INTRODUCTION

PIERRE DE BOURDEILLE, 'abbé et seigneur de Brantôme', who became known to posterity simply as Brantôme, was not, as a recent historian of French literature has called him, 'a pushing and adventurous churchman'. He was a soldier-courtier who after serving under three Kings of France, retired to his estates in early middle age and proceeded to write an account of his times. His works are a first hand account of a turbulent, violent, frightening age which was rent by fratricidal strife. They also chronicle the exploits of many of the leading figures of the sixteenth century on the field of battle and in bed.

Brantôme was born in Périgord about 1540 in the reign of François I. He came of an ancient and noble family and was the third of the six children of François II de Bourdeille, Baron de Bourdeille, and Anne de Vivonne.

His father had already exhibited the wildness which was characteristic of the age. He was the son of François I de Bourdeille, who had been cup-bearer to the Comte and Comtesse d'Angoulème, and Yvonne du Fou who belonged to an old Breton family. He spent eight years among the pages at the court of Anne of Brittany. As a young man he borrowed two hundred *écus*, took a couple of horses, a groom and a valet and departed for Naples. In the Romagna he met Pope Julius II who had heard about him and is said to have been anxious to meet him. There is a curious and surely apocryphal story of the young man playing dice with the Pope, throwing double or quits, and winning. When he returned to France his family hurriedly married him off in 1518 to Anne de Vivonne, who was only thirteen at the time, in the hope that marriage would put an end to his wanderings and encourage him to settle down. These hopes were disappointed. As soon as he was married, he set off again on his travels. We hear of him at Ardrès where he was present in 1520 at the meeting between François I and Henry VIII of England at the field of the Cloth of Gold. He died in 1546 when Pierre was some six years old.

We are not well informed about Brantôme's early years or about his private life. The manuscript of an autobiographical chapter was lost in 1712 on the death of Quinet, director of the Opera, to whom it had been entrusted with the idea of publication. What knowledge we do possess is derived largely from his account of important events in which he himself had taken part. In spite of an evident fondness for women he never married, though he was twice close to being married. We have to rely on his verse for the names of the women whom he loved as a young man : Mlle de la Guyonnière, a lady-in-waiting of the Queen-Mother; Isabelle de Limeuil, the abandoned mistress of Condé; 'la belle Rouet', whom he describes as 'the booty of our kings' and who had had a child by the King of Navarre; Mlle de Chasteauneuf and Rose de Montal. It is also thought that he is 'the estimable man' who makes an appearance from time to time in the *Vies des dames galantes*, and is the hero of some not very estimable exploits.

Brantôme spent his childhood at the Court of the Queen of Navarre, where he had been brought by his grandmother. It was probably after her death in 1549 that he was sent to school in Paris. We are told that he was 'very small' when in 1552 his elder brother, Jean de Bourdeille, who was later to die in the civil wars, returned to Paris after being dangerously wounded at the siege of Chimay. He is described in his mother's will, dated 3rd May 1557, as being 'a student at the University of Poitiers, reverend father in God, Abbot of Brantôme'. The estate and living of Brantôme had in fact just been bestowed on him by Henri II. He took possession of it on 5th July 1558, succeeding the Bishop of Lavour who had died on 20th March 1556. He already held three other ecclesiastical livings.

His studies appear to have been somewhat haphazard. He found the classics too much of an effort, 'knowing the language of Homer neither better nor worse than he knew High German, but knowing something of the language of Virgil'. He was to write many years later that there was no one in the world who having read the letters of Marguerite de Valois (for whom he had a lifelong devotion) 'does not laugh at poor Cicero with his private letters'. He did not entirely waste his time, however, and was far from sharing the contempt for books which was fashionable among sixteenth-century youths of noble birth who cared only for warlike exploits. He had proved by his example, he said, 'that there is no better emery paper for burnishing arms than literature, and that when the two are married they make a fine nuptial bed'. He claims to have read widely on 'an infinity of subjects', and never to have missed an opportunity in his life of increasing his knowledge. The result was, as his biographer puts it, that he has given us 'in a form which is as spicy as it is original, a collection of writings that represent an enormous amount of work and are a valuable source of information about the history of the sixteenth century'.[1]

When he had completed his education he went to the Court where his elder sister, Madeleine, had been a lady-in-waiting to Catherine of Medici since 1554. Two years later he saw the future Mary Queen of Scots, then a child of thirteen or fourteen, recite before the Court a Latin prayer of her own composition. A wood concession in the royal Forest of Saint-Yrieix provided him with money for the foreign travels on which he was shortly to embark.

He was more diligent in his study of modern languages than he had been in his study of 'the language of Homer', and learnt Italian and Spanish. At the end of the year 1558 he was in Italy, where he remained for eighteen months. He was indifferent to art except for works depicting battle scenes, but was, as we might expect, attracted by the women of Italy, particularly by courtesans, who provided him with some of the stories that he was later to use in his books.

We find him in Rome for the election and coronation of Pope Pius IV between 26th December 1559 and 6th January 1560. On his return to France he became friendly with the Guise family. He attended the coronation of Charles IX on 5th May 1561. Two months later he formed part of the escort which accompanied Mary Stuart, widow of François II, who

---

[1] L. Lalanne: *Brantôme: sa vie et ses écrits*, Paris, 1896, p. 11.

had been King of France for a year, back to her native land when she was driven from the French Court by the persecutions of the formidable Catherine of Medici, widow of Henri II and mother of three successive Kings of France : François II, Charles IX and Henri III.

Mary sailed from Calais on 25th July. As the vessel which was taking her back to Scotland reached the open sea, she saw a ship go down with great loss of life, and regarded it as a bad omen. Brantôme gives a moving account of the Queen lamenting her departure from France, weeping and crying out : 'Farewell France. It is done now. Farewell France. I do not think I shall ever see you again.'

The French party paid a courtesy visit to the Court of Elizabeth on their way back to France in 1562.

Brantôme fought on the King's side in the first civil war, and was an eye-witness of the assassination of Guise who was shot down by a certain Poltrot on 24th February 1563. The Edict of Amboise brought the civil war to an end less than a month later on 19th March. France then turned her attention to foreign wars and the recapture of Le Havre, which had been handed over to England by the French Protestants. It fell to the French forces on 23rd July 1563, and the war against England ended with the Treaty of Troyes on 11th April 1564.

Brantôme returned to the French Court, which began a tour of France which was to last until 1566. He seems to have grown weary of the inactivity and ceremonial of court life. He joined Philip II of Spain's victorious expedition to Morocco. He then visited Portugal, where he was invested with the Order of the Coat of Christ. From Portugal he went to Spain, where he met the Spanish Queen, Elizabeth, and was the intermediary for the meeting at Bayonne between the Queen of Spain and her mother, Catherine of Medici.

He rejoined the Court at Arles in November 1564. At the close of the following year he left France as one of an expeditionary force of three hundred volunteers who, under the leadership of his friend Strozzi, were on their way to Malta to fight against the Turks. Although as a diplomatic subterfuge they were disowned by the King of France, they were received with great enthusiasm when they landed at Malta. The death of the Emperor Soliman of Turkey put an end to the need for the expedition. Brantôme paid a second visit to Italy, where he claimed to have enjoyed the favours of a celebrated courtesan whose price had been too high for him on his first visit, but who had made a good marriage and was more accommodating the second time.

Brantôme was back at court in 1567. The second civil war, in which his brother Jean was killed, broke out the same year and ended with the Peace of Chartres on 23rd March 1568.

After the end of the second civil war Brantôme is thought to have been converted to Protestantism by his great friend Théligny, the future-son-in-law of Admiral Coligny. Although he celebrated the event in one of the best of his poems, his conversion does not seem to have lasted long, and certainly not beyond the death of Théligny, who was to perish in the massacre of St Bartholomew's Eve.

Religious peace was short-lived. Six months after the Peace of Chartres a royal edict revoked all concessions made to the Protestants and forbade the exercise of any religion in France except Catholicism. Théligny tried to persuade Brantôme to join the Protestant cause, but he refused to take up arms against the King and whatever the state of his religious beliefs again fought on the King's side in the third civil war. He was at the battle of Jarnac, where Condé was killed, on 13th March 1569, and at the capture of Mussidan by the Catholic forces on 22nd April of the same year. He then caught fever and withdrew to his estates. He has left us a curious picture of himself entertaining the Protestant leaders, the Prince of Orange and Coligny, at Brantôme. It is said that no Catholic churches were destroyed and no atrocities committed in the area.

After the Peace of Saint-Germain, which was signed on 8th August 1570, Brantôme resigned his commission. He was engaged for a time at Brouage in the preparation of a mysterious naval expedition which never took place. He expressed his horror at the St. Bartholomew massacre which started the fourth civil war in 1572, but took part in the siege of the Protestant stronghold of La Rochelle which fell on 8th July 1573. He also took part in the fifth civil war, which lasted from February 1574 to May 1575, but left the army some time during the year 1574.

He was present at the deathbed of Charles IX on 30th May 1575, and has left an eye-witness account of the strange behaviour of the French at the King's funeral. We know little about the next eight years, which seem to have been spent mainly at court. In 1583 or 1584 he met with a serious riding accident which is said to have kept him in bed for four years. At this time he lost his patron, the Duc d'Alençon, and was disappointed by what he regarded as the shabby way in which he had been treated by the King.

In 1589 Henri III, a notorious homosexual with no children, who was surrounded by *mignons*, was assassinated and Henri of Navarre became king as Henri IV with Marguerite de Valois as his Queen. The last recorded meeting between Marguerite and Brantôme took place earlier the same year. Whether or not they saw one another again, their affection continued. Each of them dedicated a piece of writing to the other, but by the time Brantôme's was ready she was no longer Queen of France. Henri IV had divorced her in 1599 and Brantôme addresses her simply as 'Queen, daughter of France'. He devoted his remaining years to his writings, to the management of his estates and to family problems. He died on 5th July 1614. Marguerite de Valois survived him by ten months.

The riding accident coupled with the disappointment of his worldly ambitions was the main cause of Brantôme's decision (warmly applauded by Marguerite) to retire to his estates and write. He was in the best sense an amateur, the talented sixteenth-century aristocrat who after a very active life sat down and wrote some account of his times. This did not prevent him from taking his work seriously. He published nothing during his lifetime, but gave detailed instructions and made financial provision for publication in his will. He would no doubt have been highly incensed if he could have known that, owing to some disobliging references to his relatives in the will, they did not hurry themselves to carry out his instructions and it was not until he had been dead fifty years that the first edition appeared in a small format in 1665-6.

When the Garnier brothers decided to publish the *Vies des dames galantes* in their edition of the French classics, they assigned it to a special section called 'Littérature Grivoise' which includes, among other celebrated works, those of Rabelais, Boccaccio, Casanova, Bussy-Rabutin's *Histoire amoureuse des Gaules*, La Fontaine's *Contes* and Laclos's *Liaisons dangereuses*. This classification at once raises the question of the author's intention. Was he an historian writing an account of his time? Was he a moralist exposing the private life of the sixteenth-century nobility? Or was he, as his dedication suggests, simply compiling a collection of bawdy stories for the entertainment of his peers?

Although the division of the book into seven parts or *discours* gives the impression of serious purpose, it is primarily a collection of stories which are strung together and frequently introduced by the words, 'I saw', 'I knew', 'I heard tell'. Brantôme is the amateur telling us what he saw and heard of the sexual life of the nobility. What he saw and heard was certainly meant to be funny. In places it is very funny indeed. For he tells his stories with immense gusto and the four-letter words come tumbling out on every page.

Each of the seven discourses has a main theme which runs through it like a thread, but the form is as flexible as an essay of Montaigne's. It provides ample room for digression and comment, enables the writer to range over the whole field of personal experience, hearsay, history and literature in his search for examples.

In his first 'discourse' he establishes his position. He does not write from the angle of the seducer, the gallant man, seeking opportunities of winning the favours of the lady or ladies of his choice. It is written from the woman's point of view. The central figure in most of the stories is the lady of very noble birth who, to put it baldly, can take all that the opposite sex can give, can often take a good deal more than a single *cavalier servant* can give her, and is prepared to pay very handsomely for what she gets. Although the intention may be basically humorous, the violence of the age breathes in the least of these stories. The timid lover, the man who does not dare or who lets slip an opportunity of tipping a great lady up in a convenient wood or garden, earns undying hate and is sent packing. Outraged husbands slaughter erring wives and their swains on the spot, while the crueller ones—usually the aged and impotent spouses—kill their wives with slow poisons. The pages echo with the sound of crashing beds, smashed by the ardours of amorous pairs. While Brantôme may appear nearly as enthusiastic about high scoring as the nineteenth century, his approach is somewhat different. A man who is only good for a couple of 'knocks' in a night simply fails to make the grade of the day in which a dozen appears to have been the qualifying mark in a highly vigorous society.

While the book is a somewhat ramshackle collection of anecdotes and while the principal aim seems to have been to entertain, the author's wide experience and natural powers of observation turn it into a social document of some importance. He moves not merely with ease, but almost unconsciously, from something which comes near to clinical observation to the equivalent of the smoke-room story. He notes, for example, that while physical deformity such as a cancer of the breast may put off an aspiring lover, there are cases when it has the opposite effect and becomes a perverse stimulus. He notes, too, the attraction of lubricious conversation to highly-sexed women and the stimulus it provides during love-making. From serious observations of this kind, he passes imperceptibly to a series of anecdotes about the calibre of the female organ which offer an outlet for his considerable verbal wit.

He does not confine himself to what might be called perverse tendencies. He deals very fully with sexual perversion in women, and describes the shocking tactics of husbands who cast a lascivious eye on their wives' young lovers, which leads in one story to an *orgie à trois*. One of the funniest of his stories is an account of a search of the belongings of the courtiers for hidden weapons which only produced, among the possessions of one 'very great lady', four large 'bilboes'.

The first of the seven 'discourses' is the most substantial and, in its way, the most serious. The remainder are in reality a development, a filling in of the canvas by a closer look at certain impulses.

While the inclination to discover Freudian tendencies in the literature of pre-Freudian ages is sometimes overdone, we also need to remind ourselves that Freud did no more than uncover impulses which are endemic in human nature, and have simply become more widespread and more serious with the development of modern civilization. Brantôme provides classic examples of what today is known as the Freudian error. One is the inadvertent use by a woman addicted to extra-marital adventures of the word 'adulterous' in place of the word 'adulatory'. The other, which is much funnier and which incidentally throws a curious light on the application of martial imagery to love, is the story of the woman who, when describing the blowing up of a bridge in the course of a military exploit, used the word *con* instead of *pont*.

From time to time a story, which in itself may appear trivial, frivolous or simply bawdy, catches the attention of the contemporary reader and illuminates the age. At one point Brantôme relates that François I arrived outside the bedchamber of one of his mistresses who happened to be engaged with an *ami de coeur*. The lover was hastily bundled into the capacious fireplace and hidden behind the sticks that filled it. The King was admitted and had his pleasure of the lady. As he was about to leave, His Majesty was taken short and finding nowhere else proceeded to relieve himself in the fireplace, thoroughly drenching the hidden lover. The comic episode, which to the memorialist was nothing more, reminds us that the age was not simply an age of high spirits, of violence and of cruelty : it reminds us that for all the splendour of its literature, the magnificence and apparent sophistication of court life, the people were still primitive by modern standards and did not expect their monarch to behave any differently from a peasant.

The historian, writing long after the events that he is describing, is naturally in a better position to place them in their true perspective, to unravel their complexity and assess their political significance than a contemporary can ever be. But political events, the public life of an age based on official sources, are only a part of the total picture. If we want to understand its climate and penetrate the hidden causes of those events, we must turn to the private records, to the eye-witness accounts of the memorialist, the letter-writer and the diarist. Although Brantôme like all good writers was very con-scious of the duty to entertain the reader, the main value of his memoirs lies in the fact that they are a first-hand *document* and a primary source for an understanding of the sixteenth century in France. It is for this reason that they have been constantly reprinted in French and that Mr. Alec Brown's admirably vigorous translation is their third appearance in English dress during the present century.

What do we see when we stand back and look at Bran-tôme's picture? He is only concerned in the *Vies des dames galantes* with one aspect of society. He is describing the sexual life of the highest in the land. While we must therefore avoid mistaking it for a complete picture and while the account of the widowhood of Queen Anne of Austria shows that there was room for sanctity and that the kingdom was not one vast cess-pool, it is nevertheless true that Brantôme was dealing with one of the fundamental urges of humanity and that its workings throw a powerful light on the age as a whole. There are moments when he heads us off, when he tells us that there are some stories which are too strong even for him to repeat; there are others when he mildly condemns the behaviour of some of the characters, and others still when he defends fornication or adultery on no better grounds than that nature must have her way, and that since she has provided men and women with certain organs they must make use of them in order to maintain the health and proper balance of the whole man. The overall picture, however, is a picture of a dissolute age, an age in which corruption and moral laxity began at the top and where their ravages were most destructive. The middle ages were not precisely remarkable for their continence, but at least there were standards of right and wrong—the standards which emerge so clearly, for example, in the work of Villon, who is essentially the laureate of the collapsing middle ages.

It was the loss of these standards which made it possible for the vigour of the Renaissance to find its outlet in such disastrous channels. For in the last resort it was the Renaissance vigour which was transformed into violence and fed the destructive, fratricidal wars of religion instead of being turned into constructive and creative work. While we may look back on the sixteenth century at a distance of four hundred years and admire its works of literature, while we may be moved by the religious poetry of a Sponde or a La Ceppède, the underside can only produce a sensation of horror. And if it seems less terrifying than it should, it is only because the outbreaks of savagery in our own time have shown that when human nature goes to it and when it is provided with more highly developed techniques of destruction, it can do far worse than what we are pleased to regard as our semi-primitive ancestors.

MARTIN TURNELL

To Milord the Duke d'Alençon[1] de Brabant
Count of Flanders, son and brother of our Kings[2]

MY LORD, since you have at court often shown me the favour of telling me yourself many of those funny stories and anecdotes, so frequent and persistent in you that one would say that, so great is your wit, so ready and so alert, and your diction too very fine one only needs to glance at your lips for one to be born, I set myself as best I could to put together these essays, such as they are, so that if there is any that please you, it may so far serve you for entertainment and when you hold your conversations remind you of those with which you so honoured me when I was in service at your court.

So, My Lord, I dedicate this book to you and beg you to back it with your name and authority, while I proceed to graver essays. You will see one of them which is separate from the others, which is almost complete,[3] in which I make a comparison between six great princes and captains in vogue today in this Christendom of ours, they being King Henry III your brother, Your Highness himself, the King of Navarre your brother-in-law,[4] Lord de Guise,[5] Lord du Maine[6] and the Prince of Parma,[7] and there I outline all your great qualities, accomplishments, merits and fine deeds, though as to these, I leave the conclusion to those more competent than I am to accomplish it.

Meanwhile, My Lord, I pray God ever to increase you in your greatness, prosperity and eminence, of which as ever I am,

Your very humble and very obedient subject and most affectionate servant,

BOURDEILLE

To the Reader

I HAD during his lifetime dedicated this second part of the study of women[8] to My Lord d'Alençon, since he used to honour me[9] by liking me and chatting with me most intimately and was eager to learn good stories. Now, for all that his great-hearted and valorous and noble body lies under a brass plaque of honour, I have preferred not to withdraw my dedication, so now re-confer it on his illustrious ashes and divine spirit, of the value of which, as of his lofty deeds and merits,[10] I speak in due course, as of other great princes and great captains;[11] for, if ever there was a great man, he certainly has been great, although he has died so young.

This is enough talk of grave matters, now I must turn a little to gay ones.

This translation is based on the French edition of 1891 published by Editions Plon. The Notes are by Maurice Rat from the 1959 edition published by Editions Garnier Frères to whom the publishers are indebted for their permission to make use of them.

FIRST ESSAY

On ladies who make love and their cuckold husbands

SINCE it is the ladies who created cuckoldry and they who put the horns on their husbands' heads, I thought it fitting to include this treatise in my book on the ladies, although I shall have as much to say about the menfolk as the women. I am well aware that I am setting my hand to a great task, one I could never complete if I wanted to go to the very end, for not all the paper in the office in Paris would furnish writing space for a half of the stories about either the women or the men. Nevertheless, I will set down what I can, and when I can add no more I will pass my pen to the devil or to some boon friend who will take it on. I apologize if in this treatise I do not observe half the system I ought, for the number of suitable men and suitable women for the purpose is too great, and they make such a motley medley, that I doubt whether even a good sergeant-major could reduce it all to order and degree.

Hence it will be as fancy dictates that I shall say whatever pleases me in this month of April which brings the open season for cuckolds round again. I mean of course, first fledglings, for the others are being made and are on show in every month and season of the year.

Now, this class of cuckolds is divided into a very large number of different kinds, but the worst of all—and, what is more, those whom the ladies fear, and rightly, too—are the crazy ones, the dangerous, the odd, the bad, the malicious, the cruel, the bloodthirsty and the moody men, who come to blows about it, who torment, who kill, some for real cause, some for none, so much does the faintest public suspicion infuriate them; and dealings with these are much to be avoided, both by their wives

1

and by the ladies' lovers. All the same, I have known many ladies and lovers of theirs who did not give a heed to this, the gentlemen being as bad as the husbands, and the ladies having pluck, to such a point that if their lovers lacked it, they made up the balance, since the more risky and dubious any undertaking, the more should it be carried through with great fervour. I have also known ladies who had neither the heart nor the mind for any elevated matters, and found no entertainment whatsoever save in low things, hence the saying: as shabby of heart as a whore.

I knew one estimable lady, and not one of the least, either, who when on one occasion the circumstances favoured indulging in love-making with her lover, but he put her off, pointing out how very unfortunate it would be if the husband, who was in the vicinity, surprised them at it—she without more ado quit him, there and then, as a lover lacking pluck, or perhaps quite plainly because he cheated her of her enjoyment, for when her heat and the whim for it takes hold of her there is indeed nothing that your love-sick lady detests or scorns her lover for, more than when for this reason or the other he either cannot satisfy her or does not want to.

One really ought to heap praise on this lady I mention for her pluck and praise others like her too, who fear nothing that may assuage their desire for love, although in this they run greater dangers and risk their fortune more than any soldier or sailor does from the greatest perils of battle or the sea.

A Spanish lady, being escorted to the King's residence one day by a gallant cavalier, heard her gentleman, as they passed a certain hidden, gloomy spot (counting on his Spanish dignity and discretion,) say: *Señora, buen lugar, si no fuera vuessa merced*, to which the only reply she made was: *Si, buen lugar, si no fuera vuessa merced*; that is: 'A lovely spot, were it any other but you,' to which she replied: 'Yes, a lovely spot, were it any other but you,' by which she meant to point and to charge him with cowardice for not having taken of her, in such a suitable spot, what he wanted and she craved, which another bolder would not have failed to do, and for this incident she loved him no more and gave him up.

2

I have heard tell of a very lovely and prominent lady who gave her lover a rendezvous, to sleep with her, on condition he did not once touch her or come to grips,[12] which he did achieve, spending the whole night in very great tension, temptation and restraint indeed, which pleased her so much that soon after she gave him his enjoyment, alleging as reasons for her conduct that she had wanted to test his love and see whether he could do what she had prescribed. And for this reason she loved him much more after that, since on any other occasion he would be capable of doing anything else as exacting as that test was, being one of the greatest of all.

Some men may praise that discreet or low behaviour, others not, I leave it to the reactions and views either the one or the other sort may have about it.

I knew one rather high-up lady who, having given her lover a rendezvous, to sleep with her one night, found him appearing in nothing but his shirt, all ready to do his duty, but as it was winter, having got so chilled on the way to her that when he got into bed he could do nothing but entertain hopes of getting warm, for all of which the lady conceived a great loathing for him and never paid any heed to him again.

When another lady parleyed about love with a certain courtier, among other things he told her that if he slept with her he would undertake six stands in a night, so greatly would her beauty stimulate him. 'You make a big claim,' she said, 'but I will give you your night.' And without fail he turned up, but only to his own misfortune, for, once in bed, he was taken with such a revulsion, chill or nervous collapse, that he could not manage even once, till at last the lady cried : 'Don't you mean to do anything more than this? Then, out of my bed, I did not hire it to you, like the bed in some inn, to sprawl at your ease and take your rest. I mean what I say ! Out with you !' And thus despatched him and thereafter maintained a great scorn of him and loathed him worse than the plague.

That nobleman would have been very fortunate had he had the constitution of the great protonotary, Baraud,[13] who was also almoner to King François, for when he slept with the ladies of the court he always ran to a dozen at least, and when morning came could still on one occasion say : 'I am so sorry, Madame, for not doing better, but I took some loosening medicine yesterday.' I saw him later. He was known as Captain Baraud, a Gascon, and he had then given up, but he certainly told me of many ladies, naming them all.

In his old age that virility and venereal force had failed him and he was poor, for although he had in course of time garnered in some fine takings earned by his prowess, he had squandered it all and when I knew him had taken up the infusion and distillation of essences. 'If only,' he remarked, 'I could distil essence of sperm as I used to in my young days, I should be in a much sounder position and more prosperous.'

During the War of the League, a high-standing lord, who was certainly a fine, courageous fellow, after a fighting excursion from the place of which he was governor failed to get back before the barrack gates closed. So he spent the night at the house of a lovely and very highly-placed great lady who was then widowed, and who suggested she might put him up, which he did not refuse, being quite exhausted. After giving him an ample supper, she put her own bedroom and bed at his disposal, all the other rooms being voided of furniture on account of the fighting that was going on, and the furniture— she had some lovely things—in store. She herself withdrew to her closet, where she had a daytime couch.

After repeatedly declining her bedroom and bed, the nobleman had no other course but to accept the lady's offer, but when he had gone to bed and was fast asleep, there was my lady fair and fine getting into bed beside him without his feeling a thing all night, so tired and drugged with sleep was he, and he slept on till broad daylight the next day when, slipping out from his side just as he began to wake up, his hostess said : 'As you see, you've not slept alone, for I did not really want to abandon my whole bed to you, but had half of it, sharing with you. Good-bye! You've missed a chance which will never come your way again.'

Cursing angrily about this good fortune he had missed (it was enough to make a man hang himself) the nobleman would have detained her and implored her to stay, but to no result, she was very peeved with him for not having comforted her as she would have liked, for she had not joined him in bed for one bout only (as the saying goes, *one bout's no more than the bed's salad*) but for the whole night. She had not come there for the singular number but the plural, which in this business many ladies do indeed prefer to the singular, quite the opposite of an estimable, lovely lady whom I knew who, having one night given her lover a rendezvous to come and sleep with her, found him in no time subjecting her to three grand attacks, when, craving quarter and an end to this multiplication of bouts, she told him, she begged him, she commanded him to get out of her bed and be off. As fresh as when he began, he tried once again, assuring her that he would now be mad all night till day broke, so little work had in no way diminished his energy. She said to him : 'Well, you will have to be content with my recognition what really wonderful, hearty virility you possess. At the right time and in the right place I might be able to make better use of it than I can now, for the truth is, you and I must not risk being discovered and my husband finding out, for I should be ruined. So farewell, till a better and a safer opportunity, and then I will use you without any constraint for the great battle, not indulge in a mere skirmish like this.'

There are many ladies who would not have had so much circumspection, but, intoxicated by their pleasure, would have kept their opponent with them on their own ground, fighting till daylight came.

The estimable lady, for instance, whom I mentioned before these last was of such temperament that when the mood was on her she was never at all timorous or apprehensive about her husband, for all that he had a good sword and was a choleric man, and yet she was always so lucky that neither she nor her lovers ever ran risk of fortune or life, since they never were caught at it, for they always planted a look-out, good, vigilant sentries, though the ladies should never trust to this, for it only needs one luckless moment, such as some time back befell a certain excellent, brave knight,[14] who was slaughtered for going to see his mistress, being betrayed and trapped by none other but the lady herself, who did so on the instructions of her

5

husband. And had this knight not been so sure of his own valour as he was, he would undoubtedly have taken care and would not now be dead, which is a great pity. Unquestionably a great example that one should never trust an amorous woman so far, since to escape their husband's cruel hand they will play whatever game he wants, as this one did, who herself survived while her lover died.

There are other husbands who kill the lady and the lover to-gether, as I heard tell of a very great lady, of whom her husband[15] was jealous, not on account of any precise thing, but just out of jealousy and love's empty show, and he killed his wife by poison and wasting away, which was a great pity, after he had first had the lover killed, an estimable man himself, saying that killing the bull first and the cow after made the sacrifice all the more pleasing and striking.

This prince was crueller towards his wife than he was re-garding one of his daughters,[16] whom he had married to a great prince, though one not as great himself, for he was all but a monarch.

This silly woman managed to get herself pregnant by some-body other than her husband, who was prevented from doing it, being away at a war, and then, having produced a fine son, did not know into which saint's hands to place herself other than her father,[17] whom she informed of it all by a nobleman whom she trusted and sent to him. And he, as soon as he learned of it sent a message to her husband on his life to take care not to take that of this daughter or he would have his and make him the most wretched prince of Christendom, which it was in his power to do, and he sent a galley with an escort to his daughter to fetch the boy and his wet-nurse and provided the boy with a fine house and with the upkeep of this and had him well looked after and brought up. But when after some time the father died, the husband straightway put her to death.

I have heard tell of another husband who put his wife's man to death in front of her and made him suffer a long time so she should die martyred by seeing the man she had loved so much and had clasped in her arms die a long, painful death.

Another prominent personage[18] killed his wife in front of the

6

whole court, after having allowed her all the liberties in the world for fifteen years, and being quite well informed about the life she was leading, to the point of remonstrating with her about it and admonishing her. However, the iron finally bit into him (the story goes that it was by the counsel of a great teacher of his[19]) and one morning he went and found her in bed, just on the point of getting up, and after getting into bed with her and joking and laughing together with her, gave her four or five thrusts with his dagger,[20] then had one of his men finish her off, after which in front of everybody he had her placed in a litter and taken to his house to be buried. After-wards he came back and put in an appearance at court, as if he had done the finest thing in the world, triumphing about it.[21] He would gladly have done the same to her lovers, but he would then have had more than he could cope with, for she had had so many and loved so much that it would have formed a little army.

I have at the same time heard tell of a fine, brave captain[22] who, having reason to suspect his wife who was of excellent birth, without hesitation went to her and throttled her him-self with his white scarf, then had her buried with all possible honour and attended the funeral in full mourning, very grieved, and wore mourning a long time after, which was of course great moral satisfaction for the poor woman, and, to cheer her up by the fine ceremony of it all, he did the same to one of her maids, who had been her accomplice in her love affairs. Nor did this man die without lineage of this wife, hav-ing a fine son by her, one of the bravest and most outstanding men in his country, whose acts of courage and merit indeed carried him high, for he served his masters the kings well.

I have also heard tell of a grandee of Italy who was another who killed his wife,[23] being unable to catch her gallant, who escaped to France, but it was alleged that he did not so much kill her for sinning (for he had known that she had love affairs for quite a time and had not heeded it at all) but in order to marry another lady he had now become amorous of.[24]

All of which points to the dangers of tackling or setting about a c— that is armed, especially when there are so many others that are unarmed, or should I say conquered, like one I knew which was really as well armed as any in the world. There was a knight,[25] a fine, courageous man if there ever was one, who wanted to have an affair with her, but that was not enough for him, he also wanted to be the great man and spread the news. He did not last long without forthwith being killed by men planted in ambush, without any great to-do; nor did the woman come to any harm, though she spent a long time very anxious and worried, the more so since, being pregnant, she thought she would get the same treatment, and would have liked her confinement to last for ever, but her husband was a kind and merciful man, and so, although one of the best swordsmen in the world, pardoned her, and there were no other consequences, though the whole affair was not without great alarm for several other suitors whom she had had, but the one paid for them all. However, after this, recognizant of the benevolence and mercy of such a husband, this lady subsequently gave him very little indeed to be suspicious about, but turned into one of the best behaved and most virtuous women of the age.

It was quite otherwise at about the same time in the Kingdom of Naples, in what happened to Donna Maria of Avalos, one of the loveliest princesses of the country,[26] married to the Prince of Venosa. She fell in love with Count d'Andriana, another fine prince of the same land, and the two had agreed to enjoy their love together, when (by means I would relate, would the story not be too lengthy[27]) the husband caught her in bed with him, and had them both done to death at once by men he had placed there, so that the next day these two lovely persons, two halves making one whole, were to be seen stretched out and exposed on the paving stones outside the front door of the mansion, dead and chill, for all passers-by to see, shedding tears for them and lamenting their pitiable condition.

Some of the relations of this lady, thus put to death, were very distressed and anguished, to the point of wishing to be avenged by death and murder, as the law of the country would have allowed, and seeing too that she had been killed by knavish valets and slaves who were not worthy of having their hands stained with such fine, noble blood. They were of a mind to seek out the husband and have their revenge, whether through the courts or otherwise, which they would not have done, had he killed her with his own hand, for then there would have been no consequences or pursuit.

There's a stupid, cranky opinion and attitude about it all, which I refer to our great debaters and fine legal minds, asking them which is the greater enormity, to kill one's wife with one's own hand, having loved her so, or by the hand of a rascal or a slave? There is much to be said on the matter, which I refrain from setting down, fearing my arguments may be too feeble beside those of the great.

I have heard tell that when he learned of the plot, the viceroy[28] warned the lover, or the mistress, but such was their destiny that so glorious a love had to end so.

This lady was the daughter of Dom Carlo d'Avalos, second brother of the Marquis de Pescayre, who, had any such thing happened in any of his love affairs that I know of, he would have been dead long since.

I knew one husband who, coming back from his travels, and not having lain with his wife for a long time, arrived home in very cheerful mood, resolved to go to bed with her at once and have a fine time, but, getting there at nightfall, through the look-out window he realized that she had a lover in bed with her. At once his hand went to his sword and he knocked at the door and as soon as it was opened entered determined to kill her, but first tried to get the gallant, who leapt out of the window, and only then came to her, to kill her. But it so happened that on this occasion she had furbished herself so well and done her hair so beautifully for the night, that in her lovely white gown and so well adorned (don't forget that she had got herself up like this to please her lover) she was lovelier than he had ever seen her got up on his account, and never so much to his taste as when in her night-shift she fell on her knees and begged his forgiveness, and with lovely and so sweet words, such as she was indeed very capable of, he had her get up off her knees and found her so lovely and so charming that his heart softened. He let the sword drop and, not having done anything for so long, and hungering for it (as the lady may have been too, nature exciting her as well) he forgave her, took her, embraced her, lay her back on the bed, tore off his clothes, locked the door and straightway got into bed with her, and she so well satisfied him by her loving charms and devices (you may imagine she left none of those out) that as a result, the next morning they were seen to be more intimate than ever, fondling each other as never before. Just like Menelaus, poor cuckold, who, having for from ten to twelve years been threatening his wife, Helen, with death if he ever got hold of her, even telling her so with her on top of the ramparts of Troy and he down below, when the city was taken, and she really was in his hands, was actually so enraptured by her loveliness that he forgave her everything and loved her and caressed her more than he had ever done.

Outraged husbands like this who turn from lions into butterflies are kind, but it is less easy to find such a case as the following :

A certain lady of the reign of King François I who was great, beautiful and young, and married to one of the great princes of France,[29] of a line than which there is non greater, escaped in a very different way, better too than the preceding one, for what happened was that either she had given her husband some love pretext or he was seized with a brainstorm or a fit of sudden rage, anyway, he came at her with bared sword in hand, to kill her. She was despairing of any human aid to get her out of that dangerous situation when she suddenly thought of consigning herself to the glorious Virgin Mary and promising to fulfil a vow at the Virgin's Loretto shrine at St Jean des Mauverets, in the Anjou country, if only the Virgin would aid her. And the moment she made that inward vow the prince in question fell to the ground and his sword flew from his hand. He immediately leapt to his feet again, but then, as if emerging from a dream, asked his wife who the saint was to whom she had consigned herself to escape from her danger. She told him it was the Virgin Mary, at the above-mentioned shrine, and that to obtain intercession she had promised to make a pilgrimage to that holy site. Her husband merely said to her : 'Then you had better go and fulfil your vow!' Which she did, and on the shrine she hung a picture of the story, together with a number of lovely large wax offerings of the sort that used to be customary, and these were to be seen there for long after. There is a good vow for you and a fine and novel escape. Just look at the *Anjou Chronicles*.[30]

I have heard it said that on one occasion King François wanted to sleep with a lady of his court whom he loved, but found her husband waiting sword in hand, ready to kill him. But the King pointed his own sword at the knight's throat and ordered him on his life to do her no harm and added that if the knight did interfere with her in the least, he would kill him or have somebody else take his head off, and for that night he sent the knight outside and took his place.

This particular lady was very lucky to find such a lusty champion and protector of her c——, for from then on the husband did not dare say a word, but let the King have it all his own way.

I have heard it said that not only this lady, but a number of others too were granted that royal cover, just as many men in time of war, put up the royal arms over their gates to safeguard their properties, so do these women sport the devices of great kings, on the edge of their c——s, inside them too, so that their husbands do not dare say a word, where otherwise they would have run them through with their swords.

I have known other ladies, thus favoured by kings and great men, who hawked these passports of theirs about everywhere, though when some of them overstepped the borderline, though their husbands did not dare take to cold steel, they did help themselves out with poisons and hidden secret deaths, which they made out to be chills, apoplexies, or heart failures. Such husbands are indeed loathsome, who see their lovely wives die lingering deaths at their side lasting many days; they are more deserving of death than the wives. Or you have them putting their wives to death enclosed in high walls, in nunneries for life, such as some very ancient ones, which we have in France, like for instance one grandee of France whom I knew who put his wife to death in this way, and she a lovely and most estimable lady, too, and did it, what is more, by a court decision, getting his wretched satisfaction at the cost of publicly declaring himself a cuckold.

Of such unbalanced and savage husbands it is most readily the older men who are the cuckolds, those who in default of virility and heat in themselves try to make sure of their wives, even when they have been so silly as to marry young and pretty ones. They are so jealous and touchy both by nature and by reason of the things they used to do themselves once or have seen others do, that they treat their poor women so wretchedly that purgatory would be less arduous than such domination. The Spanish has it: *'El diablo sabe mucho, porque es viejo'*, The devil is knowing because he is old, and likewise these old men by reason of their age and their former way of life know a great deal. Hence they are the more to be blamed in this matter, for, being unable to satisfy a woman themselves, why ever do they go and marry them? At the same time, women so beautiful and so young are very wrong to go and marry them, all because of worldly goods, thinking to enjoy these after their husband's death, which they await hourly, and meanwhile soon yield to the young lovers they come upon, for which some of them pay a grievous price.

I have heard tell of one who being caught in the act, was given poison by her husband, an elderly man, and by this suffered a slow death which lasted more than a year, till she was as sere as a piece of wood, and all the time the husband paid her frequent visits, enjoying her lingering death and laughing about it, saying she had only got what she deserved.

Another such wife the husband shut up in a room and put on bread and water and frequently made her strip naked and whipped her till he was satisfied, without a hint of feeling or the least compassion for her lovely naked flesh. That is the worst about such men; having lost any moments of heat themselves, and become as devoid of the love impulse as a marble statue, they feel no compassion for any loveliness as such but wreak their rage in cruel tortures, whereas, were they young, they might well work it off on their wives' lovely naked bodies, as I have related above.

That is why it is not a good thing to marry such cranky, elderly men, for, although with age their sight weakens and begins to fail enough always remains for them to spy with and see the frolics their wives may get up to.

Thus I once heard tell of an estimable lady who said there never was a Saturday without sunshine or a pretty woman without love affairs or an old man without jealousy, and the latter was all the result of the debilitation of their virility.

Here is why a great prince of my acquaintance[31] said he would rather be like the lion which never goes white when it gets old, the monkey, which, the more it does it, the more it wants to, to the dog, which the older it is the larger its member becomes, and the stag, which the older it is, the better it performs so that does always run to an old stag in preference to any of the young ones.

Now, to be quite frank about this, what sense is there, as I heard a prominent person remark, however great the authority of the husband may be, for him either to be obliged or able to kill his wife or even merely to repudiate her, since such authority is not given him by God, or by God's law or Holy Gospel. No mention is there in the gospels of death, of murder, of bloodshed, of torture, of prison, of poisoning or of cruelty. Oh, how well Our Lord Jesus Christ did when he reminded us that in such murders and other doings there were great abuses, indeed, he never did approve of them, for instance, when the woman taken in adultery was brought before him for him to pronounce judgement on her, with his finger he wrote in the dust : 'Let him among you who is cleanest and purest take the first stone and begin stoning her,' which no man dared do, each feeling that so sensible and gentle a reproof struck home precisely at him.

Knowing the frailty of our temperaments and the abuses some of us commit in this respect, our Creator taught us all not so lightly to condemn people to death, even for this reason, for the man who kills his wife[32] is a greater adulterer than she is, and in many cases such men put them to death innocent, being merely

13

tired of them, wanting to take a new wife, and what a number of such there are! St Augustine tells us that the adulterous man is as punishable as the woman.

I have heard tell of a very great prince of our time[33] who, suspecting his wife of making love with a gallant cavalier, had him killed leaving his palace one evening, and then he killed the lady too, who, a little previously, at a tournament held at court, had kept her eyes on her man, who was handling his horse well, and had suddenly cried: 'Heavens! how well he manages his pike! Ah, but he's aiming too high!' which had astonished him, so that subsequently the wife was poisoned by some perfumes, or something taken by the mouth.

I knew a noble of good stock who had his wife put to death, who was very lovely and of good family and extraction, poisoning her constitution, without her feeling anything, so subtle and well made was the poison, in order to marry a great lady who had married a prince, for which without his friends' intervention he would have been tortured, imprisoned and in mortal danger; then misfortune would have it that he did not marry her at all, but was deceived and sadly disgraced by her, and all the lords and ladies thought very poorly of him.

I have seen great personalities throw much blame on our ancient kings, such as Louis Hutin and Charles the Fair, for having killed their wives, one being Marguerite, daughter of Robert, Duke of Burgundy, and the other Blanche, daughter of Othelin, Count of Burgundy, charging them with adultery, and causing them to die a cruel death between four walls, at Gaillard Castle,[34] and the Count de Foix did the same to Jeanne d'Arthoys,[35] in which cases there were certainly not so many delinquencies or crimes as they made out, but these lords were merely tired of their wives and for this reason accused them of those fine doings and so married other women.

As, merely to have a change, King Henry of England,[36] had his wife, Anne de Boleyn,[37] put to death by beheading, to marry another, he being very subject to choleric fits and changing to fresh wives.[38] But would it not have been better just to repudiate them, as God said, and not thus cruelly put them to death? But they must have fresh meat, these gentry must, either to

14

have a table all to themselves and not invite any other to it, or to get fresh, new wives, to bring them property when they have used up what their previous wives brought them, or because they did not have enough to satisfy them, like Baudoin, second King of Jerusalem, who, persuading his first wife that she had lived loosely, put her aside, to take a daughter of the Duke of Mélitène, because she as dowry had a good sum of money, which he was in great need of.[39] You can find all this in the history of the Holy Land. It suits such men well to touch up God's laws and make new ones, just to put these poor women to death.

King Louis the Younger did not do the same regarding Leonora, Duchess of Aquitaine who, suspected of adultery, (maybe falsely), while he was in Syria, was merely repudiated by him[40] without his wishing to use the law of the others, invented and applied more by arbitrary authority than by right or reason, whereby he acquired a greater name than the others, and the epithet *the Good*, and the others that of the bad, the cruel and the tyrannical, so in his heart he did at least have some misgiving of conscience, and that is to be a Christian ! Even the pagan Romans mostly likewise behaved in a more Christian than pagan fashion, above all some of the emperors, most of whom were liable to be cuckolded, having very highly sexed, very abandoned wives, yet, cruel though these men were, you will read of many who got rid of their wives rather by repudiation than by slaughter, as with us Christians.

Julius Caesar did no other harm to his wife Pompeia than to repudiate her, when she was adulterous with P. Claudius, a handsome young Roman nobleman, who fell desperately in love with her, as she with him, and chose the opportunity one day when she was making a sacrifice at her house at which men were not allowed. He dressed up like a girl, since he still had no hair on his chin, and mixed in with the women, singing and playing musical instruments and thus, getting through that test, had the opportunity to do what he wanted together with his mistress. But he was recognized, hunted down and charged, though by means of money and influence he was let off, and he never repeated the act.[41] Cicero wasted his Latin on a fine speech

15

made against him.[42] True, Caesar's reply to public opinion, which assured him his wife was innocent, was that he did not merely require his wife not to be guilty of the crime, but also above any suspicion. That was a good way of throwing dust in people's eyes, for in his heart of hearts he knew very well what it all meant : his wife had indeed thus been surprised with her lover, what is more, very probably contrived the occasion and the meeting, for, as far as that goes, when a woman wants a man and lusts after him, the lover need not bother to conjure up opportunities, for she will find more in an hour than we men could think of in a century, as a society lady I know said one day to her lover : 'You just find how to give me the desire, for as far as the rest goes, I'll find all the opportunity required.'[43]

Therefore Caesar knew quite well what the measure of such matters amounted to, for he was a very great rascal himself, said to be the chanticleer of all the hens of Rome, and cuckolded many a man in that city of his, as witness the nickname his soldiers gave him at his triumph : *Romani, servate uxores, maechum adducimus calvum*[44]—'Romans, hold tight to your women, for we're bringing you this great roysterer and adulterer Caesar the Bald, who will soon cover them all for you.'

Anyway, there you have the device by which with a smart answer about his wife, Caesar got out of bearing the title cuckold that he had had others bear, but in his heart of hearts of course he felt it all very deeply.

In the same way, Octavius Caesar repudiated Scibonia[45] because of her love of loose living and did her no other harm, though she indeed had had good reason to cuckold him because of the infinity of women that he entertained, taking them publicly, in front of their husbands, at the parties he gave them, bearing them off to his bedroom, and after doing them would send them back again, their hair somewhat awry and untidied and ears red, a great sign they had come straight from lechery, though I myself had never heard before that this was a sign of just having come from it— red cheeks, yes, but not ears. Anyway, he was reputed to be a great rascal, even Mark Anthony reproved him for his ways, but his excuse was that he did not entertain the ladies so much for love-making but as the easiest way to ferret out the secrets of husbands whom he mistrusted.[46]

I have known many of the great and others too who have done the same and cultivated the ladies for the same reason, and found it worked well. I could name quite a number, and there's some subtlety about it, because the satisfaction one gets is double. Thus, the Catiline conspiracy was disclosed by a lady of pleasure.[47]

The same Octavius, regarding Julia his daughter, (Agrippa's wife) thought of killing her for having been a very great whore and disgracing him greatly, (for sometimes daughters dishonour their fathers more than wives their husbands) but only banished her, depriving her of wine and the use of fine clothes and condemning her to wearing only poor ones, and, as a very great punishment, also forbidding her any commerce with men,[48] a terrible punishment, after all, for a woman of that sort, to take these last two enjoyments from them!

When Caesar Caligula, who was a very cruel tyrant, got the idea that his wife Livia Hostilia had taken a number of knocks, on the sly from him, giving herself secretly to her first husband, C. Piso, from whom Caligula had taken her by force, (thus giving him, still living, some pleasure and charm of her gracious body, while Caligula was away on tour,) he did not treat her with his customary cruelty, but merely banished her from him, two years after taking her from her husband Piso and marrying her.[49]

He did the same to Tullia Paulina, whom he had taken from her husband C. Memmius, merely divorcing her, expressly forbidding her, however, to ply her gentle trade, even with her husband. Now that was really cruel, not letting her give herself to her husband![50]

I have heard tell of a great prince of Christendom too who put the same prohibition on a lady whom he had kept, also forbidding her husband to touch her, so jealous was he.

Claudius, son of Drusus Germanicus, merely repudiated his wife Plantia Herculalina, for having been an outstanding whore, and, what is worse, because he heard she had tried to

17

take his life. But, cruel as he was, although these two reasons were quite enough for him to have her killed, he was satisfied with a divorce.[51]

Further, for what a long time he put up with the frolics and the foul debaucheries of Valeria Messalina, his other wife, who was not satisfied with doing it with one man and another dissolutely and without any discretion, but also regularly went to brothels to give herself to men, like the worst drab of the city, going so far, as Juvenal says,[52] that after her husband had lain with her she would slip away when she saw he had fallen asleep and, disguising herself as well as she could, go straight off to a brothel and there to such an extent give herself that when she left she was at least physically exhausted, if not yet assuaged or satisfied. Indeed, she went further. To get more satisfaction and earn her reputation and really feel she was a great whore and drab, she charged a fee for every single knock or ride, just like a steward going round the country collecting in every possible penny.

I have heard tell too of a well-known highly placed lady, of quite expensive race too, who led that sort of life for a time, going to brothels disguised to try that way of living and give her body to men, till one night the town watch on its rounds caught her out. There are others too who do the same, as everybody knows.

In his book of *Celebrated Unfortunates*, Boccaccio has some nice things to say about this Messalina, representing her as advancing excuses for her conduct, as being genuinely born to it, since on the very day of her birth there were certain signs in the heavens which already then set her a-smouldering, as they have others too. Her husband knew this and put up with her for a long time, till he learned that she had been secretly married to a certain Caius Sillius, one of the finest specimens of Rome's nobility. Perceiving it to be a plot against his life, he had her put to death for this reason, but not in the least on account of her loose living, for he was quite used to seeing that, knowing all about it and putting up with it.

Anybody who has seen the statue of the said Messalina, recently found in the town of Bordeaux,[53] will admit that she certainly looked like one who led such a life. It is an ancient portrait piece found among some ruins, very lovely, and worth keeping to look at and make some study of. She was a very big woman, of very fine, tall stature, handsome of feature and with a charming coiffure in the ancient Roman style and her great height clearly reveals that she was as people say, for, from what I understand from a number of philosophers, doctors and physiognomists, tall women are most prone to this, especially when mannish, for, being like that, they share the heats of both man and woman, and these combined in one body and person make them more vigorous and energetic than a woman alone, very much, people say, as a big ship needs a lot of water to bear it up. Further, from what great authorities on the art of Venus say, a tall woman is better and more pleasing at it than a little one.

Regarding which a very great prince I once knew comes to my mind : wanting to praise a woman of whom he had had enjoyment, he uttered these words : 'She's a lovely whore, as tall as my own mother,' whereupon, challenged regarding the comparison he had just made, he explained that he had had no intention of saying that she was a great whore like his mother, but that she was big, (of the same build, that is) as his mother.

Sometimes one says things like that without meaning to, though sometimes without realizing it one is really speaking the truth.

So you see love is better made with big, tall women, if only because of the lovely charm and the majesty implicit in them, for in these matters this is as necessary and as delightful as in other acts and things done, neither more nor less than the riding of a fine upstanding Neapolitan charger is a hundred times more pleasing and delightful than riding a little nag, and gives the groom much more pleasure too, though the grooms needs to be good, to have a good seat and to show much more strength and skill. The same applies to large, tall women, for with such height they are likely to move with haughtier manner than the others, and often make a man lose his stirrups or his saddle, if he has not got a good seat, as I have heard from some jockeys who have ridden such, and such women take a pride

19

and are most scornful in unseating their riders and tipping them over on to their backsides, as I heard tell of one in this city who, the first time her man slept with her, said frankly : 'Hug me well and bind me to you with both arms and legs the best you can and hold on very tight, because I buck high, so you look out you don't fall. So, don't spare me, I am strong and practised enough to stand all your knockings, however roughly you set about it and if you spare me, I'm certainly not going to spare you. That's why the more you stake the more you stand to gain.' But she was the winner.

There you have it, one should take care how one manages the business with women who are bold and gay and vigorous and muscular and well put together like that, and although the superabundance of heat in them yields great satisfaction, they sometimes want too much through being so hot. However, as the saying has it, *Good harriers are of all sizes,* hence there are little, dwarfed women who have all got as much verve and charm and grace in these matters as the others, or want to vie with them, so are just as hot and spicy in the hunt, or even more so; I refer to masters of these skills, so that a small horse moves as fast as a big one, and, as an eminent person once said, a woman is like several animals, but principally a monkey, since all she does in bed is move about and fidget.

This divagation was due to recalling things. I must get back to our original subject.

So the cruel Nero thus merely repudiated his wife Octavia, daughter of Claudius and Messalina, for adultery, and his cruelty halted there.[54]

Domitian did still better, repudiating his wife Domitia Longina because she was so much in love with a certain actor and acrobat named Paris, that she did nothing else but play lecherously all day with him, neglecting her husband altogether, but after a very little while he took her back again and regretted their separation; you may well imagine that the acrobat had taught her various tricks of suppleness and contortioning which he thought Domitian might well find to his taste.[55]

Pertinax did the same with his wife Flavia Sulpitiana, not that he repudiated her, then took her back, but knowing that she made love with a singer and instrument player, giving herself without reservation to the man, decided to do no more than let her do so, while he for his part made love to a girl named Cornificia who was his first cousin, here following the opinion of Heliogabalus, who said there was nothing in the world more lovely than the conversation of one's relations, male and female. There are many who to my knowledge have made similar exchanges, basing themselves on these views.[56]

Thus the Emperor Severus too was not at all concerned about his wife's honour, she being a public whore without his ever thinking of correcting her of it. He said her name was Julia,[57] and for this reason she was to be excused, since from the earliest times all who bore that name had been given to being great whores who cuckolded[58] their husbands, just as in our Christendom I know many ladies bearing certain names which I will not mention, because of the respect I feel for our sacred faith, who are as a rule more given to being whores and upping their skirts in front than others who bear different names and of these very few have been observed to escape the rule.

But were I to mention the infinitude of other great ladies and ancient Roman empresses, to whom their cuckolded husbands, even when very cruel, did not apply their cruel ways or authority or use their privileges, even when they went to great excess, I would never be done, but I think there were very few prudes in those days, as the description of their way of living shows. Indeed, if one examines their effigies and ancient representations carefully, in their lovely faces one very plainly sees sheer lewdness engraved and depicted. And yet their husbands though cruel forgave them, and did not put them to death, at least, not some of them. And to think that it should have to be these pagans, who did not know God, who were so gentle and kindly regarding their wives and the human species, and that the majority of our kings, princes, lords and other Christians should be so cruel towards them for such shortcomings!

One should also prize great Philip Augustus, our French King, who, after repudiating his wife Angerberge,[59] the sister of Canute, King of Denmark, who was his second wife, on the grounds that she was his cousin in the third degree on the side of his first wife Isabel (others maintain that he suspected she had a lover) nevertheless, even though he had remarried, was by an ecclesiastical court driven to take her back, and carried her off pillion behind him, unbeknown to the Assembly of Soissons, which had been called together for this very matter, but was too dilatory about its decision.

Today none of our great men do like that, but as the least punishment of their wives lock them up for life in a nunnery, on bread and water, and cause their deaths there, poisoning them and killing them, either with their own hands or through the courts. But if they have such great longing to get rid of them and marry others, as is often the case, why do they not simply repudiate them and separate from them decently, without other harm, and request authority from the Pope to marry some other? Although man should not separate what is once joined together, we have all the same had cases of this quite recently, both in King Charles VIII and Louis XII of France.[60]

Regarding which I have heard a great theological authority speaking *à propos* of the late King of Spain, Philip, who had married his niece, mother of the present king,[61] and that by special dispensation, say : 'Either one must simply admit that the Pope is God's lieutenant-general on earth, and absolute, or he is not; if he is, as we Catholics ought to believe, we should clearly admit his quite absolute and infinite power on earth, and that without limit, and that he can join together and separate as he pleases; though if we do not hold him to be thus absolute, I am prepared to absolve those who hold such an erroneous view, but not good Catholics. And thus our holy father can remedy these dissolutions of marriage and also the great inconveniences which are thereby caused between husband and wife when they are so badly matched.'

Clearly women are much to be blamed for thus treating their husbands by breaking faith with them when this has been so approved by God, but yet, on the other hand, God has certainly prohibited killing, and from whatever side one views it, it is very detestable, and I have hardly ever seen bloodthirsty and murderous men who killed their wives who have not paid for it, for rarely have men who have loved bloodshed ended well, whereas many sinning women have sought and acquired forgiveness from God, as the Magdalene did.

Finally, these poor women are creatures more like God himself than we others are, by reason of their loveliness, for whatever is beautiful comes nearer to God, who is all beauty, just as what is ugly is of the devil.

The great Alfonso the Magnanimous, King of Naples,[62] used to say that beauty was a true sign of a good and decent way of living, just as a lovely flower is of a fine, good fruit : and indeed, in my lifetime I have seen many a lively woman who was all goodness, and though they made love, they did no harm, or aught else but think of that pleasure, putting their whole mind to it and not applying it to anything else.

I have also seen others who were very bad, pernicious, dangerous, cruel and very malicious, able nevertheless to give their minds to love and to evil at the same time.

Should it therefore be said that, thus being subjected to the uncertain, captious moods of their husbands, who are a hundred times more deserving of punishment before God, the women should thus be punished? For the character of such men is as unpleasant as the task of writing about them.

I will now mention another, who was a lord in Dalmatia, who having killed his wife's paramour, compelled her nightly to go on sleeping with his putrefying and stinking dead body, till the poor woman was choked by the evil stench, which she endured for several days.

Among the *Hundred Stories* of the Queen of Navarre you have the loveliest but most distressing story you could read on this matter, the one about that lovely lady of Germany whom her husband compelled regularly to drink from the skull of that lover of hers whom he had killed,[63] of which Lord Bernage then the ambassador of Charles VIII in that country saw the lamentable sight and put it on record.[64]

The very first time I ever went to Italy, on my way through Venice[65] I was told as genuine the story of a certain Albanian knight who, having caught his wife in the act of adultery, killed the lover. And was so irked that his wife should have not been

23

satisfied with him, when he was a real lady's man, most fit for
Venus, to the point of being able to return to the attack ten
or twelve times in a night, to punish her he went to the trouble
of seeking out a dozen roisterous fellows, all great wenchers,
reputed to be well and lavishly fashioned in their parts, and
very able and hot in the execution too, and took them on, paid
them, hired them for a fee, and locked them in his wife's bedroom (she being very lovely), and left her absolutely in their
hands, requesting them each and all to do their duty at it, with
double payment if they accomplished the task well. And they
all set upon her, one after the other, and so handled her that
in the end they killed her, to the very great satisfaction of the
husband, who when she was at her last gasp threw in her face
the jeer that as she had been so fond of that liquor she might
as well have her fill, after the fashion of what Semiramis did
to Cyrus when she stuck his head in a pot full of blood.[66]
That was a terrible sort of death.

The poor lady would not have suffered this death, had she
had the sturdy constitution of a wench in Caesar's camp in
Gaul of whom it is said that two whole legions followed each
other on her in a short time and all she did at the end was
leap up on to her feet, none the worse for it.

I have heard tell of a French townswoman, unmarried and
lovely, during our civil wars in a town which was captured,
having been raped by countless soldiers, when she came out
of it asked an excellent father of the church if she had sinned
greatly. And when she had told him her story he said : No, since
she had been taken by force and violated against her will, hating it all, to which she replied : 'God be praised then, for having had all I want once in my life, without sinning or offending
our Lord God !'

A lady of good family, having been raped in this way during the St Bartholemew massacre, when her husband was killed,
asked a man of knowledge and conscience if she had offended
God and would she not therefore be sternly punished, and if
she had not injured the shade of her husband who was but
freshly killed, and this churchman told her that if she had had
any pleasure when she was in the act, she certainly had sinned,

but if she had been disgusted, it did not matter at all. There was a fine judgement, indeed!

I must say I knew one lady whose view of the matter was different. She said there was never so much pleasure in the business as when she was half forced and flung down for it, even if by a noble, since the more a woman rebelled and refused the more the man got heated and lusty, since, once he had then forced the breach, the greater the fury and force with which he enjoyed his triumph, thereby giving his lady too much appetite, till for the sheer pleasure of it she would act as if half dead and swooning with love, though really swooning with the extreme pleasure she got out of it. This lady even said that very often she presented her husband with such antics and caprice and pretended to be so wild and queer and scornful, merely to put him on heat the more, and when he did get down to loving her, both he and she found it a hundred times better, for indeed, as many have written, a lady pleases more when she is a little difficult and resistant than when she lets the man put her on her back straightaway. Thus in war too a victory obtained by force is more outstanding, hotter and more pleasing than one given away, and men boast more of it. But the lady should also not go so far in this as to be really captious and to dismay, or she might well be mistaken for a crafty whore merely trying to make herself out to be pure, which would very often mean her disgrace. This is what I heard some ladies, among the cleverest and most skilful in this matter, say, and I base myself on them, not wishing to be so presumptuous as to give them counsel on what they know better than I do.

Now I have seen many men find great fault with some of these jealous, murderous husbands, on one point, namely, that if their wives are whores it is they themselves who are the cause of it. For, as St Augustine says, it is very silly of a man to require his wife to be chaste while he himself wallows in a cesspit of debauchery, the husband should be in the state in which he would like to find his wife. As a matter of fact, in Holy Writ we can find that there is no need at all for husband and wife to love each other so very greatly, meaning of course,

25

lascivious, loose loving, since if they put all their heart into such lewd pleasure-making and preoccupy themselves with that, always thinking of it and thus abandoning themselves to it, they fall short in the love which they owe to God, and indeed I myself have seen many women who loved their husbands very much, and the husbands them too, till both burned with such ardour that through it they quite forgot to serve God, so that the time which should have been given to this they spent and used on their debaucheries.

Further in their own beds, such husbands, which is worse, teach their wives countless lubricities, countless lewdnesses, countless tricks, counter-tricks and new ways of loving, practising on them the outrageous postures which Aretin[67] describes, till from the one hot coal they start within their bodies they breed a hundred and so become very loose, till, having been trained into all this, they cannot refrain from leaving their husbands and going to seek other mounts. And then their husbands lose their heads and punish their poor wives, in which they are very wrong, for since, once so well trained, they become conscious of their hearts, they naturally long to show others what they can do, whereas their husbands would like them to keep that knowledge to themselves, in which there is neither seemliness nor reason, any more than if a good horse-breeder had a horse which had trained well and could go through all the paces and he did not want anybody to see it about, or ride it, but expected folk to believe his mere word and buy it on such grounds alone.

I have heard the story told by a world-famous nobleman of standing that when he fell badly in love with a certain lovely lady, he was told by one of his friends that he would be losing his time, since she loved her husband too much, till it was suggested to him one day to make a hole through the floor through which he could look straight down onto their bed. When the couple retired, he did not fail to spy on them through the hole, and then he saw the greatest lubricities, debaucheries, and postures that were dirty, monstrous and outrageous, both on the part of the wife and even more of her husband, all carried through with extreme passion, to such extent that the next day he sought out his friend and told him the remarkable sights he had seen, adding : 'That woman's mine as soon as her husband goes on his trip to so-and-so, for she'll never be able to last long in the heated state that nature and art have given her, she will have to find relief for it, and so if I keep on at her, I shall get her.'

I knew another estimable lord who, being in love with a beautiful, estimable lady, and aware that in her closet she had an illustrated copy of Aretin, of which the husband knew, having seen it and permitted it, immediately concluded therefrom that he would get her, and without ever losing hope he served her so well and so assiduously that at last he did carry her off, and though he knew her now as one who had learned fine lessons and ways, whether from her husband or from others, she nevertheless denied that any of these had ever been her first masters, but said that lady nature, the best mistress in all the arts, had shown her the way. Anyway, both book and experience together had greatly served her in the matter, as she herself subsequently admitted.

One reads of a great courtesan and pimp of the days of Ancient Rome whose name was Elefantina,[68] who invented and made some of those pictures of Aretin's, and even worse ones, which great ladies and princesses[69] who indulged in whoring used to study as a very fine work. And there was that good whorish great lady, Cyrene of Corinth,[70] who was known as the 'lady of the twelve inventions' for having found a dozen ways of making love's enjoyment more voluptuous and lubricious !

Heliogabulus maintained and rewarded with large sums of money and gifts any man or woman who invented and demonstrated to him any such new invention which would stir his flagging lust,[71] and I have heard of other such cases at one time and another.

A few years back, Pope Sixtus V[72] had a secretary in Rome who had been in the service of Cardinal d'Este,[73] Capella his name was, hanged for a number of delinquencies, but among others for having compiled a book of fine drawings of that sort, depicting together a grandee whom I will not name for the sake of his robes, and a great lady, one of the loveliest women in Rome, all taken after nature and painted in life-like colours.

I knew a prince of a certain country[74] who did much better, for from a goldsmith he purchased a very lovely silver-gilt goblet, a *chef d'œuvre* and great curiosity, including the finest tooling, engraving and repoussée work one could see, on which were most daintily and finely represented some of Aretin's postures, worked with the burin, a man and a woman together —this at the base of the goblet, while in addition above these and at the top were series of pictures of the various ways in which the animals copulate, and it was from this that I first learned (for I have often seen this goblet and drunk from it, not without smiling) how the lions do it, in a way quite the contrary of all the other animals I ever heard of,[75] regardng which I refer to those who know without my telling them. This goblet was the show-piece on this prince's sideboard, for, as I have said, it was very lovely and richly worked and a pleasure to see inside and out.

When this prince entertained married and single ladies of the court, and he often gave parties, his butlers, on a word from him, never failed to offer the ladies this goblet to quaff from, and when they drank or afterwards, those who had never seen it were amazed and at a loss to know what to say; some would be abashed, the colour flying to their cheeks, others would whisper one to another : 'What was that engraved inside?' 'It looked to me like some very dirty things.' 'I'm not drinking any more.' 'I would have to be very thirsty to have another drink out of that.' But they had to come back to it again or collapse with thirst, so some would close their eyes as they drank, others, less prudish, did not do this, but those, whether married or unmarried, who had previously heard talk of this joke of the prince's would set a-laughing on the sly, while the men of the company split their sides.

When asked what they had found to laugh at and what they had seen, some of the women would say that they had only seen 'some pictures' though for that reason they would not take the goblet for another drink. Others said : 'Well, as for me, I don't see any harm in it, paintings and just seeing things doesn't leave any mark on your soul.' Some said : 'Good wine is the same out of that goblet as out of any other.' Yet others insisted that it was as good a cup to drink out of as any other, and quenched one's thirst just as well. Some were attacked for not closing their eyes when they drank, but they replied that they wanted to see what they were drinking, being afraid it might be some sort of laxative or poison, not wine. Others were asked what gave them the greater pleasure, seeing, or drinking. They replied: 'Both.' Some cried: 'What lovely grotesques!' others: 'There's nice games!' Some said: 'Those are lovely mirrors!' One comment that was made was: 'That goldsmith must have wanted something better to do, to fashion such silly things.' Yet others added: 'And you too, sire, still more, for buying this fine bauble.' Some were asked if they felt no pricking in the middle of their bodies from what they had seen. They replied that none of those games could stir them. Others were asked if they had not found the wine a bit peppery, and if it had not heated them up, especially seeing it was winter, and they replied that they had not noticed it heated, because it was very cold when they drank, though it had refreshed them a lot. Some were asked which picture out of all they had seen they would like to keep in their own beds, but they said the pictures wouldn't come off the goblet to be taken there.

In a word, there were a hundred thousand quips and japes tossed to and fro between the gentlemen and the ladies at table about this goblet, and as I see it, all together had a very pleasant bit of fun, well worth the seeing and the hearing, but above all, to my taste, the funniest thing and the best was to see the innocent unmarried ones, or rather those who pretended so to be, and some other ladies fresh to the company too, all maintaining a cold smile just at the tips of their noses and lips and forcing themselves to be hypocrites, as many of the ladies did. And note that even were they dying of thirst, the butlers would not have dared give them any other goblet or glass. And, what is more, some, to put a good face on it, swore that they would never attend such a party again. Yet they did not fail to do so, and attended very often too, for this prince was both very munificent and very hospitable. Other ladies when invited said: 'I shall go, but I shall protest and say we ought not be given that goblet to drink out of,' yet, when they were present, drank longer than anybody else. In the end they all grew so accustomed to it that they made no more scruples about drinking from it and, still better, some of them made use of the things they saw at the right time and place, while, what is more, there were some who took to debauch for the first time, just to try, for any intelligent person wants to try anything once.

There you have the effects of that lovely goblet so much told about. And from this one has to imagine the rest of the talk, dreams, acts and words that such ladies exchanged together, either in private or in company.

I think this goblet was very different from the one M. de Ronsard mentions in one of his first odes,[76] the one dedicated to the late King Henri, which begins :

> *Like the man who takes a goblet*
> *His treasury's proudest mould,*
> *And for each by rank pours out*
> *Wine that laughs within the gold.*

In this goblet the wine did not laugh at anybody, it was they who laughed at the wine, for some drank laughing, and others drank ravished, some pissed themselves as they drank, some drank as they pissed themselves, of course I don't mean exactly piss.

In short, so impressive were the pictures, visions and perspectives, that this goblet had shocking effects, which reminds me of once, in a gallery of the Count of Château Vilain, known as Lord Adjacet's[77] house, when a party of ladies came to see this lovely house, with its many paintings. *A elles se présenta un tableau fort beau, où estoyent representées force belles dames nues qui estoyent aux bains, qui s'entretouchoyent, se palpoyent, se manioyent, et frottoyent, s'entremesloyent, se tastonnoyent, et, qui plus est, se faisoyent le poil tant gentiment et si proprement en monstrant tout, qu'une froide recluse ou hermitte s'en fust eschauffée et emeue*; and that was why a great lady of whom I have heard talk and whom I knew, losing herself in this picture, turned to her man and said : 'We've been here too long, let us get into our carriage without delay and go home to my place, because I cannot bear this heat, I must go and quench it, I am too scorching hot.' And so left, taking with her her gentleman in attendance to sip that good water which her man gave her with his little pipette, water which is sweet enough without any sugar.

Such paintings and pictures do more harm to delicate minds than people realize; there is for instance one of a stark naked Venus lying down with her son, Cupid, looking at her, another of a Mars lying with Venus, another of a Leda lying with her swan. So many others are there too, both here and elsewhere, which are a little more modestly painted and better veiled than Aretin's pictures. But it almost all comes to the same thing, boiling down to that goblet of which we have just spoken, which by contraries very nearly matched the goblet found by Renault de Montauban in the castle of which Ariosto speaks,[78] which clearly depicts certain wretched cuckolds (whereas this one made them), yet that one disgraced the cuckolds and their faithless wives a little too much, but this one did not disgrace any particular person.

Today there is however no need for such books or paintings, since the husbands teach their wives enough, and there you have it, that's what such husbands' teachings serve !

I knew a good Venetian printer in Paris, Messer Bernardo by name (a relative of the great Aldus Manutius of Venice), who had his shop in the *Rue de St Jacques*, and he told me, and swore it was true, that in less than one year he had sold more than fifty sets of the two volume Aretin to many men, married and unmarried, and also to some women, of whom he mentioned three well known names to me, great ladies, whom I will not name, delivering the books directly to them, all very well bound, and under oath not to breathe a word. He did, however, tell me, and also said that after some time another lady had asked him if he had not something like what she had seen in the hands of one of those three, to which he had replied : *Signora, si, e peggio*, 'Yes, Madame, and worse,' and there at once was the cash, to purchase them all at their weight of gold's worth. There you have indeed a mad urge, to send her husband on a trip to Cornetto ['Horncastle'],[79] near Civita Vecchia.

All those positions and postures are hateful to God, so much so that St Jerome said : 'Any man who shows himself to be an unrestrained lover of his wife rather than a husband to her, is an adulterer and commits sin.' And since certain learned ecclesiastics have spoken of this, I will add a brief word in Latin, since they themselves did not wish to say it in French : *Excessus*, they say, *conjugum fit, quando uxor cognoscitur ante, retro, stando, sedendo, in latere, et mulier super virum*, like a little couplet which I once read, which says :

> *In prato viridi monialem ludere vidi*
> *Cum monacho leviter, ille sub, illa super.*

Others say, when they do it in some other fashion, that it is because their wife cannot conceive. Certainly, there are some women who do say that they conceive better by monstrous, unnatural and unusual postures than by those natural and common, because they take greater pleasure when they give themselves, as the poet puts it, [80] *more canino*, which is detestable. Yet pregnant women, at least some of them, do practise this, from fear of doing themselves harm from the front.

Other church authorities say that whatever form you use is good, but that : *semen ejaculetur in matricem mulieris, et cuomodocunque uxor cognoscatur, si vir ejaculetur semen in matricem, non est peccatum mortale.*

You will find this discussed in *Summa Benedicti*, the work of a learned Franciscan who has written very well on all sins, and shows that he has both seen and read much.[81] Anybody who cares to glance at this passage will see many abuses that husbands commit towards their wives. Thus he remarks that : *quando mulier est ita pinguis ut non possit aliter coire* to assume such positions : *non est peccatum mortale, modo vir ejaculetur semen in vas naturale.* But regarding this, some say that it would be better for husbands to abstain from their wives when they are full, as animals do, rather than befoul marriage by such bad things.

I once knew a famous courtesan in Rome, known as 'the Greek', who had been kept by a great lord there. After some time she felt desire to go and see France, by the aid of Lord Bonvisi of Lucca, a Lyons banker, very rich and enamoured of her. When she was there, she got very interested in this lord and his wife, and, among other things, whether she did not cuckold him, 'since', this courtesan said, 'I have so well trained her husband and taught him such good lessons, that if he has shown them to his wife and practised them with her, it is impossible for her not to have wanted to demonstrate them to other men, for when well learned our trade is so hot that one gets a hundred times more pleasure out of showing it to several men and practising it with them, than with merely one.' And she also said this lady owed her a good, generous present for her trouble and ability, because when the husband first attended her school he was a complete ignoramus, the most naïve, stupid beginner at it all that she had ever seen, but she had trained and shaped him so well that the wife must now find him a hundred times better. And indeed, the wife for her part also wanted to see the courtesan, and called on her in a disguise which the courtesan saw through, when she told her all I have set down here and worse things, too, unrestrained things, being a very unrestrained whore indeed. And there you have the way husbands forge knives to cut their own throats with—it means putting the horns on their heads. Thus when they abuse holy matrimony God punishes them, then they want to have their own back on their wives, though they are a hundred times more guilty themselves. So I am not at all surprised that this saintly authority should assert that marriage is almost a kind of adultery in itself. He meant it was so when abused in the way I have just described.

Hence our priesthood is forbidden to marry, for after lying with their wives and thoroughly debauching themselves with them, men are unfit to approach the holy altar. For, upon my faith, as I have heard tell, some men do more loose things with their wives than wastrels do with whores in brothels, for out of fear of catching disease these do not go very far or get very hot with their whores, as husbands do with their wives, who are clean and cannot convey disease; at least, some cannot, not all, for I have known some who did infect, just as some husbands infect their wives.

When they abuse their wives husbands are very guilty, I have heard great church authorities say, alleging that husbands do not behave as modestly as they should with their wives in bed, but do loose things with them as with concubines, whereas marriage has been instituted as the necessary means of rearing families, not for disorderly pleasure and lewdness. Which the Emperor Sejanus Commodus, otherwise known as Anchus Verus, put very neatly when his wife Domitia Calvilla, complained to him that he took to whores and courtesans and other women that which belonged to her in bed, robbing her of her little pleasures and minor acts, and he told her that she should put up with his 'satisfying my desires with other women, as the title of wife and consort is one of dignity and honour, not of pleasure and debauchery.'[82] I have never read or heard anywhere what the Empress his wife replied to this, but one can be quite sure that she was not all pleased with that gilded assertion and must have replied very bluntly, speaking moreover for most, if not all married women : 'A pox on your honour and cheers for pleasure ! That suits us better than the other thing.'

Nor should one have any doubts but that most married men among us today, and indeed in all ages, who have lovely wives do not say this, for they do not marry and tie themselves up or take their wives for any other reason than to enjoy them and have all sorts of lechery with them, and teach them rules both for the movement of their bodies and for the unrestrained and lascivious use of their speech, so their slumbering Venus may thereby the better be awakened and excited, then, having thus taught them well and debauched them, if the wives have recourse to any other man the husbands punish them, strike them, flog them, and put them to death.

Now there is as little sense in that as if anyone were to debauch a poor girl in her mother's arms and forcibly take her honour of virginity from her, and then, having had his will of her, began to beat her and force her to live again quite differently, chastely, a nice time to think of that, very timely, indeed ! Who would not condemn such a man as devoid of sense and meriting punishment? The same should be said of the many husbands who, when all is said, do more to debauch their wives, and teach them more bad ways by which they fall into lewd loose living, than their lovers do, for they have more time and leisure for it than the lovers, but if they come to discontinue their dealings with their wives, these change hands and masters, like a good horseman indeed, who finds a hundred times more pleasure in riding than the man who knows nothing about it at all. 'And the unfortunate thing is,'—thus this courtesan—'there is no trade in the world more insistent, nor more calling for the regular practice, than that of Venus.' By which husbands should take warning not to teach their wives such things, because they are too liable to corrupt them, or else, if they do see their wives being unfaithful, they should certainly not punish them, for it was they themselves who showed them the way.

Therefore I must illustrate these reflections by the case of a married woman whom I know, who was lovely and estimable and of quality and yielded to a very estimable knight really more from jealousy of a certain estimable lady whom this knight loved and kept, than from love. Wherefore, while he was having his enjoyment of her, she remarked to him : 'And now, to my great satisfaction, I am having my triumph of you and the love you have for So-and-so.' The knight replied : 'When put on her back, mastered and trodden, a woman can hardly talk of triumphing.' She took umbrage at this reply, as impinging on her honour, and at once replied : 'You are quite right.' And all at once she suddenly contrived to unseat her man and slipped from under him, then, changing roles, swiftly and nimbly mounted on him, putting him beneath her. Never before had a Roman knight or man-at-arms been so quick or agile in mounting or remounting a restive horse as in this joust this lady was with her man, and now, as she did him, she said : 'Anyway, now I can with a clear conscience say that I am triumphing over you, because I've got you on your back under me.' Now that was a lady of delightfully lecherous enterprise if you like, to mete such unusual treatment out to her man !

I have heard a very lovely, estimable and well-known lady of a certain country spoken of as much addicted to love and lewd things, yet who was so arrogant and so proud and so stout-hearted with it all that when it came to the job she never would let her man mount her, but put him under her, had him on his back, thinking it a great injury to her expansive heart and considering it great pusillanimity to be mastered and subjected like that herself, as if it had been some sort of conquest or slavery, but always insisted on maintaining the upper hand and pre-eminence. And she maintained a favourable situation for herself in the matter by never yielding to a man bigger than herself, lest, taking advantage of his superiority and strength, he were able to lay down the law and might turn her upside-down and backwards and tread her as suited him. Thus she chose men to whom she was equal in size or who were smaller than herself, whom she could order to accept the position, placing, the order and the shape she ordained that the combat of love should assume, just as a sergeant-major commands his men on the battle day, and she would instruct them too not to dare counter her on pain of losing the day altogether, that is, some merely their love-making, but others their lives too, so that they never could bring her to accept the least humiliation of submission, or get her to let them have their way for a moment, whether in a standing or a seated or a lying-down position. I base myself on the stories and reflections of those men and women who have dealt with such love, such positions, such posturings or forms.

This lady could thus insist without her alleged honour being infringed or her warm heart offended because, from what I have heard from some who have practised this, there were still sufficient ways left for the execution of her arrangements and practices.

Now was that not indeed a frightful though entertaining feminine foible, a bizarre scruple of an exaggerated conscience. Yet was she not really right, for it is an aggravating thing to put up with, for a woman to be mastered, laid out, and trodden, especially when the woman occasionally reflects on it and says: 'Think such and such a man got me under him and trod me,' for, though not actually meaning trod with his feet, but in another way, it really amounts to the same thing.

In the same way that particular lady never let her inferiors kiss her on the mouth. 'Since,' she said, 'touching and feeling mouth to mouth is the most sensitive and refined of all ways of touching, including the hand and all the other members,' and for this reason she would not put up with anybody else's breath or allow any dirty or smelly or unseemly mouth to touch hers.

Now we are on this subject, there is another matter I have seen some write of and discuss, namely, which partner has the greater glory or the greater pleasure in comparison with the other, the man or the woman, when together in these skirmishings and victories of love-making?

The man for his part adduces the foregoing argument : that the victory is by much the greater when one holds one's sweet enemy beaten down under one, subjugating her, treading her and mastering her at one's ease and pleasure, for there is no princess or lady so great but when she comes to it, even if with an inferior, a man not her equal, suffers the law and rule that Venus has written into her statutes, and therefore the glory and the honour of it remain greatly to the man's advantage.

The woman says : 'Yes, I admit you must feel triumphant when you hold me under you and tread me, but if it pleases me like that and it is merely a matter of who is on top, I am the one to triumph, by reason of being brought to it not by constraint but my gaiety of heart and sweet volition. As for your being on top displeasing me, indeed, it is really I who make use of you as if you were a slave or galley convict, in fact, I really have you harnessed like a regular cart horse, as you work away, labouring, sweating, panting, striving to achieve whatever forced labour and effort I want to get out of you, while all the time there am I, lying at my ease watching your efforts being worked up and sometimes laughing about them and getting quite a deal of pleasure out of seeing you at such strain, so that there are even times when I am quite sorry for you, according to my whim or when I deign to pity you, and when in that way I have indulged my imagination very nicely, I just leave my gallant weary, jaded, debilitated, nervously exhausted, unable to do anything more, merely craving a good rest and a good meal, a good drink, a restorative or a soothing broth. Whereas all that forced labour and all those efforts have no effect whatsoever on me, unless, my fine love-maker, it is to make me feel very well served at your expense, and with no other care than the craving for another man, to give me just as much again, till I reduce him to the same state as yourself. And so, never really yielding, but making my dear enemy yield, it is I who carry off the real victory and real triumph, since in any contest it is the one who is out who is dishonoured, not the one who fights on to the final point of death.'

Thus I have heard tell of a lovely, estimable lady who once when her husband awakened her from a deep sleep, from the rest she was taking, to make love, after he had finished said to him : 'You have finished, but I have not.' And, getting on top of him, she fettered him completely with her arms, her hands, her feet, her legs, lacing him about : 'I will teach you not to waken me another time,' she said, as she laboured away wildly. shaking him and stirring him, who was still underneath and could not get away, perspiring, gasping, worn out, crying for mercy. But in spite of himself she made him do it again and made him so tired, so exhausted, so flabby, that he simply could not get his breath and he swore that another time he would take her when it suited her, her mood and her appetite. This story is better to imagine and picture than to write.

So there you have the arguments of the lady with several others she might have adduced.

Encor l'homme replicque là dessus: 'Je n'ay point aucun vaisseau ny baschot comme vous avez le vostre, dans lequel je jette un gassouil de pollution et d'ordure (si ordure se doit appeller la semence humaine jettée par mariage et paillardise), qui vous salit et vous y pisse comme dans un pot.—Ouy,' dit la dame; 'mais aussitost ce beau sperme, que vous autres dites estre le sang le plus pur et net que vous avez, je le vous vais pisser incontinent et jetter ou dans un pot ou bassin, ou en un retrait, et le mesler avec une autre ordure tres puante et salle et vilaine; car de cinq cents coups que l'on nous touchera, de mille deux mille, trois mille, voire d'une infinité, voire de nul, nous n'engroissons que d'un coup, et la matrice ne retient qu'une fois; car si le sperme y entre bien et est bien retenu, celuy là est bien logé, mais les autres fort sallaudement nous les logeons comme je viens de dire. Voilà pourquoy il ne faut se vanter de nous gazouiller de vos ordures de sperme; car, outre celuy là que nous concevons, nous le jettons et rendons pour n'en faire plus de cas aussitost que l'avons receu et qu'il ne nous donne plus de plaisir, et en sommes quittes en disant: Monsieur le potagier, voilà vostre brouet que je vous rends, et le vous claque là; il a perdu le bon goust que m'en avez donné premierement. Et notez que la moindre bagasse en peut dire autant à un grand roy ou prince, s'il l'a repassée; qui est un grand mespris, d'autant que l'on tient le sang royal pour le plus precieux qui soit point. Vrayment il est bien gardé et logé bien precieusement plus que d'un autre!'

Voylà le dire des femmes; qui est un grand cas pourtant qu'un sang si precieux se pollue et se contamine ainsy si sallaudement et vilainement; ce qui estoit defendu en la loy de Moyse, de ne le nullement prostituer en terre; mais on fait bien pis quand on le mesle avec de l'ordure très orde et salle.

Further, if they did as a great prince of whom I have heard did, who if he dreamt during the night and soiled his sheets, had them interred so scrupulous was he, saying it was a little child arising therefrom that was dead and it was a pity and a very great loss that this blood had not been put into his wife's womb, for then the child might have lived.

He may well have been mistaken in this, since of a thousand cohabitations that a husband has with his wife in the course of a year, it is, as I have said, quite feasible for her not to become pregnant at all, indeed, not merely once in her life, but never, for there are women who are quite barren and sterile, and never do conceive. Whence arose the error of certain miscreants that marriage was instituted not so much for procreation as for pleasure, which is bad faith and bad talk too, since, for all that a woman is not made pregnant every time one takes her, that is by the purpose of the Almighty, which is hidden from us, by God's wishing to punish the particular husband and wife, since the greatest blessing that God can send us in marriage is good offspring and not that concubinage which many wives like to get from their lovers. Others however are different, refusing to let one leave anything inside them, both so as not to plant children on their husbands which are not theirs and so they might think they did their husbands no wrong and did not cuckold them at all, if no dew got into them—rather as a poor, delicate stomach cannot be upset by bad or indigestible food if one merely puts it in one's mouth, masticates it and then spits it out again.

This is why men are called cuckolds, which is really the same name as those April birds bear, who are thus called because they go laying in others' nests—they are cuckolds by antinomy, that is, when others come and lay in their nest, that is, in their wives' parts, which is the same as saying when others come injecting them with seed and giving them children.

This is how it is that many women think they are doing their husbands no wrong by just putting it in and having all the fun they want without taking in any seed, so they have a clear conscience in the matter, like one great noblewoman I heard tell of, who said to her gentleman-in-waiting: 'Knock as much as you like and give me pleasure, but on your life take care not to sprinkle me inside, not a single drop, or your life is at stake!' So that the knight in question had to be very careful and watch out for the moment when the bore came up and was about to break.

I heard a tale of that sort from Baron de Sanzay of Brittany,[83] a very upstanding and fine aristocrat who had the misfortune to be captured by pirates and taken to Algiers, (a great sailor, had not death taken him hence at an early age, for he had made a good start in that calling, and had all the marks and signs of it, having lost an arm carried away by a cannon shot at sea.) His master, who had him as slave, was the Grand Mufti of the local mosque, and he had a very lovely wife who fell deeply in love with Sanzay, so much so that she ordered him to come and take his pleasure love-making with her, and said she would see he was treated very well, better than any other slave of hers. But above all she ordered him very particularly, and on his life too, or under threat of stern imprisonment, not to eject a single drop of seed into her body, since, she said, she did not want any pollution or contamination by Christian blood, by which she thought she would be greatly offending her law and her great prophet Mahommed, and she further instructed Sanzay that even if when she was at the height of her pleasure she told him a hundred times to let the whole packet go in, he was never to do so, since it would merely be her immense enjoyment getting the better of her that made her say such a thing, and not the will of her heart.

In order in spite of being a Christian to have good treatment and the greatest freedom, Sanzay turned a blind eye to that offence to his faith, for a poor slave who is roughly treated and wretchedly chained may well forget himself a little. He obeyed the lady and was so careful and so attentive to her instructions that he ruled his pleasure very well, pounding away at his lady's mortar most steadfastly and stoutly, without ever letting any water trickle, for just as his sluice was about to give way and flood over, he would draw it out, hold it tight and then drain it off wherever else he could, for which this woman loved him still more, being most rigorous about her strict orders. And even when she cried: 'Let it go, I give you full permission!' he never would, being afraid of being beaten in Turkish fashion, as he had seen his companions suffer before his face.

That was a terrible woman's whim, yet it still seems to me that she did a great deal, both for her soul, which was Turkish, and for the man, who was a Christian, since he never did have an emission when joined with her, though he told me that never in all his life had he had such trouble.

He told me another story, the most delightful one too, of a trick she once played on him, but as it is very dirty I shall remain silent about it, for fear of offending chaste ears.

Later this Sanzay was ransomed by his own folk,[84] men of honour and good family in Brittany, for he was related to many great men, including the Constable of France,[85] who was very fond of Sanzay's eldest brother,[86] and helped a great deal towards this deliverance. And when it was accomplished, Sanzay came to court and told Lord d'Estrozze[87] and me a great deal about several matters, including this.

What now are we to say of certain husbands who are not satisfied with getting satisfaction and lewd pleasure from their wives, but give others, that is, their comrades or their friends, an appetite for them? Thus I have known several men who will praise their wives to their friends, talking about their beauties, going into a description of their limbs and the parts of their bodies, or even depicting the pleasures they have with them and the tricks they get up to with them, or have them kiss and touch and feel their wives, even see them naked.

What do men like that deserve, if not to be very thoroughly cuckolded indeed, as by means of his ring Gyges cuckolded Candaulus King of the Lydians, who, fool that he was, had praised the rare beauty of his wife to Gyges, as if holding his tongue hurt or damaged him, and then actually showed him her stark naked, which made Gyges so amorous of her that in the end he had his full pleasure of her, secured the assassination of the King and took over his kingdom.[88] It is said that Candaulus's wife was so outraged by having thus been shown to Gyges that she forced the latter to commit this evil deed, saying: 'Either the man who urged and suggested such a thing to you must die by your hand, or you, who have seen me naked must die by the hand of some other.' This king must really have been at a very loose end thus to give another man an appetite for fresh meat which was so lovely and so good, but which he should himself have set more store by.

Louis, Duke of Orleans, killed at the Barbette Gate[89] of Paris, did quite the contrary (he was a great debaucher of the court ladies, and invariably the most eminent among them).[90] One day when he had in bed with him a certain very lovely and great lady and her husband entered the room to bid him good morning, he quickly covered the head of the lady (the other man's wife) with the sheet, thereby uncovering her whole body, to be looked at and even fondled by the visitor at his pleasure, though strictly forbidding him on his life to pull the sheet away from her face or indeed to uncover any more of her, but repeatedly asking him what he had to say about that lovely stark naked flesh. The other man got very worked up and had tremendous satisfaction from this.

Then the Duke said he might go, which he did without ever succeeding in realizing that it had been his own wife!

Had he really seen her before this without anything on, (as I have many women,) he would, I imagine, surely have recognized her by various points, so it is a good thing sometimes to look at your wife's body.

This lady, when her husband had left, was asked by the Duke of Orleans whether she had not been alarmed and afraid. I leave you to guess what she said, and the torture and strain she was in for a quarter of an hour, for it had only needed a trifling indiscretion, or the least disobedience on the husband's part, lifting the sheet! True, the Duke had forbidden this and would immediately have killed the husband to prevent his harming his wife.

The good part of the story, however, is that when night came and the husband slept with his wife, he told her that that day the Duke of Orleans had shown him the loveliest woman he had ever seen, though he could say nothing about her features, as seeing her face had been forbidden him! I leave it to you to imagine what the wife must have thought. The issue of that great lady and the Duke of Orleans, I may add, is said to have been that fine, courageous, illegitimate son of Orleans who was the support of France and the scourge of England —the originator of the noble and great-hearted line of the Dunois.

Now, to go back to these husbands prodigal of the sight of their naked wives, I know one who one morning when a friend of his went to see him in his room while he was dressing, showed him his wife stark naked stretched straight out, sound asleep, having herself pulled the sheets off her, as it was very hot, and the husband had drawn back half the curtain, so as it rose the sun fell straight on her, and thus the visitor had ample time to study her to his fill, and saw nothing which was not perfectly lovely, and was able to feast his eyes, not as much as he would have liked, but as much as he was able, after which the husband and he went to wait on the King.

The following day, the knight, who was an assiduous attendant on that great lady, told her the sight he had had, even describing to her many points about her lovely limbs which he had noticed, including the most concealed things, whereupon the husband confirmed this story and said it was he himself who had drawn back the curtain. The lady in question was so annoyed by the wrong she thought her husband had done her that merely for this reason she let herself be swayed in favour of her husband's friend, which was something all his courtship had never gained him.

I once knew a very great prince who, one morning, when he wanted to go hunting, and his knights had come round to him as he was at dressing—just as his breeches were being made ready, in fact, with his wife in bed beside him, holding his member firmly in her hand—he pulled off the counterpane so sharply that she had not time to take her hand away from where it was, and they all saw what she was doing and half her naked body too, whereupon the Prince laughed and said to the knights present: 'Well, gentlemen, have I not now shown you enough of my wife?' But she was so put out by this trick that she bore a great grudge against him, especially for being taken by surprise with her hand like that, and most likely afterwards she got her own back very thoroughly.

I know another story of a great lord who, knowing that a friend and relation of his was amorous of his wife, either to augment his craving, or because of the grudge and disheartenment he might feel because his friend had so lovely a wife whom he could have no taste of, showed her to him one morning when the friend came into their room when they were both in bed together, half naked, and then went much further, for he actually did it in front of his friend, riding her as if she had agreed to it, and what is more, called on his friend to watch it all, saying he was doing this purposely to please him. I leave it to you to imagine whether after that indiscretion of her husband's the wife did not find the opportunity to let the friend have everything too, and with good reason indeed, thinking that if her husband had nothing better to do than that, he might as well wear the horns.

I have heard tell of another, a great lord too, who did the

same to his wife in front of a great prince, his master, but that was at the prince's request and orders, because he found pleasure in such enjoyment. But are these not really the guilty ones, if, after being pimps themselves, they should think also to be their own executioners?

One should never show one's wife naked, nor one's lands, country or places, was what a great captain told me *à propos* of the late Duke of Savoy,[91] who when our last King Henry[92] was on his way back from Poland and passing through Lombardy, counselled him not to enter the city of Milan, for the reason that the King of Spain might be offended. This however was not the real reason, what he feared was that if the King did enter Milan and saw the whole city, and was able to contemplate its loveliness, its richness and its greatness, he might be tempted by excess of envy to ravish it and reconquer it, as by good and just right indeed, it having been his forbears'. And that was the real reason, as a great prince said who had had it direct from the late King, who knew the crux of the matter. However, to please Savoy and cause the King of Spain no umbrage, he did by-pass Milan, although he had all the desire in the world to go there, as he did me the honour of telling me when back at Lyons, so that in the whole business one suspects that Savoy was being more Spanish than French.

I also consider those husbands worthy of censure who, having been granted their lives by reason of their wife's favours are so ungrateful as to treat them very roughly, to the extent of trying to kill them, merely because of suspicion that the wives have made love with other men. I have heard for instance of a prince against whose life certain conspirators had plotted, when his wife by entreating them made them desist, thereby certainly saving him from slaughter, but for which she subsequently had very poor recognition, but was in fact treated very harshly.

I have also seen a nobleman[93] who, having been charged and put on trial for having fallen very short of his duty in support of his general in a battle, to the point of letting him be killed without offering him any aid or assistance, for which this nobleman was all but tried and condemned to decapitation, and that notwithstanding the offer he made to ransom his own life with twenty thousand crowns' payment, but whose wife approached a certain great prince and then, with the permission and indeed on the entreaty of this husband of hers, slept with the prince, so that what money had not been able to buy her beauty and her body achieved, and saved the husband's life and liberty, yet afterwards the nobleman treated her as badly as any man could. Such cruel, insensate husbands are undoubtedly very wretched creatures.

I have however known other husbands who have not done this, but were sensible enough to see where their good fortune had come from, and all their lives honoured that excellent hole for saving them from death.

There is yet another sort of cuckolds, those who are not satisfied with having been quarrelsome fellows all their lives, but when it comes to dying and they are on the point of departing from this world, are still captious, such as one I knew who had a very lovely, estimable wife, but who however had not quite strictly reserved herself to her husband only. Well, when he was dying, he said to her: 'Oh, my dear one, I am going to die. Would that God granted you could keep me company, so you and I went to the other world together, then my death would be so much less hateful to me, and I would be more reconciled to it.' But the wife, who was still very lovely, and young, being only thirty, did not at all want to follow him or pay any attention to that wish, nor did she want to pretend to be a fool, as we read of Evadne,[94] daughter of Mars and Iphis, Capaneus's wife, who loved him so much that when he was dead, as soon as his body was cast onto the pyre she threw herself on after it, alive as she was, and burned up and was consumed with him, by this great constancy and steadfastness thus accompanying him into death.[95]

Alcestis did far better, for, having learned from the oracle that her husband Admettus, King of Thessaly, was soon to die if his life were not ransomed back by the death of one who loved him, without hesitation did a way with herself and thereby saved her husband.

Today we have no more women so great-hearted as to be ready of their own volition to enter the grave with their husbands or quickly follow them there. No, they are no more. The mares are all dead, as the Paris horse-jobbers say when you cannot find one horse any good.

That is why I thought the husband just mentioned quite wrong to make such a suggestion to his wife, indeed, outrageous to call on her to die too, as if it were some pleasant party he could invite her to. Fine jealousy it was indeed that made him speak so, imagining how unpleasant he might find it down in hell when he saw the wife he had trained so well in the arms of one of her lovers, or of some fresh husband.

What a strange jealousy that was! The husband should have seen this at once and at every whip and turn told her that if he succeeded in avoiding it he would not put up any longer from her what he had already put up with, and that as long as he was alive he had never suffered from it and let her follow her own bent.

The worthy Tancred[96] did not do this—the one who was formerly so outstanding in the holy war. When on the point of death, with his wife grieving beside him together with the Count of Tripoli, he begged them after his death to marry one another, indeed, gave his wife orders to that effect, and they did marry.

You will realize that he had seen some love preludes while he was alive, since she could be as much a strumpet as her mother, the Countess of Anjou,[97] who, after the Count of Brittany had maintained her a long time, passed to King Philippe of France who also kept her and made him that bastard girl, Cecily by name, and then gave her in marriage to the glorious Tancred who with his great exploits behind him certainly did not deserve to be cuckolded.

An Albanian who had been condemned beyond the mountains to be hanged for some delinquency committed when in the service of the King of France, when about to be taken to execution asked if he could see his wife to bid her farewell, she being a very lovely and very forthcoming woman. And when he was bidding her farewell and kissing her, what did he do but suddenly bite off her nose with his sharp teeth and rend it from her lovely face. When the authorities questioned him as to why he had done such a foul thing to his wife, he replied that he had done it from keen jealousy. 'Since,' he said, 'she is very lovely, and I know that for that reason after my death she would at once be sought after and moreover would at once give herself to one of my comrades, for I know her to be very hot and she would waste no time forgetting me without delay. But after my death I would like her to remember me and weep for me and be saddened, if not by my death, at least because of her disfigurement. Anyway, none of my comrades will now have the pleasure with her that I have had.' Now that was a monstrous jealousy!

I have heard tell of others[98] who, feeling themselves growing old, decrepit, crippled, debilitated and near to death, have from sheer spite and jealousy secretly speeded on the ageing of their better halves, even when they were beautiful.

Now, regarding the strange humours of such cruel, tyrannical husbands, who encompass the death of their wives in this way, I once heard a discussion which amounted to this, whether, if they detect or suspect the cruel and murderous intentions of their husbands regarding the wives, they should be allowed to take the lead, make the first move, and, to save themselves, ensure that their husbands die first, sending them on ahead to secure room for them both in the other world.

I have heard it argued that yes, they may do so, not according to God, since any murder is forbidden, as I have remarked, but certainly by the common view, readily, those who say this basing themselves on the thought that it is always better to forestall than to be forestalled, for after all, every person is bound to cherish his own life, and since God had granted it, should indeed preserve it till by our death he summons us. Otherwise, seeing death before them, to rush into it and not avoid it when they can would be for such wives to commit suicide, an act which God greatly abhors, whence it is better to send the husbands in advance as ambassadors and ward off their blow, as did Blanche d'Awrebruche with her husband, Lord de Flavy, Captain and Governor of Compiègne, who betrayed and was the cause of the loss and the death of the Maid of Orleans. For this Lady Blanche, learning that her husband intended to have her drowned, forestalled him and with the aid of his barber suffocated him and strangled him, for which King Charles VII immediately gave her pardon,[99] in all of which the treachery of the husband almost certainly worked in her favour more than anything else. The matter is related in the *Annales de France*, principally the part dealing with Guyenne.[100]

The same step was taken by a Lady de la Borne[101] in the reign of King François, who denounced her husband and handed him over to justice for a number of foolish acts and crimes, perhaps great, which he had committed with her and others, first getting him imprisoned and then pulling strings against him till in the end he was decapitated. I have heard my grandmother tell the story of this, and she said that Lady de la Borne came of a good family and was a handsome woman. This was a clear case of forestalling.

Queen Jeanne I of Naples did the same with her third husband, the *Infanta* of Majorca, whom she had decapitated for the reason I give in her speech,[102] (in another of my works), though it may well have been that she was afraid of him, and wanted to get rid of him first, in which she was quite right, and all her like, to do the same when they suspect their gallants.

I have heard of many ladies who made a grand escape in this way, and I even knew one who, having been found by her husband together with her lover, he said nothing to one or the other, but, heartbroken, left them, so there she was, abandoned in the room where she was found with her lover, and aghast and upset at thus falling so low in her husband's estimation. Even so, this lady had will enough to say: 'He has neither said nor done anything about this, I am afraid he may be storing it up against me. But if I felt sure he intended to cause my death, I would see to it that he suffered death the first.' Her luck was so good that some time after this, he died naturally, which was a great relief to him for since that moment he had been unable to touch food, whatever his wife did to try to get him to do so.

There is yet another sort of debate and open question regarding such mad and insensate husbands, such dangerous cuckolds, namely, whom they should make their victim and have their revenge on, their wives or the wives' lovers.

There are those who say solely on the wife, basing themselves on the Italian proverb which runs : *morta la bestia, morta la rabbia o veneno*—'with the beast the madness or poison dies too'—thinking, as it seems to them, that they are well quit of their trouble when they have killed the woman who caused their grief, in exactly the same way as those who have been bitten or stung by a scorpion, when the most sovereign remedy is to take the creature, kill or rather macerate it and apply it to the bite or wound it has made. So, as a rule, people at once say that it is the women who are most to blame. This I take with reference to great ladies, ladies of prominence, not the little and common ones or the common herd, for it is the great ladies who by the attraction of their beauties, by their intimacies, by the orders they give and the things they say start the skirmishing. All the men do is play up to them, just as it is those who seek and start wars that are the guilty ones, more than those who defend themselves; and since as a rule men do not rush into such dangerous situations at too high a level without the ladies, they feel for them, similarly as in the case of a large, handsome, strong frontier town it is very difficult to undertake any surprise military action, unless there has been secret espionage among some of the inhabititants or there are some inhabitants of the town who prompt and invite the assault and lend the attacking force a hand.

Now, the womenfolk should be forgiven also because they are a trifle less robust than are men. One should remember too that once they take it into their heads to love and to put the notion of love into your mind, they go through with it, whatever the cost, not satisfied (though not all of them) to harbour it in their hearts and gradually be eaten up by it, becoming haggard and run down, thereby losing their good looks—which is why they so crave to be cured of it and get pleasure from it, not to die of ferret sickness, as folk call it.[103]

True, I have known many a lovely lady of that temperament herself to be the initiator, seeking her other half. They do so more often than the men, and for various reasons; some because they find the man fine, handsome, plucky and pleasant, others to pocket a nice little sum of money, others to get pearls or precious stones or cloth of gold or silver gowns out of it. Indeed I have seen them making it as difficult for a man to get out of it as to get free from a merchant selling his wares. Besides, there is the saying that she who takes, gives; others do it to curry favour at court, others like many lovely women I have known, give themselves to judges, because, not really having the law on their side, they manage to get a point stretched by their fine looks and by their c——s, while there are yet others who make love merely to draw the luscious substance from the man's body.

I have seen many women so in love with their lovers that they all but followed them round and took them by force, and the whole world blushed with shame for them.

I knew one very lovely lady who was so amorous of a famous noble that whereas as a rule it is the gentlemen-in-waiting who sport their lady's colours, here she sported those of her man. I could name the colours too, but that would be to reveal too much.

I knew another lady who when her husband insulted her man in a tournament held at court, when later he was in the ballroom having his triumph, dressed herself up in man's clothes and made off to find her lover and under cover of her fancy-dress have him take her for a moment, she was so dying of love for him.

I knew an estimable lord, one of the less scandalous figures at court in fact, who, wanting one day to serve a lady who was lovely and estimable if there ever was one, because she had for her part given him many indications, though at the same time he was very circumspect for many reasons and considerations—however, notwithstanding, the lady in question had set her heart on him, and risky though it was she had cast the die, (this was her own story,) and thereafter never desisted trying to win him to herself by the fairest words of love she could

51

find, among others saying: 'At least if you do not love me, allow me to love you, do not count my qualities but have regard for the impulses of heart and soul,' though there was no question but that she outweighed the lord in question in her fine qualities. So what could he do, seeing that she loved him so, but love her, and serve her, after which he requested payment and recompense for his devotion, and got it too, which was only right, since a man's services should always be paid for.

I could adduce endless examples of ladies like this who courted more than they were courted. That indeed is why the ladies are more to blame than their lovers, for once they have set their hearts on their man, they never give up till they get what they want and will attract their man, by little magnetic glances, by their points of beauty, by their sweet charms, which they study a hundred thousand ways of bringing out, by creams cunningly applied to their cheeks if their complexion is not good, by finery of all sorts, by lavish, delightful hairdressings all wonderfully arranged, by their impressive, their superb gowns, but above all by their ever rich and suggestive talk, further by charming, extravagant little gestures and intimacies, and by presents and gifts. There you have what captures the men, and once they are taken on the hook, they cannot fail to take the ladies, which is why some hold that the husbands should have their vengeance of the women.

Others however say that where possible it is the men who should be punished, exactly as one would those who besiege a city, for they it is who first sound the attack, they who first call on the women to yield, they who make the first open move, who prepare the first bridge-heads, build the first earthworks, dig the first trenches, prepare the first batteries. They it is first assault the walls and parley for the city to yield. That is what is said of the lovers. Seeing that the boldest of them, those who are courageous and determined, do indeed attack the fortifications of modesty of the ladies who, after going through all the motions of counter-attack against such great importuning, in the end find themselves obliged to run up the white flag and receive their sweet enemies in their castles. In which however it does not seem to me that they are so much to blame as might be said, since it is never easy to get rid of a besieger without some loss of one's own forces. Thus I have seen many men who by dint of lengthy service and perseverance, had their pleasure of the ladies on whom they attended, although at the outset these would, to use a plain expression, not have let them kiss their backsides, and the men press the ladies to such a point, (at least, some of them,) that tears are brought to their eyes. And it is all done much as one gives alms to beggars outside the churches in Paris, alms often enough given more because the beggars do pester one so than for love of God. Thus many women do it more from being too much pestered than for being amorous, and much the same applies in the case of some great men, it is because the ladies are afraid of them and have not the courage to refuse them because of the power they wield that they do it, they are afraid of displeasing them and thereby being disgraced afterwards for it, or publicly insulted, or made to suffer some even greater derogation of their honour, for I have seen such things happen in cases of this sort.

This is why bad husbands, who delight so much in bloodshed and murder and treating their wives badly should not be so hasty, but first quietly enquire into all the circumstances, however grievous what they thus learn may be, giving them much to scratch their polls about, although some husbands, wretched creatures that they are, give them all the opportunity in the world.

Thus I knew a great foreign prince who had married a very lovely lady of standing, but stopped paying her his attentions, to transfer them to some other woman, who was generally said to be a courtesan, though others said it was a lady of honour whom he had led astray. But that was not enough for him, when he made this other woman sleep with him, it was in a bedroom downstairs, under his wife's room, immediately under her bed, and when he was about to ride his mistress he was not satisfied with the wrong he was doing his wife, but to jeer and mock her he would take a short pike and give two or three raps on the floor of the room above and call out to his wife : 'My respects to you, dame !' This mockery and scorn went on for some days, and made the wife very angry, and she was so outraged and so wanted her revenge that she approached a very estimable knight and one day, contriving to be alone with him, said: 'Sir So-and-so, I want you to take your pleasure of me. If you don't, I know a way of ruining you.' The knight in question was only too pleased with such a fine adventure and was not saying no. So now, when her husband took his mistress in his arms, she took her lover, and when her husband shouted: 'My respects to you!' she replied in like coin: 'And mine to you!' and then pledged his toast, and these toasts and pledgings of toasts, these matched ridings of theirs lasted quite a time, till at last this prince, who was both perspicacious and of a suspicious nature, suddenly wondered, and, having had a peephole made, discovered that his wife was cuckolding him very nicely and as her revenge toasting him back very finely. And when he saw this really was so, he at once turned the farce into a tragedy. For the last time he toasted her, and when she pledged him back, he rushed upstairs, broke open the door, entered the room and charged her with the wrong she was doing him, whereupon she stood up for herself and said: 'I know I am a dead woman, kill me, don't hesitate, I am not afraid of death, but I die gladly, I can tell you, because I've had my own back on you and cuckolded you and put the horns on your head nicely! But it was you showed me how or I would never have done this wrong, for I had sworn absolute loyalty to you and would never have broken my oath, not for all the handsomest men in the world. But you were not worthy of a woman as decent as I. Come on, kill me, at once! But if you have a drop of pity in you, do, I beg you, forgive this poor knight who took no initiative at all in this. I both invited and urged him to help me thus to have my revenge.' Too cruel by far, without the least consideration, the prince killed them both. But what else could that poor princess have done in response to the indignities and scorn shown her by her husband, save, seeing that she cared no more for this world, do what she did? Some will say she was not at fault, some that she was. There are a lot of things to be said on the matter.

In the *Hundred Stories* of the Queen of Navarre there is one,[104] and a very nice story too, almost identical to this, about a Queen of Naples who in the same way avenged herself of the King her husband, but here the end was not so tragic.

And with this let us leave these demoniacal madly insensate cuckolds and say no more about them, for they are hateful and not very prepossessing, and I would never end were I to attempt to describe them all, but the subject is neither pretty nor prepossessing. Let us say a little about kindly cuckolds, those who are pleasant fellows, pleasant tempered, good company and as patient as saints, cheerful, amenable, jolly good fellows who turn the blind eye.

Now, there are cuckolds dyed in the wool, some of them cuckolds who know they are cuckolds before they marry, that is, those whose ladies, whether widows or unmarried, had already taken the leap, while there are yet others who have not a clue, but marry the women on their own faith and that of their fathers and mothers, their relations and their friends.

I have known many men who married women and girls whom the husbands knew quite well to have been thoroughly tested out by certain kings, princes, lords, knights and many another too, yet who were so enraptured by their love, as well as the property, the jewellery, and the money they had earned in the trade of love, that they had no scruple about marrying them. For the moment I will confine myself to the unmarried girls.

I have heard of a daughter of a very great man, one of the royal blood,[105] who, being in love with a knight, so let herself go with him that when he had taken the first fruits of her love she acquired such a taste for love-making that she kept the knight in her dressing-room for a whole month, feeding him up with tasty broths and restoratives, and fine carminative meats, the better to alembic him and draw out his substance, and having done her apprenticeship under him, went on taking occasional lessons from him till he grew old, and then studied under others, after which, at the age of forty, she married a prince who had not a word to say in objection, but was in fact very glad to be able to make so good a match.

Boccaccio mentions a proverb[106] current in his day, that a *pair of lips kissed* (in some versions *a girl that is* f——) *never lose their fortune but monthly renew it like the moon*. He quotes it *à propos* of a story he tells of that very lovely daughter of the Sultan of Egypt[107] who went the rounds on the pikes of nine different lovers, one after the other, doing it at least three thousand times, in the end to be given in marriage as a perfect virgin to the King of Garb,[108] making out she was as much a virgin as if she had been affianced to this King at the start, and he too had not a word to say, but was quite content. A very nice story.

I once heard a great man say that among some of the great (of course not all), such girls are not scorned at all, even though three or four may have handled them and piked them before these great ones became their husbands, and this he said *à propos* of a certain prince who was much in love with a great lady who was of rather higher standing than he was, and who loved him too, but where it so happened that they did not marry, as they had thought they would, upon which this great man I am speaking of at once enquired : 'Has So-and-so at least had a ride on the little nag?' And when the other said that as far as he knew, gossip had it that he had not, the great man's rejoinder was : 'More's the pity, for then at least they would have had that satisfaction one of another, even if it did go no further.' For among the great all those rules and stipulations about virginity are not respected, since for the unions of the great everything has to be allowed. What is more, these good, kindly dyed-in-the-wool cuckolds are really too lucky.

When King Charles made the tour of his kingdom, a daughter of a very good family[109] who had just given birth to a daughter in a fine town which I could name was left behind. The child was put in the charge of a poor woman of that town, to provide board and lodging and bring her up, two hundred crowns being paid in advance for keep. The poor woman fed her and brought her up so well that in fifteen years she was very lovely and then she yielded, for her mother no longer cared about her, but four months later she had married a grandee.[110] Oh, how many cases of both sexes like this I know of which nothing has ever leaked out.

Once, when I was in Spain, I heard the story of a great

prince of Andalusia who had married one of his sisters to another very great prince who three days after the wedding said
to him : *Señor hermano, agora que soys cazado con my her-
mana, y l'haveys bien godida solo, yo he hago saber que siendo
hi ja, tal y talgozaron d'ella. De lo passado no tenga cuydado,
que poca cosa es. Del futuro guardate, que mas y mucho a vos
toca*, that is : 'Señor, my brother, now that you are married to
my sister, and have yourself well f—— her, I have to tell you
that when she was a girl, so-and-so and so-and-so enjoyed her.
But don't you worry your head about what's past, as that's a
trifling matter. Look after the future, that concerns your
honour more than the past.'

There are indeed men who see things like that, holding it
lesser cuckoldry when it has occurred in the green corn than
in the ripe, in which there is indeed something.

I have also heard tell of a great foreign prince[111] who, having
one of the loveliest girls in the world as his daughter, who was
sought in marriage by another great prince who was well
worthy of her, was given to this man by the father, but before
he would let her leave his house for ever, the father wanted to
try her, saying he was not so easily going to let such a fine
mount of his own training go without getting in the saddle
once himself, so he might know what she was going to be capable of. I do not know if this is true, but it is what I heard
was once told, moreover, that not only did he try the girl
out, but another fine and handsome knight did too, and yet
even after that the husband found nothing bitter in the bever-
age, it was all sugar to him. He would have been a very unper-
ceptive man had he done otherwise, for this girl was one of the
beauties of this world.

I have heard tell of many other fathers, and particularly of
one very eminent one, who regarding their daughters were
no nicer about it than the cock in Aesop's fable who, when
the fox met him and threatened him with death, told the fox
all the good things he did in the world, particularly all the
fine poultry originating from him. 'Oh!' said the fox, 'that's
just what I have against you, my fine fellow, you are such a
loose living bird that you have no scruples about treading your

daughters as much as any other hens,' and on this ground killed him. A great and sage judge, indeed !

In our time Ferdinand, King of Naples, in like fashion knew his aunt by marriage, the daughter of the King of Castile,[112] at the age of thirteen or fourteen, though this was by dispensation of the Pope. There were then objections raised as to whether she ought to have or could have let him do it. This recalls the Roman Emperor Caligula, who seduced and slept with all his sisters,[113] one after the other, the one he loved extremely, more than any of the others, being the youngest, Drusilla, whom he had deflowered[114] when still a small boy, and whom later, when she was married to Lucius Cassius Longinus the consul, he took from him, and maintained her openly, as if she were his legitimate wife, so steadfastly, indeed, that when on one occasion he fell ill he willed all his worldly goods, even the empire, to her.[115] But she then died, which he mourned so much that as sign of mourning he ordered the courts to stop work and all others to stop work too, and tried to persuade the populace to join with him in public mourning, and for long after he refrained from cutting his hair or shaving his beard. And when he addressed the Senate, the populace and his soldiers he used no other name than that of Drusilla to swear by.[116]

As for his other sisters, when he had had enough of them, he prostituted them all, handing them over to grown-up serving-boys whom he had brought up and known very dirtily. It would not have been quite so bad had he done the sisters no other harm, since they had become accustomed to this and it is a nice sort of misfortune, as I have heard some deflowered girls and some raped women say, but he subjected them to endless indignities, sent them into exile, took away all their rings and jewellery to turn to cash, when he had squandered and frittered away very foolishly all that the great Tiberius had left him,[117] and yet, just imagine, those poor girls, when after his death they came back from exile and found their brother's body badly and very poorly buried under a rubbish heap, had it exhumed and burned and entombed in the most decent way they could, which was certainly great kindness of the sisters towards so shabby and unnatural a brother.[118]

To excuse illicit love with near relatives, the Italian says: *quando messer Bernardo il bucieco sta in colera et in sua rabia, non riceve legge, et non perdona a nissuna dama,* 'when Mr. Bernardo is on heat and in one of his brainstorms he recognises no law and lets no woman off.'

We have many an example of the ancients doing the same. But, to get back to our discussion, I have heard it related of a certain man that when he had married a lovely and decent girl to a friend of his, boasting that he had given him a lovely and decent mount which was both healthy and sound, 'without splint or malanders', as he put it, whereby the friend ought to be jolly thankful, one of the company replied in an aside to one of his companions: 'All very good and true had she not been ridden so young and too soon, so she's a bit too hollow in the front.'

But another thing I would much like to learn from these husbands of ours is whether, if such mounts often had not a little something, a feature wrong or some other defect or fault or shortcoming, they would have been quite as cheap or would not have cost more. Or rather, were it not for the fault, they would have fixed up with many another worth more than those they did marry—just as our horse-jobbers get rid of their ruined hacks as best they can, when, being unable to get rid of them otherwise, those who know all their marks give them to these gentry who know nothing about them, the more so since (as I have heard several fathers say) such dealing is a good job of work done, getting rid of a daughter that's unsound, or beginning to be, or tends and looks like being.

What a lot of girls I have known in various parts who did not bring their virginity to the marriage bed, but nonetheless were well taught by their mothers or other relatives and by artful women friends who were very knowing pimps how to put a good face on the first charge, helping themselves out by a variety of means and inventions of the most cunning, to make the goods seem sound to their husbands and suggest that the way had never been broached. The majority help themselves out in this by putting up a stout resistance and defence at the height of the attack, proving stubborn to the very limit, which quite satisfies some husbands, who remain quite sure that in the end theirs was all the honour, they like fine, resolute soldiers, made the first pike insertion, and the following morning, as red-crested as pet cocks and fighting birds who have eaten their fill of millet the evening before, tell their story to their comrades, including quite likely those who were really the first, without the husband's knowing it, to have penetrated that fort, and who now laugh till their sides ache in secret together with these wives who were once their mistresses, and can now boast of having played their cards well and tricked their husbands marvellously.

There are however some touchy husbands who take such antics of resistance as a bad sign and are not at all pleased at finding their wives so fractious, like one of my acquaintance who asked his wife why she pretended to be so wild and so difficult and if she disliked him so much, upon which, thinking to get out of it and not have it put down to any dislike for him, she replied that she was merely afraid he might hurt her. His answer was : 'So you must have tried already, because you cannot know it hurts without having experienced it.' But she, being crafty, denied this and said she had merely heard some of her friends who had been married say it hurt. 'Fine talk and fine counsel !' he said.

There is another remedy to which these women resort, and this is, on the morning following the first night to display linen spotted with the blood shed by the poor girls during the arduous forcing of their maidenhood, as is done in Spain, where this linen is shown publicly, hung out of the window. with the loud shout : *Virgen la tenemos*. 'We deem her a virgin.'

And indeed, I have heard that this custom is still observed at Viterbo, and as those who have previously suffered a pike charge cannot thus show their own blood, they have thought, as I have heard tell, (and many courtesans in Rome themselves assured me) in order the better to sell their virginity, of staining the same linen with drops of pigeons' blood, which is the cleanest of all, and when the following day the husband sees it he is most soothed thereby and firmly convinced that it is the virginal blood of his wife, and feels himself no end of a man, but is very mistaken.[119]

Touching which I will relate the charming story of a knight who had a tied foreskin when he came to his first night of his marriage, but whose bride, not being one of the best and most complete virgins, fearing he might carry on about it, had on the counsel of her good girl friends, married women, women relations and dear friends made certain in advance by having her linen stained, but the misfortune was that her husband having this tied foreskin, could not do anything at all, nor had he at all counted on her displaying that fine emblem, making the best show she could, for which reason when they went to bed she was as meek and mild as could be, with onlookers hidden in the usual way to tell the tale, so she might the better conceal that she had already lost her maidenhood, but of course, nothing happened.

That evening, the wedding supper being brought in the usual way, there was one fellow who as part of the usual wedding fun stole the sheets, which were found to be well stained with blood, and were at once displayed, with much shouting to all present that the bride was no longer a virgin, her virginal membrane had now been tackled and broken, which all left the husband, who was quite sure he had done nothing, nevertheless pretending to be the gay, plucky champion, but most astonished, quite at a loss to understand what that blood-stained sheet meant, till, after much thought on it, he did wonder a bit if there had not been some crafty, lewd trickery, but held his tongue.

The bride and her intimates were thus most vexed and put out by the husband's having missed fire like that, and they felt their scheme had gone all awry. However, no hint of it was given till a week later, when managing the job at last, the husband went at it more fierily, afterwards telling the whole company that now there was no question about it, he really had given proof of the stuff he was made of and had made his wife a real wife if there ever was one, and admitted to his friends that till that night he had had a fit of impotence, which of course gave rise to all manner of talk among those present, with much gossip about the wife, whom everybody had taken to have been made a wife by her stained linen, so now she was quite disgraced, not so much by her own fault as by that of her husband, who from debility, flaccidity and limpness had ruined his own case.

There are some husbands who by these signs do know whether their wives came to them as virgins on their first night and see whether it is they who have forced the breach or someone else by how they find the going, like one whom I know who married a woman who had been married before and was persuaded by her that her first husband had never touched her, being impotent, so she was a virgin and maiden as much as before her first marriage, yet found her so large and so copious, so broad, in fact, that he said at once : 'Hm, what is this, do you still say you are one of those Marollan virgins, so tight and so narrow, that I have been told about, you've got a very big span, the road is so broad, and well trod that I am in no danger of losing my way.' But he had to travel by it and drank it all as sweet as milk, for, if her first husband had never touched her, which was true enough, there had been many another.

What shall we say of certain mothers, who, seeing the impotence of their sons-in-law who have a tied foreskin or some other defect, are their daughters' pimps, and to get their dowry have them give themselves to other men and very often get pregnant by them, in order to have children for heirs after the father's death.

I knew one who certainly advised her daughter to do that and indeed spared nothing in the matter, but the misfortune was that she was quite unable to conceive. I also know a man who, being unable to do anything to his wife, called in a big lackey of his, a handsome fellow indeed, to sleep with her and deflower her when she was asleep and so save his honour that way, but the wife noticed it, so the lackey did not do anything, which was the cause of a long dispute between them, till in the end they had the marriage annulled.

King Henry of Castile[120] did the same, as Baptista Fulguosius relates, for, seeing he was not capable of giving his wife a child, he had recourse to the assistance of a handsome young knight of his court to make one for him, which the knight did,[121] and for his trouble the King gave him great estate and advanced him in honours, grandeurs and dignities,[122] and one need have no doubts but that the wife loved him for it too and was happy and well off. Now that was a good cuckold.

As for these tied foreskins, there was a case on at the Paris high court recently between the Lord de Bray, treasurer, and his wife, to whom he could do nothing, having a tied foreskin or some other defect, for which the most disgusted wife had sued him. The court order was that both he and his wife should be examined by great expert doctors. The husband chose his and the wife hers, and a really delightful sonnet about it all was made at court, which a great lady herself recited to me, then gave me a copy while I was dining with her. It was said that it was composed by a lady, though others said it was a man. Here is the sonnet :

The wisest doctors Paris could produce
For learning, know-how and experience
Were called as expert judges to pronounce
If Lord or Lady de Bray 'twas of no use.
De Bray chose only three—Short, Droop and Truce,
For he was careful how he spent his pence,
Lavish his wife, with greater commonsense,
Chose Doctors Long and Strong, and Last and Spruce
To say which side might be victorious,
If last and strong, or droop and short, were glorious.
De Bray of course was found the faulty spouse,
And loser on the account of evidence.

I have heard mention of another husband who, the first night, holding his new bride in his arms, brought her to such delight and satisfaction that she could not hold herself back from making a certain little hitch or spasmic contortion not usual in young brides. But all he said was : 'Damn and blast,' and plodded on. And there you have our green cuckolds, of whom I know a myriad tales, I could never get through them all. And the worst I can see in them is when, so to speak, they marry both cow and heifer, and get brides already pregnant. Like one I know who, having by the favour and desire of the prince and liege lord of them both, who was very fond of this particular knight and had insisted on his taking her, married a very lovely, estimable young lady, at the end of a week found she proved to be pregnant, indeed declared it herself, to conceal her little game. The prince, who had always suspected there had been some love-making between her and another noble, then said to her : 'Now, So-and-so, I made a careful note in my diary of the day and hour of your wedding, and when they are compared with the day and hour of your confinement, you may be put to shame !' But all the response she made to this was to blush a little, and that was all there was about it, otherwise she still bore herself as a *dona da ben*.

Now there are girls who are so afraid of their father and mother that it would be easier to tear the life out of their bodies than the membrane of their maidenhood, for they fear their parents a hundred times more than they do their husbands.

I have heard of one very lovely, estimable young lady[123] who, being much sought after for the pleasure of love by her gentleman-in-waiting, replied to him : 'Wait a little, till I am married and you will see how we shall make love when we are under the curtain of marriage which conceals everything, and when my belly is opened up and big.'

Another girl, much sought after by a nobleman, said to him : 'Try to get our prince to find the expenses for the wedding he has promised me soon and marry me to the man who wants me; the day after the wedding, if you and I don't come together, it will be a poor show.'

I know a lady who was approached with a love-making proposal by a noble who was a relation of her husband-to-be, only four days before her wedding, and within the week after the marriage the noble had enjoyment of her, or at least, he boasted that he had. And it was easy to credit it too; for the two showed such intimacy that one would have thought they had been brought up together from infancy, he even spoke of signs and marks which she had on her body, and they carried on like this for a long time afterwards. The noble said that the occasion which had made it possible for them to reach this intimacy had been when for a fancy-dress rout they had changed into each other's clothes, he taking his mistress's and she her lover's, and the husband just laughing at them, nobody in fact seeing anything in it to reproach them with or think badly of.

There was a song made at court of a husband who was married on the Tuesday and cuckolded on the Thursday, now that *is* putting the clock on!

What shall we say too of a girl whom a noble had long courted, a man of good family, rich, too, yet at the same time a nincompoop, quite unworthy of her? And when her parents counselled her and pressed her to marry him, she replied that she would rather die than marry him, and let him take his love elsewhere, and would people stop talking about it, either to her or her parents, for if they forced her to marry him she would cuckold him in no time. Yet in the end she had to go through with it, because the command went out from the greatest lords and ladies who had authority over her, and even from her parents too.

The evening before the wedding, when her husband saw her sad and pensive, he asked her what was the matter, and she angrily replied: 'You never would listen to me and cease pursuing me, well, you know what I have always told you, that if I ever had the misfortunte to be your wife, I would cuckold you into cuckoldom, and I swear now that I will do so, and will keep my word.' She at least did not pretend to any of her girl friends or any of her admirers to be a straitlaced person, and you may rest assured that in due course she did not fail to do exactly what she did, and showed him that she was a very charming wife, indeed, for she kept her word!

I leave it to you to decide whether she should be blamed for this, for frank confession halves the wrong, and she certainly had given him warning about the difficult position he would find himself in. And why then did he not take care? The truth is, he did not worry much about it.

These girls who thus yield to lovers immediately after going to the altar, do as the Italian has it: *La vacca, che è stata molto tempo ligata, corre più che quella che quella che ha havato sempre piena libertà*—'The cow which has long been tethered runs more than the cow which has always had complete liberty.' Thus the first wife of Baudoin, King of Jerusalem, of whom I spoke earlier,[124] who, having been forced into a monastery by her husband, broke out and got away, when she made for Constantinople, where she lived so loosely that she would give herself to any passer-by coming in or out of the city, men of arms or pilgrims on their way to Jerusalem, without regard for her Royal condition. But the great love-fast she had endured while in prison was the reason for that.

I could name many another. Now, there you really have got a goodly company of cuckolds. It includes those who give their wives free rein if they are lovely and men court them, and allow them to yield themselves, in order to get advantage and favour thereby, in goods and position. One can see many such in the suites of great kings and princes, sitting pretty, for, having formerly become poor, whether because of burdens on their estates or through litigation, or even through going to the wars, and down to bedrock, there they are up again, aggrandized and well away, all by means of their wives' holes, in all of which they see no loss to themselves but merely increase, except in the case of one fair lady whom I heard of, who by chance lost half of hers, though it was said that it had been her husband who gave her syphilis or some other sort of chancre which had eaten the part away. There is no gainsaying it, to a chaste soul, the favours and benefits granted by the great are staggering, and do give rise to many cuckolds. I have heard much talk of one foreign prince who, having been made a general by his sovereign, and head of a great expedition of war, the command of which was given to him, and having left his wife at his master's court, and she one of the beauties of Christendom, the sovereign proceeded to pay such court to her that he shook her constancy, got her down and mastered her, so thoroughly indeed that he made her pregnant.

Coming home thirteen or fourteen months later and finding her in this condition, her husband was most aggrieved and sore with her. No need to ask how she felt. But she was very good at finding somebody else to blame—namely, one of her brothers-in-law. At last all the talk boiled down to the following : 'My lord,' she said, 'it is your going away that is the cause, because it was looked on with such ill favour by your master' (he clearly had not made any proper arrangements in that quarter) 'that while you were away you were charged with so much that you had omitted to do that had your lord not begun to be interested in me, you would have been a ruined man, so that to save you I lost myself. My honour is as much or more at stake in this than yours is. To support you I never spared what is most precious to me. Now ask yourself if I have fallen short as much as you say, for without what I have done not only your honour and your favour but even your life were at stake. Now you stand better than ever. The news is not so widely spread that the slur on you is very obvious. So you now pardon me and forgive me.'

The brother-in-law, who was one of the best talkers, and who may well have played his part in the pregnancy, added some more fine words of advocacy, and all this produced the desired result. Thereby agreement was reached and they got on better than they ever had before, living in utter frankness and good friendship, though for this reason their master the prince, who had done the seducing and caused the trouble, never held the same opinion of him (so I have been informed) as he had before for having paid so little heed to his wife and for having accepted her story so easily, for this reason never again thinking him to be a man of such stoutness as he had believed him to be, despite the fact that inwardly he was very glad the poor lady did not really suffer for having given him pleasure. I have known both men and women to make excuses for the lady concerned and hold that she did well to ruin herself to save her husband and restore him to favour.

Oh, what a lot of such examples there are, including one of a great lady who saved her husband's life when he had been condemned to death in open court on conviction for great peculation and malversation in the affairs of government entrusted to him, for which the husband loved her all his life.

I have also heard talk of a great lord[125] who, having been condemned to decapitation, had already reached the scaffold when pardon reached him,[126] obtained by his daughter, who was one of the loveliest of girls, and yet as he came down from the scaffold he had only one thing to say : 'God save my daughter's fine c—, which has so well got me out of this.'

St Augustine was not sure whether a Christian citizen of Antioch did sin when, to deliver himself from a large money debt on account of which he was in strict confinement, he allowed his wife to sleep with a very rich lord who promised to pay the debt.

If St Augustine leans towards this opinion, what latitude is he going to allow the many wives, widows and unmarried girls who to ransom their fathers, relations, even their husbands, yield their sweet bodies to buy off the vexatious forces which are visited against them, such as prison, slavery, loss of life, assaults on cities and their capture, and countless others, or do so even to win over captains and their men to fight valiantly in support of their family causes, or to sustain a long siege or recapture a place (I could tell of a hundred instances) without their having any fear that they were prostituting their chastity, and what harm was there in it, what disgrace, merely great benefit.

Who indeed will contradict the assertion that it is sometimes a good thing to be cuckolded, if by it one gets such benefits as preservation of one's life, restoration of favours, award of high positions, dignities and goods? I know many cases of it, and have heard tell of several men who made great advancement by means of the good looks and the private parts of their wives.

I have no wish to offend anyone, but I will certainly venture this—I have been told by both men and women that the ladies have served such husbands well, and there is no question, all the valour of the men has never been equal to what the women could give.

I know one great and very clever lady who acquired the Order[127] for her husband, the only man to get it apart from the two greatest princes of Christendom. She often remarked to him in front of everybody (for she was an easy-going person, most forthcoming) : 'Ha! my love! What a long time, poor dear, you would have had to run around in the wilderness without getting that damn thing[128] dangling round your neck!'

I have heard tell of a grandee[129] of the time of King François who, having acquired the Order and wanting to show off one day in front of the late Lord de la Chastigneraye (my uncle)[130] said to him : 'Ah, I am sure you would like to have, as I do, the Order dangling round my neck.' My uncle, who was a quick, fly, hot-tempered man if ever there was, replied at once : 'I would rather be dead than have got it through the hole yours came by.' The other then shut up, knowing very well the man he had to deal with.

I have heard the story told of a grandee whose wife it was by her solicitation that brought into the family the charter of one of his country's great appointments, granted him by his sovereign in return for his wife's favours, but which he absolutely refused to accept, particularly knowing as he did that his wife had spent three months at the sovereign's court, in great favour and not without suspicion. By this refusal he certainly manifested the greatness of heart which he had shown all his life. Yet even he accepted in the end, after doing something which I would rather not relate.

And there you have the way that great ladies have certainly made as many or more great lords than all the battles I could list, for though I would rather not slander or disgrace them, I know them as well as anybody does. And if they have brought honours they have also brought a lot of wealth too.

I knew one who was wretchedly poor when he brought his wife to court, she being very lovely, but in less than two years they were both well set up, and became quite rich.

All the more should one prize those ladies who thus raise their husbands materially without turning them into both rascals and cuckolds, as was said of Marguerite of Namur, who was so foolish as to undertake and give all she could to Louis, Duke of Orleans, the one who was such a great and powerful prince, brother of the king too, sucking all she could out of her husband till he became poor and was forced to sell his county of Blois to the same prince, the Duke of Orleans—and you may imagine he paid for it with the money and very substance that the man's stupid wife had given him. Very foolish indeed she was, giving as she did to one greater than herself.[131] And what do you think, afterwards Orleans poked fun at both her and her husband, for he was just the man to do such a thing, flighty and inconstant in love matters as he was.

I knew one great lady, who, becoming very amorous of a noble at court, so that in the end he had his enjoyment of her, gave him most of her jewellery, which amounted to more than thirty thousand crowns' worth, since she could not give him any money, as her husband kept his cash-box as well hidden as a priest, till it was court gossip that he might easily build a mansion with them, so many precious stones had he accumulated, and then, after that, having inherited a large estate and got her hand on twenty thousand crowns of money, no sooner was it hers than her gallant had a good part. And she said that had she not had that legacy, she would not have known what to give him, and he would have had even her gown and her shift. Such spendthrifts and squanderers are indeed very much to be condemned, for thus alembicking and drawing out all the substance of such poor female devils with their capricious, crazy brains, for no purse so often drawn upon can remain what it was in the way that that other purse which a woman carries between her legs does, which is always in the same state, always ready to sin and quite dumb as to what prisoners it lets in and out. That worthy knight whom I have mentioned as having acquired so many precious stones some time after this died, and then in typical Parisian fashion all his goods and chattels were auctioned and then by several persons seen and recognized as having been this lady's, not without much disgrace for her, indeed.

There was once a great prince who, loving a very prominent lady, had a dozen very sparkling diamond studs bought and nicely worked with Egyptian letters and hieroglyphs all with some hidden meaning, and made a present of these to a mistress of his, when after staring at them for some time she said she had no longer any need now for hieroglyphic letters since all the necessary writing between the two of them had been written, just as between the knight and the lady above.

I knew a lady who often told her husband that she would rather *beggar* him than *cuckold* him, but as *coquin* and *cocu* are in French really much the same word, both lovely conditions might well have been said to be present in them both.

I have however known many, indeed, very many ladies who did not do so, but tied the strings of their purses much tighter than those of their lovely bodies, for though they may have been very great ladies, they would never give more than a few rings or favours or other trifling things, such as sleeves or scarves, as tokens of their love.

I knew one very great lady indeed[132] who was most lavish and liberal in this respect, for the least of the scarves and favours she gave her attendants was worth five hundred crowns, others being worth a thousand or three thousand, all embroidery, pearls, embellishments, figuring, hieroglyphics and fancy work, nothing lovelier could be seen anywhere. She was right too, for her presents, once made, were not hidden away in chests or purses, like those of many ladies, but were publicly displayed, her lover making full use of them, feasting his eyes on them in glorious memory of her, whereas the other sort of presents, those made in cash, smack of common women and their paramours, not great ladies of real distinction. She would sometimes also make gifts of a number of fine rings with rich stones, for favours and scarves of that sort are not worn every day, but on fine and notable occasions, whereas a ring on the finger is a more normal, usual thing for its owner to put on.

But then, surely any decent, noble-souled knight should be big enough of heart to serve his lady for her resplendent beauties rather than for all the gold and silver with which she shines.

I can without boasting pride myself on having served a number of estimable ladies in my time, not of the lowest station, indeed. Had I been willing to accept from them all they offered me and to exact too all I could, I should today be the richer either in goods or money or furniture to the tune of thirty thousand crowns. But I was always glad to manifest my affection from warmth of heart, not avarice.

True, since a man gives of his substance to the purse of a

woman's belly, there is some logic if in return she should tip something of hers into his, but in any such exchange one must put everything in the scales. For just as the man can never shoot or give as much to that purse of hers as she would like, he on his side should show restraint and never drain her purse of all he might like, there should be some sense of fairness and balance in the matter.

I have in fact seen very many knights lose their mistresses' affections because of their importunate demands and their greed, so that seeing them such persistent askers, so pressing for money, the ladies quietly disentangled themselves and put such men in their proper place.

This is why any man who values decent standards should be tempted rather by carnal appetite than appetite pecuniary, for if the lady is too free with her cash, when the husband sees the funds shrink he is a hundred times more upset by this than by ten thousand freedoms of her flesh.

Next, there are also men who are made cuckolds from vengeance. I mean this; that quite a number of men who hate certain lords or knights or others for slights or insults they may have been shown by them, take their revenge by making love to their wives, seducing them and cuckolding the husbands.

There was one great prince[133] I knew who when some signs of rebellion in a great principality tributary to him came to his notice, and he was unable to have his revenge of the rebel, (because he went into headlong flight, so that he could nohow be apprehended,) when one day the wife came to the prince's court to solicit the settlement of some of her husband's affairs, the prince gave her an appointment to discuss the matter in a garden with a room handy, in order to talk to her of making love with her, which he was able very promptly to enjoy without any difficulty or great resistance, for she was a very full-blooded woman. Nor was he content with mounting her himself but procured her to others, including some of his valets, and thereby, so he said, felt he had had ample revenge of his rebel subject, by thus mounting his wife and decking his head with a lovely crown of horns for wanting to set himself up as a kinglet and sovereign on his own, so that instead of a crown with the fleur-de-lys he provided him with a nice one of horns to wear.

On his mother's prompting this same prince did the same when he took his pleasure of a girl, a princess,[134] deflowering her and having great pleasure of her, because he knew she was to marry a certain prince who had both caused him umbrage and greatly upset his brother, two months after which she was delivered to the prince in question as virgin intact, to become his wife—a very sweet instalment of revenge, pending another form of it which followed soon after.

I knew a very estimable noble who, serving a lovely lady of good origin, asked her for some recompense for his services and love-making, to which she replied flatly that she would not give him a penny even for double the service, particularly since she was very convinced that he did not love her so much for love's sake, nor had such affection for her beauty as he maintained, but in having his pleasure of her was really out to have his revenge on her husband, who had done him some disservice, for which reason his first thought was to get satisfaction for that, and also some other advantage out of it, but with assurances that it was quite the contrary, this noble went on serving her two years more so faithfully and with such ardent love that this greatly impressed her, to such an extent indeed that she then granted him what she had hitherto persistently refused, assuring him that had she not really thought vengeance on his part had really been his motive, she would have satisfied him as he wanted at the very beginning of their liaison, her natural instinct being to love him and also to show him such favours. How well, you may note, this great lady controlled herself, seeing that love did not oversway her, to do what was her strongest impulse, but steadfastly wished to be loved for herself alone, not merely to serve her lover's vindictiveness.

The late Lord de Guast,[135] in every respect one of the world's perfect gallants and nobles, one day at court invited me to go to dine with him. He had brought together a dozen of the cleverest men at court, among others the Bishop of Dol, by birth one of the d'Espinays[136] of Brittany, and Milords de Ronsard, de

Baïf, Des Portes and d'Aubigny[137] (the two latter are still alive, and could confirm what I say) and some others whose names I forget, the only soldiers present being de Guast himself and me.[138] Talking, after dinner, of love and the advantages and disadvantages, the pleasures and the displeasures, the good and the evil that its enjoyment entailed, our host, after each in turn had given his views on both sides, wound up by saying that the sovereign boon of love's enjoyment lay precisely in vengeance of this sort, and he then requested all those great personalities to make an impromptu quatrain about it, which they did. I would have liked to have had the text of them to include here. It was de Dol, who spoke and wrote gold,[139] who won the day.

There was no doubt about it, Lord de Guast had good reason to maintain this against two great princes whom I know, because he put horns on their heads in return for the animosity they showed him, and as their wives were very beautiful, he did indeed get double satisfaction out of it, both revenge and pleasure, and I have known quite a number of men who have thus had both revenge and pleasure in this way, so would be of the same opinion.

I have also known lovely, eminent ladies who said and insisted that when their husbands had ill-treated them or been discourteous to them, taking them to task or censuring them, beating them or doing them some other mischief or outrage, it had been their greatest pleasure to cuckold them, and as they did it to keep them in mind, lampooning them and making mock of them and laughing about them with their lovers, and they even went so far as to say that they got a greater appetite and a quite indescribable enhancement of the pleasure out of this.

I have heard tell of one beautiful, famous lady who, when once asked whether she had ever cuckolded her husband, replied : 'But why ever should I do so, when he has never beaten me or threatened me?' As if to say that, had he done either, the champion she carried between her legs would soon enough have avenged her.

And as for mockery, I knew one very lovely, estimable lady

who when in the sweet ecstasy of love's pleasure, lapped with her lover in a bath of delectation and easement, it so happened that a horn of plenty ear pendant of hers which was no more than black glass, (such as were then worn), was broken, so much clasping and playing about and wriggling was there. All at once she said to her lover : 'Just observe how provident Nature is, for merely by breaking one horn I've made a dozen others for my poor nincompoop of a husband to wear any festival day if he likes.'

Another, having left her husband sound asleep in the conjugal bed, paid a visit to her lover before at last going to bed herself. And when the lover enquired where the husband was, she replied : 'Looking after his bed and cuckoo nest, in case anybody else tries to drop an egg in it, but it isn't in his bed or between his sheets or in his nest that you are going to drop it, because I've come here to you, and left him on guard there, sound asleep.'

Talking of being on guard, I have heard the tale told of a valorous lord who, one day coming to words with a very estimable lady whom I knew also, by way of insult he asked her whether she had ever been to see St Mathurin[140] (reputed to cure looneys). 'Oh yes,' she said, 'but it was no use, the church was so full and so well guarded by cuckolds that they just wouldn't let me in, and you were up in the bell-tower, one of the ring-leaders, a master of ceremonies.'

I could tell a thousand other funny stories, but there would be no end to it, though I hope to get some in somewhere else in the course of this book.

There are cuckolds who are cheerful cuckolds, self-invited so to speak to the feast of cuckoldry, much as I have known some men who would say to their wives : 'So-and-so is quite in love with you, I know him well, he is often at our receptions, but it's all for love of you, my dear. So do be kind to him. He might be of great service to us, it is very useful indeed knowing him.'

Others say to this or that nobleman : 'My wife is very fond of you, she simply adores you, do come and see her, it will please her so much, you can while away a pleasant hour talking and discussing the world together.' Thus do men bring about their own discomfiture, as, for instance, the Emperor Hadrian, who, one day, when in England conducting the wars (this is in his Life),[141] received a number of reports that his wife, the Empress Sabina, was carrying on wild love-making in Rome with a number of noble Roman gallants. And as luck would have it, just at this time she wrote a letter from Rome abroad to a young Roman nobleman who was with the Emperor in England, and in this letter she complained that he had forgotten her and no longer cared about her at all, he really must be having some other little love affairs in those far-off parts, and some affected little hussy must have borne him off on the lakes of her fair looks. This letter happened to fall into Hadrian's hands, and when, a few days later, the young nobleman asked him for leave of absence, alleging a need to go to Rome at once on family business, Hadrian had his fun with him and said : 'Very well, young man, off you go, but you needn't worry, my wife the Empress is very loyal, she's waiting for you.' When the young Roman thus saw that the Emperor had discovered the secret, and might well play him some dirty trick he left without so much as a good-bye the very same night and—took refuge in Ireland.

He need really not have worried so much, for as the Emperor himself often said, being swamped, as he was, by his wife's excessive love demands : "I assure you, were I not Emperor, I would soon get rid of my wife, but I do not want to set a bad example,'—as if to suggest that eminent personalities should always remain steady and never wash their dirty linen in public. But what a judgement on them this is, and a course of conduct which some certainly did follow, though not for these reasons. Anyway, that is how this worthy Roman Emperor lent a fine hand to his own cuckolding.

Excellent Marcus Aurelius's wife Faustina was a fine fast one too, and he was advised to get rid of her. But he replied : 'If we part from her we shall also have to part from her dowry, which is the Empire.' Who indeed would not gladly be cuckolded for a morsel like that—indeed, even for less.

His son, Antonius Verus, known as Comodus, for all that he

turned very cruel in the end, nevertheless made a very neat reply to those who counselled him to have the said Faustina, (his mother)[142] put to death, for being so amorous and hot after a certain gladiator that she never would have been cured of her infatuation unless it were by taking the step of killing the rascally gladiator and making her drink the man's blood.[143]

Many husbands in the past and in the present too have done the same as worthy Marcus Aurelius, fearing to have their drabs of wives put to death from fear of losing the great estates that went with them, preferring by far to be rich and cuckolded than poor and mere beggars.

Heavens, what countless cuckolds have I not known who were always inviting their relations, their friends, their comrades to come and see their wives, even arranging parties to attract them more, and when they did come, leaving them alone with their wives in their bedrooms or their dressing-rooms, then going off on business and saying to them : 'I leave my wife for you to look after.'

There was one man I knew in my travels of whom you would have said that his whole happiness and satisfaction were based on being cuckolded, for he went out of his way to provide opportunities for it, and above all would say : 'My wife dotes on you, do you love her as much as she does you?' And when he saw his wife together with her attendant, more often than not he would take the company out for a walk and leave the two of them together, giving them ample leisure to indulge in their love-making. And if he should have reason to come back unexpectedly, he would start shouting from the bottom of the stairs, hawking and coughing and asking if there was anybody about, so as not to catch the lovers in the act, for however much one may know or suspect, such sights and surprises are hardly pleasant for either party.

Thus one day, when this prince I speak of was having a fine house built and the master mason had asked him if he would not have some embellishment on the cornices, he replied : 'I don't know what cornices are, you ask my wife, she knows, she's a specialist on that sort of geometry, you do whatever she says.'

77

One that I know did much worse when, selling one of his pieces of land to another for fifty thousand crowns, he took forty-five thousand in gold and silver and a unicorn's horn for the other five thousand. That meant a hearty laugh for all who heard—'As if,' they said, 'he hadn't enough horns on him already, without adding that one too.'

I knew one very great prince, a fine man of courage, who visited a prominent lord to tell him he was greatly beholden to him, adding with a laugh : 'Monsieur So-and-so, I don't know what you have done to my wife, but she is so taken with you that she's always day and night talking about you, and praising you to me. The only answer I give her is to tell her that I have known you longer than she has and I am well aware how great your qualities and merits are.' Who was the astonished one but the noble, for he had just come from escorting the lady in question, giving her his arm, to vespers, where the Queen too went. Nevertheless, he pulled himself together quickly and said : 'Sire, I am your very humble servant, as I am that of Madame your lady, and much obliged to her for the good opinion she has of me, and I respect her greatly. But I don't make love to her,' he added, playing the fool, 'I only pay court in pursuance of the good counsel you recently gave me, especially as she could do a great deal in the quarter of my mistress, whom by her intervention I might marry, and so I do hope she will assist me in the matter.'

The prince outwardly did no more than laugh and advise the noble in question to court his wife more than ever, which he did, now with this excuse feeling quite free to serve so lovely a lady and princess, who soon made him forget that other mistress he would have liked to marry. Indeed, he hardly bothered about that proposal now except as a cover which stopped talk and disguised everything. But this could not go on without the prince at last being jealous, when one day, in the Queen's chamber, he saw this knight wearing on his arm a scarlet Spanish ribbon, a fine novelty just brought to court, and having handled it and felt it while chatting with him, went to his wife, who was beside the Queen's bed and wearing one just the same, which he handled and touched too, finding that it was identical, cut off the same piece, indeed, yet did not say a thing or do anything else about it. Such love-affairs need well covering up by such ashes of discretion and good counsel that they cannot be found out, for often enough the disgrace thus revealed angers the husbands against their wives far more than when it is all done on the sly. In other words, one should be guided by the proverb: *si non caste, tamen caute*, if not prudishly, at least privily.

What great disgraces and troubles have I not known in my time through the indiscretions of ladies and their attendants! Their husbands quite likely may not care a fig, but they for their part might at least better do it all *sotto coperte*, under cover, not blazoned abroad.

There was one lady I knew who suddenly blazoned her loves and favours abroad, behaving just as if she had no husband at all and was subject to no authority, refusing to pay any heed to the counsel of her attendants and friends who expostulated with her as to what unseemly results there would be, and very serious in the end they were too.

This lady never did what several others have done, who carried on their loves nicely, giving themselves a good time without letting the world know anything about it, unless it were by some faint whisperings, but never enough to reveal the truth even to the most perspicacious, for in public they addressed their attendants so skilfully and maintained them with such address that all their lives neither their husbands nor any spying eyes ever had anything to get their teeth into. And when their lovers went on any expedition or happened to lose their lives, such ladies masked and hid their grief so wisely that nobody ever knew a thing.

I knew one lovely, eminent lady who on the day when a great lord who was attendant on her died appeared in the Queen's chamber with countenance as cheerful and smiling as on the day before. There were lords who prized her greatly for this restraint and circumspection, which she observed from fear of displeasing and annoying the King, who had not liked the man who had just died, but others found fault with her for it, holding that the gesture revealed a deficiency of affection, as they put it, there was not much real love in her, any more than in any other lady at court who led such a life.

I knew two lovely, high-born ladies[144] who when by hazard of war they lost their courtiers so lamented and sorrowed and by the dun garments that they wore, together with their use of holy-water and engraved gold aspergillums with death's heads and all sorts of symbols of death in their trinkets, jewels and the bracelets they wore, so revealed their sorrow that they were greatly lowered in people's estimation and it did them great harm, though their husbands remained quite indifferent.

This is how these ladies will overstep the bounds, making their love-affairs public knowledge, though at the same time one should value and praise them for their constancy, but not their discretion, for this really does them a great disservice. But while they are to blame in this, there are many of their attendants who deserve reproof as much as the ladies, for they act the transports and langours of a goat in labour. It is they who cast their eyes on them and make these their ambassadors, they who make passionate gestures and sighings in public, they who sport their ladies' colours so blatantly, they, in short, who permit themselves so many ridiculous indiscretions that a blind man would see them, and some of them as often do this quite falsely as genuinely, just to make out to the whole court that they are in clover, they are in love with this or that great lady. Whereas Heaven knows one would not give them a farthing if they were beggars, even if it meant losing all the benefits of charity.

I know a lord and prince who, wanting to persuade the world that he had become amorous of a beautiful, estimable lady of my acquaintance, one day had two of his men or pages stand holding his little mule outside her door. It so happened that de Strozzi[145] and I came along and came upon that dubious mule, with the lackeys and pages, and de Strozzi at once asked them where their master was. They said he was in this lady's house, at which de Strozzi roared with laughter and remarked to me that he would take any bet this was sheer invention. And at once he set one of his own pages to stand guard and see if the alleged lover did come out of the house. From there we went

straight on to the Queen's Chamber, to find our man there—
and you may imagine we had a good laugh, both of us. Towards evening we tackled the fellow and, pretending to challenge him, asked him to tell us where he was at such and such
an hour of the afternoon, and of course he could not get out
of it, for we had seen his mule and his pages outside the lady's
door. So he pretended to take offence at our having seen this,
and made out that we were only picking a quarrel with him
for making love to so eminent a lady, and he maintained that,
yes, indeed, he had been there, but would we please not
breathe a word, or we should be endangering him, and the
poor lady would be disgraced and badly treated by her husband. Which we promised him (laughing heartily all the time
and making fun of him, although he was a fairly highly rank-
ing noble of standing himself) said we would never speak of it
and not a word would escape our lips. But when he continued
those trickeries with the mule too frequently, we disclosed the
whole device and challenged him point blank about it and in
a good company too. Then from shame he gave up, for through
what we had done the lady in question learned about it, and
one day set a look-out for his mule and pages and had them
chased away from her door just like beggars outside a church.
Then we went one better and told her husband the whole
story, in such funny detail that he was most amused and had
a really good laugh about it. He remarked that he would never
have any fears that fellow could cuckold him, and he said that
if he now found that mule and the pages stationed at the courtyard gate he would have his men open it and let them in to give
them a little protection from the heat and the cold or the rain.
Others however did cuckold him. But that is how this other
worthy lord tried to make a show at the cost of that eminent
lady, and without a thought for any disgrace.

I knew a knight who caused scandal by the way he behaved
towards a very lovely eminent lady. He had for some time
been amorous of her and trying to persuade her to grant him
that little titbit which was reserved for the husband to munch,
but she refused him outright, till, after several rebuffs, he lost
all patience and said to her : 'I can see now that you are not

going to give me what I want. Very well, then I swear I will ruin your good name.' And to do so, he conceived the notion of making so many covert goings and comings, yet by design not so secretly as not to be observed, by several people, to whom he afforded the opportunity of being seen as if going to her house both by day and by night, while at the same time he began to boast largely of how lucky he was, and in public would address the lady with more intimacy than he really should, making himself out to his comrades far more of a gallant than he really was, to such a point that one night he went to this lady's chamber very late, well wrapped in his cloak, hiding his face from the household servants, a trick he repeated several times, till the majordomo of the house grew suspicious of him and had a watch set. And though the husband failed to catch him, he nevertheless boxed his wife's ears several times, and then, egged on by the majordomo, who said this was not sufficient, took his dagger and killed her—and had no difficulty in obtaining the King's pardon for the act. It was a great pity, for she was a lovely lady. The nobleman who had caused it all did not get very far after that. By the grace of God he was killed in a war skirmish for having so unjustly robbed that estimable lady of both her honour and her life.

To tell the truth about this case and so many another that I have come across, there are ladies who are themselves much to blame, and are the real causes of their own disgrace and dishonour, for they themselves venture into skirmishes and give gallants a lead, and from the outset lavish the finest caresses, intimacies and familiarities in the world, on them, by languishing glances and pretty words, raising their hopes, yet when it comes to the point flatly refusing anything. So that such estimable gentlemen, who had begun to envisage all manner of delectations for their bodies, but then are unceremoniously rebuffed by these women, lose all patience and are offended, and for this reason proceed to disgrace them and label them as the greatest strumpets in the world, alleging a hundredfold more than anything that happened.

That indeed is why an estimable lady should never venture deliberately to attract a gallant noble or allow him to attend on her, unless in the end prepared to satisfy him according to his merits and his attentions. If she does not want to be ruined, even if she has to do with a gallant, estimable man, she should envisage this as the final goal of it all. Otherwise, from the start, if he approaches her and she can see he is paying attentions to her to get that most-coveted favour, she should turn him straight away from her door, for, to be frank, no lady who allows herself to be loved and paid attentions to but takes on such an obligation that subsequently, however slow she may be, she cannot withdraw from the combat, she must come to it sooner or later.

There are however ladies who delight in getting men to pay them attention for nothing, or merely for the sake of their pretty eyes, and even say they wish to be paid attentions, it is their pleasure—but not to go so far. They say they find their pleasure in the desire but not the execution. I have seen some who told me as much. But there is no question about it, they should not adopt such an attitude, for once they start desiring, there is not a shadow of doubt but they must eventually come to the execution of it, the laws of love will have it so, and once any lady desires or craves or even dreams of thinking of craving a man, the deed is done, if the man makes her acquaintance and presses his attack steadfastly, he will bag her, on foot or on the wing, by feather or fur, as the saying is.

There you have the way the poor husbands are cuckolded by these ladies who think they can merely desire without doing anything, for without ever really intending to do so, such do singe their wings in the candle-flame, caught, that is, in the fire they have laid for themselves, rather like simple-minded shepherdesses who to warm themselves, when in the hills watching their sheep and ewes, build a little fire without any thought of misfortune or trouble, not realizing that their little fire may sometimes kindle a conflagration so great that it consumes a whole district of heath and brushwood.

Such ladies, to make them see sense, should take note of the case of the Countess d'Escaldasor, in Pavia, whom Lord de Lescu,[146] who was later known as the Marshal de Foix, then studying at Pavia (whence his title of Protonotary of Foix, since he had dedicated himself to the Church, though later he abandoned the cassock to take up arms)—whom, I was saying, this lord courted, particularly since at that time she took the prize for beauty above all the lovely women of Lombardy. Seeing how assiduous he was, she did not want to disappoint him too harshly, let alone send him packing, for he was a near relative of the great Gaston de Foix, Lord of Nemours,[147] under whose universal fame all Italy trembled,[148] and so it came about that one day when there was a great festival and fête at Pavia, attended by all the great ladies, including the loveliest of the city and surroundings, and the Countess put in an appearance, more lovely than any, sumptuously dressed in a gown of sky-blue satin, full-cut and flowing, simply smothered all over with torches and flying butterflies fluttering and blazing all over her, all in gold and silver embroidery in the fashion in which the Milan craftsmen have always been so superior, so that she bore off the crown and was considered to be the finest dressed lady of the whole assembly and company. Partnering her in a dance, Protonotary Lord de Foix was then curious to learn the meaning of all the symbols on her gown, having a shrewd notion that there was some hidden sense not to his liking in them. Her reply was : 'My Lord, I have had my gown made in the way that cavalrymen and soldiers fit their difficult, vicious mounts, who buck or kick. They fasten a large silver bell to their crupper, so that this may serve as a signal to their comrades, whenever they ride in company, to warn them to take care of the vicious horse which kicks, for it might strike them. Likewise, by these butterflies fluttering and blazing about these torches I give notice to the estimable gentlemen who do me the kindness of loving me and admiring my looks not to come too close or crave more than merely to look, because they will prosper no more than the butterflies do, all they can possibly have from it will be their craving plus some burns, nothing more.' This story occurs in Paolo Giovio's[149] book on the signs of arms and love. In this way this lady gave notice to her attendant to take care of himself in good time. Whether he approached any closer or what he did I do not know, all I can say is that when he was mortally wounded at the battle of Pavia and then taken

84

prisoner, he asked to be taken to this Countess who lived in that city, and was very well received and well treated by her. And there too he died, after three days, to the great sorrow of the lady, as I heard Lord de Montluc[150] relate one night when we were entrenched outside la Rochelle and he was in conversational mood, and I had told him the story of that device. He assured me he had seen the Countess in question, and she was indeed very lovely, and very fond too of the said Marshal, and he was very decently treated by her, though de Montlac did add that he could not assure me that they had not gone further on previous occasions. This example should serve for many and for the various ladies I mention.

Now there are the cuckolds who are so kind-hearted that they have their wives lectured and admonished by prominent religious men, with a view to converting the ladies and putting them straight, when the false tears and deceitful language they make great vows and promise mountains and wonders of repentance and say they will never do it again, yet their oaths do not last any time. For the vows and the tears of such ladies are worth precisely as much as the oaths and protestations of lovers such as I have seen, for I knew one great lady whom a great prince, her sovereign, disgraced by finding a monk, whom he appointed to go and seek out her husband, (who was in one of the provinces on the king's service,) as coming from the King in person, to warn him of his wife's wild love-making and the malicious gossip which was spreading about the harm she was doing him. This messenger said that His Majesty felt it his duty by his station and vocation to warn him in good time so he might bring that sinful soul back to decent ways. Though astounded to receive such a message and kindly act of charity, the husband showed no other reaction than to thank the monk and say he trusted he could cope with the business, yet when he returned, treated his wife no worse. Indeed, what use would it have been to him to do so? Once a woman has taken that road there is no diverting her from it, any more than you can get a post-horse which has always been accustomed to gallop to proceed in any other way.

Ah, how many eminent ladies have not been caught doing it

and then scolded and beaten, enjoined and reproved, by means both forcible and gentle, not to behave so again, but to promise, swear and protest they will be chaste, only afterwards to apply the proverb *passato il pericolo, gabbato il santo*—'danger over, mock the saint'—and go back more vigorously even than before to the battles of love. Then there are also those, many, indeed, who feel some worm of remorse inwardly gnawing and on their own promptings make most secret, solemn vows, yet hardly ever keep them, repenting instead for having repented, as Lord du Bellay[151] said of repenting courtesans in his lines to the mother of love.

> *Mother of love, by vows that once I took*
> *I crave return to your most gracious laws*
> *Which now I see I ought not have forsook,*
> *Repenting of repentance without cause.*

And such women maintain that seeing they are able to spend so little time in the brief stay they make in this world, it is very arduous indeed to deprive themselves for ever and aye of a habit and custom so delightful.

I could so easily instance too what certain lovely girls, who repent young, take the veil and forsake the world would say if one were to ask them to declare in all faith and conscience how much they would very often give to have the high walls around them flattened and to escape therefrom without delay.

This is why husbands should never think of making their wives behave, once they have taken the first step to betraying their word, by any other means than to let them have their head, merely counselling them to be discreet in it and make sure there is no public disgrace, for it is vain to apply even all the cures for love that Ovid ever advised[152] or the infinity invented by others or even those authentic ones of Master François Rabelais, which he taught venerable Panurge,[153] they will never do any good. Indeed the best thing to do is to apply the chorus of an old song of King François I's time, which ran :

> *The man who wants to keep his wife*
> *From whoring if she's once begun*

*Would have to barrel her for life
And take his pleasure through the bung.*

In the days of King Henri,[154] there was an ironmonger who took to the St Germain Fair[155] a dozen contraptions for bridling a woman's parts. They were made of iron and consisted of a belt and a piece which came up under and was locked in position, so neatly made that once a woman was bridled it was out of the question for her to indulge in the gentle pleasure, as there were only a few little holes for her to piss through.[156]

It is said that there were five or six madly jealous husbands who each bought one and bridled their wives, so these might well say : 'Farewell, good times.' But there was one wife who took it into her head to approach a very skilful locksmith, and showed him the appliance and her parts and all when the husband was out in the country, and he set his mind to it so well that he fashioned a skeleton key, so the lady could open and close her bridle whenever she wished. The husband never had any complaint to make, and she had all the good pleasure she wanted, despite her foolish cuckold of a husband, who thought he was quit of cuckoldom for ever. But it was the wretched locksmith who made the key who really spoiled it all for him. Indeed, the man did better than that, for the story goes that he was the first to try it and put horns on his head, nor was he in any danger, for Venus, who was the loveliest of women and biggest whores, had Vulcan, ironworker and locksmith, who was a very dirty, rascally, limping, ugly fellow, for husband.

What is more, it is said that there were a number of gallant estimable nobles of the court who so seriously threatened that ironmonger that if he ever dared bring any more such rotten goods to market they would kill him, he was not to show his face again, and must throw all the other bridles he had made in the privy, which he did, since when they have not been heard of.[157] Which was very sensible of the man, for it was enough to ruin half the world, not to say de-people it, inventing such bridles, locks and seals of nature, hateful, despicable things, inimical to the multiplication of humanity.

There are some who appoint eunuchs to keep a watch on their wives. This the Emperor Alexander Severus practised[158] with stern orders to the ladies of Rome never to make love. But such men got caught there too. Not that eunuchs ever impregnate or that ladies conceive by them, but they certainly do obtain certain emotions, and many light pleasures from them, almost amounting to the complete act. That however does not worry some husbands, who maintain that their principal worry about adultery is not the mere fact of their wives giving themselves to other men, but the great subsequent annoyance of feeding and bringing up and recognizing as their offspring children not begot by them. For without that, what their wives did would be the least of their cares, so that I have in fact known some, even many, who, when they found it fitting and easy, have had those who gave their wives children pay a good annuity, to keep the children on, and so they do not worry at all, merely advise their wives to request such payments, indeed, to ask their lovers for it, insisting on some such maintenance allowance to feed and bring up the boy they have had of them. As I heard of a great lady who was the mother of Lord de Villeconnin, who was a child of François I.[159] Before he died she asked the king to give her or assign to her a decent sum for the child he had made, which he did, making over to her two hundred thousand crowns, lodged in a bank, to increase and bring in continuous interest and be turned over and over, so that when the boy was grown up the income was so large that he spent so magnificently and seemed so affluent, even in gambling at court, that everybody was astonished. The first conclusion to which people jumped was that he had it all from some lady whom nobody could guess at, nobody imagining it was his own mother, till, as he never left the great lady in question, it was imagined that the great expenditure he made came from enjoying her, which was not at all the case, for she was his mother, which however very few persons knew. Indeed his origin and birth remained a great secret, so that when he came to end his life, at Constantinople, he was held a bastard and his escheat was given to the Marshal de Retz,[160] who was sharp-eyed and wily enough to sniff out that pot of roses, to his own advantage, and snatched at it and proved the bastardry which had been concealed for so long and cornered the escheat, right under the nose of de Teligny,[161] who had been made formal heir to the said Villeconnin.

There were however others who maintained that this lady had had the child by somebody else, not the King, and had set him up as he was from her own estates, but de Retz plucked the case so well and made such good research in the banks that he found the money and King François's deed of assignment, though others still maintained that it was some other prince, not quite so great as the King, or even a lesser person altogether, but that to conceal and hide it all and provide for the child it was not a bad idea to impute it all to His Majesty, as one can also see in other cases too.

I think there are many women in high society, even in France, who if they meant to produce children at such a price, would have been easy prey for Kings and grandees to mount the bellies of. Indeed, they very often allow the mounting without getting any great provender from it, whereby such ladies are greatly disappointed, for they never give themselves to such great suitors except to get a nice little sum, a *galardón* as the Spanish has it.

There is a very ticklish point regarding such putative and uncertain children, namely, whether they should inherit their paternal or maternal estates, and whether it is not a great sin on the part of the women to have them inherit from the husbands, *à propos* of which some theologians have declared that the wife should tell the husband the whole truth. Thus says the great thinker, Doctor Subtil.[162] But others hold this not to be a good opinion, because in revealing what has happened a woman defames herself, without being obliged to do so, and, as Solomon said, a good name is more valuable than any earthly goods.

It is therefore better for the paternal estates to be taken up by the child than for a good name to be lost, for, as the proverb says, a good name is better than a gilded belt. From this the theologians draw the maxim that when we find ourselves bound by two different precepts or orders, the lesser must give way to the greater. Now it is the case that the injunction to preserve one's good name is greater than that which enjoins one to give up others' goods, so this must be preferred to the latter.

Further, if the wife tells the husband about it, she puts herself in danger of being killed by her husband himself, which is sternly forbidden, and punishable with death. It is not even allowable for a woman to kill herself from fear of being raped or after the act, for that too is to commit mortal sin. So that it is better for a woman to let herself be raped, if she can do nothing about it by flight or crying out, than to kill herself, for the violation of the body is not a sin, unless inwardly consented to. This is the reply made by St Lucia[163] to the tyrant who threatened to have her taken to a brothel. 'If you have me forced,' she said, 'my chastity will acquire a double crown.'

For this reason, some men complain of Lucrece.[164] It is true that St Sabina[165] and St Sophronia,[166] together with other Christian virgins, who took their own lives rather than fall into the hands of the barbarians, are excused by our church fathers and theologians, who say that they did this moved by the Holy Spirit, by which Holy Spirit, after the capture of Cyprus,[167] a newly christianised Cypriot maiden, seeing herself being taken as slave together with several other Cypriot women, to be meat for the Turks, secretly put a light to the gunpowder magazines in the galley, so well that in an instant all was consumed in flames, herself included. She had cried : 'God grant our bodies be not polluted and known by these villainous Turks and Saracens!' Though Heaven knows, perhaps hers already had been known by them, and this act was really a form of penitence, or perhaps it was because her master had not wanted to touch her, so as to get more money for her by selling her in a virginal state, seeing that in those parts, (indeed, in all others too,) men are always greedy for the taste of an intact morsel.

Now, to come back again to the noble guardians set over those poor women I was speaking of, apart from procreation as I say, these eunuchs never cease committing adultery with them and cuckolding their husbands.

I knew two ladies in France who took to love-making with

two castrated nobles so as to be sure of not getting pregnant, but who nevertheless had their pleasure and without any public disgrace too. But in Turkey and Barbary there have been husbands so jealous that, when they saw through this fraud, they have decided to castrate their poor slaves completely, slicing everything off clean. Of which cruelty, as those who have lived in Turkey say and write, not two out of twelve survive, they just die, but those who do survive the Turks love and worship as true, reliable, chaste guardians of their wives' chastity and guarantors of their honour.

We Christians do not resort to such unpleasing rigour, which is far too horrible, but instead of such castrates we sometimes give them aged sexagenarians, as is done in Spain, even at the court of the Queens of Spain, where I have seen such old men made guardians of the daughters of families of their court and suite. And yet, God wot! there are old men a hundred times more dangerous and more likely than any young man to ruin a girl or a married woman, they are a hundred times hotter too, more inventive and more industrious about winning and corrupting them.

In my opinion such guardians are not at all more reliable than the young ones by reason of being hoary headed and hoary chinned, just as older women are not safer than young ones, as, for instance, when an elderly Spanish governess was taking her girls somewhere, and passing through a large hall where she saw men's private parts depicted to advantage in wall paintings, and very big too, out of all proportion, took it into her head to say : *Mira que tan bravas no las pintan estos hombres, como quien no los conociese,* 'But those men are not splendidly enough painted, you'd think the painter did not know what they are really like.' And the girls all looked up at her and took due note, except for one that I know, who, pretending to be naïve, asked one of her companions what sort of birds these were—for some of the men were depicted as having wings. The other girl replied that they were 'Barbary birds', and they were even lovelier in nature than in paintings. Heaven knows she had really never seen any, but she had at least to pretend she had.

Many husbands very often make a mistake about these guardians, thinking that as long as their wives are in the hands of elderly women, whom as title of respect they all call 'mother', the said wives' privy parts are very well protected, whereas in such matters there is nobody so easy to get at and suborn as these elderly women, for it is in their avaricious nature to accept open-handed whatever is offered them as price for their charges.

Governesses are unable always to have their eyes on your young women, who are always quick-witted, even when in love, for governesses usually sleep in a corner of the ingle nook and cuckolds are freely made in their presence without their noticing it or knowing anything about it.

I know one lady who once did it in front of her governess so subtly that the governess never even noticed. Another did the same once in front of her husband, almost openly, when he was fencing.

Other elderly governesses have bad legs which are incapable of keeping up with their young ladies, so these get to the end of an alley or a copse or to a closet first, and conceal their copulation under their skirts, without the governess noticing anything, being feeble-legged and poor-sighted. There are yet other elderly women governesses who, having enjoyed life themselves, feel pity at seeing the young folk made to fast, and are so gay themselves that it is they who show their charges the path to take, indeed, egg them on to take it, and do all they can to assist them. Further, Aretin observes that the greatest pleasure of a lady who has been through it all, her greatest satisfaction, indeed, is to aid another to do the same.

This is why, when one really wants the assistance of a good messenger of love, one employs or one applies to an old pimp rather than a young woman. Thus I have it from a very gallant man that he expressly forbade his wife to keep company with elderly women, whom he himself did not favour, as being too dangerous, but told her to have as many young women friends as she liked, and he gave me many excellent reasons which I leave it to better talkers than myself to expatiate on.

This is also why a famous lord I know confided his wife,

about whom he was jealous, to a woman cousin of his, who moreover was unmarried, to keep an eye on her, which she did very well, though she had only half the nature of the gardeners' dogs which though it never eats its master's cabbages itself, will not let anybody else have them either, for this wife did nibble some greens, though without offering her cousin any, though the other one did quite often manage a bout fully dressed, which smart though she was, the cousin either did not notice or else pretended not to notice.

I could adduce an infinity of remedies used by poor jealous cuckolds to bridle, lock up and curtail their wives and prevent them from taking the leap, but in vain do they practice all the old methods they may have heard of or think up new ones, they always lose the match, for once the wives have got that rascally worm into their heads, they are for ever sending their husbands to Guillot the Dreamer,[168] as I hope to show in an essay which is half ready,[169] dealing with the tricks and subterfuges of women in this matter, all of which I compare with the stratagems and military subterfuges of soldiers. And the best remedy, a reliable, delightful protection which the jealous husband can give his wife is to let her go on just as she chooses, as I heard of one gallant married man doing, since it is a woman's nature that the more she is forbidden to do something the more she wants to do it, particularly in matters of love, where the appetite is more heated by prohibition than by letting it have its course.

Here now is another sort of cuckold, one which is debatable, I mean : if a man has had all his pleasure of a woman during the life of her cuckold husband and the husband dies and he who paid her attentions comes to marry her in her widowhood, thus marrying her as her second husband, is he to be called a cuckold? For I have known and heard many other men, even great ones, say that he is.

There are some who say that he cannot be, seeing that it was he himself did the work, and nobody cuckolded him but he himself, any horns are of his own fashioning. All the same, there are many armourers killed by the swords they make, and armourers who kill each other.

There are others who maintain that such a man really is a cuckold, by reason of the deed itself, a cuckold in the green.[1] They adduce many arguments in support of this view, but as the cause is still undecided, I leave it for examination at the first hearing that may be given it.

I would however add the following, of a very great lady, married, who after marrying promised herself to a man who still keeps her. This was fourteen years ago, since which time she has constantly awaited and wished for her husband to die. But it would be a rare man who died by such wishing, so she had every reason when she said : 'Cursed be the husband and partner who has lived longer than I wished !' He has had many an illness and bodily complaint, but he has not died. So that the late King Henry,[170] having granted the reversion of the estate of the said cuckolded husband to a very eminent, worthy noble, often used to say : 'There are two people at my court very impatient to see so-and-so die, one so he can have his estate, the other so she can marry her lover, but so far both the one and the other have been cheated.'

You see how wise and thoughtful the Almighty is, not to send down to us the evil we desire, for the truth is, I have now been told that quite recently these two have been on quite bad terms. They have burned that promise of eventual marriage and broken the contract, to the great mortification of the woman and the delight of the proposed husband, seeing that he has now conceived a desire to find what he wants elsewhere, getting tired of waiting for the death of the other husband who, mocking people, so often gave the alarm as at death's door, only, thus, to outlive the intended husband. Unquestionably, this is God's punishment, since it is a great, indeed, an enormous wrong to conclude and grant a second marriage while the first is still undiminished.

I would as soon have another lady, who is great (but not so great as the one I have just spoken of), who, when sought after in marriage by a knight, married him, not because she had any love for him, but because she saw how thin and debili-

---

[1] 'in the green'—corn just above the ground, as distinct from ripe, harvest corn.

tated and sickly he had become, so that the doctors were telling him he would not see the year out, and all this even after having known this lovely woman several times in her bed. And for this reason she craved his early death, and would have lost no time after his death getting hold of his goods and estate, fine furniture and great benefices which he gave her by marrying her, since he was very rich, a noble who was well established. She was very disappointed, for he is still among the living, a gay fellow, better in health than ever he was before he married her. Then her death ensued. It is said that in this case the noble concerned was merely pretending to be sickly and ailing, so that this woman, whom he knew to be extremely greedy, should be prompted to marry him in the hope of getting all his wealth, but the Almighty here arranged things in quite contrary fashion and to its mortification the goat had to crop where she was tethered.

What shall we say of some who marry whores and courtesans who have been very notorious, as is quite commonly done in France, but above all in Spain and Italy, counting on saving their souls by such acts of charity, *por librar una anima christiana del inferno*, 'by delivering a Christian soul from hell,' as they say, bringing it on to the road of sanctity.

It is very true, and I have known men who held to the opinion and maxim, that if they married their wives for that holy, kindly reason, they need not count as cuckolds, because what is done for the glory of God should never be made a reason for opprobrium, and they also argued that as their wives have been put on to the right road and did not depart from it at all or go back to the other, as I have known some do in those two countries, becoming greater sinners after marriage than before, some of them never able to cure themselves of it, but turning aside to plough the same furrow over again.

The first time I went to Italy[171] I fell in love in Rome with a very lovely courtesan called Faustina, but as I had not much money and she was too expensive, taking from ten to twelve crowns for a night, I had to content myself with conversation with her and with seeing her. After the lapse of some time I was back in Italy a second time, now with a fuller purse, so by the

95

intervention of another woman, I went to see her at her house, for I found her now married to a magistrate, who was living there with her. She welcomed me warmly and told me all about the great fortune of her marriage and how far behind her she had cast the follies of her past, to which she had said good-bye for ever. I showed her some good French crowns, as I was dying more than ever for love of her. She was tempted and let me have what I wanted, telling me that when she married she had settled and agreed with her husband that she should have complete liberty, so long as she did not disgrace him or hide it from him and got a big fee, so they might both maintain a high standard of living, and was ready, indeed, glad to do it for big sums, but not for small money. Now that was a man truly cuckolded, both *en herbe et gerbe,* in sprout and ear.

I have heard of a lady of station who when she married insisted on her husband leaving her at court to make love, and this was agreed upon, she reserving to herself whatever use she made of her pool and her grove, except that as recompense she would pay him a thousand francs a month for his own little pleasures, her only other concern being to give herself a good time.

Thus it follows that women who have been free cannot easily keep from breaking any restricting locks on their doors, or any other restraint, especially where gold chinks and gleams, as witness that lovely daughter of King Acrisius[172] who, though completely restricted and locked in her thick-walled brazen tower, allowed herself a path of delight where Jupiter's lovely gold dripped.

Ah, said a certain gallant man, how hard it is to keep a woman who is lovely, ambitious, money-loving, ever craving after show and fine clothes and ornament, and also in good health, without her rooting not with her snout, but her behind, and as the saying goes, however well protected her parts are, in other words, however fine a husband she has, however brave he is and however good a swordsman in her defence.

I have known so many fine brave men who have gone through it, and a sorry sight indeed it was to see such worthy, valiant men fallen so low, and after having gained so many fine victories too, and achieved so many outstanding conquests of their foes, to have to be brought down to finding horns peeping out of their lovely coronet of flowers and foliage that garnishes the helmet of triumph, to their utter disgrace, in spite of all finding more satisfaction in their grand doughtiness and estimable enterprise in war, in their acts of martial bravery and other exploits, than in keeping a watch over their wives and a light shone on their dark dens. And thus without realising it do such men find themselves finally taking the city of Cornwall, or rather Hornwall, which is really very pitiable. For instance, I knew one valiant, worthy knight who bore a very eminent title too,[173] who when one day he was spreading himself in an account of his acts of bravery and his conquests, heard an eminent and great noble who was his ally and bosom friend remark to another : 'Here he is telling us of his conquests, which really does surprise me, for his wife's part is bigger than any other he has ever quested or ever will.'

And I have known many others, too, who, whatever the distinction, their majesty or their standing nevertheless had all the markings of the cuckold, which annulled it all, for such marks and taints can never be hidden or dissimulated, a man can put as good a face and show on it as he likes, it all comes out quite clear. As for me, I have never in my life seen any such who did not bear the markings, the face, the taint of it, except one whom I knew in whom the most clear-sighted person could have found nothing to pick hold of and find fault with, so distinguished and grand of bearing was he, so estimable and grave his appearance—until he knew the wife.

I would really like to implore wives who have such perfect husbands not to play them such tricks or do them such injury. But they of course might well ask : 'But where are those perfect husbands you speak of ? Whom do you really mean ?'

Indeed, my ladies, you are right, for all men cannot be Scipios or Caesars, such men are no more. So my conclusion really is that in this matter you should follow your promptings, for, after all, speaking of Caesars, the most gallant of them certainly went through it, even the most virtuous and perfect, as I said, and as we see in the case of that gifted Emperor Trajan, whose fine qualities could not keep his wife Plotina from giving herself to the pleasure of Hadrian, (who became emperor after him,)[174] whence he acquired great benefits, profit and greatness, for it was she who was the cause of his advancement, though when he reached his high position he was at least not ungrateful, for he always loved her and respected her, so much that when she died he went into deep mourning, falling into such a melancholy that for a time he was utterly unable either to eat or to drink, so grieved that he was quite unable to return from Narbonian Gaul, where he learned this sad news, for three or four months, during which time he wrote to the Senate to declare Plotina one of the goddesses of Rome, giving orders that very lavish and very sumptuous offerings were to be made *in memoriam*, after which he spent his time having a very lovely temple[175] near Nemausus, now known as Nimes, with much ornament of fine marble and porphyry works and other treasures, built and furnished in her honour and memory.

There you see how in respect of love and its satisfaction one has to turn a blind eye. After all, Cupid, the lover's god, is blind too, as we see in some ladies, who, having husbands who are the most handsome, most decent and most accomplished of men one could find, yet turn to making love with others so ugly and so dirty that they could not be worse.

I have seen many women who made one wonder which is the worst drab, the lady with a very handsome, estimable husband who takes a lover who is ugly, morose and quite the opposite of her husband, or the one who has an ugly, morose husband, but finds a handsome, very charming lover, yet does not cease loving and caressing her husband, as if he were the handsomest of men—as I have seen many women do?

There is no doubt about it, the general opinion is that the woman who has a handsome husband and leaves him to love an ugly lover is really a very great whore, neither more nor less than that anybody who leaves good meat to eat bad meat is a very greedy person. Likewise in the case of the woman who leaves good looks to love ugliness, it does look rather as if she does it from sheer lust, for there is indeed nothing more lustful or more suitable to satisfy lust than an ugly man, who is more conscious of his stinking, foul, lewd sex than her husband is. And the handsome and decent men are without question rather more delicate, so less able to satisfy any excessive, unbridled craving for an orgasm than a huge, corpulent bearded, rustic, satyr-like roisterer of a fellow.

Others however say that the woman who loves a handsome lover and an ugly husband and caresses them both is just as bad a whore, because she is so concerned not to miss any possibility of daily practice of love.

Such women are like the men who wander about the country, (it is certainly true now of France,) and when at their lodging they come to the evening meal never fail to ask their host to give them the baggage-horse's portion, and they have to have it too, even if they are already full to the lips. These women likewise when they go to bed always want their baggage-horse portion, like one I knew who had a husband who filled out a pair of trousers as well as any man. Yet despite what their husbands have, they want to increase and double it, no matter by what means, and for the daytime want a lover with obvious good looks, which by the aid of the lovely daylight so much the more increase my lady's lust and satisfaction, and a husband for the night, since, as the saying goes, all cats are grey in the dark, and so long as such a woman satisfies her appetite she does not care a jot if her husband is ugly or handsome. For, as I hear from more than one person, when in the throes of the act of love neither man nor woman thinks at all of anything else, there is no other idea in their heads, only what they are doing in the given moment, although I have it from a good source that many ladies have made their lovers believe that when they are with their husbands they do not think of them at all, but really think of their lovers, so as to get more pleasure, just as I have heard husbands say that when with their wives they think of their mistresses, for the same reason. But those are abuses.

Natural philosophers have told me that solely the aim of the moment dominates in such moments and never what is absent, and they adduce many arguments for this, but I am not good enough or learned enough a philosopher to argue it out with them. Besides, there are some women who are very dirty. I merely wish to put on record what is said. But, to return to these choices of ugly lovers, I have seen many such in my life and been astonished a hundred times over.

Coming home once from a journey into certain foreign parts,[176] which I will not name, lest the person I mean to speak of be recognized, and in talk with a great and eminent lady[177] happening to mention another great lady and princess[178] whom I saw there, she asked me with whom she made love. I named the person whom she kept as favourite, who was neither handsome nor very presentable, and of very poor quality.[179] My interlocutor's reply was : 'Really, she is doing herself no good at all, and great harm to love, being as lovely and as estimable as she is held to be.'

This lady had every right to say this to me, since she did not counter it herself or attempt to conceal it, for she had an estimable lover herself whom she greatly favoured. And when all is said and done, a lady will never reproach herself for choosing to love or selecting a handsome person, nor does she wrong her husband, unless for reasons bearing on love of their line, as there are husbands who are so ugly, so stupid, so silly, so gumptionless, so unpresentable, so cowardly, such worms and of so little valour that when their wives have children by them and the children resemble them they were better if they had had none, for I have known several ladies who, having had children by such husbands, had them all turn out just like their fathers, but whenever they borrowed a child from a lover, the child surpassed its legal father, and its brothers and sisters, in everything.

There are too some of the philosophers who have touched on this subject and always held that such borrowed or stolen children, made in secret and sometimes in most improvised fashion, are far more gallant and have much more in them, (all coming from the delightful way used to make them so featly and neatly, with such skill in fact,) than those made cumbersomely, dully, ponderously, at leisure in a bed, and half asleep too, with only thought of satisfaction of the animal pleasure of it.

Similarly I have heard those in charge of the horse-studs of the King and of great princes say that they have often seen better horses foaled by the mares' own going to stallion than those produced by the ingenuity of the stud masters when they deliberately select and lead on special stallions. It is just the same with people.

What a lot of cases I have known of ladies producing handsomer, finer, grander children, whereas had their putative fathers made them they would have been real bullocks, mere animals.

This is why women are well advised to produce good stock, to seek the aid and assistance of good, fine stallions. Though I have also seen more than one with a handsome husband who sought the aid of an ugly, wretched stallion, which pro-created hideous bad stock.

There you have one of the marked advantages or disadvantages of cuckoldom.

I knew a lady of eminence who had a very ugly and very ill-mannered husband, and of the four daughters and two boys she produced there were only two which were any good, these being made by her lover, whereas the others, being by her steadfast husband (though I would rather call him *chathaunt* than *chaland*, rather *caterwauling* than *conforming* husband) were most surly.

In this matter the ladies should take care and be skilful, for as a rule boys are like their fathers, and they are sensitive about their honour when they are not. Thus in my experience I have known many ladies make quite a point of getting everybody to say and believe their sons to be the image of their father rather than like themselves, whereas they are not a bit like the former, for this is the greatest pleasure you can give them, especially when it looks as if they had borrowed from elsewhere, even if that is not the case.

I once found myself in a great company at court examining a portrait of two daughters of a very great Queen.[180] Everybody added his opinion as to whom they were like, and the result was that all the lords and ladies present said they were the image of their mother, but I, who was the very humble gentle-

man-in-waiting of the mother,[181] held the positive side and said
that they were the image of their father, and if one had seen
and known him as I did, everybody would have agreed. Upon
which the sister of the mother in question thanked me and was
very grateful to me, extremely so, indeed, particularly since
there were people who deliberately said the opposite, so she
should be suspected of illicit love and having, as the saying
is, some dust in her recorder. Thus my opinion about the children's likeness to the father completely repaired the situation.
Wherefore à *propos* of this matter of any man having love relations with a lady, if the children are seen to be of his blood
and bones, it is always better to say they are the image of their
legal father, and certainly not the opposite.

True, there is no harm in saying that they have a little of
the mother in them too, as did a noble at court, a great friend
of mine, when speaking to two nobles, brothers,[182] rather favourites of the King, who, when asked whom they resembled, the
father or the mother, replied that the one who was cold was
like the father[183] and the other, who was hot-blooded, was like
the mother, by which opinion he certainly credited the mother
well, for she is a hot piece if there is one,[184] but it was quite
true, the boys did show those two different qualities, one cold,
the other hot.

There is one class of cuckolds who are made by their own
scorn for their wives, and I have known several such, men with
very lovely, estimable wives, but whom they did not prize at all,
despising and disdaining them. Being clever and full of pluck,
and of good family, the wives, when they felt themselves thus
scorned, had their revenge by scorning their husbands in turn,
which they did immediately they found a good lover, which
produced the right result, for, as the Italian has it in a Neapolitan ditty : *Amor non si vince con altro che con sdegno*, 'only
disdain overcomes love.'

Thus, if she has any heart at all, any lovely, estimable lady,
especially if aware of herself and taking pleasure in being
so lovely and estimable, will, when she sees her husband despise her in spite of her offering him the greatest conjugal love
in the world, and even if you plead and remind her of the

law's stipulations about loving, put the husband in his proper place by taking an additional lover to aid her in her little needs, so that she thus finds her own satisfaction.[185]

I once knew two ladies of the court, sisters, lovely both of them. One had married a well-favoured husband, a courtier of great ability, but who did not pay the attention to his wife that he should, seeing her position, and even spoke to her in front of other people as to a savage, treating her very roughly. She was patient and put up with him for some time, till her husband fell somewhat into disfavour. The wife was not slow to find the occasion opportune, for by now she had a nice grudge against him, and without more ado, she returned his scorn by nicely cuckolding him, which her lovely sister did too with her husband, taking an example from her, for she had been married very young, at a most tender age, and her husband did not pay her attention, treating her as if she was only a silly little child, and not according her the love he owed her. However, since she by now saw the years were mounting up, and she was conscious of her power to love and aware of her own beauty, she paid her husband back in the same coin and as recompense for the past made him a present of a nice pair of horns.

Formerly I also knew a great lord[186] who, having taken two courtesans, of which there was a multitude, for his greatest delights and loves, to the neglect of his wife, for all that she was attentive to him with all the honours, signs of love and respect for marriage that she could offer, and he never had even a pleasant word for her, never an affectionate embrace, and out of every hundred never accorded her more than a couple of nights. What was she to do, poor thing, after such indignities, except just what she did, that is, choose another bed with space going and join with another half, taking of him what she needed.

At least this husband might have done what another of my acquaintance did. This man was of such temperament that when once pressed by his wife, who was very lovely, for taking his pleasure elsewhere, said frankly to her: 'Find your satisfaction too elsewhere, I give you full leave to do so. Do on your part whatever you like with another man, I grant you your liberty to do so, but you do not worry about my loves, let me do whatever I may choose. I shall not hinder your convenience and pleasure, so do not interfere with mine.' So from that point on they both went at it cap and bells, one to the right, 'tother to the left, without a care about one another, and life was immediately more pleasant.

I would equally approve of an impotent, sickly, gouty old man whom I knew who one day said to his wife (who was very lovely, but whom he could not satisfy as she wished) : 'I am well aware, my love, that my impotence is not sufficient for your full-blooded age. For this reason I might become very hideous to you, and it would be impossible for you to be my affectionate wife, as you would be if I accorded you the usual offices of a strong, healthy husband. But I have come to the decision to grant and give you complete liberty to make love and to call on some other man better able to satisfy you than I am, but above all, I would have you choose one who is discreet, modest and will cause neither you nor me or our house, any disgrace, and who might make you a couple of handsome sons whom I will love and regard as my own, to such point that all the world will be convinced that they really are our legitimate sons, since I still am a sufficiently vigorous man and look as if capable of such boys being my own.'

I leave you to conceive how delighted that lovely young woman was to hear that pleasing and handsome little homily, with the licence to enjoy such delightful liberty, which she applied so well that in no time she had filled the house with two or three handsome sons, in which indeed, since he did have relations with her occasionally and sleep with her, he felt he had played some part, and, since he was so sure, so the world and everybody else was, and thus husband and wife were very happy and had a fine family.

Here now is another sort of cuckolds, those who are made by the charming views that some women hold, namely, that there is nothing more handsome or legitimate or to be recommended than the act of charity, which they maintain does not merely embrace giving to the poor who need help, aiding them with the goods and resources of the rich, but also quenching the fires of these wretched, miserable lovers who are to be seen a-glow with the hot combustion of love : 'For,' these ladies say, 'what could be more charitable than to give life to one whom one sees dying or to completely restore one whom one sees thus consumed?' As, bearing out lovely Genevieve in Ariosto,[187] that fine paladin Lord de Montauban says it would be justice were one to take the life of the woman who robbed her courtier of life, not the one who gives life to the man who pays her attention.

If Ariosto could say that of an unmarried girl, all the more are such charities to be recommended to women, for unmarried girls' purses are not unfastened and open yet, as are those of married women, who have bags (at least, some of them have) which are very ample indeed and most fitted for lavish alms-giving.

A propos of which I recall a story of a very lovely lady of the court, who, dressing one Candlemas in a gown of white damask, with all her suite in white too, so that you could not have seen a lovelier or whiter sight on that day, found herself, together with one of her ladies-in-waiting who was also a lovely lady, but a trifle older and better with her tongue, at whom too one of her gentlemen-in-waiting had set his cap, standing the three of them, looking at a very lovely picture depicting a *Charity* in all purity in white veiling, felt prompted to say a word for him, so remarked to her companion : 'You are wearing the same dress as this *Charity* today, but if you resemble it in this respect, you should also resemble it in practice with regard to the noble who is paying you attentions, for there is nothing so meritorious as acts of mercy and charity, in whatever form they are clothed, provided they are given with the good intention of aiding your neighbour. So do exercise charity, and if you are afraid of your husband and have your marriage vows before your eyes, that, believe me, is a vain superstition we women folk should never feel, for Nature has not granted us our various kinds of goods to be parsimonious with them, like a foul miser with his hoard, but to distribute them decently to the poor who are suffering and necessitous. It is very truly said that our chastity is like a hoard of gold, not to be frittered away on mean things, but to be spent grandly, without stint, on lofty things. Likewise should we dole out our chastity, which should be stretched for persons of merit and virtue and those who are suffering, and denied to those men who are base, valueless and little in need. As for our husbands, fine idols they are indeed, to be granted our exclusive vows and vigils and never to be quit for any other handsome form. For it is only to the Almighty that we owe a vow of exclusivity, not to any other being.'

This speech was not at all displeasing to the lady, nor did it in the least offend the gentleman-in-waiting, who with a little perseverance obtained the benefit of it. Nevertheless, such advocacy of charity is dangerous for poor husbands. I have heard tell (I do not know if it is true, so will not vouch for it) that when the Huguenots first founded their churches, they preached their faith at night and in secret, from fear of being caught, found out and prosecuted, and there was one occasion in the *Rue de St Jacques* in Paris, in the time of Henry II, when great ladies of my acquaintance went to get this charity because they counted on being surprised! When the minister finished his sermon he ended by recommending charity, and immediately after that all the candles were put out and there and then, pairing off, men and women, Christian brother and sister showed each other charity, sharing it all out one with another according to their whim and ability. I cannot really affirm that all of this was so, but I was certainly assured that it was, though it is quite possible that it is all pure falsehood and deception.

All the same, I do know for sure that at Poitiers in those days there was a certain lawyer's wife who was known as 'fair Gotterelle', whom I actually saw, and she was one of the loveliest of women, of the most superb charm and bearing, and one of the most desirable in the city at the time, so that every man had his eye on her and desired her. Now, when she came out of the church after the sermon she was mounted one after the other by a dozen collegians, some doing it in the consistory itself, some under a penthouse roof, while I have even heard that some took her under the scaffold in the old market place, without her uttering a sound or refusing any single one of them, but, relying solely on the word of the sermon, meekly accepted them one after the other, as her true brothers in Christ. She kept these almsgivings up for a long time, too, yet she would never let a Catholic touch her, not even for a doubloon. Nevertheless there were several Catholics who picked up the language and jargon of their Huguenot meetings from comrades of theirs, and also had their pleasure of her. Others then went to these sermons for that express purpose and pretended to be of the reformed church, learning it all just to be able to enjoy that lovely woman. I was a young student in Poitiers[188] at the time, and a number of good friends who had their share of it told me about it on oath. Indeed, it was the talk of the town. Now there's nice charity for you, and a woman of conscience too, thus choosing between human kind by their faith !

There is another form of charity which, in the case of the wretched men held in prisons and deprived of the pleasures of the fair sex, is practised today, as it has often been in the past, by the women gaolers and other women who have charge of them, that is, the mistresses of great houses who have prisoners-of-war in their castles, and take pity on them and give them a share of their love, doing so from charity and pity, as a Roman courtesan once said to her daughter, of whom a gallant was extremely amorous, but to whom she would accord nothing, not even for a doubloon. Her words were : *E dagli, al manco per misericordia*—'Come on, let him have it, at least by charity !'

Thus women gaolers, mistresses of castles and others treat their prisoners who, although captive and wretched, still feel the prick of the flesh, as they did in better times. Thus the old proverb says : 'Desire is born of poverty', and no matter, Master Priapus raises his head on straw or hard stone just as much as he does in the softest and finest bed in the world.

This is why beggars and prisoners in their hostels and prisons are as lusty at love-making as kings, princes and grandees in their fine palaces and soft royal beds.

As confirmation of what I say I will cite the story told me one day by Captain Beaulieu,[189] Captain of Galleys, whom I have mentioned a number of times. He was attached to the late Lord the Grand Prior of France, of the Lorraine family,[190] and was much loved by him. Going to see him one day in a frigate at Malta, he was captured by the Sicilian galleys and taken prisoner to Castel-a-Mare of Palermo, where he was confined in a very constricted, dark, wretched prison and badly treated for three months. But it so happened that the master of the castle, who was a Spaniard, had two very lovely daughters, and when one day they heard him complaining and found he was falling into a melancholy, they asked their father for permission to visit him, *ad majoram gloriam Dei,* which he freely did. And as Captain Beaulieu was a very gallant man and a fine talker, he was so able to convince them at this very first interview that they got their father to let him out of this miserable prison and have him quartered in a fairly decent room where he was better treated. This was not all, for they also obtained permission from their father to visit him daily and talk to him.

And Captain Beaulieu was so diligent about it that both the girls fell in love with him, though he had no good looks and they had, with the result that, tempted by these liberties, and regardless either of the most rigorous confinement or the danger of death, he began to take his pleasure of them both, to complete satisfaction, and their dalliance went on without any publicity and he was so fortunate in this conquest which lasted eight months that there was no scandal at all, no ill, nothing wrong, not even a swollen belly, nor were they ever caught at it or discovered, for the two sisters agreed well together and so they aided one another, taking turns at keeping *cave,* so that nothing untoward ever did happen. He swore to me—and he was a very great friend of mine, too—that even when he was as free as a bird he had never had such a good time, or greater ardour or appetite for it than in this prison, which for all that it is said that no prison can ever be lovely, became really lovely to him. And this he enjoyed for the whole of eight months, till a truce was concluded between the Emperor and King Henry II by which all prisoners were freed and came out. And on oath he assured me that he was never so annoyed as he was when he had to leave so good a prison, and really upset at leaving those lovely girls, being so favoured by them, who when he went were all lamentation.

I put it to him as to whether he had not feared trouble had he been found out. He said of course, not that he had exactly feared it, for the worst that could have happened would have been that they would have put him to death, and he would as soon have died as gone back to his first prison. Further, he said, that what he had really been rather afraid of was not satisfying these worthy girls, for they put such great demands on him, and he was afraid lest they took a spite and scorn of him, for then he would have been still worse treated, so for this reason alone he blinded himself to everything else and staked all on this lovely good fortune.

One really could not find praise enough for these kind Spanish girls for being so charitable, though they were neither the first nor the last so to be.

It is said that earlier on in our own land of France the Duke d'Ascot, taken prisoner in the Bois de Vincennes, escaped by the aid of a worthy lady,[191] who certainly risked suffering for it, for it concerned the royal service. Such charities are indeed to be condemned which impinge on the public weal, but when there is nothing special involved and it is only a lovely body that is risked—and there is little harm in that—they are very good and praiseworthy.

I could adduce very many excellent examples of this if I wished to make a special study of it, which would indeed not be too unpleasant. But I will not say more than tell the following story, as a charming instance from the ancient world, and then no more.

In Livy[192] we find how when the Romans had sacked Capua, some of the inhabitants came to Rome to petition the Emperor regarding their wretchedness and beg for his pity. The matter was put to the Senate, and among the speakers was M. Atilius Regulus, who held that no mercy should be shown the Capuans, 'For,' said he, 'one could not find a single Capuan of whom since the rebellion of their city it could be said that he had revealed the least trace of friendship or affection for the cause of Republican Rome, save two estimable ladies, one, Vesta

Opia, of the city of Atella, then domiciled in Capua, and the other Faucula Cluvia,' both of whom had formerly been prostitutes and courtesans, trading publicly. The one had not let a day pass without offering prayers and sacrifices for the prosperity and victory of the people of Rome and the other he commended for having secretly helped wretched prisoners-of-war with provender when they were dying of hunger and misery.

Those were certainly very lovely, charitable and pious acts, *à propos* of which a worthy noble, an estimable lady and I, one day coming upon this passage in our reading, remarked both at once to each other that since these two estimable ladies had already made such good progress in the study of such pious and worthy works, they must certainly have passed this on to others and given them too a share in the charity of their bodies, for, being courtesans, they had given alms many times previously to other men, and they may indeed still have been of the same profession, though the book says nothing about that, leaving a hint of uncertainty, so that this can only be presumed. But even if it was a resumption of the business after once having given it up for a time, that was no difficulty, for there is nothing so easy to do, and possibly too they knew and accommodated some of their excellent previous lovers, old acquaintances who had mounted their bodies on previous occasions, and had a mind to tread familiar ground, so to speak, or it might well be that among the prisoners they were able to find complete strangers, men they had never seen before, but whom they considered handsome, debonair, valiant presentable fellows who were certainly in need of all possible charity, and it was for this reason that they were not sparing with the lovely enjoyment of their bodies. It could not well be otherwise. Anyhow, whichever way it be, these estimable ladies certainly deserved the courtesy that the Republic of Rome showed them by its recognition, for it secured the restoration of all their possessions, and they subsequently enjoyed what was theirs as peacefully as ever. What is more, they were given to understand that whatever they liked to ask for, they would have. And to tell the truth, had Livy not been so bound as he was to be truthful and discreet, he would probably have set it all down quite frankly and told us plainly that these two women did not stint them their charming bodies, which would have made this passage of history so much the finer and more pleasant to read, without this resort to curtailment, leaving the loveliest part of the tale still clinging, so to speak, to the tip of Livy's pen. This anyway is what we said at the time.

When a prisoner in England, King Jean received the same charity from the Countess of Salisbury,[193] and so good were those particular favours, too, that he was unable afterwards to forget them and the good times she had given him, and went back to England expressly to see her, as she made him swear and promise he would.

There are other ladies who are amusing in this matter about a certain scruple of conscience in their charity, like one, for instance, who, however much her lover slept with her, would never allow him to kiss her lips, adducing as argument for this prohibition that it was her lips that had taken the oath of faithfulness and loyalty to her husband, and she did not wish to sully either these lips which had made the promise and taken the vow, whereas the abdominal mouth, so to speak, having not said a single word or promised a thing, she allowed to do whatever it pleased, and made no scruples about lending that, holding that the upper lips had no power to assume obligations for those below, just as those below had none *vis-à-vis* the upper ones, and the common law ordains that one cannot assume obligations for any other person without the express consent and word of both parties, nor can one part only involve the whole in such a matter.

Another conscientious, scrupulous lady, giving her lover the enjoyment of her body,[194] would always insist on being on top, making the man lie underneath, and never departed one instant from that rule, but, observing it as she did on every single occasion, most stringently, she said that like this, if her husband or any other asked her if such and such a person had done so-and-so to her, she could confidently protest, swear and deny without offending God that the man mentioned had certainly never mounted her.

111

This oath she was so good at swearing that she satisfied her husband and others too by the restrictions under which she acceded to their demands, and they all believed her, because of what she replied, but, so she said, 'It never entered their heads to ask if I had ever ridden him, a question which would certainly have put me at a loss and given me something to think about.'

I think I have said enough about this subject, but one cannot always remember everything, though I have the impression that there is more in this part than the other.

As a rule, the ladies of this trade are great liars, and never speak a word of truth, for they have learned so much and grown so accustomed to lying to their husbands and lovers on these subjects and changes of love, and to swearing that they never give themselves to any but them, (or if not, they are very silly, and bad cess to them) that when they do happen to come upon other important matters, or business, or treatises, they never do aught but lie and cannot be credited.

There are other women I have known and have heard pronounce on it who only give their lovers enjoyment when they are pregnant, so as not to be impregnated by their seed, making it a great matter of conscience not to saddle their husbands with progeny to feed, provide for and bring up as their own, which are not theirs. I have discussed this already. But these women feel it is no offence to their husbands, nor does it cuckold them, to prostitute themselves thus once they are pregnant.

It may be that some have done it for the same reasons that were given by Augustus's daughter Julia, (Agrippa's wife,) who in her day was an arrant tart, which angered her father more than the husband. Asked one day if she was not apprehensive of being made pregnant by her lovers, and her husband noticing it and being angry with her, she replied : 'I see that things are all right, by never accepting anybody in my little boat, however momentarily, unless it already has a full cargo.'

Here again is another kind of cuckolds, though these are real martyrs, namely, men with wives who are as ugly as imps of Satan, yet crave to dabble and taste the sweet pleasure just

112

as much as do the lovely ones whose only privilege, as the proverb says, is: 'Handsome men to the gibbet and lovely women to the brothel.' And yet these ugly charcoal-merchants go wild just as much as the others, with the same nature, merely not so beautiful. I have seen ugly women, at least in their youth, put as high a price on themselves as the lovely ones, thinking that a woman's worth is to be measured solely by what value she puts on herself, so that in a good market all goods are sold and cherished, some more, some less, according to what one wants of them and also depending on how late after the others one comes to the market, and also according to the good prices one finds there, for, as people say, even if the goods are not the best, one always goes to the best market, it depends on the ability of the seller, man or woman.

So it is with ugly women, of whom I have on my faith seen some who were as hot and lewd and addicted to love-making as the loveliest, and those set themselves right in front of the market displaying their goods and sticking the price up notwithstanding their looks.

But the worst thing about them is that instead of the buyers making the offer, as they do to the lovely ones, here it is the sellers who ask the buyers to take and purchase their goods, which they are ready to let go for a mere song. They even go further, for more often than not they will give a man money to accommodate their cravings and serve them, which is lamentable, for such service calls for no small sums of money, so that the supply costs more than the supplier is really worth, let alone the suds one has to put into it to swab it out well, but here all the same Monsieur the husband is made both a fool and cuckold by an ugly wife, which is a much harder morsel to digest than being the victim of a lovely one, not to mention that it is the limit of wretchedness to have one of hell's demons lying at your side instead of an angel.

A propos of this, I have heard more than one gallant man crave a wife who was beautiful and a bit of a strumpet, rather than one who was ugly and the chastest in the world, for in ugliness is but sheer wretchedness and displeasure, there is not a grain of happiness in it, while in a lovely woman, according

113

to some, a man has every pleasure and happiness in abundance and very little wretchedness. I am relying here on those men who have trodden this particular path and road.

I have heard some men say that sometimes it is not so essential to husbands to have their wives so very chaste, for love makes them so magnificent, I mean those who have that very rare gift by which you could almost say of them that they would rule not only their husbands, but the heavens and the stars as well, they are so proud in their chastity they have the impression that God owes them some return. But such women are very mistaken, for I have heard great theologians say that God better loves a wretched sinner of a woman, if she is humble and contrite (as the Magdalen became) than one who is haughty and supercilious and thinks she has attained paradise without doing anything else to earn God's mercy and good judgement.

I have heard of one lady so arrogant about her chastity that she came to despise even her husband to such an extent that when she was asked if she had slept with him she said : 'No, he slept with me.' What arrogance ! And I leave it to you to imagine how such foolish arrogantly chaste women nag their husbands, even when they have nothing whatever to reproach them with, just as do those too who are both chaste and rich, for such, the chaste and rich in their own right, get above themselves, becoming haughty and supercilious and outrageous *vis-à-vis* their husbands, to such extent that because of the excessive opinion they have of their chastity and their so well guarded parts, they are quite unable to restrain themselves from being imperious, nagging at their husbands for his least shortcoming, as I have known some do, particularly his bad management. And if he gambles, if he spends freely, if he squanders, she shouts still more, she rages, in fact, making the house more like hell than the home of a noble family, and if he is obliged to sell some of his possessions to cope with the costs of an attendance at court or to go to the wars, or for litigation, or some other need, or even for his lesser pleasures and trivial expenses, it does not bear talking of, for the woman has assumed such an imperious position over him, all based on her excessive prudery, and if she is backed by this the husband

simply has to submit to her condemnation, which was all expressed very well by Juvenal[195] in his satires :

> .... *Animus uxoris si deditus uni*
> *Nil unquam invita donabis conjuge; vendes,*
> *Hac obstante, nihil; nil haec, si nolit, emetur,*

'if you have been such a simpleton as to let your wife be the
master of your spirit, you will never hand out a thing without
her, you will sell nothing if she is against it or buy anything
she does not want.'

From these lines of his we see clearly that such temperaments in the women of Ancient Rome were exactly like those
of some of our own age in this respect, but, on the other hand,
when a woman is a bit of a strumpet, she does thereby make
herself much more genial, she is more submissive, more docile,
more yielding, sweeter altogether and more agreeable in temperament, humbler and more ready to do what her husband
wants and in short to submit to him in everything, as indeed I
have seen in many instances, the wives simply not daring to
scold or nag or make savage attacks, lest their husbands tackled
them about their own misdemeanours and confronting them
with their adultery made them pay a little for the life they led,
and if your gallant then wanted to sell some piece of family
property which was the wife's, one saw her signing up the deed
of sale almost before the husband suggested it. I have seen
many such instances. In short, such women do what their
husbands want.

Are not such men thus really rather spoiled by being cuckolded by their wives, since from it they draw such goods and
commodities as these, not to speak of the fine, delightful
pleasure they have making frenzied love with such lovely
women, swimming with them so to speak in so fine, so clear a
stream, not in a filthy, ugly cesspool? And, as a great captain
of my acquaintance once said, if one has to die, is it not better
to die by a lovely young sword which is bright and clean and
gleaming, and cuts clean, than by an old, rusty, badly-cleaned
blade which cries out for more emery powder than all the
cleaners of the city of Paris could supply?

And what I say of young ugly women I say all the more of some elderly women who would like to be furbished and kept as clean and bright as the loveliest women in the world (I am making a special treatise on this) and therein lies the misfortune, for when their husbands cannot cope, the wretched creatures call in assistants, and they are as hot or hotter than the young ones, as I have seen some, who were prone to get quite frenzied, not at the beginning or midway, but at the end. No wonder it is said that in these matters the end is more frenzied in wanting it than the other two stages, the commencement and the middle, for what such men lack is vigour and ability to perform, a lack which causes them very grave sorrow, for, as the old proverb puts it, it is a great and lamentable misfortune when a backside is all lust and no thrust.

Thus there are ever wretched old women who adore being ridden and distribute great largesse with both their purses, though it is the one that dispenses gold that makes men declare the other, the one of their bodies, both firm and narrow. Thus is it said that liberality in all things is more to be prized than miserliness and niggardliness, except in women who, the more free they are with their parts, the less they are esteemed, and the miserly and niggardly so much the more.

This is what a great prince once said of two great ladies, sisters, whom I know, one of whom was niggardly with her honour, but liberal with her purse and expenditure, the other tight-pursed in expenditure and very free with her belly.

Now here is another breed of cuckolds, which is without doubt most abominable and execrable before God and man, those who, being enamoured of some fine Adonis, abandon their wives to him to enjoy.

The very first time I went to Italy,[196] I heard of an instance at Ferrara, in the story told me of a man who, being taken with a handsome young man, persuaded his wife to confer enjoyment of herself on this young man who was in love with her, and said she was to appoint a day for him and do whatever he wanted. The lady made no objection whatever, for there was no venison she liked so much. At last the day was fixed and the hour came round for the young man and the woman to indulge in these sweet doings and they were all athirst for it, when the husband, who by the arrangement between his wife and himself had hidden, broke into the room and, catching them in the act, held his dagger at the young man's throat, accounting him worthy of death for such a misdemeanour, according to the laws of Italy, which are rather more rigorous than those of France. The young man was compelled to give the husband just what he wanted, and they struck a bargain by which the young man prostituted himself to the husband and the husband abandoned his wife to the young man, so that here was a husband cuckolded in a very disreputable way.

I have heard tell[197] that in a certain part [198] (I am not going to name it) there was once a husband, one of high quality too,[199] who was shabbily in love with a young man[200] who in turn loved the man's wife greatly, as she did him, and whether the husband had won his wife over to conspire with him or he did genuinely surprise them together, anyway, he caught his wife and the young man in bed, coupling, and threatened the young man with death if he did not yield to him, and took him at once as he lay there, solving the problem as to how three lovers could all three have their pleasure at one time.

I have heard tell of a great lady who was desperately in love with an estimable noble whom she had taken for lover and favourite, and when he expressed fear lest the husband did her some harm, consoled him and said : 'Do not fear, for he would never dare do anything, as he is afraid I might charge him publicly with wanting to enjoy me in a way for which, if I spoke the least word and revealed him to the law, he could pay with his life. But by that means I keep him in check and uncertain of himself, so that as he is afraid I may charge him he does not dare say anything.'

It is true, such a charge would indeed have put the man's life in question, for the lawmakers say that sodomy is punishable merely in intention. But it may be that the lady in question did not want to speak right out, because he in fact went the whole hog with her and did not stop at mere intent.

I have been told the tale that in recent years there was a young French noble, a handsome fellow who had been seen at court for some time, who went to Rome like some of his companions to learn the military arts, and was so much admired and marvelled at both by men and women for his looks that he was all but taken by force, and wherever it was known he would go to mass, or any other public place of assembly, all and sundry never failed to be present, to see him, and in the end several husbands gave their wives permission to give him love assignations in their homes, so that they might surprise him there and effect a bargain, one giving his wife, the other himself. So he was counselled never to yield to these ladies' importuning, it was all merely a trick to trap him, and he became circumspect and thought more of his good name and his conscience than of all the hateful pleasures, thereby earning great commendation. At last, however, he was killed by his groom. There are various accounts of why, but it was certainly a great pity, for he was a very decent young man, of good origin, and with much of promise in him, equally in his looks, in his noble behaviour and also this fine, noble feature, for, as I was told by a very gallant man of my own time, and it is true, there never was either a b—— or a sodomist, who was upstanding, valiant and great-hearted except the great Julius Caesar so that by the great dispensation of the Almighty such loathsome persons are all marked and most disapproved of. Regarding which, I am amazed that several men who have been seen to indulge in that shameful vice have nevertheless been permitted by Heaven to continue in great prosperity. But God awaits them and in the end we shall see them get their due.

The truth is, I have heard it said that many a husband has been badly infected with this perversion, wretched, abominable creatures indeed. Thus do they treat their poor wives. Then are such wives not to be excused if they cuckold their husbands?

*　　*　　*

What a great number of women there are in the world who, were they examined by midwives and doctors and expert surgeons, would be found to have been made love to unlawfully and could at any moment bring a charge against their husbands, but conceal it and dare not reveal it, for fear of the disgrace to themselves and their husbands. Or is it feasible that they do get some pleasure from it, greater than we might imagine? Or are they silent for the scheming reason I have mentioned, to keep their husbands in a state of subjection when they themselves make love elsewhere, (although of course there are husbands who allow this). Nevertheless, there is no good in it all.

Summa Benedicti says : if a husband wishes to accomplish his act counter to the ordering of Nature, he commits mortal sin, and if he thinks he can plead that he has a right to dispose of his wife as he pleases, he thereby falls into the hateful and disgusting heresy of certain Jews and evil rabbis, of whom it is said that *duabus mulieribus apud synagogam conquestis se fuisse a veris suis cognitu sodomico cognitas, responsum est ab illis rabinis: virum esse uxoris dominum, proinde posse uti ejus utcumque libuerit, non aliter quàm is qui piscem emit: ille enim, tam anterioribus quàm posterioribus partibus, ad arbitrium vesci potest.*

I have put this in Latin without giving a French translation because it sounds very bad in ears which are really decent and chaste. How disgusting they are, to neglect a lovely, pure, specially granted part of the body and take a disgusting, dirty, filthy prohibited part, put in a prohibited direction too.

And if a man wants to take his wife like that, it is allowable for her to separate from him, if there is no other way of correcting him, and so, *Summa Benedicti* says again, those women who fear God never need consent to it, but should rather shout for help, without regard to the scandal which might arise, or the dishonour or fear of death, for it is better to die, says the law, than to consent to evil. Yet the same book says something that I find very strange; in whatever a husband knows his wife, provided she can conceive, it is not a mortal sin so much as it may be a venial one. For when all is said and done there are some ways of doing it which are very dirty and disgusting, at least, as Aretin depicts them in his pictures, and not at all fitting for marital chastity, although, as I have remarked, it may be permissible with pregnant women, also with those who are short of breath or have stinking breath either by mouth or nose, whose kiss or breath is as bad as a privy hole, or even, as I heard tell of one very great lady—I repeat, very great—of whom one of her ladies-in-waiting one day remarked that her breath reeked worse than a bronze piss-pot. Those were her very words, and one of this lady's very intimate lovers, who was sometimes very close to her, confirmed to me that it was so, though it is true that she was then rather getting on in years.

Now, in such a situation what can a husband or a lover do, save have recourse to some extravagant way.

I would go further, but it disgusts me to speak of it, indeed, I am vexed to have said so much already. Yet there are moments when one should reveal the vices of people so they may be cleaned up.

Now I find myself obliged to utter the bad opinion which has been held by many and is still held by the Court of our Kings, namely, that the unmarried girls and the wives at court are very given to going astray, indeed, do so regularly; those who allege this are often mistaken, for there are some who are very chaste, very decent, very virtuous, indeed, more than in other spheres, and one finds virtue too at court, indeed more than in any other place, which should most emphatically be taken as proved.

I will evidence merely the example of the present Grand Duchess of Florence, of the house of Lorraine.[201] She reached Florence the same evening that the Grand Duke married her, and when he wished to sleep with her at once to take her virginity, he first had her make water in a lovely crystal chamber-pot, the loveliest and clearest vessel he could find, and after examining the urine, he held a consultation with his doctor, who was a very great and very learned and expert personality, to learn from him by this inspection whether the girl was a virgin, yes or no. When the physician had made a thorough, learned examination, he found the girl as she was when she left her mother's belly, and said that the Grand Duke could go ahead without hesitation, and would certainly not find the road in any way open, either torn or trodden, which the Grand Duke did do, and found it was exactly as his doctor said, whereupon the next day he said in wonder : 'Now that is a real miracle, a girl coming from the French court still a virgin!' What suspiciousness, and what an opinion! I do not know if this is true, but I was assured it is exactly what happened.

There you have a fine opinion of our courts, though, it is true, not of today, but of long ago, when it was held that none of the ladies of the court of Paris were as circumspect with their bodies as those of the Netherlands, who never leave their own homes. There were men so careful as never to marry a girl or woman who had travelled abroad and seen the world, however little. So that in our Guyenne, in my young days, I heard many gallant men say—and have known them to swear it, too —that they would never marry a girl or a woman who had gone beyond Port de Pille[202] and travelled the French way. Poor fools, for all their ability and gallantry in other things, they were in this thinking that there was no cuckoldom established in their own homes, on their own hearths, in their own bedrooms and closets, whereas there was just as much, perhaps even more, according to circumstances, than in the royal palaces and great royal cities, for their wives were equally prone to be persuaded, sought after, gained and put on their backs, either when they themselves were at court, or the wars, hunting, at the law-courts at litigation, or on other journeyings forth, and so well too that they would never notice it, but they were simple enough to imagine that their womenfolk never dared talk of love matters, merely of household business and the garden and their own hunting and of birds, and so, thus convinced and credulous, were even more cuckolded than men elsewhere. For everywhere, any woman who is lovely and clever, just like any man who is estimable and gallant, knows how to make love and how to fit it in. What poor fools, what idiots these fellows were ! Could they not see that Venus now has no fixed abode, such as she once had on Cyprus, at Paphos and Amatonte, but

121

dwells everywhere, even in the huts of shepherds and on the laps of shepherdesses, including the naïvest of them all?

In this matter for some time now men have been losing such silly notions, for, having observed that there is a danger of being sadly cuckolded anywhere, they have taken wives wherever they pleased and were able, and this is better done. They have sent them or taken them to court, to show them off and have their beauty appreciated, and make this or that other man envious, and in the end to get themselves horns.

Other men have sent their wives or taken them to institute lawsuits and plead, though some of them had no case before the courts at all, merely pretended they had, while if they had they dragged it out as long as they could, to make their love-affairs last. Sometimes husbands even left their wives with the High Court bailiffs, or in the gallery or the hall, and went home themselves, thinking the ladies would conduct the cases better and win more, as indeed they did, for I know several who gained the suit, but rather by the dexterity and charm of their bodies than for any sound legal reason. In this work they often became pregnant, when, not to be disgraced (if drugs had failed to prevent pregnancy) they would hurry off home to their husbands, under pretence of a need to find the deeds or some other papers required, or to make some sort of research, or to bide their time till St Martin's Day, when the court would reassemble, and so as they could do nothing during the vacation they came to stud, to see their households and their husbands. Indeed it was a coming to stud, but already impregnated.

I could refer to many a counsellor, reporter and president of the court about the good titbits of the wives of such nobles that they all tasted.

It is not long since that one very lovely, estimable and great lady of my acquaintance[203] whent to pursue her case at Paris and somebody remarked: 'What has she gone there to do? She will lose it, she has no legal grounds whatsoever.' But did she not carry her legal grounds in her loveliness, and between her legs, as Caesar did his on his saddle and the point of his sword?

Thus are nobles cuckolded at the High Court, as recompense for the cuckolds such good nobles themselves make with the wives of the counsellors and presidents of the court, as there are some of those wives too whom I have seen who could be paraded quite well side by side with several great ladies, both unmarried and married, of princely, noble and grandee families of the Royal Courts, and others.

I knew one great lady who had formerly been very lovely, though the years had blotted that out. Having a lawsuit at Paris, and seeing that her looks were no longer any use for the solicitation and winning of her case, she took with her a neighbour of hers who was young and beautiful and reimbursed the neighbour for it with a nice sum of money, upwards of ten thousand crowns and what she could not though would have liked to do herself she used this lady for, by which she was well away. So was the younger lady too, in two fine ways, indeed.

Not so very long since I saw a lady with daughters take one of them, although married, to aid and assist her in her lawsuit, for the daughter had no other business at Paris, and she certainly was very lovely and well worth the cause.

It is time I ended this long treatise on cuckoldry, for in the end my flow of words might be submerged in these deep waters and great torrents, and I would never get out of the subject, any more than from that great labyrinth there once was, no, not even if I had the longest and strongest thread in the world to guide me and keep me on the right track.

To wind up I will conclude that if we make these poor cuckolds the object of troubles and torments, martyrising them and playing them sorry tricks, it is but to pay the price, as people say, and at triple interest too, for most of their persecutors and love-makers, these ladies' men, have quite as many troubles too, for they are the victims of jealousy because of both the husbands and also their own rivals, they too suffer torments and tricks of fortune, risking death itself, mutilation, wounds, outrages, insults, altercations, fears, torture and death, and bear with cold, rain, winds and heats. I leave syphilis and chancres and all the other ills and ailments they acquire, either with the great or the lesser ladies, out of it, but the general result is that they pay a high price for whatever they get and it is really all not worth the candle.

We have seen such men die a wretched death who could have conquered whole kingdoms, as witness Lord de Bussy, of whom in his time there was no equal,[204] and many another.

I would adduce countless others, whom I leave out, to wind up by admonishing these love-makers to put into practice that Italian proverb which runs : *Che molto guadagna chi putana perde!* 'that the man who loses a whore gains a lot'.

Count Amédée of Savoy II often used to say :

> *All a man's philandering and soldiering*
> *For one delight a hundred troubles bring*

He also said that rage and love were very unlike in that the first quickly passed and left his body untouched, not so love.

This just shows that one really should be wary of such love-making, which costs quite as much as it is worth, and very often brings many misfortunes. And to tell the truth, most patient cuckolds have a hundred times better a time, so long as they are able to get to know their wives and have an understanding with them, and I have indeed seen many a one who, when he got horns on his head, mocked us and laughed at all the fancies and fashions of us who carried on affairs with their wives, and especially when we had business with crafty wives who had pacted with their husbands and betrayed us. There was for instance one very fine, estimable noble who, having long loved a lovely, estimable lady, and had the enjoyment of her which he had wanted to have for a long time, one day noticed that the husband and the wife were making fun of him about something, when he took such umbrage against her that he left her and so doing did well, after which he went on a long journey to cleanse his mind of her and, so he told me, never approached her again. And one should indeed be as wary of such crafty women, so cunning and fickle, as of wild animals, for to satisfy and appease their husbands they will leave those who have served them long, but then afterwards take up with others, because they cannot do without making love with somebody.

For instance, I knew one very estimable and great lady[205] who had that element of misfortune in her that of the five or six whom I saw pay her attentions in my time, there was not one but died, they went one after the other, not without her showing great sorrow, so one could have said of her that she was the mare of Sejan,[206] in so much as that all who mounted her thereby ended their lives, yet there was in her this good quality, that whatever happened she never changed or abandoned any of her lovers while alive, to take another, it was only when they were on their death bed that she would find another mount, so as not to have to go on foot, just as in the same way legal authorities put it, that one may have one's estates and land cultivated by anybody when the real owner is incapable. Such steadfastness was very outstanding in that praiseworthy lady, but if she was reliable to that point there have also been countless women very unreliable.

So, to speak quite frankly, one should never allow oneself to get old in one hole only, and no man of heart ever did so, one should be enterprising on all sides, in love as in war and in other matters, for if one secures one's vessel by one sole anchor and this gives way, one can easily lose the ship, particularly if out of harbour in a storm, when a ship is more affected by tempests and stormy waves than in a calm or in port.

And on what higher or rougher sea could one venture and sail than that of making love to only one woman? For even if they are not crafty and cunning when we start, we men so train and sharpen them by all our dealings with them that we often suffer from it, because we make them capable of waging war on us, our fashioning rendering them more martial. So that, as one gallant man once said, it is better to marry some lovely, estimable lady even if at risk of being touched by horns and by this cuckoldry trouble, than go making others cuckolds, all at cost of such rough passages, though this is contrary to the opinion of Lord de Guast.[207] When one day, as representative of a great lady who asked me to intercede for her, I asked him if he would marry her, his only reply was that he had accounted me one of his greatest friends, but by making him such a suggestion, and thus pressing a matter he detested more than any other, proposing he should be married and cuckolded, instead of cuckolding others, I was risking making him change his mind, and he added that he married a sufficiency of women during the year, giving the appelation 'marriage' to his reputation of debauchery and liberty, by a fine law, indeed. The worst part of all this, as I see and have remarked, is that most, if indeed not all of those who thus find their pleasure in making others cuckolds, when they themselves came to marry, are cuckolded in turn, and I have never seen it otherwise. As the proverb has it : *Ce que tu feras à autruy, il te sera faict,* 'what you do to others will be done to you.'

Before I end I will add the following : that I have heard a debate which is still not really settled, as to in which provinces and parts of our Christendom and our Europe are there most cuckolds and whorish women? It is said that in Italy the ladies are very hot, hence very whorish, as Lord de Beze has said in an epigram, that where the sun is hottest and gives the most, it heats the women more, and one line runs :

Credible est ignes multiplicare suos,[208] 'one may conclude that it adds to their fires'.

Spain is in the same position, for though it lies more to the west, the sun heats the ladies there as much as it does in the east.

The Flemish women, the Swiss, the German, the English and the Scottish, though leaning towards the centre and north, hence towards the cold regions, participate none the less in this natural heat, for I have known some of them quite as hot as those of other nations.

The Greek women are right so to be, since they are so far towards the Levant. Thus in Italy one has the greeting : *'Greca in letto!'* 'May you have a Greek girl in bed!' And indeed they have many points and qualities which are attractive so that not without reason in the past they were the darlings of the world, and have taught the Italian and Spanish ladies much, from ancient times to modern, so well that they almost surpass their ancient and present mistresses. Thus the Queen and Empress of whores, that is, Venus herself, was a Greek woman.

As far as our lovely Frenchwomen go, in past times they have been seen to be very coarse, satisfied with doing it brusquely, but for the past fifty years they have borrowed from other nations and learned so many nice fashions and cossetings, so many attractions and fine qualities, so many little devices and subtle modes and lascivities, and further have made such a good study of their own in the invention of them, that now one has to admit that they surpass all the others in every way, till, as I have heard even foreigners say, they are now worth far more than the others are, apart from the fact that the French vocabulary of love-making is more spicy, it sounds better and stirs a man more than any of the others.

Further, the lovely freedom of France, more to be prized than anything, makes our ladies more desirable, lovable, and approachable, and better givers than any others, and further since all adulterers are not publicly punished here as in other parts of the world, by reason of the far-seeing provisions of our great French senates and legislators who, seeing the abuses which resulted from such punishments, reduced them a little and somewhat pruned down the rigorous laws of the past which were made by men who had given themselves all liberty to take their pleasures but taken liberty away from the women, to the extent that an innocent wife was not allowed to charge her husband with adultery by any imperial law of canon (so Cajetan says).[209] The men however made that law for the reasons expressed in the following Italian lines :

> Perche, di quel che Natura concede
> Cel'vieti tu, dura d'honore,
> Ella à noi liberal largo ne diede
> Com' agli altri animai legge d'amore.
> Ma l'uomo fraudulento, e senza fede,
> Che fu legislator di quest' errore,
> Vedendo nostre forze e buona schiena,
> Copri la sua debolezza con la pena.[1]

To conclude, in France it is good to make love—I base myself on our real authorities on the subject, that is, our courtiers,

[1] Harsh law of honour why do you prohibit what nature makes possible? Nature has given us like other animals the law of love liberally, grandly. But men, cheating and faithless, made this mistaken law protecting honour. Seeing our great female powers and loins, they hid their weakness behind a penalization.

who are better able to discourse thereon than I am. And, to be frank, there are whores and cuckolds everywhere, as I can vouch, having seen all the spheres I have listed, chastity dwells no more in any one part than in any other.

Whence I will put the following question and one moreover which I think has never been examined by anybody, nor I think even conceived, namely—if two ladies are amorous one of another, as one can find, for such pairs are today often seen sleeping together, in the fashion called in imitation of the learned Lesbian Sappho, *donna con donna*, can they be said to commit adultery and by their joint act make their husbands cuckolds?

If we are to take Martial's first book, epigram CXIX,[210] they certainly do commit adultery. In this epigram he introduces and apostrophizes a woman named Bassa, a *tribade*, attacking her very fiercely on the grounds that no man was ever seen to go to her house, so she was taken to be a second Lucrece, but she had just been found out, because many women and girls had been seen to enter, and it was discovered she served them, playing the rôle of man and adulterer, and copulated with them, Martial says of them : *geminos committere cunnos*. Then, expostulating, he gave the following riddle to be solved in one line of Latin verse :

Hic, ubi vir non est, ut sit adulterium,

'A fine situation indeed, no man and yet adultery.'

I knew a courtesan in Rome, old and knowing if ever there was one, called Isabella da Luna,[211] who took another courtesan named Pandora as lover, one of the loveliest of the time in the whole of Rome, who had just been married to a butler of the Lord Cardinal d'Armagnac,[212] though without relinquishing her old trade, and she was kept by this Isabella and regularly slept with her, and, unrestrained and disorderly in her speech as this Isabella was, I often heard her say that she had made Pandora more of a whore than before and caused her to put the horns on her husband's head more than any roisterer with whom she had made love. I do not know in what sense she meant this, unless she was basing herself on Martial's epigram.

It is said that Sappho of Lesbos was a very fine mistress of this trade, indeed, what is more, that she invented it, and since her the ladies of Lesbos have imitated her in it and continued in it to this day. This is what Lucian[213] says—such women, who will not let a man touch them, but approach other women, just as men do, are 'Lesbians.' And women of the sort who like this practice will never let a man touch them, but yield themselves to other women, just as if these were men, and these are called *tribades*, a Greek word derived, so I have been told by Greeks, from *tribo, tribein*, which means to rub or fret or mutually fret, and those who play at this game of *donna con donna*, as seen today, are called *tribades* or in French *fricatrices*, or frickers.

Juvenal also is referring to such women when he speaks of . . . *frictum Grissantis adorat*, in a passage about a similar *tribade* who adored and loved the fricking of a woman called Grissanta.[214]

That good fellow Lucian devotes a whole chapter to them,[215] and goes on to tell us that such women meet to copulate like men, copulating with lascivious devices, far-fetched and monstrous, sterile things, and that the name, now rarely heard, for such frickers, then used freely everywhere for these of feminine sex, should be Philenises, after Philenis,[216] who imitated certain masculine actions in the love act. However, Lucian adds that it is still far better for a woman to be given to a libidinous leaning towards acting the male than for a man to become effeminate, so feeble-spirited and ignoble does such a creature become. In this view, you see, the woman who thus counterfeits the man can have the reputation of being more courageous and plucky than another, as indeed I have known some to be, both in body and in spirit.

In another place Lucian introduces two ladies discussing this form of love, and one asks the other if such and such a woman had ever been in love with her and had she slept with her, and what had she done to her? the other replied frankly: 'First, she kissed me as men do, not merely with joined lips, but parting them too' (this means pigeon kisses, with the tongue inserted in the mouth), 'and although she had no male member, and was made just like we other women, she said she had the heart and the impulse and all the rest masculine, and then I embraced her as if she were a man, and she copulated with me, kissing me and "going" (a word I do not quite understand) and as far as I could see she had the greatest pleasure from it, and copulated in a way which was much more agreeable than that of a man.' So much for what Lucian says.

Now, from what I have heard, in many places and regions there are many such women and many Lesbians too, in France, in Italy and in Spain, in Turkey, Greece and other places. And where the women are recluses, and do not enjoy complete freedom, the practice is most developed, for such women, when hot in the body, really, so the women say, do need the aid of this remedy to refresh themselves a little, or completely from their heat.

The Turkish women go to their steam baths more for this lechery than any other reason and are much given to it. Even the courtesans, who have men at their beck and call at any hour, also make use of these frickers, and they seek each other out and have loves together, as women in both Italy and in Spain have told me. In our own France too such women are quite common, and yet it is said that they have not long been addicted to it, the fashion for it having been introduced from Italy by a lady of quality whom I will not name.

I have heard the late Lord de Clermont Tallard the younger who died at La Rochelle[217] say that when he was a small boy, and had the honour of being school companion to The Duke of Anjou, later to become our King Henry III, and studied regularly with him, Lord de Gournay being their tutor, one day, when they were at Toulouse, working with the said tutor in his study, Clermont Tallard, sitting in a corner by himself and through a little crack (the rooms and closets here were all of match-boarding run up at short notice, in haste, on requisition by the Lord Cardinal d'Armagnac, the Archbishop of the region,[218] the better to receive and accommodate the King and his court) saw into another closet in which were two very great ladies, *toutes retroussées et leurs callesons bas, se coucher l'une sur l'autre, s'entrebaiser en forme de colombes, se frotter, s'entrefriquer, bref se remuer fort, paillarder et imiter les hommes; et dura leur esbattement près d'une bonne heure, s'estans si très fort eschauffées et lassées, qu'elles en demeurerent si rouges et si en eau, bien qu'il fist grand froid, qu'elles n'en purent plus et furent contrainctes de se reposer autant.* And he said he saw them at this sporting on several other days, in fact, as long as the court was there, always in the same way, but never had any opportunity of seeing this sort of pleasure elsewhere, for that particular place gave him a particular opportunity which he had nowhere else.

He also told me more than I dare write, and named the ladies. I do not know if it was all true, but he swore to it, and backed what he said a hundred times by solemn oaths. And it was indeed quite feasible, for those two ladies had always had the reputation of making love in that way and so passing their time.

I have known many others to speak of the same kind of lovemaking, and among them I once heard tell of a great lady who was quite outstanding in it and loved a number of other ladies, honouring them and serving them more than any men did, and making love to them as a man to his mistresses. And when she took them into her house, she provided their board and lodging and gave them everything they wanted. Her husband was very resigned to this, indeed, he was quite pleased about it, as have been many other husbands I have known, who were very satisfied to have their wives carry on such love affairs rather than make love with men, holding that in this way their wives were neither so wild nor so lewd. But in my opinion they were very mistaken, for, from what I have heard, this little practice is merely the apprenticeship to the great business with men, for after getting heated and put in rut one by another, their heat is in no wise diminished, they need to be douched by a fresh natural spring, which I have heard from good surgeons, is more refreshing than still water, and indeed, have I also seen that anybody who seriously wants to heal a wound should not medicament and dress it merely round about, on its edges, but should probe deep in and apply a really good compress to it.

How many of these Lesbians have I not seen who despite all their frickering and mutual rubbings did not fail also to have recourse to men—even Sappho, who was the prime mistress of that art, for did she not turn to love with her great lover, Phaon,[219] after which she died? For, after all, as I have heard many ladies say, there is nothing like a man for it, and despite all that they can get with other women, such play is merely a decoy leading to the greediest of love-making with men, and these *fricarelles* merely serve them when they have not got a man. And if they find a suitable occasion, without possibility of disgrace, they quickly quit their female partners and fling themselves at the men's necks.

In my time I knew two lovely, estimable girls of good family, cousins, who, having slept together in the same bed for three years, became so accustomed to this fricking that in the end they decided it was very meagre and faulty compared with what a man could provide and so started to try doing it with men, and then they did become very great whores, and subsequently they confessed to their lovers that nothing had so debauched them and stirred them up to love-making as the *fricarelle*, which they now loathed as having been the sole cause of their debauchment. And yet, notwithstanding, whenever they met, or found themselves with other women, they always took a little snack of this fricking, just because thereby they could get greater appetite for the other way, with men. And this is also what a decent girl I once knew told me. When one day asked by her gentleman-in-waiting if she did not indulge in the *fricarelle* with her friend, with whom she usually slept, she said : 'Oh, no!' and laughed. 'I am too fond of men,' she added. And yet the truth is, she enjoyed both ways.

I know an estimable noble who when at one time he wished to seek an extremely estimable girl in marriage, asked the opinion of a woman relation, and she told him frankly that he would be wasting his time, as, she told me[220] such-and-such a lady (whom she named) and about whom I myself had heard certain things, would never let her marry. I suddenly realized the whole situation, and became aware that she was supporting the girl in question and reserving her for her personal consumption alone. The noble thanked this cousin of his for her good advice, though not without teasing her some deal about it, saying that here she was speaking for herself as well as for the other girl, for she too, she was far from denying, sometimes had a little fun in that way on the sly.

This trait reminds me of some men who in the same way have their own special whores, whom they even love so much that they would never let them go for all the goods in the world, even to a prince or grandee or their closest friend or comrade, so jealous are they of them, but cling to them like a leper to his mug, though indeed these will let anybody have a drink from it. But this lady I speak of wanted to reserve her girl entirely to herself, without letting anybody else have any share in her, and yet all the same the girl did cuckold her secretly, and with some of her own girl friends !

It is said that weasels are touched with this sort of love, and one and another of them will take pleasure together, and live together, which is why in hieroglyphics women who made love with each other used to be represented by weasels. I have heard people talk of a lady who always kept some as pets and always eavesdropped on their sort of love and delighted in watching these little weasels cohabiting.

Here is another point : these feminine love-makings are practised in two different ways, some by *fricarelles* and, as the poet put it,[221] by *geminos committere cunnos*. This method does no harm, some men say, as it does when they make use of a device fashioned from . . . for which the name (in French) 'godemichy' has been chosen.[1]

I have heard tell of a great prince who, suspecting that two ladies of his court made use of one of these, had them watched so closely that he surprised them at it, so much so that they were much taken aback to be caught, one with a big one between her legs, so neatly fastened on by little belts passing round the body that it looked like a natural member. She was so surprised that she did not have time to take it off, so much so, indeed, that the Prince persuaded her there and then to demonstrate how the two of them did it.

It is said that many women have lost their lives from en-

[1] A word (for the material from which bilboes were fashioned) is lacking in the original text. A.B.

gendering in their wombs growths caused by movements and by frictions which are far from natural. I certainly have known some such instances, and a great pity it has been too, for they were very lovely and very estimable ladies and girls, and it would have been far better had they had the companionship of some estimable nobles, who, far from causing a woman's death by what they do, aid her life, refreshing her, as I hope to show in another place, indeed, even curing some ailments, since there is nothing better, I have heard some surgeons say, for thoroughly cleansing them out inside than the natural member of a man, which is superior far to any pessary used by doctors and surgeons, made up with ointments, and yet there are still many women who, in spite of the evil consequences which they often see, have to go using these imitation devices.

I heard the story told when I was at court that one day when the Queen Mother had given orders for all the rooms and chests of all the company staying at the Louvre to be inspected, without sparing either great lady or unmarried girls, to see that there were no arms, including pistols, concealed during the troubles, there was one girl who was surprised by the Captain of the Guard not with any pistols in her chest but four big very finely fashioned bilboes, which amused everybody very much indeed, and certainly surprised the Queen a lot. I knew the girl too. I believe she is still alive, but she never had a good complexion. Such instruments are in fact very injurious. *Je feray encor ce conte de deux dames de la cour qui s'entr'aymoient si fort, et qui estoyent si chaudes à leur mestier, qu'en quelque endroit qu'elles fussent, ne s'en pouvoyent garder ny abstenir que pour le moins ne fissent quelques signes d'amourettes ou de baiser qui les escandalisoyent si fort, et donnoyent à penser beaucoup aux hommes. Il y en avoit une veufve, et l'autre maryée; et comme la maryée, un jour d'une grand'magnificence, se fust fort bien parée et habillée d'une robbe de toille d'argent, ainsy que leur maistresse estoit allée à vespres, elles entrerent dans son cabinet, et sur sa chaise percée se mirent à faire leur fricarelle si rudement et si impetueusement, qu'elle en rompit soubs elle, et la dame maryée, qui faisoit le dessous, tomba avec sa belle robbe de toille d'argent à*

134

*la renverse, tout à plat sur l'ordure du bassin, si bien qu'elle se
gasta et souilla si fort, qu'elle ne sceut que faire de s'essuyer le
mieux qu'elle peut, se trousser, et s'en aller à grande haste
changer de robbe dans sa chambre, non sans pourtant avoir esté
apperceue et bien sentie à la trace, tant elle puoit: dont il en
fut ry assez par aucuns qui en sceurent le conte; mesmes leur
maistresse le sceut, qui s'en aydoit comme elles, et en ryt son
saoul. Aussy il falloit bien que ceste ardeur les maistrisast fort,
que de n'attendre un lieu, et un temps à propos, sans s'escanda-
liser.*

Another point—unmarried girls and widows may be excused
for liking such frivolous, vain pleasures, and preferring to give
themselves to each other thus and so get rid of their heat than
to resort to men and be put in the family way and dishonoured
by them, or have to get rid of their fruit, and several have
practised Lesbian love for this reason, thinking thereby not to
offend God so much and not to be such whores that way as if
with men, just as there is a great difference between actually
pouring water into a pot and merely moistening it all round
and about. I refer back to the women themselves. I am not
their censor nor am I their husband, if indeed they do find
it bad, for I myself have not seen any who were not very
glad when their wives fell enamoured of their women friends,
hoping they would never commit greater adultery than this,
for after all, such cohabitation is very different from that committed with a man, and whatever Martial likes to say,[222] the
men are not cuckolded by it, and his words are not a gospel
text, but those of a crazy poet. This is why, as Lucian says,[223] it
is much better for a woman to be virile, or a real amazon, or
lubricious in this way, than for a man to be feminine, like a
Sardanapalus or Heliogabalus, or many others like them, for
the more mannish they are the more courageous they are, and
in the whole matter I rely upon the decision of the court.

One day Lord de Guast[224] and I were reading a little Italian
work entitled *On Beauty*, cast in the form of a dialogue by
Lord Agnolo Firenzuola,[225] and we came on a passage in which
he says that some of the women made by Jupiter at the outset
of things were created with such a nature that they turned

to men for love, others were made who preferred each other's beauty, while there were yet others who loved purely and in sanctity, and, as the author remarks, we find an example in our own day, in the very illustrious Marguerite of Austria,[226] who loved the fair Laodomia Forteguerra, while others loved lasciviously and lewdly, like Sappho the Lesbian, or in our time that great courtesan of Rome, Cecilia the Venetian, and these by nature hate marriage and avoid dealings with men as much as they can.

Here Lord de Guast took the author up and said that it was wrong that the fair Marguerite loved that fair lady with a pure, saintly love, for since she had conferred more love on her than on others who might be said to be as lovely and virtuous as she was, it was to be presumed that she did so in order to make use of her for her pleasures not less if not more than others, and it was to cover her lasciviousness that she proclaimed and widely advertised this notion of loving her in a saintly fashion, just as we see many others like her who cloak their love affairs by similar talk.

There you have what Lord du Guast said about it, and any who wishes to take up the discussion is at liberty to do so.

This fair Marguerite was the loveliest of all the princesses of her time in the whole of Christendom. And with whatever love it is, beauty and beauty match in love, but more so with sensual love than the other. She was married a third time, her first husband having been King Charles 8th, and the second John, son of the King of Aragon. The third marriage was with the Duke of Savoy known as the Fair, and in her day they were said to be the handsomest match and the handsomest couple in the world, but the Princess had little enjoyment of that union, for he died very young, and at his most handsome too, which she lamented very greatly, and on that account never married again.

She it was who had that lovely church near Bourg in Bresse built, one of the handsomest and most superb buildings of Christendom.[227] She was aunt to the Emperor Charles,[228] and she aided her nephew greatly, for she was anxious to give satisfaction all round, as indeed she and the Lady Regent did, by the Treaty of Cambrai,[229] at which they met and compounded, and I have heard it said by former grandees and great ladies that these two Princesses together made a glorious sight.

Corneille Agripa wrote a short essay on the virtues of women, all in praise of the same Princess Marguerite.[230] What he wrote on the subject is very lovely, and could not help being so because of the glorious nature of his subject, and of the author too, for he was a very great personality.

I have heard tell of a great lady of Royal blood who among the girls in her suite preferred one to all the others, and loved her more passionately too, which surprised everybody, for there were other girls who surpassed this one in everything. Then it was found out and disclosed that the girl was really a hermaphrodite, who provided the Princess with her pleasure without any inconvenience or disgrace. This was a case a little different from that of the *tribades*, the pleasure penetrating somewhat deeper.

I have heard a great lady named who is a hermaphrodite too, and likewise has a male member, though it is very small, since she has more of the woman in her composition, for I have seen her and she is very lovely. I have heard great doctors say that they have seen quite a number of such cases, some who have been particularly lustful.

Here, to wind up, is what I would say as a general observation on the subject of this essay (which I could have gone on adding to endlessly, far more than I have done, for I have ample material and lengthy too)—if all the cuckolds and all the wives who make them were to join hands in a ring, I think it would go half way round the world.

In the days of King François there was a very old song which I have heard a very estimable lady of older times recite, which ran :

> *When the time comes, I do declare,*
> *For all our cuckolds to confer,*
> *Mine will lead and bear the banner,*
> *The rest behind, yours at the tail*
> *No end to them as they march past,*
> *'Twill be a very lengthy trail.*[231]

Nevertheless I do not mean to slander greatly all the many estimable, circumspect married women who have borne themselves virtuously and in constancy in the loyalty which they vowed to their husbands in the sacrament, but I hope to make a separate essay in their praise and give the lie to Master Jean de Mun in his *Roman de la Rose* says : 'All you ladies. . .

> *. . . either are, or were,*
> *Whores in fact, or in intent*'[232]

whereby he incurred such dislike of the ladies of the court at the time that by the advice of the Queen, plotting together with her consent, they undertook one day to strip him naked, and whip him, and indeed were just about to begin to lambaste him when he asked that at least the one who was the biggest whore of all should strike first, when from shame not one dared strike him, and so he escaped his whipping. I have seen the incident depicted in an old tapestry on some antique furniture in the Louvre Palace.

I would as soon have a preacher who, preaching one day before a select congregation, was reproving some ladies for their conduct, and their husbands for putting up with being cuckolded by them, when he suddenly cried : 'Yes, I know them, and I see them too, and I am now going to throw these two stones at the heads of the greatest cuckolds in this congregation,' and drew back his arm as if about to throw, when not a man present but ducked his head or held up his cloak or cape or forearm to ward off the blow. Then, refraining, he said : 'Did I not tell you? I thought there were only two or three cuckolds listening to my sermon. But as far as I can see, there is not one who has not got horns on his head.'

But whatever these crazy fellows say, there are many circumspect and estimable ladies who, were they to have to fight a battle with those of the opposite sort, would win, not by force of numbers, but by virtue, which easily defeats and slays its contrary.

And if Master Jean de Mun, to whom I have referred, attacks those who are whores at heart, I find that he is really praising them and exalting them to the skies, since though they burn so ardently in both flesh and spirit, they never come to the deed, which goes to show their virtuousness, their constancy and their greatness of heart, since they would rather burn and be consumed in their own fires and flames, like some rare phoenix, than forfeit or sully their honour, or like the white ermine, which would rather die than be dirtied (the emblem of a very great lady I once knew) though she however did not herself embody it, for, since it is in their own power to remedy the matter, they rule themselves so greatheartedly, nor moreover is there any virtue or victory more lovely than that of ruling and mastering oneself. In the *Hundred Tales* of the Queen of Navarre[233] we have one very lovely story of that estimable lady of Pampeluna who, though she was by heart and intent a whore, and was consumed with love for so handsome a prince as Lord d'Avannes,[234] she preferred death in her own conflagration to seeking the remedy, as indeed she found occasion to tell him in her last words before she died.

That worthy and lovely lady certainly caused her own death very iniquitously and unjustly, and, as I heard an estimable lord and lady say when she died, it was all not without grave offence to the Almighty, for she could have so easily saved herself from death, and to seek death and thus hasten it should really be called self-murder. And there are also many others like her who by such great continence and abstaining from the pleasure of love cause their own deaths, both spiritually and physically.

I have it from a very great physician (and believe he has given such lesson and instructions to numerous estimable ladies) that human bodies can almost never be in good condition if all their members and parts, from the greatest to the smallest, are not employed and if they do not function all together, and that Nature in her wisdom has thus ordained things for the health of men and women, and if they do not create general harmony, as an ensemble of musicians does, for there is no reason why any of the said parts or members of the body should work while another is idle, just as in any commonwealth all its officers, artisans, workers and all others should all do their work in concert, without anyone refraining or putting his work on to the others, if one wishes that common-wealth to prosper and its body remain healthy and whole; and so it is with the human body.

Such lovely ladies, whorish at heart and chaste of body, merit eternal praise, but not those who are cold as marble, limp, flaccid and unmoved, worse than rocks, not like flesh at all, devoid of feelings (however, there are hardly any such), those who are neither lovely nor sought after; for indeed, as the poet has it : *Casta quam nemo rogavit*[235]—'chaste is she whom no man wants.'

A propos of which I know a great lady who remarked to certain of her ladies-in-waiting who were lovely : 'God was very kind to me not making me lovely like you, my ladies, for I should have made love just like you, and would have been a whore as you all are.' So one may praise those who are lovely and yet though of such a nature, are chaste.

Thus we are very often deceived by such ladies, for some there are who to see them are prim and prude and priggish, chill, chary, so restrained and modest in speech and their protestant garb that one might well take them to be saints and really pure wives, though inwardly, in intent, and out-wardly too, in frank deeds, they are great whores.

Others we see who, from their charm and their lively talk, their gay gestures and their worldly and chic attire, might well be thought to be most debauched, and on the very point of yielding their bodies to some man, but yet are in public essen-tially strictly well-behaved women—regarding their hidden lives, we should have first to find out the reality thus concealed.

I could adduce many examples that I have seen and known, but I will be content to cite the following, which Livy relates[236] and Boccaccio tells us still better,[237] of a charming Roman lady, Claudia Quintenna[238] by name, who in Rome in her days was supreme over all others in the gaudiness and immodesty of her appearance and who in her worldly, gay and free be-haviour went further than she should, thus, as far as her honour went, acquiring a very bad name, yet when the day for the reception of the goddess Cybele[239] came round silenced it all, for it was she who had the honour and the glory, over and above all the others, of receiving the goddess as she stepped forth from her barge, touching her and leading her into the city, by which the whole of the public was amazed, for it was held that only the leading lady and the leading gentleman were worthy of that duty. There you have the way the world at large is deceived by many of our ladies. One needs first really to know them intimately and examine them very carefully, before pronouncing judgement, no matter of which kind they are.

Therefore, before finally concluding I must declare another fine virtue and quality of cuckoldom, which I had from a very estimable and lovely lady of good origin.[240] When I entered her closet one day I found her on the point of completing the writing of a story in her own hand, which she without more ado showed me, for I was one of her good friends, and she hid nothing from me. She was very entertaining and had a ready tongue, and was much attracted to love-making, and the beginning of her story was as follows :

'It seems,' she had written, 'that among the other fine advantages that cuckolding may offer is the excellent, subtle way in which it reveals how excellently the mind works towards the pleasure and satisfaction of human nature, since it is the mind that watches over matters and invents and designs all the artifice required to achieve cuckoldry, nature providing merely the initial desire and the sensual appetite, the mind however showing how by many a ruse and trick those who practice this commerce of love, which is the one that plants the horns on a man's head, may conceal it all, for one has always to deceive a jealous, suspicious, hot-tempered husband, one has always to cheat and veil the eyes which are most ready to perceive the wrong and divert the most prying glance from recognition of the truth, one has to cause a conviction of faithfulness where there is nothing but deception, suggest the greatest frankness where there is nothing but dissimulation, and the greatest timidity where there is most licence. In short, because of all these difficulties, and in order to surmount all these considerations, those are not acts which any simple instinct can achieve, but one has to make all possible room for the play of the intelligence, which it really is that provides the pleasure, building more horns than the body which actually plants them and dibbles them in.'

These are the actual words this lady wrote, without any editing, as preface to her story, which was really all about herself, though she veiled it by other names. After this introduction, following the loves of the lady and the prince with whom the lady had dealings, and to get what she wanted and enjoy it to the full, she argued that the form love takes is merely that of satisfaction. Love is utterly devoid of shape until complete enjoyment and possession have been achieved, and very often one thinks these attained when one is still far from the goal, when as recompense all one gets out of it is a sense of time lost, which one greatly regrets. (One should carefully weigh and note these last words, for they do strike home, and give food for discussion.) If for the man and the woman alike there is to be no regret of the time on it, love must have its completion. So this estimable lady who wrote this story gave her gentleman-in-waiting a rendezvous in a wood, in a very lovely ride where she often went walking. At the entrance to this she left her ladies behind her, and went on, to find him under a fine, broad-spreading, shady oak-tree, for it was summer-time. 'There,' says the lady in the story in her own words, 'where one should have no doubts about the life they led for a little while and the fine altar which, for all they were not at Delos, they erected to the poor husband in the keratonic[241] temple,' an altar of course made entirely of horns, and you may imagine that a good gentleman-in-waiting founded it, too.

This is how this lady made mock of her husband, not only in her frolics and deeds, but also in what she wrote. But all she says should be carefully noted, how able it is, being uttered and written down by so able and so estimable a lady.

The story of it all is very beautiful, and I would gladly have inserted it here, but it is too long, for the preamble, before one gets to the point, is also fine and lengthy. In it she reproaches her gentleman, who praised her excessively, for being passionate rather subjectively than in regard to any good that was in her, although she was one of the most lovely and estimable of ladies. And, to counter that opinion, the gentleman in question had to give great proofs of his love, all of which are clearly specified in the story. And then, when they are in agreement, one sees in it all the tricks, the finesse and the deceits of love of all kinds, both of the husband and of the world, all of them unquestionably very fine and very subtle.

I begged this estimable lady to give me a copy of her story, which she did very gladly, and would have none other but herself do the copying, lest it be seen, and I guard my copy very carefully indeed.

This lady was quite right to assign that virtue and quality to cuckoldry, for, before she began lovemaking she was not at all clever, but once she had thus made love, she became one of the cleverest and ablest ladies of France, both in this respect and others too. And I must say that this is not the only woman I have seen who became intelligent by having made love, for I have seen an infinity who were very stupid and short-witted when they started it, but who had not been in the school of Cupid and his mother Venus a year before they emerged very able and very estimable ladies in every way, and as far as my experience goes, I have yet to see the whore who was not clever and good at throwing dust in your eyes.

I would now add this further question: in which season of the year are most cuckolds made, and which is the season the most suited to love-making, to making a woman excited, whether widow or unmarried? Certainly the most general opinion is that there is nothing for it like the Spring, that awakening of body and mind, which have slumbered through the dismal, aggravating Winter, for, just as all birds and animals are delighted by the Spring and begin to make love, so with all their additional senses and feelings human beings feel it too, and so much more, above all the women (in the view of several philosophers and doctors) who in that season become more ardent and love-inclined than at any other time, as I have heard various estimable and lovely ladies say, including a great lady who asserted that when Spring came round she never failed to be more moved and pricked by love than in any other season; she said she could feel the grass sprouting through, and it made her whinny like the mares and stallions, and she felt she had to enjoy love too, or she would waste away, which, I can assure you, she did, and then became still more lustful. Thus with three or four fresh loves which I saw her have in her life, she started each of them in the Spring. And not without cause, for of all the months of the year April and May are those most consecrated and dedicated to Venus, the period when lovely ladies begin more than they have recently done to dress, to embellish and to ornament themselves nicely, with romantic hair-dressings and all those light gowns that they don. Indeed, one might almost say that all these new changes of clothes and styles tend to engender lust and to people the earth with cuckolds to walk it, exactly as the heavens and the very atmosphere produce flying creatures in April and May.

Further, one should not imagine that when, as they take their walks in their woods and forests, their warrens and parks, their meadows, gardens, groves and other places of recreation lovely women, girls and widows see on all sides how the animals and birds make love together, with lustful dalliance, they themselves do not feel strange prickings of their flesh, and suddenly crave the same remedies. Indeed, this is one of the most persuasive remonstrances that some lovers and their mistresses make each other, when they see one another without warmth of flame or love, and protest that the animals and the birds, both those of the fields and those of the courtyard, like the sparrows and the lascivious domestic pigeons, do nought else but play at love, fertilizing, engendering and multiplying, and even the trees and plants as well. This indeed is just what a sweet Spanish lady intended to say one day when she addressed an attendant gentleman who was too cold or too respectful : *Ea, gentil cavallero mira como los amores de todas suertes se tratan y triunfan en este verano, y Vs. queda flaco y abatido!* That is : 'Just look gentle knight, and observe the triumph and practice of love by all species in this springtide, yet you, sir, remain flaccid and drooping.'

Spring passing gives place to Summer, which follows and brings the heats, and as one heat leads to another, the lady in consequence doubles hers, and no refreshment is there that

144

can so assuage it as a good hot, tempestuous bath of love. This is not to cure the contrary with contrary, but like by like, for even were she every day to dive and bathe in the clearest fountain pool of the whole country, that would not help her any more than wearing the lightest garments she can find to obtain freshness, or drawing up her skirts as much as she chooses, or even leaving off her drawers or wearing her flounced petticoat outside them,[242] with nothing underneath, as many in fact do. And that is the worst of it all, for in such a state the ladies look at each other and get enraptured by that sight alone, admiring themselves in the lovely bright sunlight, and seeing themselves so lovely, so white, so daintily dressed, so dainty and plump, and suddenly come into rut and temptation, and then they have to go to the male or they burn up altogether, which one rarely sees them do, for that would be silly. And when in their lovely beds they are unable to bear coverlets or sheets on them, but lie there uncovered, their shifts drawn half up, and their bodies half naked, and in the morning the rising sun falls straight on them, when thus they come to examine themselves, still more at their ease, from all sides and all parts, they cannot but crave their lovers and wait for them. So that if these happen to appear at a moment, they are at once welcome, accepted, embraced. 'For now,' the women say, 'now is the finest embrace and enjoyment of any hour of the day.' 'Since,' said one great lady, 'the c— is then well soused, because of the soft warmth and fire of the night, which thus cooks and marinades it, making it much better and more savoury.'

However, there is an old proverb which runs : '*In June and July the lips are moist and the v— is dry.*' Some add the month of August. That goes however for the men, who are in danger when they get too heated in this time of the year, and even in the dog days, which they should take great care about, so that if they do choose to singe themselves in those candles, that's up to them. Women never risk this, for all months, all seasons, all times, all signs are good for them.

Now the good fruits of the Summer come in, which one would think should refresh these estimable and hot-blooded ladies. Some I have seen eat little, others a lot. But not in one have I seen any noticeable change in their heat, neither in the one direction nor the other, either of abstention or indulgence, for the worst is that though there are some fruits which tend to refresh, there are also very many others which are equally heating, and to these the ladies have recourse most frequently, just as there are several simples which in their virtue are good and pleasant to eat in potages and salads, such as asparagus, artichokes, morels, truffles, buttons and pumpkins, and new meats which on their orders their cooks know well how to dress and cook so as to augment greed and lust, and which their doctors also sometimes order them. So that any man who was very expert and gallant, were he to undertake to apply what I say here, would come off far better than I have done.

When such good food is being served out, take care, poor lovers and husbands, for, if you are not well prepared, you will be disgraced, and very often be quit for somebody else.

This is not all, for to these fresh fruits and garden and field crops one should add fine big pasties, such as have been recently invented, with a-plenty of pistaccios, pine-kernels and other apothecary's carminative drugs, but above all cocks' crests and privy parts, all the produce of Summer, more abundant then than in Winter and other seasons, whence too the great massacreing of all the young cockerels and chantecleres, only the little ones being good and suitable, by being hot, fervent and with more spunk in them than the others. There you have one among many of the good pleasures and advantages which Summer brings to love-making.

As for those patties thus made of cockerels' giblets and artichoke stumps and truffles or other hot tasty things, some ladies I have heard of often have recourse to them, and when they eat them and fish about in them, either sticking in their fingers or using forks, to convey merely an artichoke or a truffle or a pistaccio nut or a cock's comb or other such titbit to their lips, with dismal sadness they say they have drawn a *blank*,[243] but when they come upon such titbits as the privy parts of a cockbird and get their teeth into them, they cry in delight : *benefice*, all in imitation of the cries customary at the drawing of

Italian lotteries, so that when their cry is *benefice* it is a sign they have fished out some very precious, rich treasure.

Thus are they obliged to the cockerels and first-crowers of Summer and the first-half of Autumn, a season which also gives us many other fruits and little fowls which are a hundred times more carminative than those of the second half of Autumn and the Winter, when, though one might and should join them together, one cannot so easily gather all these good simples in their vigour, nor anything else as in the hot season, though the Winter does try to produce what it can, such as good chard which whether taken raw or cooked, engenders much good heat and concupiscence, also including the hot little milk-thistles, on which donkeys live and bray the better, and which the Summer makes tough but Winter makes tender and deli-cate, so that from them can be made many fine recently in-vented salads. And apart from all this, there has been much research too into good drugs at the apothecaries', druggists' and perfumers', so nothing is forgotten, whether for pies or for soups. And one can hardly complain of their heat in Winter for this reason and to the best of their ability they look after themselves in this way, 'For,' say the ladies themselves, 'seeing that we are at pains to keep the outsides of our bodies warm by means of heavy coats and good furs, why should we not do the same with the insides?' The men say likewise : 'And what is the use of their adding heat to heat, like silk lining silk, all against the Pragmatic Restrictions, when they in themselves are so hot that at any time that one thinks of tackling them they are already naturally ready, without any added device? What would you do about that? Perhaps they are apprehen-sive lest their hot, seething blood if not fed should get lost and congeal in their veins and become cold and icy, like that of a hermit who feeds on nothing but roots.'

Now let them get on with it; it is all good for boon com-panions, for as the ladies are so steadfast in their ardour, the least love approach one makes to them, one has them, and my lords their poor husbands are as cuckolded and horned as satyrs. And they do even better, do these estimable ladies ! Sometimes they give their lovers a share of their good patties and soups and potages, out of commiseration, so they may be bolder and not so debilitated when they come to the job, but feel in better trim and master them more abundantly, and they also give them recipes for having their own kitchens too prepare such foods, by which some men are well deceived, as I heard of one gallant noble who, having thus taken his broth, came all jaunty to tackle his mistress and boasted what a fine time he would give her, saying he had taken her broth and eaten her pasty. Her reply was : 'You'll do no more than right, but first let me try you.' And when they embraced and coupled, it proved that those dainties had served him for only two shots, whereupon she told him straight that either his cook had deceived him badly or he had been miserly about the drugs and compounds required, or he had not made all the necessary preparations for the great medicine, or his body at the moment had been too poorly disposed to take it in and give it out again, and this is how she mocked him.

All simples, however, all drugs, all meats and medicines, do not suit everybody, on some they work, with others they draw a blank.[244] Besides, I have also seen women who, when they ate these heating foods and were teased that perhaps thereby there might be excess of heat or something untoward happen either when with husband or lover, or else in some nocturnal orgasm, they swore and asserted and alleged that after eating such food their lusty appetite just did not hold. But Heavens, who knows, they must have been putting it on !

Now, the ladies who stand for Winter, say that they know enough recipes for such broths and carminative foods to make them as good in Winter as in the other seasons. They certainly experiment enough, and say Winter is very fitting too for making love, for, just as that season is gloomy, dark, obscure, retiring, shy of company and secretive, so should love too be properly made in secret, in some dark, withdrawn place, in a separate closet, or in an ingle-nook near a good fire which, when one stays a long time by it, engenders as much venereal heat as any Summer.

Thus it is well when done in the narrow space between a dark bed and the wall, where, if at the time they are round the fire warming themselves, the eyes of other people can only with difficulty see anything at all, or else seated out of the way on chests and beds, thus making love, because then, seeing them hugging close one to another, one thinks it is merely because of the cold, just to get warm, while with the torches at a distance, well to the side, or perhaps on the table or the sideboard, they do nice things.

For after all, who is better off when in a bed? Why, there's all the pleasures in the world for lovers and their mistresses in thus embracing each other and hugging and clasping and kissing and riding up the one on the other from fear of cold, not for a moment only, but for a long time so as softly to get warm again on each other, without feeling anything of the excessive heat that Summer brings, with that extreme sweat which greatly incommodes the completion of love, for instead of holding one another close and hugging and holding tight they then have to hold each other well away, which say the ladies, is, by the advice of doctors, best, the men are then, in Winter, more apt, more ardent and more given to it than they are in Summer.

Formerly I used to know a very great princess who had a very fine mind and talked and wrote as well as anybody. One day she began to write some stanzas in favour and in praise of Winter, and its aptness for love. You may conclude therefrom that she had found Winter very favourable and conducive in herself to loving. (They were well written stanzas too, I kept them in my cabinet a long time, and would much have liked to have inserted them here, for one would then have seen and observed the great virtues of Winter and its particular qualities for love-making.)

I knew a very great lady, one of the loveliest in the world indeed, who, freshly widowed, pretended in her new condition and state not to desire to go to court, or to the ball, or to the Queen's retiring, after supper, so as not to be thought too worldly, and so did not stir from her own room, but let each gentleman and each lady go to the dance as they would, her son and all, while she herself withdrew behind the bed. Here came her lover, who had previously been well treated, and

149

loved and favoured by her even when her husband was alive, or else he would sup with her and then stay on, till at last a brother-in-law of hers who was on the watch went to bed, and then, there behind the bed, he served her and renewed his old love ways, and found new ones for her second marriage, which followed the Summer after. Since then, having thought over all the circumstances, I believe that the other seasons would not have been nearly so suitable as the Winter was in this case, and as I heard one of her procuresses remark.

Now, to wind up, I maintain and affirm that, when taken properly and with regard to the whims of the men and the women who undertake the business, all the seasons are suitable for love-making, for, exactly as war, which was instituted by Mars, is made in all seasons and all kinds of weather, and victories are granted as Mars pleases and as he finds his warriors equipped and in a mood to engage in battle, so does Venus with the ladies, according to whatever bands of lovers and their mistresses are in a real mood for this combat, and the seasons hardly affect it at all, neither when favourable or unfavourable do they affect it much, nor do all those simples, nor those fruits, nor their drugs nor their druggers, nor does any other trick to which one or another has recourse, either to augment their last heat or reduce it, have any great effect. For, as a last example, I know a great lady whom her mother, from an early age, seeing she had hot, seething blood which was one day going to lead her straight along the road to a brothel, made regularly, at all meals, for thirty years, use sorrel-leaf juice, either in her meats or her soups and broths, or as a drink in great handled bowls without any admixture, so that, in short, her one sauce was sorrel juice. But in vain this girl took all those occult blood-coolers, for in the final resort she was a most famous whore and a tremendous tart, certainly one who had no need whatsoever of any of those pasties which I mentioned to give her heat, for she had enough naturally, though she was greedy enough to eat them like everybody else.

Now, though I might have said more and brought more arguments and examples, I do conclude, for one should not over-gnaw one's bone. And so I yield the pen to a better essayist than I am who will be able better than I am to speak up for this or that season, referring back to a wish and desire once made by an estimable Spanish lady who wished and craved for it to be Winter, which would be her season, and her lover to be the fire, so that when because of the great cold she felt she came to warm herself at him, he might have the pleasure of warming her, and she the delight when she warmed herself at him, taking his heat, and further to present herself and reveal herself to him often at her ease, warming herself straddling, with her skirts pulled up, her thighs and legs bare, so he might participate in the sight of the lovely limbs hidden till then under her linen and her gowns, and thus warm herself up still more and have him feed her other inner fire and lustful warmth.

Then she craved for Spring to come and her lover to be a garden full of flowers with which to deck her head, her lovely throat, her beautiful bosom, and revel in her lovely body naked between the sheets.

Then she craved for it to be Summer, so her lover would be a pellucid fountain or a gleaming stream, to receive her in its lovely fresh waters when she went to bathe and delight, and to her fill reveal herself to him so he would touch and touch again and handle all her lovely, lustful members.

And then, to conclude, she craved for her Autumn to come round again as it first was and she be a woman and her lover a man, for them both afterwards to have the intelligence, the feeling and the mind to contemplate and remember all their past delight and live in those lovely imaginings and re-flections of the past and to know and discuss together which season they had found the most suited and delightful.

That is how that estimable lady shared out and combined the seasons, and in this I will rely on the judgement of better debaters than I am as to which of the four seasons in these matters can be the sweetest and most pleasant.

And now I do most definitely relinquish this discussion. Whoever may wish to know more and learn the various tem-peraments of cuckolds should go back to an old song made at court fifteen or sixteen years since on cuckolds, the refrain of which was:

> One cuckold leads to another, and they are always a sorry
> kind
> Like the blind leading the blind.

I beg all worthy ladies if they happen on them, who come to read some of the tales in this chapter, to forgive me if they are rather salty and spicy, for my not having been able to wrap them up more modestly, because of the bite they demand. I will merely emphasize that I could have given others still stronger and more spicy, were it not that as I could not satisfactorily cloak them with fine modesty, I would have feared I might offend any estimable ladies who may take the trouble and do me the honour of reading my books. And I will further add that these stories which I have told here are no mean-born tales of town or village[245] but all come from excellent, elevated places, hence are not of vile or low persons at all, as, though I am humble of speech myself, I preferred to couple only great, eminent personages, and as I do not use names, I do not think I shall disgrace anybody.

> Wives who turn your husbands into birds,
> Do never tire of it, it is a lovely way,
> For did you leave them in their former skins
> They'd seek to keep you ever under their sway,
> And as men do would think to take their pleasure
> Whereas, they being birds, you have their measure.

ANOTHER

> Those who would cast stones at the charming wife,
> Who secretly plants horns on husband's head,
> Loose-tongued, do make a very great mistake,
> They are most kind, 'tis charity, when all is said,
> And charity's a law that governs all
> So please don't be so hypocritical.

AN ANCIENT RHYME ON THE GAME OF LOVE
(which I came upon among some old papers.)[246]

The game of love, where youth has pleasure
Can be compared to a gaming board,
Upon this board we stand ladies in array
And then 'tis time to open up the game
For this we need nought else but pretty dresses,
When some fill all the holes. 'Tis grand!
Is't not a game like this which teaches
How gladsomely our human hearts can live,
Though if perchance a hole is not too clean
What was a game's transformed to agony.

SECOND ESSAY

On the question as to what gives most satisfaction in love-making, the sense of touch, the sense of sight, or speech

HERE we have a question concerning love-making which really deserves a more profound and better essayist than myself, namely, what gives the greater satisfaction in the enjoyment of love, the tactile sense, which means touching, or speech, or sight? Etienne Pasquier,[247] unquestionably a very great figure in the realm of law, which is his profession, as he also is in other excellent humanitarian fields of knowledge, discusses it in the letter[248] he has left us. But he was far too brief, and, being so great a man, should not have been so sparing with his fine words on the matter as he was, for, had he but condescended to expatiate a little and frankly and freely declare all he might have done, the letter he wrote on the matter would have been a hundred times more entertaining and satisfactory.

He bases his main theme on some ancient rhymes of Count Thibaud de Champagne which apart from the little fragment which Pasquier cites in his letter,[249] I have never seen. And I find that that worthy, valiant gentleman of old spoke very well, not perhaps in such fine language as our gallant poets of today, yet nonetheless with great wisdom and fine argumentation; besides, he had a very handsome, fitting reason for speaking so well, namely, Queen Blanche of Castile, the mother of St Louis, of whom he was rather fond, indeed, very fond, taking her as mistress.[250] Though what was there in that with which to reproach the Queen, for despite her being very wise

154

and virtuous, could she prevent people loving her and burning with fire at her beauty and her qualities, since it is the very essence of virtue and perfection to attract love? It merely boils down to not letting oneself yield to the will of the man who loves.

This is why one should not find it strange, or reproach that Queen for being so loved and for there having been divisions of opinion, seditious uprisings and warrings in France during her reign and under her sceptre, for, as I once heard a very great person say, there are divisions of opinion as much over love's passion as over state intrigues, and in our fathers' day there was an old saw which ran that everybody wants his share of the c—— of a crazy Queen.

I do not know for which Queen[251] this saying was first coined, but it was probably concocted by that same Count Thibaud, very likely for not being treated as he would have liked by Queen Blanche, or simply for being slighted by her, or somebody else preferred to him, anyway he conceived a grudge which prompted him to ruin himself in these wars and tumults, as often happens when a lovely or great queen or lady or princess tries to run a state, every man wants to pay her attentions and honour and respect her, as much in order to be lucky enough to have her favour and be in her good books as to boast of ruling and governing the state with her and drawing profit therefrom. I could give a number of examples, but I will refrain.[252]

The long and the short of it is that it all resulted in this Count Thibaud's undertaking to put pen to paper as I have just said, on this fine subject, as Pasquier tells us; and without citing any of the verse here, I will refer the enquiring reader to him, for to quote would be superfluous here. All I need do for the moment is give my own views on the matter, that is, those of myself and of men more gallant than I am.

Now, as for flesh to flesh touching, one really must admit that it is very delightful, the more so since the acme of love-making is having the culminating enjoyment and that enjoyment cannot come about without joining flesh to flesh with the other person, for just as hunger and thirst cannot be assuaged or ease quenched except by eating and drinking, likewise love is not experienced by ear or eye but by flesh to flesh touching, by embracing and by the act of Venus, to which that idiotic jackanapes Diogenes Cinicus with japing mood, though dirtily too, rejoined that he wished he could assuage his hunger by rubbing his belly as he assuaged his craving for love by rubbing his cock.[253] I would have liked to put my opinion of this in franker language, but I had better treat lightly of it, as that other lovesick fellow did with Lamia[254] when she demanded too high a price for enjoyment of her love and he either could not or would not hear of paying so much, and for this reason thought fit to debase himself and pollute himself, while thinking of her, and thus in imagination get rid of his desire, whereupon she, hearing of it, summoned him before the magistrate, with the requisition that he should satisfy her too and then pay her, to which the magistrate replied with the court judgement that she should indeed be paid and her desire satisfied, but by the mere sound and tinkle of the money, which he was to show her, so that just as he had done, so also should she satisfy herself in imagination.

It is very true that against me I can have cited many kinds of Venus which the ancient philosophers disguise, but regarding such forms I refer back to them and to those more subtle than I am who may wish to discuss the matter. For all that, since the fruit of worldly love is naught else but enjoyment, one should never imagine one can really have it otherwise than by bodily contact and embracing. Yet it remains a striking fact that many have been of the opinion that it is a very meagre pleasure without sight and speech, and of this we have a fine exemplification in the *Hundred Tales* of the Queen of Navarre,[255] that one of the estimable nobles who, having had his pleasure several times of an estimable lady at night, she being masked with her kerchief[256] (real masks not yet having come in)[257] in a dark, shadowy gallery, was not satisfied with that favour, for all that he was well aware by touch that it was all very good and delectable and exquisite, but wanted to know who exactly it was he was having business with. So when one day he embraced her and held her in his arms, he marked the back of her gown, which was of black velvet,[258] with chalk, and then, at the party held after supper, (for their assignations were always at a definitely appointed hour in the day) as the ladies were entering the ballroom,[259] he hid behind the door and watched them all carefully as they passed, till he saw his particular one, marked on the shoulder, one too he would never have thought it was, since by her public behaviour, her expression of countenance and her discourse one would have taken her for the Wisdom of Solomon itself, which is how the Queen does describe her.

Who was more amazed than the noble, to find his good fortune embodied in a lady of whom he would the least have thought it of all the ladies of the court. Now indeed he wanted still more, not to stop there, and he insisted on disclosing to her what he had done, so as to find out why she hid from him as she did and had herself thus served covertly, in hiding. But she was very sly indeed and denied it all quite flatly, swearing by her share of paradise and by the damnation of her soul, that it was not her, as is the way with womenfolk if ever you bring up against them any act of their privy parts which they do not want to have known, even though you may be quite sure about it and know it to have been done. She then took umbrage and thus this noble lost his good fortune. And it had been good fortune indeed for the lady in question was really great and it was worth continuing with and what is more, it was worth it just because she did pretend outwardly to be so sweet and chaste and prim and circumspect, he could have had a double pleasure from it, one from so delectable, so good, so delicate an enjoyment of love and the other from often gazing at her in public when she had on that shy, deceptive, chill, modest countenance, and her speech all that was chaste, strict, and prim, while inwardly she thought of all the lascivious, frolicsome, lewd things she did when she and her lover were together. That is why this noble was very wrong to have spoken to her at all, he should just have kept on knocking away, enjoying his food, whether it was without as much as a penny dip or with all the torches of the front bedchamber. Certainly, on the other hand, he needed to know who she was, and his inquisitiveness in itself is praiseworthy, particularly since, as the tale tells us, he had begun to be afraid he was having business with some sort of succuba, for such demons admittedly do change their shape and take the form of women, to cohabit with men and thus deceive them, and, from what I have heard some knowledgeable magicians assert, they find it much easier to assume the form and countenance of a woman, than her power of speech. This is why the noble was right to want to spy on her and find out who she was, for by what he said himself, her abstaining from speech alarmed him more than his not seeing her and made him think of Satan's work, whereby he certainly showed he was a god-fearing man.

However, once he had found out everything, he should have held his tongue. But how so, somebody will object, both friendship and love are far from being perfect if not made manifest by heart and by word, which was precisely what the noble wished to convince her of, but all to no avail at all, for he lost everything. Moreover, anybody who knew the temperament of the noble in question would excuse him, since he was not cold or circumspect enough to play that game and cloak himself with like discretion, and from what I have heard of my mother, who was a lady-in-waiting of the Queen of Navarre and knew the background history of several of her stories, (one of the inspirers of them, indeed,)[260] the noble in question was my late uncle, La Chataigneraie, a brusque, mercurial and rather testy man.[261]

However, the tale was wrapped up, the better to disguise it, for this uncle of mine was never in the service of the great princess who was this lady's mistress, though he was in that of her brother the King, which amounted to much the same since he was much liked both by the King and the Princess.

The lady I will not name, beyond adding that she was a widow and a lady-in-waiting of a very great Princess and that she could contrive the most prim facial expression of any lady of the court.

I have heard tell of one lady of the court of our last kings whom I knew who, being in love with a very estimable noble attached to the court, had a mind to imitate the manner of making love of the preceding lady of whom I have told, but who, every time that she left her lover, went straight to her bedchamber and had one of her girls or maids examine her all over to see that she was not marked in any way, and in this way she avoided being recognized and disgraced. In fact, she was not marked at all till her ninth meeting, after which a sign was at once discovered and recognized by her woman, and for this reason, from fear of being disgraced and falling into opprobrium, she broke off with her lover there and then and never went to the meeting-place again.

It would have been better, somebody remarked, if she had let him make as many marks as he liked and removed them as many times, for then she would have had double pleasure, once from her satisfaction in making love with him, the other from outdoing her man who strove so hard with his philosophical stone to test her and get to know who she was, though never with any success.

I have heard another story told of the days of King Francis, about that fine groom Gruffy,[262] who worked in the stables of that monarch, and died in Naples, a member of Lord de Lautrec's expedition,[263] and of a very great lady of the court who fell greatly in love with him, he being a very good looking man, commonly known as 'handsome Gruffy', I have seen his portrait which shows him very handsome indeed.[264]

One day she called one of her footmen, in whom she had confidence, to her room, though without anybody seeing or knowing, and he one day called on Gruffy, so well dressed he was like a noble, to say that a very estimable and lovely lady sent him her compliments and was so in love with him that she wished to make his acquaintance more than that of any man of the court, though on one condition—not for anything in the world would she have him see her and know who she was, but when it was time to withdraw and all the court had dispersed, he would come and find him at a certain spot which he would now indicate, and would take him and conduct him to where he would sleep with the lady. Further, by this proposed pact he, that is Gruffy, was to consent to be blindfolded with a fine white handkerchief, like a man taken to parley with the men of an enemy city, so that he would neither recognize the place nor the room he was taken to, and a footman would hold his hands so he should not slip the handkerchief up, for this was what the messenger's mistress had ordered him to stipulate, so she might not be recognized till a certain date and time fixed beforehand which the envoy told him and promised. He should therefore think it over carefully, as to whether or not he was willing to go on such conditions, so the messenger might give the answer on the morrow, when he would come and pick him at a place which he would now appoint, but he must come alone, and he would then take him to such a lovely spot that he would never regret having gone. There now was a nice rendezvous for you, tied up with a strange stipulation.

I would almost as well like that of a Spanish lady, who called a man to a rendezvous, provided he came with three S's[265] as his qualities, which were *sabio, solo* and *segreto*—circumspect, sole and secret, and the other said he would go provided the lady for her part prepared and equipped herself with three F's, namely, not to be *fea, flaca* or *fria,* that is, not fearful flabby or frigid.

Well, to resume, the messenger left Gruffy. And troubled and pensive, Gruffy had good reason to fear lest this was a trick arranged by some enemy of his at court, to put him in an awkward position which might well cost his life or at least his good name in the King's eyes. He also wondered whoever the lady could be, whether great, or intermediate or a small person, lovely or ugly, which despite the saying that all cats are grey in the dark and any c—— is a c—— without a light, worried him the most. So, anyway, after having discussed it all with one of his most intimate friends, he decided he would risk it, thinking that in the case of the love of a great lady, which he presumed it must be, there would be nothing to fear or be apprehensive of. So the next day, when the King, the Queens, the ladies and all the courtiers male and female had withdrawn to go to bed, there without fail he was at the site the messenger had appointed, and the man duly turned up too, with another one, to assist him and keep watch to see that he

160

was not followed by any page or lackey, whether servant or knight. When the man appeared, all he said was, curtly : 'Let us go, sir, my lady awaits you.' At once he blindfolded Gruffy and led him by a strange path, by narrow alleys and unfamiliar crossings, till the other man said that even he did not know where they were, then he entered the lady's bedchamber, which was so dark and so shadowy that he could make out no more than he would inside an oven.

And there she certainly was, sweet smelling and excellently perfumed, which made him hope for something good. She had him undress at once, indeed, the messenger undressed him, then, having taken off the handkerchief, led him by the hand to the bed of the lady, who was trustfully awaiting him, and he at once took his place at her side, feeling her, embracing her, caressing her, and finding nothing that was not very good and fine, so lovely were her skin, her linen and her bed, which he felt, and so he spent the night very gladly indeed with this lovely person, whose name, I must say, I have been told, till she satisfied him in every possible way and he was highly conscious of having been most excellently quartered for this night. Yet nothing irked him so much as not being able to get a word from her.

She was very wise not to speak, since he had occasion to talk to her often enough during the day as he did to the other ladies, and so would at once have recognized her. Of love-frolicking, of cosseting, of caressing, of feeling and of all the other ways showing love and lechery she made no stint at all, so that he had a very good time indeed.

At daybreak the next day there was the messenger, duly come to waken him, get him up and dress him, bandage his eyes and take him back to the original meeting-place and there bid him God speed till next time, which would be soon. And the man did not fail either to ask if he had not told the truth and was not Gruffy glad he had believed him, and asked what Gruffy thought of him for having served him so well as quartermaster, and asked if the billet he had provided had not been satisfactory?

Handsome Gruffy thanked the man a hundred times and

161

bade him goodbye, with the assurance that for so good a deal he would always be prepared to come back and repeat the turn, whenever the other wished, which indeed he did, and this jollification lasted a good month, at the end of which Gruffy had to leave on that expedition to Naples, and bade his lady farewell and expressed his great regret, but still without extracting a single sound from her lips, nothing but the sighs and the tears, which he could feel streaming from her eyes. So he parted from her without seeing through it or ever finding out who she was.

Subsequently this lady was said to have led the same sort of life with two or three others, in just the same way, thus having a very good time, and it was said that this trickery suited her, since she was very miserly and in this way saved her money and was in no need to make the gentlemen who waited on her any presents, for after all any great lady for sheer honour's sake should give a man something, whether little or much, some cash, or rings or jewels or at least some costly favours. In this way the gallant lady provided her c—— with its pleasure but spared her purse, without ever revealing who she was, and so, as she never let it be known who she was, she did not have to draw on both purses. Now that was a terrible character for a great lady to have.

Some men of course will find the system good, others will condemn it, others will account it very wily, some will hold that she was a good business-woman, but however you take it, this lady cannot incur the reproach, but the Queen[266] did who stayed in Nesle's Paris mansion,[267] the one, I mean, who used to spy out for men passing by and no matter of what origin they were, had those who suited her and pleased her most summoned in to her, and after getting out of them what she wanted, had them thrown from the top of the tower, which is still standing, down into the water, so that they drowned. I cannot assert that this is all true, but the common folk, at least, most of the people of Paris, affirm it; and point out the tower to someone and ask him what he knows about it, and most likely he will on his own initiative tell you all this. But let us leave such love-making, which is more the abortion of it than real love-making, and today many of our ladies abhor such women, and love to have talk with the gentlemen who serve them, not treating them like stones or marble statues, but, selecting them carefully, contrive to have them serve them and adore them all very gallantly and decently, and then, once they get to know their loyalty and see how faithfully they persevere, from fervent love they prostitute themselves to them and give themselves pleasure with them, not masked at all or in dumb silence or in the night and the dark, but in lovely daylight, letting their lovers see them, touch them, feel them, embrace them, and entertain them too with lovely, lascivious conversation, with words and expressions which are all fond and conducive to love. Nevertheless, some do still make use of masks, and indeed there are a number of ladies who are sometimes forced to use them when they make love, if they do it in the full sunlight, simply from fear of ruining their complexions, or as a general precaution, in case they are suddenly caught when too heated, so their red faces and aghast expressions, (such as I have seen,) may never be seen, for a mask hides everything, and in this way they deceive the world. But I have heard several ladies and cavaliers who have made love say that without seeing and talking they would think themselves more like mere brutes which know no other consideration or any friendship, but merely seek to assuage their body's frenzy and heat.

So it is that I have heard many lords and gallant nobles who have slept with great ladies say that they have found them a hundred times more lascivious and unrestrained in their speech than any common women and others.

They know how to entertain a man delightfully with their talk, and this is the more pleasurable since it is out of the question, however vigorous a man be, for him to heave at the yoke in incessant ploughing, so that when the man comes to his orgasm and pause he finds it so very good, so appetising, indeed, when his lady entertains him with lascivious talk and with spicy suggestions which even when Venus seems most sound asleep, can sometimes awaken her again immediately, and this goes to the point that when in conversation with their lovers in the presence of others, even in the presence of Queens and

Princesses and so forth, many ladies can work the men up by utterance of words so lascivious and so delectable that both they and their lovers have an emission, just as if they were in bed, while we others look on, imagining the talk to be of anything but that.

This is why Mark Antony was so fond of Cleopatra and preferred her to his wife Octavia, who was a hundred times lovelier and more pleasing than Cleopatra. Cleopatra, you see, was one of those women with this sort of highly charged talk, and had such lascivious grace and manner and such a fine sense of words that Antony abandoned all else for love of her.

Plutarch informs us[268] of certain expressions or terms which she used so neatly that when Mark Antony tried to follow suit (and he was most anxious to be a great lady's man) he was in comparision with her and her verbal graces like nothing so much as a common soldier or clumsy man of arms.

Pliny[269] tells a tale about her which I find very pleasing, so I will give part of it here. It is that one day, when in one of her most high-spirited moods, and dressed extremely grandly, ready for anything, above all having on her head a garland of various flowers, when everything in short was suitable for any lechery, and they were at table and Mark Antony wanted to drink, she entertained him with some delightful talk and while she discoursed away, one by one, plucked the lovely flowers of her coronet, these however all being doctored with powder she had sprinkled on them, and tossed them as she did so into the goblet in Mark Antony's hand, from which he was about to drink, but just when she had concluded this operation and Mark Antony was on the point of putting the cup to his lips, to drink, Cleopatra suddenly restrained him, summoned to her a slave or criminal whom she had had placed ready, and made the man drink what Mark Antony was about to swallow, upon which the man fell dead on the spot. Then, turning to Mark Antony, she said : 'Did I not love you as I do, I would have got rid of you just now, and done so deliberately, too. But I suddenly saw clearly that my life would be nothing without yours.' Here were device and language well calculated to confirm Mark Antony in his love and make him snuggle closer to her side.

That is how Cleopatra's eloquence worked and history does assure us that she was a most able talker. Mark Antony never called her otherwise than plainly 'Queen', for her greater honour, as he wrote to Octavius Caesar,[270] before they fell out, saying: 'Who has changed you? Is it because I embrace the Queen. She is my wife. Is this the first time I have done this? You embrace Drusilla, Tortala, Leontifa, or Rufila or Salura Litisema, or all of them, what concern is it which you turn to, when that is your whim?'

By these words Mark Antony meant to praise his own constancy and reprove the other's fickleness, loving so many at once, while he loved only his Queen, so that I am astonished that Octavius did not love her after Antony's death. Perhaps he had his pleasure of her when he saw her and had her come to his room alone and she harangued him there, or possibly he did not find what he thought to discover in her, or else scorned her for some other reason, so preferred to make her part of his triumph in Rome, and show her in the great parade, a proposal that she countered by her untimely death.

There is no doubt about it—to return to our original theme —when a woman's mind is set on love or she has begun an affair, there can be no more eloquent orator.

Just look at how Livy,[271] Apianus[272] and others have described Sophonisba[273] for us as so eloquent to Massinissa when she came to him to love him, win him and make him hers, and later too when he made her take poison. In short, to be well loved any lady must be a good talker, and admittedly we see few who are not, with a vocabulary fit to move heaven and earth, even when in the depths of winter this is iced up.

Above all, ladies who undertake love-making and cannot talk are so dull that the trifle they give you lacks taste and savour, and when à propos of his courtesan, describing her way of life, Lord du Bellay says she was:

Sober of speech but frisky in her bed[274]

he of course means sober of speech when in the company of

others, in conversation with all and sundry, for when in private with her lover every gallant lady desires freedom of speech, to be able to say what she pleases, so as to stimulate Venus to the maximum.

I have heard several men who have had their pleasure of ladies great and fair tell their stories of how fascinating it was to hear them talking to another person in bed, saying they were as free and uncontrolled in their speech as any whore one ever knew, and it is a remarkable fact that despite being used thus to entertain husband or lover alike with words and suggestions and conversation which are salacious and lewd, even freely naming the goods they carry at the bottom of their bag freely without any disguise, yet when they are in polite conversation they never go too far nor let a single one of such salacious words come to their lips, so that one must admit them to be great masters of self-control and dissimulation, for there is nothing so fidgety as the tongue of a great lady or a prostitute.

But in my time I knew one very lovely and estimable lady who was once discussing the events of the recent civil wars with an estimable noble at court when she suddenly said : 'I've heard that the King has blown up all the c—— of such-and-such a country,' putting a "c" instead of "p", that is, saying not *ponts*, c——s, that is to say not "bridges", "——" blown up. As you may imagine, having just slept with her husband or else dreaming of her lover, she had that other little word on the tip of her tongue and the noble in question fell hotly in love with her for that very slip of the tongue.

Another lady whom I knew, entertaining another lady greater than she was, and praising and expatiating on her fine qualities, added : 'Lady So-and-so, I assure you, I'm not saying this to be adulterous about you,' meaning to say adulatory about her. Now, that was a clear sign that she was really thinking of adultery and committing it.

In a word, speech in the game of love-making is a powerful instrument, and where it is lacking the pleasure is so much impaired. Besides, if a lovely body has not got a lovely spirit, it really is more like a statue of itself than a human body, and

166

if it is to be truly loved, however beautiful it may be it does need to be backed by a lively intelligence, so that such a body as has not naturally got an able tongue must needs fashion one by artifice.

The courtesans of Rome make much mock of the charming ladies of Rome for not being so good at talking as they themselves are. They say of them that *chiavano come cani, ma che sono quiete della bocca come sassi,* that they come on heat like bitches but their mouths as dumb as tombs.'

This is precisely why I have known many estimable nobles who have refused to have any dealings with quite a number of ladies, and very lovely ones too, I can tell you, because they were stupid, soulless, without any spirit, and bereft of speech, so that they left them quite alone, saying they would as soon have dealings with a lovely statue in fine white marble, like the man in Athens who loved one to the point of taking his pleasure of her.[275]

For this reason, indeed, men who travel in foreign parts are little given to loving foreign women and do not at all readily conceive a desire for them largely because of their not being able to understand each other, for what a foreign woman says makes no impression on a man's heart, and I understand any man who does not pay attention to their call, for if then he does have any dealings with them, it is merely more or less to satisfy nature and extinguish the natural fire in brute fashion and then *andar in barca,* reimbark, to use the words of an Italian one day who had gone ashore at Marseilles on his way to Spain, and asked where women were to be found. He had been shown a place where a wedding dance was in progress, but when a lady approached him, to persuade him to join in, said *Vs. mi perdona non voglio parlare, voglio solamente chiavare, e poi me n'andar in barca,* 'Madame will pardon me, I do not wish to talk, all I want to do is have a knock, then reimbark.'

Your Frenchman does not much enjoy it with a German or Swiss or Flemish or English, Scottish or Slav woman or any other foreign woman, even were she to chatter away in the finest way in the world, if he does not understand her, but he takes great pleasure with his French woman or with an Italian or Spanish woman, for as a rule most Frenchmen today, at least, those who have seen a little of the world, know how to talk or at least can understand those languages, and God knows if they are agile and fitted for love-making, for any man who has to do with a French, Italian, Spanish, or Greek lady who is a talker might as well confess without more ado that he is caught and conquered.

Formerly our French tongue was not so lovely or so well stocked as it is today, but Italian, Spanish and Greek have been rich for a long time, and I doubt if I have ever seen a lady speaking those tongues who, if she had any experience worth speaking of in love-making, did not also know very well how to talk. I refer you to men who have had dealings with such women.

There is this to be said, that a lady who is both lovely and has ample fine words satisfies a man doubly.

Now let us talk of sight. There is no doubt that, since it is our eyes that make the first assault in the skirmish of love one must admit that they afford us great satisfaction when they show us something which is lovely and, as loveliness, rare. Ah, and what in all the world is there more lovely to be seen than a lovely woman, whether well dressed and well groomed or stark naked between two sheets? When she is dressed, all you see naked is her face, yet even so, when a lovely body, equipped with a lovely, lavish figure, with fine carriage and charm, of imposing appearance and superb majesty, appears in its entirety before us, what lovelier sight or more delightful show could there be in the world? And even when you come to have pleasure of her thus covered and grandly dressed, your craving and your delight are increased, although you see only her face, out of all the parts there are to the body, yet one cannot really have one's full pleasure of a great lady with all the boons that one really craves if one is not in a bedchamber at one's ease, in a secret place, or in a bed specially designed for pleasure, where she is so well revealed.

And this is why a great lady, of whom I have heard tell, whenever she happened to come upon her gentleman-in-waiting conveniently, out of sight, I mean, where discovery would be impossible, she took immediate advantage of it to get her satisfaction as promptly and as quickly as she could. And one day she said to him : 'How silly women were in times gone by who from excessive desire to be dainty in their love-affairs and their pleasure, used to shut themselves away, either in their dressing-rooms or in some other concealed place, and there dragged out their sporting and frolicking so long that in the end they were found out and everything was made public. Today one should snatch one's moment as quickly as one can, no sooner seen, than taken advantage of and done. Like that we cannot be disgraced.'

I think this lady was right, for those men who have dabbled in that sort of love have always held to that rule, that there is nothing like love stolen on the spur of the moment. Besides, the mere thought in such circumstances of how one is forcing one's way under the clothes, treading on cloth of gold and silver canvas and rustling silks with all those pearls and precious stones, crushing, spoiling, flinging down, dragging on the ground tends to augment and build up one's ardour and satisfaction unquestionably far more than with any herd-girl or other woman of like quality, however lovely she may be.

Why indeed was Venus in olden times found to be so beautiful and so desirable, if not that with her loveliness she was always finely attired and invariably perfumed, so that she smelt good at a hundred paces? This is why it is maintained that perfumes greatly prompt love-making.[276]

This is why the Empresses and great ladies of Rome paid great attention to their appearance, as also our great ladies of France have done, but even more so, those of Spain and Italy did, who were for long more enterprising and tasteful than ours, both in perfumes and in ornaments and fine clothes, our ladies subsequently having taken patterns and fine inventions from them, while they had learned of them from ancient reliefs and statues of those Ancient Roman ladies, which one can still see among the many antiquities still in Spain and Italy in which anybody who examines them closely will find that their hairdressing and clothes are perfect and very conducive to loving them. But today our French ladies surpass them all. It is to the Queen of Navarre[277] that they owe this great benefit.

This is why it is good and fine to have dealings with these lovely ladies, who are so well dressed, so richly and grandly got up, to such point that I heard certain courtiers, comrades of mine, when we were talking together, say that they liked them better so than when undressed and naked between two sheets, even were the bed the most lavish with embroidery that could be made. Others however maintained that there was nothing like the natural state, without any make-up or artifice, for instance, one great prince of my acquaintance[278] for this reason had his courtesans or ladies lie between sheets of well tucked-in black taffeta, so that against the black their whiteness and delicacy of skin should show the better and yield him more delight.

It is indeed unquestionable that of all the lovely sights in the world there is none more delightful than that of a lovely woman, all perfection in her beauty, though such is not so easy to find. Thus one can find it on record that when once asked by certain estimable ladies and girls of his acquaintance to give them a picture of Helen the Fair[279] and depict her as lovely as she was said to have been, that excellent artist Zeuxis did not want to refuse them, but before making this portrait of her, examined them all very closely and then, taking from one and the other all that he could find that was most lovely, he made them a picture of those lovely features all combined together, and by them jointly depicted Helen so fair that there was no gainsaying it, and she was the cynosure of them all, though it was by God's grace all due to them for having helped so well by their own loveliness and their own features as much as Zeuxis did by his brush. This indicates that it would have been out of the question to find such perfection of beauty in Helen, though she was indeed very lovely.

And to support the truth of this the Spanish has it that for a woman to be absolutely perfect and her beauty complete, she must fulfil thirty conditions of beauty,[280] as a Spanish lady once told me at Toledo, that city of so many very lovely and very charming and very cultivated ladies. These thirty conditions are :

Tres cosas blancas: el cuero, los dientes, y las manos.
Tres negras: los ojos, las cejas, y las pestanaas.
Tres coloradas: los labios, las mexillas, y las unas.
Tres lungas: el cuerpo, los cabellos, y las manos.
Tres cortas: los dientes, las orejas, y los pies.
Tres anchas: los pechos, la frente, y el entrecejo.
Tres estrechas: la boca, (l'una y otra,) la cintra, y l'entrada
      del pie.
Tres gruesas: el braço, el musto, u la pantorilla.
Tres delgados: los dedos, los cabellos, y los labios.
Tres pequenas: las tetas, la naris, y la cabeça.

which, for comprehension, means :

Three white things : skin, teeth and hands.
Three black : eyes, eyebrows and eyelashes.
Three red : lips, cheeks and nails.
Three long : body, hair and hands.
Three short : teeth, ears and feet.
Three broad : bosom, forehead and between the eyebrows.
Three narrow : mouth, waist and instep.
Three plump : arms, thighs and buttocks.
Three supple : fingers, hair and lips.
Three tiny : breasts, nose and head.
                    That makes thirty altogether.

There is nothing impossible about it, one could conceivably have all these traits in one lady, but she would have to be cast in the mould of perfection, and to see them all combined together, without anything to complain of or any shortcoming, does seem out of the question. I refer you to those who have seen lovely women (or may yet do so) and like to take care to pay attention and let us see what they will be able to say. Yet, notwithstanding, without being perfect or embellished in all these points, a lovely woman will always be lovely if she has but half, merely the principal of the points that I have just mentioned, for I have seen many who had more than half of them who were really very lovely and very delightful, neither more nor less than as a shrubbery is always found lovely in the Spring, for even if not full of all the little shrubs one would really like, yet you do see some handsome, large trees, all tufty with buds, and there are enough such lovely points to blot out the defectiveness of the other small ones.

Lord Ronsard will I hope forgive me if I say that that mistress of his whom he made out to be so lovely never attained such beauty as this,[281] nor did any other lady in the times in which he wrote, not even his lovely Cassandra, who, I am well aware, was lovely, though hidden by him under a false name;[282] nor, as far as she went, his Marie, who never had any other name but that,[283] but it is allowable to poets and painters to say and do what they please, as you have in *Orlando furioso* and the fine beauties described by Ariosto,[284] Alcine and others.

All that is fine, but, as I have it from a very great personality, Nature could never make a woman so perfect as the vivid and exquisite soul of a divine painter can depict one. *Basta!* Human eyes ever delight in seeing a lovely woman, handsome of countenance, white-skinned, well made, and even if dark, it is all the same, indeed, a dark woman is sometimes better than a fair one. As the Spanish has it : *Aunque io sia morisca, no soy de menos preciar,* 'Even if I am swarthy, I am no less to be prized.'[285] Thus, as the Italian has it, the lovely Marfisa[286] *era brunetta alquanto,* 'was a trifle dark.' But let the dark not eclipse the fair too much! So fine a countenance needs to be borne by a body fashioned and made to fit, I say the same of the great as of the small, but those who are tall surpass all.

But we can quite well do without seeking such exquisite features of beauty as I have just mentioned or are described, and enjoy the sight of our ordinary beauties, not that I mean ordinary in any other sense, for we have some so rare that, on my faith, they are worth more than all those women that our fantastic poets and crackbrained painters and our pindarizers of beauties could ever depict.

But here, alas, comes the worst : such lovely beauties, in the sense of such handsome countenances, some of us do indeed see and we admire them and desire their lovely bodies for love of their lovely faces, but nevertheless, when they come to be uncovered and laid bare, these take away all our desire, for they are so ugly, so faulty, so blotched, so marked and so hideous that they belie the faces and that is how we are often cheated.

We have a fine example of this in a nobleman of the Island of Majorca, whose name was Raymond Lully,[287] of a very fine, rich and ancient line, who when in his prime, on account of his nobility, his sterling qualities and his courage was called upon to govern the island. While in that responsible position he fell in love, as often happens to the rulers of provinces and cities, with a lovely lady of that island, one of the cleverest, loveliest and best spoken ladies of the place. He paid her attentions very assiduously for a long time, ever craving of her that fine point of enjoyment. After having refused him as long as she could bear, she one day gave him a rendezvous, which he did not fail to keep, nor did she, but appeared lovelier and better dressed than ever. But, just when he thought he was about to enter paradise, she laid bare her bosom and showed it to be covered with a dozen plasters, which she then tore off, one after the other, disdainfully throwing them to the ground, to reveal to him a frightful cancer and then, with tears in her eyes, reveal to him all her tribulation and misfortune, telling him all about it and then asking him if there was sufficient left in her for him to be as much in love with her as he was before, and went on to speak to him so piteously that he was overcome with pity for that lovely lady, yet left her. He uttered prayers to the Almighty for her health, conferring her to God's care, then resigned his post and became a hermit. When he had returned from the holy war, where he took his vows, he went to Paris to study under Arnaldus de Villanova,[288] a wise philosopher, and when he had completed his studies, he withdrew to England, where the King then reigning took him in and welcomed him principally for his great learning, and he there transmuted several ingots and bars of iron, copper and brass, scorning the common, trivial way of transmuting lead and iron into gold, because he knew that many men of his time could do that as well as he did, whereas he knew how to perform both operations, but wanted to perform one above all others.

This story I have from a gallant man who told me he had it from Oldrade[289] the legal authority who speaks of Raymond Lully in his commentary on the law *De false moneta*.[290] In turn Oldrade says he had it from Carolus Bovillus, a Picardy born man[291] who wrote a Latin work on Raymond Lully's life.

This is how Lully got over his love of that fair lady though others might not have done as he did, but would undoubtedly have loved her with their eyes shut, and thus got what they wanted of her, for it would have been all the same, the part which interested him was not touched by any such complaint.

I knew a noble who regarding a widowed lady in my time was for instance not so squeamish, for though the lady was suffering from a large malignant cancer of the breast he did not fail to marry her or she to accept him, against the counsel of her mother, and, gravely ill and diseased though she was, both she and he got so worked up and moved so violently all their wedding night that they broke the bedstead and fell through.

There was also a very estimable noble whom I knew, a great friend of mine, who told me that one day, while he was in Rome, he chanced to love a Spanish lady who was one of the loveliest women there had ever been in that city, but when he coupled with her she would not let him see or touch her naked thighs except in drawers, and when he wanted to touch her would say in Spanish: *Ah! no me tocays, hareis me quosquillas!* which means: 'Don't touch me, you tickle.' But, one morning, passing her house, he saw her door open, and went in unannounced, without coming upon page or maid or anybody else, he entered her bedroom, found her so sound asleep that he could see her stark naked on the bed and examine her at his ease, for it was very hot weather, and he said he never saw anything so lovely as that body of hers except that while one thigh was lovely, white and smooth and full-fleshed, her other thigh was quite withered, shrunken and erysipelitic, a limb no larger than a young boy's arm. You may imagine how astonished that noble was. Though he pitied her greatly, from then on he never once visited her again or had anything to do with her.

There are many ladies to be seen who though not thus erysipelitic and suppurating, yet are so thin, so shrunken, wasted, withered and de-fleshed that they can show nothing more than their bones, like one very great one of whom the Bishop of Cisteron[292] spoke the best word of any man at court when he jocularly said better go to bed with a brass-wire rat-trap than her, and, as also a certain noble knight of the court whom we were attacking for having to do with a rather elevated lady once said : 'You are quite wrong, for I am too fond of flesh and she's all bone,' though to see those two ladies, so lovely of countenance, one would have thought them both very well-fleshed, delectable morsels.

A very great prince I came upon once fell in love with two lovely ladies at once, as often happens to great men, with their love for variety. One was very fair, the other dark, but both were very lovely and very lovable. When one day he had just seen the dark one, the jealous fair one said to him : 'You've just been fluttering round a she-crow.' To which the prince, who was a trifle irritated and annoyed by the remark, said : 'And when I am with you, what am I fluttering round?' 'A phoenix !' The prince, who had a very ready tongue replied : 'You had rather have said a Bird of Paradise, seeing that they are more feather than flesh,' by this taunting her with being rather thin, for she was too young to be plump, since as a rule fat only settles on women getting on in years, when they begin to build up and get heavy in limb and elsewhere.

A certain noble gave a good rejoinder to a great prince of my acquaintance. Both men had lovely wives. The great prince found the noble's wife very lovely and charming. One day he said to him : 'So-and-so, I shall have to sleep with your wife.' Without hesitation the noble, who was good at repartee replied : 'Agreed, if I can sleep with yours.' The prince replied : 'What would you do with her, for mine is so thin she'd never be to your taste.' The noble answered : 'I'll pack her so tight with my bacon that I'll put a bit of taste into her.'

So many other women are to be seen whose gentle, doll-like

175

faces excite lust for their bodies, but when one gets to these one finds them quite fleshless, so that pleasure and temptation soon pass. Among other points, one finds the *mons veneris* so dry and fleshless that it chafes and scrapes you more than jig-jogging along on a mule does, indeed, such ladies are wont to use very soft, yielding little pads to take the brunt and stop the chafing, for I have heard of some who often used them, or else drawers softly lined and made of satin, so that anybody who did not know who touched them would find everything quite all right and be quite sure it was their natural plumpness, since over this satin they wore fluffy little white knickers, so that whenever a lover had a quick one with them on the sly he left his lady so satisfied and repleted that he held her to be a very good find.

There are yet others whose skin is much blotched and marked, like marble, or some mosaic, as spotted as fallow deer, scratchy and given to floury, farcy pustules, in a word, so sickly that the sight was hardly pleasant.

I have heard of one great lady, (and knew her too, as I know others,) who was quite hirsute, with a hairy pelt on her bosom and stomach, over her shoulders and down her spine, and on her arms, just like any savage. I leave it to you to imagine what that meant. If the proverb is to be believed, a woman so hairy is either rich or lubricious, but she, I assure you, was both, and at great pains to give herself lavishly too, to be seen and desired.

There are other women who have permanent goose-flesh or starling-flesh, with skin dried and grainy, darker than that of a real imp of Hell. Yet others have the the hugest empty dugs, dangling looser than the udder of a cow suckling her calf. I am sure these are not the lovely bosoms of Helen who when one day she wished to present a fine cup to the Temple of Diana[293] in connection with a certain vow she was taking, and engaged a goldsmith to make it for her, had him model it on one of her lovely breasts, and he made it of white gold too, which could not be more admirable, neither the goblet nor the resemblance to the breast on which it was modelled, which seemed so gracefully shaped and so dainty that the craftsman's hand must have made one crave the original breast. Pliny tells us this as of special interest where he speaks of there being white gold, which is most unusual, and informs us this goblet was made of such metal.

Anybody who wanted to make gold goblets modelled on those huge dugs I have mentioned (and I know some), would have to provide his goldsmith with the metal and would have to put up with a deal of mockery afterwards, when people came to say : 'Those are the goblets modelled on the breasts of ladies so-and-so and so-and-so !' Such goblets would not be at all like goblets but regular swill-tubs, like those one sees, flat and round, used to feed porkers.

And there are other women the tips of whose breasts are like nothing else but over-ripe black cherries. There are others, to go lower down the scale, who have so rough and wrinkled a belly that one might take them for sergeants' or innkeepers' wrinkled old game-bags, which happens to women who have children without their midwives taking proper care and massaging them with whale-oil. But there are others who have bellies as lovely and smooth and breasts as erect as if they were still virgins.

D'autres il y en a, pour venir encore plus bas, qui ont leurs natures hideuses et peu agreables. Les unes y ont le poil nullement frizé, mais si long et pendant que vous diriez que ce sont les moustaches d'un Sarrazin; et pourtant n'en ostent jamais la toison, et se plaisent à la porter telle, d'autant qu'on dit: Chemin jonchu et c— velu sont fort propres pour chevaucher. *J'en ay ouy parler de quelqu'une tres-grande qui les porte ainsi.*

J'ay ouy parler d'une autre belle et honneste dame[294] *qui les avoit ainsi longues qu'elle les entortilloit avec des cordons ou rubans de soye cramoisie ou autre couleur, et se les frizonnoit ainsi comme des frizons de perruques; et puis se les attachoit à ses cuisses; et entel estat quelquesfois se les presentoit à son mary et à son amant; ou bien se les destortoit de son ruban et cordon, si qu'elles paroissoyent frizonnées par aprés, et plus gentilles qu'elles n'eussent fait autrement.*

Il y avoit bien là de la curiosité et de la paillardise et tout:

car, ne pouvant d'elle-mesme faire et suivre ses frisons, il falloit qu'une d ses femmes, de ses plus favorites, la servît en cela; en quoy ne peut estre autrement qu'il n'y ait de la lubricité en toutes façons qu'on la pourra imaginer.

Aucunes, au contraire, se plaisent le tenir et porter raz comme la barbe d'un prestre.

D'autres femmes y a-il qui n'y ont de poil point du tout, ou peu, comme j'ay ouy parler d'une fort grande et belle dame que j'ay cogneu; ce qui n'est guieres beau, et donne un mauvais coupçon: ainsi qu'il y a des hommes qui n'ont que de petits boucquets de barbe au menton, et n'en sont pas plus estimez de bon sang, ainsi que sont les blanquets et blanquettes.

D'autres en ont l'entrée si grande, vague et large, qu'on la prendroit pour l'antre de la Sibille. J'en ay ouy parler d'aucunes, et bien grandes, qui les ont telles qu'une jument ne les a si amples, encore qu'elles s'aydent d'artifice le plus qu'elles peuvent pour estrecir la porte; mais, dans deux ou trois frequentations, la mesme ouverture tourne; ainsi que j'ay ouy parler d'une dame grande et belle, dont le mari de laquelle se mettant sur ses jactances et louant ses conquestes, il y eust un galant seigneur de par le monde qui luy dist: 'Vous avez raison, par Dieu, le cas de votre femme est plus grand que toutes les conquestes que vous fistes jamais.' Et, qui plus est, j'ay ouy dire que, quand bien on les arregarde le cas d'aucunes, il leur cloyse comme celuy d'une jument quand elle est en chaleur. L'on m'en a conté trois qui monstrent telles cloyses quand on y prend garde de les voir.

J'ay ouy parler d'une dame grande, belle et de qualité, à qui un de nos rois avoit imposé le nom de pan de c—,[295] tant il estoit large et grand, et non sans raison, car elle se l'est fait en son vivant souvent mesurer à plusieurs merciers et arpenteurs; et que, tant plus elle s'estudioit le jour de l'estrecir, la nuict en deux heures on le luy eslargissoit si bien que ce qu'elle faisoit en une heure, on le defaisoit en l'autre, comme la toille de Penelope. Enfin, elle en quitta tous artifices, et en fut quitte pour faire election des plus gros moules qu'elle pouvoit trouver.

Tel remede fut tres-bon; ainsi que j'ay ouy dire d'une fort belle et honneste fille de la court, laquelle l'eut au contraire si petit et estroit qu'on en desesperoit à jamais le forcement du pucellage; mais, par l'advis de quelques medecins ou de sages-femmes, ou de ses amis ou amies, elle en fit tenter le gué ou le forcement par des plus menus et petits moules, puis vint aux moyens, puis aux grandes, à mode des talus que l'on fait, ainsi que Rabelais ordonna les murailles de Paris imprenables;[296] et puis, par tels essais les uns aprés les autres, s'accoustuma si bien à tous que les plus grands ne luy faisoyent la peur que les petits paravant faisoyent si grande.

Une grande princesse estrangere, que j'ay cogneu,[297] laquelle l'avoit si petit et estroit qu'elle ayma mieux de n'en taster jamais que de se faire inciser, comme les medecins le conseil-loyent. Grande vertu certes de continence, et rare!

D'autres en ont les labies longues et pendantes plus qu'une creste de coq d'Inde quand il est en colère; comme j'ay ouy dire que plusieurs dames ont; non seulement elles, mais aussy des filles. J'ay ouy faire ce conte à feu M. de Randan:[298] qu'une fois estans de bons compagnons à la cour ensemble, comme M. de Nemours,[299] M. le vidame de Chartres,[300] M. le comte de La Roche, M.M.[301] de Montpezat,[302] Givry,[303] Genlis[304] et autres, ne sachans que faire, allerent voir pisser les filles un jour, cela s'en-tend cachez en bas et elles en haut. Il y en eut une qui pissa con-tre terre: je ne la nomme point; et d'autant que le plancher estoit de tables, elle avoit ses lendilles si grandes, qu'elles passerent par le fente des tables si advant, qu'elle en monstra la longueur d'un doigt; si que M. de Randan, par cas, ayant un baston qu'il avoit pris à unlaquais, où il avoit un fichon, en perça si dex-trement ses lendilles, et les cousit si bien contre la table, que la fille, sentant la piqûre, tout à coup s'esleva si fort, qu'elle les escerta toutes, et de deux pars qui y en avoit en fit quatre; et les dictes lendilles en demeurerent decoupées en forme de barbe d'escrevisses; dont pourtant la fille s'en trouva très mal, et la maistresse en fut fort en colere. M. de Randan et la compaignie en firent le conte au roy Henry,[305] qui estoit bon compagnon, qui en rit pour sa part son saoul, et en apaisa le tout envers la royne,[306] sans rien en desguiser.

Ces grandes lendilles sont cause qu'une fois j'en demanday la raison à un medecin excellent, qui me dit que, quand les

filles et femmes estoyent en ruth, elles les touchoient, manioi-
ent, viroient, contournoient, allongeoient et tiroient si souvent,
qu'estans ensemble s'en entredonnoient mieux du plaisir.

Telles filles et femmes seroyent bonnes en Perse, non en
Turquie, d'autant qu'en Perse les femmes sont circoncises,
parce que leur nature ressemble de je ne sçay quoy le membre
viril (disent-ils); au contraire, en Turquie, les femmes ne le
sont jamais; et pour ce les Perses les appellent heretiques, pour
n'estre circoncises,[307] *d'autant que leur cas (disent-ils) n'a*
nulle forme; et ne prennent plaisir de les regarder comme les
chrestiens. Voilà ce qu'en disent ceux qui ont voyagé en
Levant. Telles femmes et filles (disoit ce medecin) sont fort
sujettes à faire la fricarelle, donna con donna.

J'ay ouy parler d'une tres-belle dame et des plus qui ait
esté en la cour, qui ne les a si longues: car elle luy sont
accourcies pour un mal que son mary luy donna; voire qu'elle
n'a de levre d'un costé, pour avoir esté tout mangé de chancres
si bien qu'elle qeut dire son cas estropié et à demy demembré;
et neantmoins ceste dame a esté fort recherchée de plusieurs,
mesmes elle a esté la moitié d'un grand quelquefois dans son
lict. Un grand disoit à la cour un jour qu'il voudroit que sa
femme ressemblast celle-là, et qu'elle n'en eust qu'à demy,
tant elle en avoit trop.

J'ay aussi ouy parler d'une autre bien plus grande qu'elle
cent fois, qui avoit un boyau qui luy pendilloit long d'un
grand doigt au dehors de sa nature, et, disoit-on, pour n'avoir
esté bien servie en l'une de ses couches par sa sage-femme; ce
qui arrive souvent aux filles et femmes qui ont fait des couches
à la derobade, ou qui par accident se sont gastées et grevées;
comme une des belles femmes de par le monde, que j'ay cog-
neue, qui, estant veufve, ne voulut jamais se remarier, pour
estre descouverte d'un second mary de cecy, qui l'en eust peu
prisée, et, possible, mal traittée.

Cette grande que je viens de dire, nonobstant son accident,
enfantoit aussi aisement comme si elle eust pissé: car on disoit
sa nature tres-ample; et si pourtant elle a esté bien aymée et
bien servie à couvert; mais malaisement se laissoit-elle voir là.

Aussi volontiers, quand une bell et honneste femme se met

à l'amour et à la privauté, si elle ne vous permet de voir ou taster cela, dittes hardiment qu'elle y a quelque tare ou si, que la
veue ny le toucher n'approuvera guieres, ainsi que je tiens
d'une honneste femme: car, s'il n'y en a point, et qu'il soit
beau comme certes il y en a et de plaisants à voir et manier,
elle est aussi curieuse et contente d'en faire la monstre et en
prester l'attouchement que de quelque autre de ses beautez
qu'elle ait, autant pour son honneur à n'estre soubçonnée de
quelque defaut ou laideur en cet endroit que pour le plaisir
qu'elle y prend ellemesme à le contempler et mirer, et surtout
aussi pour accroistre la passion et tentation davantage à son
amant. De plus, les mains et les yeux ne sont pas membres
virils pour rendre les femmes putains et leurs marys cocus,
encore qu'aprés la bouche aydent à faire de grands approches
pour gaigner la place.

D'autres femmes y a-il qui ont la bouche de là si pasle
qu'on diroit qu'elles y ont la fivre; et telles ressemblent aucuns
yvroignes, lesquels, encor qu'ils boivent plus de vin qu'une
truye de laict, ils sont pasles comme trespassez; aussi les
appelle-on traistres au vin, non pas ceux qui sont rubiconds:
aussi telles par ce costé là on les peut dire traistresses à Venus,
si ce n'est que l'on dit: pasle putain, et rouge paillard. Tant
y a que cette partie ainsi pasle et transie n'est point plaisante
à voir; et n'a garde de ressembler à celle d'une des plus belles
dames que l'on en voye, et qui tient grand rang, laquelle j'ay
veu qu'on disoit qu'elle portoit là trois belles couleurs ordin-
airement ensemble, qui estoyent incarnat, blanc et noir: car
cette bouche de là estoit colorée et vermeille comme corail, le
poil d'alentour gentiment frizonné et noir comme ebene; ainsi
le faut-il, et c'est l'une des beautez; la peau estoit blanche
comme albastre, qui estoit ombragée de ce poil noir. Cette
veue est belle celle-là, et non ces autres que je viens de dire.

D'autres il y en a aussi qui sont si bas ennaturées et fendues
jusqu'au cul, mesmes les petites femmes, que l'on devroit faire
scrupule de les toucher, pour beaucoup d'ordes et salles raisons
que je n'oserois dire: car on diroit que, les deux rivieres
s'assemblant et se touchant quasi ensemble, il est en danger
de laisser l'une et naviger à l'autre, ce qui est par trop vilain.

I have heard Lady de Chalandray, (known as the fair Torcy)[308] relate that when attired and dressed Queen Eleanor of Austria, her mistress,[309] seemed a very lovely princess,[310] and there are indeed still many alive who saw her at our court to be so, of tall, well-built figure, moreover, but when undressed she was seen to have the trunk of a giantess, so long and so big was her body, yet, going lower, she seemed quite a dwarf, so short were her thighs and legs compared with her trunk.

Of another great lady I have heard it said that she was quite the contrary, for she was quite a dwarf in her body, so short and slight was she, yet otherwise down below, she was a giantess or colossus, so sturdy and lanky and bowed were her legs, though well fashioned and fleshed, that if he were small she could quite easily have concealed a man under her, like netting when hunting.

Il y a force marys et amis parmy nos chrestiens qui, voulans en tout differer des Turcs, qui ne prennent plaisir d'arregarder le cas des dames, d'autant, disent-ils, comme je viens de dire, qu'ils n'ont nulle forme; nos chrestiens au contraire, qui en ont, disent-ils, de grands contentemens à les contempler fort et se delecter en telles visions, et non-seulement se plaisent à les voir, mais à les baiser, comme beaucoup de dames l'ont dit et descourvert à leurs amants; ainsi que dit une dame espagnole à son serviteur, qui, la saluant un jour, luy dit: Bezo las manos y los pies, señora; *elle luy dit:* Señor, en el medio esta la mejor stacion; *comme voulant dire qu'il pouvoit baiser le mitan aussi bien que les pieds et mains. Et, pour ce, disent aucunes dames, que leurs marys et serviteurs y prennent quelque delicatesse et plaisir, et en ardent davantage: ainsi que j'ay ouy dire d'un tres-grand prince, fils d'un grand roy de par le monde, qui avoit pour maistresse une tres-grande princesse. Jamais il ne la touchoit qu'il ne luy vist cela et ne le baisast plusieurs fois. Et la premiere fois qu'il le fit, ce fut par la persuasion d'une tres-grande dame, favorite de roy, laquelle, tous trois un jour estans ensemble, ainsi que ce prince muguettoit sa dame, luy demanda s'il n'avoit jamais veu cette belle partie dont il jouissoit. Il respondit que non: 'Vous n'avez donc rien fait, dist-elle, et ne sçavez ce que vous aymez; vostre*

plaisir est imparfait, il faut que vous le voyez.' Parquoy, ainsi
qu'il s'en vouloit essayer et qu'elle en faisoit de la revesche,
l'autre vint par derriere, et la prit et renversa sur un lict, et
la tint tousjours justques à ce que le prince l'eust contemplée à
son aise et baisée son saoul, tant qu'il le trouvoit beau et gentil;
et, pour ce, continua tousjours.

There are other women who have such poorly proportioned
thighs, so poorly outcurved, with so little oval about them
that they do not deserve at all to be looked at and desired, any
more than their legs do, being just the same, some of them
indeed so fat that you would think the calf was a rabbit doe's
belly in young. Others have them so frail and slight and so
gawky that you might take them for musicians' pipes rather
than thighs and legs. The rest I leave to your imagination.

They are not at all like one lovely and estimable lady, of
whom I have heard talk, who was in good condition, and not
over-fat, either (for in all things there is a golden mean), who
after letting her lover sleep with her, asked him the next morning how he felt. He replied that he felt very fit, and her good,
plump flesh had done him good. 'At least,' said she, 'you've
ridden your stage without needing any padding on the saddle.'

D'autres dames y a-il qui ont tant d'autres vices cachez, ainsi
que j'en ay ouy parler d'une qui estoit dame de reputation, qui
faisoit ses affaires fecales par le devant; et de ce j'en demanday
la raison à un suffisant medecin, qui me dit: parce qu'elle
avoit esté percée trop jeune et d'un homme trop fourny et
robuste; dont ce fut grand dommage, car c'estoit une tres-belle
femme et veufve, qu'un honneste gentilhomme que je sçay la
vouloit espouser; mais, en sçachant tel vice, la quitta soudain,
et aprés un autre la prit aussitost.

J'ay ouy parler d'un gallant gentilhomme qui avoit une des
belles femmes de la court et n'en faisoit cas. Un autre, n'estant
si scrupuleux que luy, habitant avec elle, trouva que son cas
puoit si fort qu'on ne pouvoit endurer cette senteur; et, par
ainsi, cogneut l'encloueure du mary.

J'ay ouy parler d'une autre, laquelle estant l'une des filles
d'une grande princesse,[311] *qui petoit de son devant: des mede-*
cins m'ont dit que cela se pouvoit faire à cause des vents et

*ventositez qui peuvent sortir par là, et mesmes quand elles
font la fricarelle. Cette fille estoit avec cette princesse lorsqu'elle
vint à Moulins, la cour y estant, du temps du roy Charles
IX,*[312] *qui en fut abreuvé, dont on en rioit bien.*

There are others unable to retain their urine, and they always have to have a little sponge between their legs, like two
I knew, who were more than mere ladies, too, one of whom,
when a girl, let it go where everybody saw it in the ballroom.
This was during Charles IX's time, and it shocked him greatly.

Of another great lady I have heard that when one did it to
her she pissed herself right and proper, either during the act
or after it, like a mare when mounted. They ought to have
pitched a bucket of water over her to restrain her, as people
do mares.

There are many others who are constantly in period, and
others who are corrupted, spotted, marred and marked, either
by the syphilis they have caught from husband or lover or
by their own bad ways and humours, like those who have
wolfine legs and discharges and other markings which they
bear on their person as a result of the impressions their mothers
had when pregnant with them, as one of whom I once heard,
half of whose body was quite red the other not, so she looked
like a city sheriff.

Other women are so subject to their menstrual flow that
almost without exception their nature streams out as if from
a freshly slaughtered sheep's throat, not a great consolation to
husband or lover, because of the way Venus requires frequent
usage, and if such women are clear and free from it for one
week in the month, and that is all, this loses them a good part
of the year, since out of twelve months they have not five or
six clear, even less. Much like our banded soldiery, who are
made to lose more than four out of twelve months in the year
by the commissaries and treasurers who have them parade only
fourteen or fifteen days a month, so that their twelve months'
service boils down annually to less than eight months. That is
the position in which the husbands and lovers of such wives
have or who served them would find themselves, unless, driven
to it, to assuage their lust, they choose to soil themselves in a

beastly way, without any regard for the disgrace of it, and the children which arise from such unions are poor and bear the marks of it.

If I choose to tell of yet others, I should never be finished, moreover, my essays would thereby be made too dirty and displeasing, though what I said or might say would not be of lesser, common women, but of great and medium ladies, whose lovely faces though not what they conceal are fatal to society.

Si feray-je encor ce petit compte, qui est plaisant, d'un gentilhomme qu'il me le fit, qui est qu'en couchant avec une fort belle dame, et d'estoffe, en faisant sa besogne il luy trouva en cette partie quelques poils si piquants et si aigus qu'avec toutes les incommoditez il la put achever, tant cela le piquoit et le fiçonnoit. Enfin, ayant fait, il voulut taster avec la main: il trouva qu'alentour de sa motte il y avoit une demie douzaine de certains fils garnis de ces poils si aigus, longs, roides et picquants, qu'ils en eussent servy aux cordonniers à faire des rivets comme de ceux de pourceaux, et les voulut voir; ce que la dame luy permit avec grande difficulté; et trouva que tels fils entournoient la piece ny plus ny moins que vous voyez une medaille entournée de quelques diamants et rubis, pour servir et mettre en enseigne en un chappeau ou au bonnet.

Il n'y a pas long temps qu'en une certaine contrée de Guyenne, une damoiselle mariée, de fort bon lieu et bonne part, ainsi qu'elle advisoit estudier ses enfants, leur precepteur, par une certaine manie et frenesie, ou, possible, pour rage d'amour qui luy vint soudain, il prit une espée qui estoit de son mary sur le lict, et luy en donna si bien qu'il lui perça les deux cuisses et les deux labies de sa natures de part en part; dont depuis elle en cuida mourir, sans le secours d'un bon chirurgien. Son cas pouvoit bien dire qu'il avoit esté en deux diverses guerres et attacqué fort diversement. Je croy que la veue amprés n'en estoit guieres plaisante, pour estre ainsi ballafrée et ses aisles ainsi brisées: je les dis aisles, parce que les Grecs appelent ces labies himenea*; les Latins les nommenf* alæ*, et les François labies, levres, landrons, landilles et autres mots; mais je trouve qu'à bon droit les Latins les appellent aisles: car il n'y a animal ny oyseau, soit-il faucon, niais ou sot,*

comme celuy de nos fillaudes, soil-il de passage, ou hagard,
ou bien dressé, de nos femmes mariées ou veufves, qui aille
mieux ny ait l'aisle si viste.

Je le puis appeller aussi animal avecque Rabelais,[313] d'autant
qu'il s'esmeut de soy-mesme; et, soit à le toucher ou à le voir,
on le sent et le void s'esmouvoir et remuer de luy-mesme,
quand il est en appetit.

Some women, from fear of chills and catarrhs cover their
heads with kerchiefs in bed, God wot, more than witches, but
otherwise, well dressed, they are as appetising as little dolls,
while others are made up and painted like pictures, lovely in
daylight, but with paint that comes off in the night, when they
are very ugly.

One should inspect such ladies before loving them or marrying or having one's pleasure of them, as Octavious Caesar did,
for together with his friends[314] he had some great Roman ladies
and matrons stripped and examined them from one end to the
other, as if they were nubile virgins, or slave-girls on sale by
a certain pimp named Torana who dealt in them, and as and
when Octavius found one to his taste and requirement, and
not damaged goods, he had his pleasure of her.

The Turks do the same in their *bezistan* [market] in Constantinople and other large towns when purchasing slaves of
either sex.

Now I am saying no more about this, indeed, I think I have
said too much, but you see how deceived we are about many
things we see and think lovely. But though we are deluded by
some ladies, we are also just as much edified and contented by
some others, who are lovely and so clean, so trim, so fresh, so
cream-curdy, so delightful and so delightfully plump, in a
word, so perfect in all parts of their bodies, that after them
all other sights in the world are feeble and vain, and there are
men who get so sunk in such contemplation that all they can
think of is getting to work, and hence it is that very often such
ladies are pleased to exhibit themselves without any trouble, so
they may not be supposed to be blemished, and just to make us
more tempted and lustful.

One day when we were at the siege of La Rochelle,[315] the

poor late Lord de Guise,[316] who did me the honour of liking me a lot, chose to show me a writing-block which he had just taken from the King's brother,[317] our general,[318] out of his breeches pocket. He said to me : 'The Prince just now was displeased with me and attacked me on account of the love of a lady, but I mean to have my revenge, see what I have put in here, read it.' Handing me the writing-block. I found these four lines written in his hand, which he had just composed, and he wrote out f—— in full too :

> *If you have not f—— me yet,*
> *The fault was never in me,*
> *You've had a good look at me stripped*
> *And I'm certainly something to see.*

Then he told me who the lady, or rather, the girl, was, which I had certainly wondered, and I told him I was most surprised that the Prince had not touched her and cohabited with her, the more so since they had both got so near it and the rumour of it was all over the place, but he assured me he had done nothing and it had been his fault only. I replied : 'Then the Prince must either have been tired and worn himself out somewhere else, to be able to do nothing, or else was so thrilled by the sight of such beauty naked that doing anything never even occurred to him.' 'Maybe,' replied de Guise, 'he could have done something, but there's how it is, he just did not, and I have been taunting him about it, and mean to put the writing-block back in his pocket, which of course he will find and then read what he ought to know, and that will be my revenge.' Which he did and not without having a good laugh after, both of us, in fact, and thus teasing the Prince delightfully, for at the time there was very great friendship and intimacy between those two, though it all changed so markedly later.[319]

A lady or rather girl of the great world who was much liked and was the intimate of a great princess,[320] who was one day taking a rest in bed, as was customary, when a noble[321] who was passionately in love with her, but who had nothing else to offer, came to see her. This lady-in-waiting, still unmarried, as I say, being so much beloved of and so intimate with her mistress as she was, what did she suddenly do but go up to her, without giving a hint of what she proposed to do, and all at once stripped the coverlet off her, so that the noble, whose eyes were active enough, flashed his glance on her at once and saw everything, and told me about it afterwards, saying that it was the loveliest sight he had ever seen and he would never see anything so beautiful as that naked body, its lovely parts and all that white, magnificent, with flesh so pretty, that he thought he was seeing the beauties of paradise. But this hardly lasted an instant, for the lady snatched at the coverlet at once, as the girl had made good her escape but the more she strove to cover herself, the more did she reveal, which in no way spoiled the sight or the pleasure of the noble, who was in no hurry to cover her up. And very silly that would have been too. However, in the end she did cover herself, grumbling rather charmingly about the girl, telling her she would pay her out for this. From a little distance the girl then said : 'Madame, you played one on me, forgive me if I have now played one on you,' and then, being near the door, slipped away. But they made it up at once.

However, this noble felt so cheered by what he had seen, and was so ecstatic with pleasure and contentment that I heard him say a hundred times that he desired no more in his life than to live in thought of that simple sight, and indeed he was right, for by thus showing her incomparable countenance and that lovely bosom with which she had so fed society, she was able to make clear enough that underneath she had concealed the most exquisite thing of all, and he did tell me that among her lovely points she was a lady with the loveliest long flanks he had ever seen, which is quite feasible, for she was very lavishly built and among her fine points her thighs may well have been so shaped, neither more or less than frontier fortresses.

After this noble had told me this, I could not say aught else but : 'Then live, my dear friend, live with divine contemplation and such beatitude that you may never die; and may I myself at least have such a sight before my death !'

The noble in question for ever felt grateful to this girl and ever after had great respect for her and loved her with all his heart, and so became her most loyal attendant. Yet it was not him that she married, for another who was richer than he was bore her off, for it is the way with everybody to run after worldly things.

Such sights as this noble had are lovely and pleasing. But one should take care lest they do one harm, as the sight of fair Diana did poor Actaeon,[322] or as another woman I know of did harm.

In his time a famous King dearly loved a very lovely, estimable and great lady who was widowed.[323] He was so badly in love that people said she had bewitched him,[324] for he took so little heed of other women, even his own wife, save at rare intervals, for this particular lady persistently garnered all the finest flowers of his garden. This vexed the Queen[325] very much, since she felt she was as lovely and as great and as good for loving and as worthy of having just such tasty morsels from him, so was most astonished by his behaviour, to such a point that one day she poured forth her woes to one of her favourite great ladies,[326] and plotted with her to find out if there was any real reason for this—in short, plotted to spy out the game that her husband and this lady played. So she had a number of holes bored through the floor above the bedroom of this lady, to see it all, and discover what sort of behaviour these two got up to together. But she and her companion saw nothing but very fine things, for what they beheld was a woman, very lovely, white, delicate and very fresh, half in a shift, half naked, caressing her lover and cosseting him with very subtle inventions, and he doing the same to her, till they left the bed and lay down as they were, in their shifts, on the pile rug which they had beside the bed and took their fun there, so as to avoid the heat of the bed and get more fresh air, for this was in the hottest season of the year—and I knew a very great prince who took his pleasure with his wife, who was the loveliest woman in the world, in like fashion to avoid, as he himself said, the stuffiness which came from the great Summer heats.

Well, once she had seen and taken note of everything, this princess began to weep and groan, sigh and grow melancholy, because she felt, and said so too, that her husband did not give her anything like this and never did the wild things with her which she had now seen him do with the other.

The other lady, her companion, tried to console her and reproved her for getting so melancholy, or rather, reminded her that it was she herself had chosen to see these things and they at least ought not make her lose hope.

All the Queen could reply was : 'Alas, yes, I did want to see it, and I should not have wanted to, because the sight hurts me.' Nevertheless, the fact remains that after being consoled she became more resolute, till she ceased altogether to care, but instead to the best of her ability continued with her pastime of watching, and turned it into a joke—or perhaps into something else.

I have heard tell of a great lady of renown—I repeat, a very great lady indeed—who was not satisfied with her natural store of desire—and she was a great whore indeed, married, but now widowed, and very lovely but, who, to stir herself up and excite herself more would have her ladies and girls strip naked, I mean, the loveliest of them,[327] then would slap their bottoms with a loud clapping noise, hitting them quite hard too, while any girls who did anything wrong she beat with short canes, when it was her pleasure to see them writhe and twist and twitch their bodies and their buttocks which, as they received the blows, they stuck out most strangely and delectably.

At other times, without stripping them, she made them pull up their skirts (for at this time drawers were not worn) and slapped and whipped their buttocks according to the cause they gave her, and whether she wanted to make them laugh or cry. And with such sights and peepshows she used so to sharpen up her own appetite that afterwards she often went on to have the girls copulate in front of her in all reality with some very strong, robust gallant.

What a feminine whim that was ! She went so far with it that it is said that when once through her castle window out in the street she saw a tall cobbler of remarkable proportions pissing against the castle wall, she coveted his so fine, stalwart proportions and from fear of losing the effect of her sudden desire at once sent a page out to summon the man to a covert alley in her gardens where she at once went herself and there prostituted herself to him so violently that she became pregnant. That is how peepshowing served that lady.

What is more, I have heard it said that as well as her own women and girls, those, that is, of her suite, whenever they came to see her, she would quickly, in only two or three days, train strange women to the game, first with her own women, in front of the strangers, showing them how to do it, then they following suit, and some were amazed by these antics, others not. I must say those were fine goings on!

I have heard tell of a great man who in the same way found pleasure in seeing his wife in that position, naked or dressed, and beating her with the flat of his hand to watch her wriggle her bottom.

I have heard tell of an estimable lady who when a girl was every day twice whipped by her mother, not for doing anything wrong at all, but merely because it was the mother's idea that she found pleasure in thus seeing her daughter wriggle her thighs and her bottom, thereby herself gaining appetite in another part, and as the girl drew on to the age of fourteen, she persisted with such fierceness that in the end she watched her even more than earlier.

I have I must say heard worse of a great prince, more than eighty years since, that before he went to cohabit with his wife he used to have himself beaten, since he could not get excited or get his limp nature to stand without that stupid remedy. Now, I would much like a good physician to tell me the reason for that.

That great person, Picus Mirandula, related[328] having seen a gallant in his day who the more he was leathered with great stripes with saddle straps, the more on heat for a woman did he come, and was never so keen on women as he was after thus being leathered, for then he was wild with it. Now those are frightful human foibles. Looking at others is at least more pleasant than this last.

When I was in Milan[329] one day I was told the story in a good quarter of how the late Marquis de Pescayre, who died recently as Viceroy of Sicily,[330] fell greatly in love with a very lovely lady, so that one morning, thinking her husband had gone out, he went to see her and found her still in bed and, while talking with her, got no more from her than seeing her and contemplating her at his ease under the linen and fondling her with his hand. While he was at this game, in came the husband, a man who was not the Marquis's match in anything, and came in so suddenly too, surprising them, that the Marquis had not time to get his glove out, and it got lost, I don't quite know how, between the sheets, as often happens.[331] After this, with a few words to the husband, he left the room, the noble seeing him out. Then, when the husband had returned, he happened to find the marquis's glove lost in the sheets, which the lady simply had not noticed. He took it, crumpled it up, scowled at his wife, and for a long time after would neither sleep with her or touch her, till one day, alone in her chamber, she put hand to pen and wrote the following quatrain :

> *Vigna era, vigna son,*
> *Era podata, or piè non son;*
> *E non so perqual cagion*
> *Non mi poda il mio patron.*

'A vine I was, a vine I am
Once well hoed, now no more,
And I don't know why my vineron
Doesn't hoe me as he did before.'

She had just left this quatrain, written out, on the table, when her husband came in, saw the lines, took the pen and wrote this reply :

> *Vigna eri, vigna sei,*
> *Eri podata, e più non sei.*
> *Per la granja del leon,*
> *Non ti poda il tuo patron.*

'A vine you were, a vine still are
Once well hoed and now no more,
But if you let a lion scratch,
Your vineron won't hoe.'

This he in turn left on the table. Both quatrains were then taken to the marquis who replied :

> *A la vigna che voi dite*
> *Io fui, e qui restai;*
> *Alzai il pampano; guardai la vite;*
> *Ma, se Dio m'ajuti, non toccai.*
> 'As to this vine you talk about
> I went to peep at it 'tis true,
> I raised the haulm to see the grapes
> But by God never did use my hoe.'

This was taken to the husband, who, satisfied and pleased with so honourable a reply and such just satisfaction, took his vine and hoed it again as much as he had ever done, and never were husband and wife better off.

Of course, the lion's scratching referred to that glove, which he found lost between the sheets.

Now there you have another good husband who did not take too great offence and, once his suspicions were allayed, forthwith forgave his wife. There are indeed ladies who so delight in themselves that they look at themselves and contemplate themselves naked till they get quite ravished, seeing how lovely they are, just like Narcissus. So what are we men then to do when we see them and observe them?

Marianna, Herod's wife, a lovely, estimable lady, when one day her husband wanted to lie with her at full noon and see all she had properly, refused him flat, Josephus[332] tells us. He did not resort to his powers as husband, like a great prince whom I knew, with regard to his wife, who was a lovely lady, for when that man attacked her in broad daylight, although she vigorously refused him, he simply stripped her naked. Afterwards, he sent her women in to her to dress her, and they found her weeping and terribly ashamed.

There are other ladies who deliberately do not greatly scruple to reveal all their beauties freely and strip naked the better to work up and stove their gentlemen and to attract them more powerfully, though for some time they will not allow them that touch which is most valued, for they do not like to halt when on the right good road, but go the whole hog, as I have heard of several ladies who thus kept their gentlemen fed on such lovely views alone.

Very fortunate are those men who can hold their patience and not get too badly sunk in temptation, though the man must be very bewitched by virtue indeed whose eyes are not dazzled by the sight of a lovely woman. As Alexander was wont to say to his friends, the girls of Persia did great damage to the eyes of any men who saw them, so when he held Darius's daughters prisoner he never greeted them except through half-veiled eyes and even so looked at them as little as he could, lest he be too much taken by their outstanding beauty.[333]

Not only in those times, but today too, among all the women of the Orient the Persians are praised and prized as being the loveliest and most perfect in bodily proportions and natural beauty and the most charming and featly in clothing and footwear, even, above all, more than those of the ancient and royal city of Shiraz,[334] who are so much praised for their beauties, whitenesses and charming graces and lovely manner, that the Moors, in an ancient popular saying, say that their prophet Mohammed would never go to Shiraz from fear lest he ever cast eyes on those lovely women and after his death his soul never came to Paradise. Those men who have been there and have written about them[335] tell this story, which merely goes to show the hypocritical play-acting of that fine rake and rascally prophet, as if it were not to be found, as Belon remarks, in an Arabic work entitled : *Concerning the good customs of Mohammed*,[336] which, praising him for his bodily powers, says that he boasted of making it a rule to cover all his eleven wives in one hour, one after the other. To hell with the rascal ! Not another word about him ! After all, it is time wasted for me to speak of him.

I have seen the question debated regarding that characteristic of Alexander's I have just mentioned, and Scipio the African, as to which of the two was most praiseworthy for his continence.

Mistrustful of the staunchness of his own chastity, Alexander refused to see the lovely ladies of Persia at all. Scipio, after the capture of the new Cathage,[337] did see the lovely Spanish girl whom his soldiers brought to him, and offered him as his share of the booty, and she was so outstanding in beauty and at such a lovely age that wherever she went she dazzled and fired the eyes of all the men who saw her, including Scipio, who, saluting her most courteously, enquired from which town of Spain she came and asked about her parents. Among other things he was told that she had been betrothed to a young man named Alucius, Prince of the Celtiberians, whereupon without touching her at all, Scipio handed her to that person together with her father and mother, whereby he obliged the lady, her parents and the fiancé so greatly that they subsequently became most devoted to the city of Rome and its Republic.[338] Yet who knows if at heart that lovely lady had not also some desire to be a little meddled with and pricked first by Scipio —yes, I repeat, by him, who was handsome and young too, a fine, valiant and victorious young fellow? It may be that had some intimate friend, man or woman, of his asked her in good faith and trust if she would not have wished it—well, I leave it to you what her reply would have been, whether she would not have made some little facial gesture as much as to say yes, she would have liked it—indeed, if you like, I wonder if her Spanish climate and western sun had not been such as to make her, (and many other ladies of today in that land too who are lovely and like her) hot and eager for it, as I have seen many of them to be. No, one should have no doubts but that had that lovely, estimable girl been solicited and sought after by handsome young Scipio, she would have taken him at his word, or rather, on the altar of his profane gods.

In this matter I know, Scipio has been praised by some men for his great gift of continence, yet others have blamed him, for towards a lovely, estimable lady how else can a fine, valorous cavalier show the warmth of his heart but by showing her what effect her beauty has had on him and how much he loves her, without any of those chill, respectful modesties and discretions which I have heard many cavaliers and many

195

ladies call rather follies and faintheartedness than virtues? No, it is not such continence that in her heart of hearts any lovely, estimable lady loves, but good enjoyment of love-making, steadily, discreetly and secretly accomplished. In a word, as one day an estimable lady said when she was reading this story, however fine and warm-hearted a captain he may have been, Scipio was a fool, to go and put responsibilities on folk to be loyal to him and to the Roman cause by such silly means, when he could have achieved the same in some more suitable way, and especially seeing that this girl was war booty, of which more than of any other thing he should have one's triumph.

The great founder of his city did not do so with the one he took for himself when the lovely Sabine ladies were ravished, but had his good pleasure with her without any scruple, which she found very gratifying and was scarcely worried at all, neither she nor her girl friends, who at once made their peace with their husbands and ravishers and were not at all rigid about it, as their fathers and mothers were, who stirred up a great war over it all.

True, there are men and men and women and women who absolutely reject making acquaintance in this way, though all women are not like the wife of King Ortiagon, one of the Gaulish kings of Asia Minor, who was lovely to perfection and when she was captured by a Roman centurion in the rout of the Gaulish forces, and her honour was assailed, showed herself firm to him, having a horror of prostituting herself to him, a person so vile and so low, whereupon he took her by force, violently, seeing that the fortunes and chance of war had delivered her in his hands with rights over her as a slave. But of this he soon repented, and she had her vengeance, for, when she had promised him a large ransome for her liberty and they had both gone to the appointed place to get the money, just as he was counting the money she had him killed and then took the head to her husband, to whom she freely confessed that this man had actually violated her, but added that she had had her vengeance in this way, which her husband approved of, and honoured her greatly. And ever after, history tells us,[339] she preserved her honour to the last day of her life, with holiness and gravity, but after all, she did have one good morsel, though it came from a man of no substance.

Lucrece did not do the same, for though she was sought by a fine king, she tasted nothing at all, in which she was doubly silly, not to comply with his wishes on the spot, but to commit suicide for so little.

To go back to Scipio again, he was still unaware that it is for booty and pillage that war is waged, for, from what I have from one of our great captains, there is no better meat for the purpose than a woman captured in war, and he made fun of some of his comrades who in the storming and capture of cities, and even in other circumstances and encounters, put women's honour above all other things, for the women always prefer soldiers to any other men, for the very roughness of men of arms conduces to greater lust, and indeed there is nothing to gainsay here, for after all, they do have their pleasure from it, when taken thus by force, while the honour of their husbands is in no wise impaired, so that in truth they are very well favoured. And, what is more, they save the goods and the lives too of their husbands, as did fair Eunoe,[340] the spouse of Bogud or Bocchus, King of Mauretania, for whom Caesar did her husband great service, not so much, it is to be believed, because she actually pleaded his cause at all, as Juba, King of Bithynia, did Pompaea's, but just because she was such a lovely woman and Caesar had sweet enjoyment from his cohabitation with her.

There are many other advantages of such loves that I omit, and besides, as this great captain said, his other great comrades like him, who take an interest in the customs and rules of war, stipulate observation of the honour of womenfolk from whom one should first of all secretly and in confidence ascertain their opinion, and only then decide, or of course they may be men of Scipio's character, who could not refrain from being a dog in the manger and preventing others eating what he did not want, as he did in the case of poor Massinissa who had so often risked his life for him and the Romans, and laboured, sweated and toiled so much to win him glory and victory, yet refused him this privilege and took from him fair

197

Queen Sophonisba, whom he had captured and chose as his principal, most valued booty, and would have had her taken away from him to send her to Rome to live out the rest of her days as a wretched slave, had Massinissa not remedied it.[341] Scipio's fame would really have been all the finer and greater, had Sophonisba taken part in the triumph as a glorious, superb Queen, now wife of Massinissa, for as they saw her pass people would have said : 'There goes a lovely result of Scipio's conquest,' for there is more glory implicit in grand and lofty things than in low.

To conclude, in all this matter under discussion, Scipio committed great mistakes, indeed, in every way showed himself to be either misogynist or one completely unable to satisfy a woman, although it is indeed said that in his old age he turned to making love with one of his wife's serving women[342] which she bore with very patiently for the reasons which might be adduced.

Now, to get out of the digression I have been making and back to the main road from which I have strayed, as conclusion to this essay I would observe that there is nothing in the world so fine to see and behold as a lovely woman, whether sumptuously dressed or daintily undressed and on her back, but all provided she is healthy and clean, without blemish, without any sore or mallander, as I said before.

King Francis[343] used to say that however grand a noble was, he could not better receive any prince, however great, in his house or castle, than by offering as first sight for his eye, first thing on arrival, a lovely wife, a good horse and a fine greyhound, for then, casting his eyes first on one, then the other, then the third, they could not possibly fail to be charmed by the house, for the King considered those three lovely things to be all pleasing to see and admire and the practice of them very pleasant.

Queen Isabel of Castile used to say that she found very great satisfaction in seeing four things : *Hombre d'armas en campo, obisbo puesto en pontifical, linda dama en la cama, y ladron en la horca:* 'A man of arms in the field, a bishop in his robes, a lovely lady in bed, and a thief on the gallows.'

I have heard the late Lord Cardinal of Lorraine, recently deceased,[344] tell that when he was on his way to meet Pope Paul
IV in Rome, to break the truce made with the Emperor,[345] he
went to Venice, where he was received with great honours.[346]
This one need not doubt at all, seeing that he was a great
favourite of a great king. All the great and magnificent Senators of Venice came out to meet him and as they passed along
the Grand Canal, with all the windows of the houses lined
with all the women of the city, and most lovely ones too, all
come there to behold this triumphal entry, one of the greatest
of the lords of Venice was engaging him very eloquently on
affairs of state, but, noticing that his eyes were fixed on those
lovely ladies, suddenly said, in his Venetian dialect : 'My lord,
I fear you are not paying attention to me, and you are quite
right too, for there is far more pleasure and entertainment in
seeing these lovely ladies at these windows and being ravished
by them than in hearing the chatter of an annoying old man
like myself, even though he was talking about a certain great
victory gained by yourself.' But the Lord Cardinal, who was
not lacking in wit or memory, at once repeated word for word
all the Senator had said, which left that worthy veteran very
pleased with him, and greatly admiring him, too, for not having missed or forgotten anything of what he had said, for all
the distraction of seeing those lovely women.

Any man who had seen the court of our Kings François and
Henry II and other kings their sons, whoever he be and even
if he had seen the whole world, would be sure to have said
he had never seen anything so lovely as our ladies who were
at the court, all our Queens the consorts, the mothers and
sisters of our Kings, but somebody remarked, would have seen
something yet finer had the grandfather of Master Gonnin[347]
been alive, who by his inventions, illusions and magic and
sorcery could have displayed them all unclothed and naked,
as it is said he once did at a private party which King François had ordered of him, for Gonnin's grandfather was a man
very expert and subtle in his craft[348]—his grandson, as we have
seen, was not a patch on him.

I think such a sight would have been as delightful as in

ancient times was that of the Egyptian ladies of Alexandria, at the reception and assembly given for their great god Apis, before whom they gravely paraded, raising up their gowns, their petticoats and their undergarments as high as ever they could and straddling and stretching out their legs as much as they could, completely revealing their privy parts, after which these were never seen again. As you may imagine, they counted on being liberally paid for that peepshow. Who cares to see the story, let him read of Alexander ab Alexandro, the sixth book of the *Merry Days*.[349] I think that was a very delightful show, for at the time all the ladies of Alexandria were lovely, as indeed they still are today.

If the old and ugly women did the same, avoid it, for sight should never be expended save on what is lovely, one should avoid the ugly as much as one can.

In Switzerland men and women all pile into the steam-baths and cold dips together, without thereby doing anything unseemly, they merely holding a piece of linen in front of them,[350] and if this is rather loose one can get quite a glimpse of things delightful and otherwise, according to whether they are handsome or ugly.

Before ending this essay, I will add the following word: What temptations and what refreshment for the eyes the young princes, cavaliers, nobles, plebs and other Romans could enjoy in times gone by on the day of celebration of the festival of Flora in Rome. Of Flora it is said that she was the most charming and most triumphant courtesan that ever plied the trade of whore in Rome or any other place, and what was most in her favour in it was that she came of good family and great lineage, and for such purposes ladies of this sort of good blood are certainly more pleasing and relations with them are better than with others.

Further, this lady, Flora, was superior to Lais, and finer, for she prostituted herself to the common herd, but Flora to the great, hence on her doorplate she had the words: *'Kings, princes, dictators, consuls, censors, pontiffs, questors, ambassadors and other great lords received, no admission to others.'*[351]

Lais always insisted on being paid in advance, but not so

Flora, who said that she treated the great as she did so that they, as great illustrious persons, would treat her the same, and also said that a woman of great loveliness and high lineage should always be taken at her own price, hence accepted only what was given her, saying that any lady of sensitivity should make her lovers happy for love's sake, not for avarice, as everything had its price, except love.

To wind up, in her time she made love with such charm and gave herself so grandly that sometimes when she left her house to walk in the city it was enough for tongues to wag for a month, about her beauty, her lovely rich jewellery, her sumptuous style, her wonderful charm and also about the great suite of courtiers and gentlemen in attendance on her and the great princes with her, following her, accompanying her like so many slaves, all of which she put up with most patiently, while foreign ambassadors returning home all told more tales about the loveliness and the outstanding qualities of the lovely Flora than of the greatness of the Republic of Rome, speaking above all of her great liberality, in which she was so different to most such ladies. But then, Flora was out of the ordinary, being noble.

In the end she died so rich and so opulent that the value of her money, furniture and jewels was sufficient to rebuild the walls of Rome, and also free the Republic of debt. She made the people of Rome her principal heir and for this was honoured in that city by a very sumptuous temple which was named Florian,[352] from Flora.

The first feast that the Emperor Galba[353] ever observed was that of amorous Flora, at which feast Romans, men and women alike, were allowed to commit every debauch, impropriety, lewdness and excess they chose, and on that day it was the woman who behaved most loosely, improperly and outrageously who was considered the most holy and the most gallant.

You may imagine that there was no *fiscaigne*, (the dance which the chamber-maids and Moorish slaves dance on Sundays on Malta in the open in front of everybody,) nor any *saraband* which could touch it, and the women dancers never left out a single possible movement or contortion that was lascivious or gesture that was lewd, and the more dissolute and uncontrolled the act any lady could contrive, the more gallant she was, as in Rome it was held that anybody who went to the temple of that goddess in dress or with gestures and style that were highly lascivious and lewd, must have the same charm and be as opulent in worldly goods as Flora was.

There indeed were fine opinions and a fine thing the observance of that festival was! But these were pagans. And we need have no illusions about it, they forgot no kind of lasciviousness and those good ladies studied the lessons they had learned so painstakingly beforehand, exactly as ours study the ballet, and so they were all well trained for it. The young men and the old ones too vied with one another to see and to watch those lascivious antics, and indeed were such shows to be given among us today, people would take advantage of them in every way, and to be at such sights people would risk their death in the crowds.

There is food enough for thought, and I leave it to worthy gallants to ponder well. Let them read Suetonius, Pausanias the Greek and Manillus the Latin[354] and consult the books these men wrote about famous and amorous ladies and they will see it all.

Just the following story, then no more.

One reads that the Lacedemonians once went to lay siege to Mycaenae, whereupon the Mycaenians forestalled them, making a sally against them all, when they pulled out and hurried on to Lacedemonia, thinking to take it by surprise and pillage it while the Lacedemonians were having their fun outside their city, but they were valorously repelled and chased away by the Lacedemonian women, who had remained behind, hearing which, the Lacedemonians made their way back straight for their city. From afar off, however, sighting their womenfolk, all under arms, after having given chase to the enemy, they were quite alarmed, but the women recognized them at once and proceeded to tell how they had fared, whereupon the men in their delight at once fell to kissing them, embracing and caressing them; till losing all sense of shame, and without even the patience to take off their weapons, neither the men nor the women, they made love valiantly just wherever they happened to meet, and there were all sorts of strange sounds to be heard, plus a most pleasant din of clanking weapons and armour, in remembrance of all of which they built a temple with a statue of the goddess Venus which they called *Venus Under Arms*, in distinction from all other statues of her, which depict her stark naked. There was a pleasant cohabitation for you, and a very fine idea too, erecting an armed Venus and calling her by that name.[355]

Often in armies, for instance at the taking of cities by assault, one sees many soldiers taking their pleasure of the women fully armed, not having the time or the patience to take off their armament before assuaging their frenzy and appetite, so tempted are they, but to see an armed soldier cohabiting with his own wife also armed, now that is a rare sight! One can just imagine the pleasure likely to ensue therefrom, and indeed what greater satisfaction could there be in that lovely mystery, either in the doing or the observance of it, as also in that clattering of their weapons. It stirs one's imagination to think of all that might arise from it, both for the principal actors and any others near at hand who happen to see.

But that now really is enough. Let us conclude. I could easily have extended this essay with several examples, had I not been apprehensive of getting a bad name for being too lewd.

Nevertheless, having so greatly praised the lovely race of women, I must just tell the tale of a Spaniard who had a grudge against a woman and painted her one day as she deserved, by saying : *Señor, vieja es como la lampada azeitunada d'Iglesia, y de hechura del armario, large y desvayada, el color y gesto como mascara mal pintada, el talle como una campana o mola de molino, la vista como idolo del tampo antiguo, el andary vision d'una antigua fantasma de la noche, que tanto tuviese encontrarla de noche, como ver una mandragora. Jesus! Jesus! Dios me libre de su mal encuentro! No se contenta de tener en su casa por huesped al provisor del obisbo, ni se contenta con la demasiada conversacion del vicario ni del guardian, ni de la amistad antigua del dean, sino que agora de*

*nuevo ha tomado al que pide para las animas del purgatorio,
para acabar su negra vida.* 'Look at her, she is like an old, greasy
church lamp, in shape and style she is shapeless, badly built
like a big cupboard; her colour and appearance like a badly
painted mask; her figure like a church-tower or a windmill;
the face like that of an ancient idol; walk, gait and glance like
a nocturnal phantom of the ancient world; so that I would be
as afraid to meet her by night as I would to see a mandrake.
Jesus! Jesus! God preserve me from such an encounter! She is
not satisfied with having with her as regular visitor the bishop's
vicar-general, she is not satisfied with the excessive chatter of
the curate, or the persistent visits of the sexton, or the long-
standing friendship of the dean, now what does she do but
take up with the man who prays for souls in purgatory, just
to end her shabby life.'

That is how the Spanish puts it when it chooses to devalue
women, whereas, just as I said earlier in this essay,[356] the same
language describes the thirty fine points of a lady.

THIRD ESSAY

On the beauty of a lovely leg and the virtue there is in it

AMONG the many fine points which I have known to be praised on occasion among us courtiers as calculated to excite love, one notes that in a lovely lady a very lovely leg is much prized, a feature I have seen several ladies possess, and they were well aware of it too and sensitive to keeping them lovely. Among others, I have heard tell of one very great princess of renown whom I knew[357] who loved one of her ladies above all the others solely because she drew on her stockings so tight and so well arranged the calves and fitted her garters so neatly, better indeed than any other, so that the princess was most forthcoming towards her, even made her some handsome presents. But, with this eagerness of hers to keep her legs so lovely, one may well imagine it was not done to hide them under petticoat or skirt or gown, but to show them off at times with lovely drawers of cloth of gold or of silver or of other material, all very neatly and daintily made,[358] which she usually wore, for nobody finds such pleasure in themselves but wishes to have others enjoy the sight and so forth.

Moreover, this lady could not make the excuse that it was to please her husband, as most of them, even elderly women, will say when, in spite of being old, they dress themselves up so gaily and gaudily, for she was a widow. True, in her husband's time she had done the same, which was really why later, when she had lost him, she did not want to discontinue.

I have known many lovely, estimable ladies and girls equally eager to keep their lovely legs shapely and exquisite, and they

205

are all quite right to do so, for there is more lascivity in this than people realize.

I have heard tell of one very great lady, of the time of King François, very lovely, too, who when she broke a leg and it was set, thought it had been done right, but was twisted, and was so determined that she actually had it re-broken by the surgeon and set properly, as it had been before, to make her as lovely and erect as she had formerly been. There was one lady who was most astonished at this, but yet another lovely lady was heard to make this rejoinder very loudly : 'I see you just don't know all the amorous virtue there is in a lovely leg.'

I once knew a very lovely and estimable girl of high society who, when she fell deeply in love with a great prince, to draw him to her and secure a good time with him, had been constantly frustrated, when one day in an alley of the park, seeing him approaching, she pretended her garter had slipped down, so, stepping to one side a little, raised her leg and began drawing her stocking tight and adjusting the garter again. The great prince cast a keen eye on her and found she had a very lovely leg, and he was so entranced that that leg did more to him than her lovely face had ever done. He came to the conclusion that two such lovely pillars must sustain a very handsome building, and after that he did make her his mistress, when she did just what she wanted with him. Mark the ingenuity and the subtle manner of making love.

I have heard also of a lovely, estimable lady who was above all very clever, and of a charming, gracious temperament, too, who when one day she had her chamber-boy draw on her hose for her, asked him whether he was not aggrieved, tempted, made lustful by doing so. Thinking it the right thing to say because of the respect he owed her, the valet said he was not. Whereupon she upped with her hand and gave him a sound box on the ears. 'Away with you,' she said, 'I won't have you waiting on me any more, you are a fool, you're dismissed.'

There are today many girls' gentleman-servants who are not so continent when they assist their mistresses to rise, to dress and to draw on their hose, and there are also nobles who would have acted differently had they seen such a lovely sight.

It is not merely a modern fashion to value beauty in lovely legs and shapely feet (which are really one and the same thing,) for in the days of the Romans we read[359] that Lucius Vitellius, father of the Emperor Vitellius, when he was much in love with Messalina and wanted to find some way of being in her husband's good books, one day asked her to honour him with a favour. 'What would you like?' the Empress asked him. 'This, Madam,' he said, 'be so kind one day as to allow me to remove your shoes for you.' Always very gracious to her subjects, Messalina did not feel she could deny him that favour. But when he had taken them off, he kept one and he always carried it about thereafter next his skin, under his shirt, kissing it as often as he could, in this way worshipping the lovely foot of his lady by means of her shoe, since he could not dispose of the foot itself or of her lovely leg.

Then there is that English Lord in the *Hundred Tales* of the Queen of Navarre[360] who in a like manner carried his mistress's glove at his side, and was equally rewarded. I have known many a nobleman who before wearing a pair of silk stockings would beg a lady or mistress to try them on and wear them in their presence for eight or ten days, the longer the better, and then wore them themselves with great pride and satisfaction, both spiritual and bodily.

I knew a famous prince who, when at sea with a very great lady, one of the loveliest in the world[361] who was on a tour of her dominions, her women fell seasick, and were so little fit to wait on her, that he had the good fortune to have to put her to bed and get her up, but doing this, and drawing her hose on and off, fell so in love with her that he became quite heart-broken, especially as she was a kinswoman, for such temptation can indeed be excessive and there is no man who has so mortified his flesh as not to be stirred by it.

We read of Nero's wife,[362] Poppea Sabina, who was the favourite wife of this Emperor, that apart from being most lavish with all manner of gewgaws, ornaments, sumptuous trifles and costumery, she wore slippers and shoes of pure gold. That fastidiousness was not meant to conceal either her foot or her leg from her cuckold of a husband, Nero, but he was far from being the only one, he did not have all the pleasure and sight of them, there were many others.[363] But she might well be so fastidious about herself, seeing that she shod with silver the mares which drew her carraige.

St Jerome sternly reproved a lady of his time who was very fastidious about the beauty of her leg, in these words : 'By those dark little bootees of hers, so neatly drawn on and so gleaming, she serves as bait to young men, and the sound of her buckles is like bait to them.' You will realize that this refers to some sort of footwear common at the time which was too fanciful, little suitable for a lady of prudent taste. Footwear consisting in such bootees is indeed still in use today among the ladies of Turkey, including the greatest and the most chaste of them.

I have seen much discussion and enquiry as to which is the more attractive and tempting leg, the naked one, or a leg covered, with stocking on? Many believe that only the natural leg counts, particularly when this is well turned, to perfection, fitting the requirements which the Spanish lay down, as I have already quoted above, and the leg is nicely white, handsome, smooth-skinned, and suitably displayed in a fine bed. For otherwise, were a lady to choose to show it quite naked when walking or otherwise, even though with shoes on her feet and she were the most sumptuously dressed woman in the world, she would never be found really decent or lovely, as she would be wearing fine coloured or white silk cord stockings, as made in Florence for summer fashions, such as I often used to see our ladies wear before the very wide use of silk stockings which has since come in, but such stockings must be drawn tight and stretched like the skin of a tambourine and also well attached with pins, or otherwise, as the lady chooses and pleases, and with them should go a fine white slipper with an over-mule of black velvet or of some colour or a dainty little patten, made as well as man can fashion, such as I have seen one very great lady of the world wear, made most excellently and daintily.

And here one also has to consider the beauty of the foot

itself, for if this is too large it is not handsome, while if it is too small it gives its lady a bad name and report, as the proverb runs : *small foot big c——*, which is rather nasty. Thus the foot really does need to be more average for I have seen many which induced great temptations, for instance, when their owners made the foot peep out, half revealed under their skirts, shifting and fidgeting with certain little twists and lascivious movements, with a handsome lightly bast-soled little patten on, and the slipper white and pointed at the toe, not square. White is certainly the handsomest. But such little pattens and slippers are all for large women, who are tall, not for dumpy, stumpy ones, with clumping great pattens with two feet of bast sole on them. Besides, when they make play with such feet it's like toying with a giant's club or a fool's bauble.

There is something else a lady should take care to avoid, and this is, disguising her sex, she should not dress up as a boy, either for a masked-ball or any other reason, for even though she may have the loveliest leg in the world, when she does so dress up it looks shapeless, for all things have to have their decent and proper setting, and when ladies thus belie their sex they completely ruin their loveliness and natural grace.

This is why it is not fitting for a woman to try to appear lovelier by making a boy of herself, even if it is only to effect a charming Adonis effect with a fine bonnet with a Guelf or Ghibelline feather, that is, at one side or the other, according to party, or even dead in front, not to offend either side, as latterly our ladies have begun to practice, but this does not suit everybody. A lady needs to have a dainty face, one just made for it, as one saw in our Queen of Navarre, who was so well suited to this style that to see only her face when thus got up one could not have told what her sex was, whether she was a handsome youth or the very lovely lady that she really was.

A propos of which I recall one lady whom I knew in my time who once when twenty-five years old and far too tall and well developed, tried to disguise herself. She was a masculine sort of woman, recently come to court, and, thinking to play the gallant came to the ball-room dressed up like that one day, and was much stared at and mocked at, among others, by the

King,[364] who at once pronounced his opinion. He was one of the ablest men in the realm for a neat phrase, and the way he put it was that she was awfully like a woman juggler, or, to be more exact, like one of those paintings of women that men hawk round in Flanders and people set up over the mantelshelves in inns and bars, with German recorders in their mouths. So startling, in fact, was she that the King had her told that if she appeared again in such get-up and looking like that he would send her a personal request to tootle on her pipe and enliven and entertain the company with a little *aubade*. He mocked her quite as much because that way of doing her hair ill suited her as because he disliked her husband.

This is why such disguisings do not really suit all ladies for even had the Queen of Navarre, the loveliest woman in the world, cared to disguise herself by her headdress, she could never be as lovely as she really was. Impossible, for what shape more lovely than her own could she have taken? There was no shape in the world she could have borrowed more beautiful. And had she wished to show her legs, as I have heard some of her women say, and make them seem the loveliest and best shaped in the world, how do it otherwise than by showing them in their natural form, at least, properly clad with stockings, under her lovely dresses, for never would any be found more beautiful. That is how lovely ladies should appear and display their beauties.

In a Spanish book entitled *El Viage del Principe*,[365] the Prince's Tour, which described the progress of the King of Spain[366] in his Low Countries in the days of the Emperor Charles his father,[367] among the lovely gifts which he received in his rich and opulent cities there was that of the Queen of Hungary[368] in her lovely city of Bains,[369] whence the saying: *Mas brava que las fistas de Bains,* 'Lovelier than the fêtings at Bains.'

Among other wonders there was one at which, during the besieging of a mock castle which had been built, and was invested as if in real warfare (I describe this elsewhere)[370] she gave a fête to Queen Eleonora, her sister,[372] to the King her nephew[373] and to all the lords and nobles and ladies of the court. At the end of the fête a lady appeared accompanied by six mountain nymphs, dressed in ancient fashion, like maids of the virgin huntress, clad from head to foot in green and silver cloth, with a diamond covered crescent on their foreheads, so that they seemed to imitate the light of the moon, each bearing a bow and arrow, a full quiver at her side, and bootees made of the same cloth of silver, all equally neatly fitting. They came into the hall thus attired, leading their dogs at their heels, presented themselves to the Emperor and placed before him all sorts of pasties of venison which they had supposedly caught in the hunt.

Next came Pales, the goddess of shepherds, with six nymphs of the vales and dales, all dressed in white and cloth of silver, with pearly-covered headdresses of the same, and also stockings of the same cloth with white slippers, and they bore all sorts of milk products, which they set before the Emperor.

Then, as a third band, came the Goddess Pomona, with her water nymphs, and these brought the final service of fruits. And this goddess was the daughter of Doña Beatrix Pacecho,[374] Countess of Antremont, Lady-in-Honour of Queen Eleonora, then about nine years old, the one who today is the lady of the Admiral de Chastillon, whom he married as his second wife, and this girl and goddess and her companions brought in all the fruits which could be found at the time, for it was summertime and the harvest of them was lovely, exquisite. And these they presented to the Emperor, with so eloquent, so lovely a speech from the goddess, uttered with such fine charm that she earned the love and admiration of the Emperor and the whole company, seeing how young she was, and it at once presaged what she would be and indeed is to-day, a lovely, estimable, discreet, virtuous, clever and intelligent lady.

She was dressed like a nymph as all the others were, with their silver and white cloth, and she had the same stockings and footwear, with many precious stones to decorate her head, though hers were all emeralds, to stand partly for the colour of the fruits she brought, and in addition to the gift of fruit she presented the Emperor and King of Spain with a triumphal branch which was all green enamel, the twigs

211

laden with large pearls and precious stones, all very lavish to
the eye, priceless too, and she presented Queen Eleonora with
a fan, with a mirror in it, all garnished with precious stones
of great value.

There is no question, that Princess and Queen of Hungary
certainly showed that she was in every sense an estimable
lady, and she was as dexterous socially as she was skilled in
the arts of war, and from what I heard, the Emperor her
brother was greatly pleased and gratified to have so estimable
and worthy a sister.

Now, it may be questioned critically why I have made this
digression from the straight course of my subject. It was to say
that all these girls who played these parts had been selected and
chosen as the loveliest of all by the Queens of France[375] and
Hungary and by Lady de Lorraine, and they were variously
French, Italian, Flemish, German and Lorrainian, and not one
among them but was lovely, and God alone knows how exacting the Queen of Hungary had been to select the loveliest
and most charming of them all.

Lady de Fontaine Chalandry, who is still among the living,
who was at the time one of Queen Eleonora's girls, and one
of the loveliest could vouch for this. She was known as *fair
Torcy*. It was she in fact told me all about it, and it is from her
that I have it, as well as from other sources, that the lords,
nobles and knights of this court found great pleasure in observing and contemplating the lovely legs, the calves and the
lovely little feet of those ladies, for, clad as they were as
nymphs, they were dressed short, and thus offered a very lovely
display, more even than their lovely faces, which the menfolk
could see every day, but not their lovely legs, and there were
some men there who were made more amorous by the display
and the sight of those lovely legs than by their lovely faces,
the more so since at the top of such lovely columns there are
as a rule lovely cornices with curly friezes and lovely archi-
traves, lavish capitals, all exquisitely polished and deeply
cut too.

Thus, now we are on disguises and representations, I find
myself obliged to add this further digression and let my fancy

212

roam. At about the same time that these lovely fêtes were held in the Low Countries, above all at Bains, to receive the King of Spain, there was the entry of King Henry on his return from touring his lands in Piedmont and his garrisons at Lyons,[376] which was unquestionably one of the loveliest and most triumphal of receptions, as I have heard estimable ladies and nobles of the court who were present declare.

For, if this show and representation of Diana and her hunt was found lovely at that royal fête of the Queen of Hungary, this fête made at Lyons, which was very different, was even better staged, for as the King made his progress he came upon a large obelisk[377] in ancient style on his right hand and then a fenced-in-ground along the main road, with a wall of upwards of six feet height about it. The ground within this had been raised, and systematically planted with moderately-headed trees, all interspersed with groves and much compact placing of shrubs, and also with many fruit trees, and in this little forest were many little deer at play,[378] living there, with does and squirrels, all tame. His Majesty then suddenly heard a number of horns and trumpets sounded and immediately thereupon, coming through this forest, beheld Diana at the hunt with her companions and forest virgins. In her hand she had a splendid turquoise bow, with quiver dangling at her side, and she was attired like a nymph, as to this day antiquity represents her, on her body a low-cut, short tunic with six long rounded scallopings of black cloth of gold sewn with silver stars, the sleeves and the body of gold fringed crimson satin, caught up by a waist-cord to half-way up her legs, revealing all their loveliness, both her lovely calves and her bootees in ancient style, of crimson satin covered with pearls and embroidery. Her hair was interwoven with heavy ropes of splendid pearls with a quantity of precious stones and jewels of great value, and on her forehead she had a little silver crescent gleaming with tiny little diamonds, for gold would not have been so good to represent the natural crescent moon, which is bright and silvery.

Her companions were attired in dresses of varying form made of gold-barred taffeta, some broad, some thin, all in ancient style, and many other antique colours, all varied both for the strangeness of it and the brightness, with stockings and bootees of satin, and their heads decorated likewise in nymph style, with many pearls and precious stones.

Some had bloodhounds, some whippets, some spaniels and other leash dogs,[379] with leads of white and black silk, the colours of the King, all in honour of a lady named Diana, whom he loved[380] while others were accompanied in the chase by pack dogs making a great baying.[381]

Others bore little lances of Brazil wood, the ironshod heads gilded, with little dangling loops of white and black silk, trumpets and hunting horns of gold and silver dangling from sashes and cords of silver and black silk thread.

And just as they observed the King, out of the wood ran a lion which had been tamed and taught to do as it did—run up to the goddess and lay down at her feet, paying her homage. And when she saw it was so gentle and tame she took it on the leash with a thick cord of silver and black silk, and at once presented it to the King, and going—with the lion—to the edge of the wall enclosing this park bordering on the road, only a pace from His Majesty, and in a ten-line poem[382] such as was in fashion in those days, though it was not too polished and eloquent, she offered him the lion, and by this poem which she recited with very fine great charm, under the sign of that gentle, charming lion she now offered him his own city of Lyons, itself all gentleness, and submissive to his laws and commands.

This done and said with very great charm, Diana and all her companions made a profound curtsey to the King who, having greeted them all and cast a lively eye over them, to show he had been very pleased with their hunting, bid them goodbye and continued on his way to enter the city. Now note that this Diana and all her lovely companions were really the most striking and lovely married women, widows and daughters of Lyons, in which there was nothing wrong, for they enacted their masque so well and with such good grace that most of the princes, lords, nobles and courtiers were quite bewitched. I leave it to you to imagine that they had good cause.

This Lady de Valentinois, known as Diana of Poitiers, to whom the King was paying attentions, and in whose name this hunt was arranged, was equally happy and conceived an affection for the city of Lyons, which never left her. In any case, it was a neighbouring city to her, because of the Duchy of Valentinois being very close by.[383]

Now, since we are discussing the pleasure which there is in seeing a lovely leg, one may well imagine, as I have heard it said, that not only the King, but all these gallants of the court found wonderful pleasure in contemplating and admiring the legs of those lovely nymphs, so fancifully attired and with their skirts so knotted up that they gave one as much if not more temptation to climb to the second floor as to marvel and praise such charming ingenuity.

To abandon our digression and go back to what I had started on, I maintain that at our courts we have seen very delightful ballets indeed made and presented by our Queens, especially the Queen Mother,[384] but as a rule among us courtiers it was the feet and legs of the ladies performing in such ballets on which we really cast our eyes, finding our supreme pleasure in observing how daintily they manipulated their legs and twisted and fidgeted their feet, all with the acme of featliness, their skirts and gowns very much shorter than usual, though nevertheless not quite nymph-like, nor quite as high as they should have been or one would have liked. All the same, we did lower our glances a little, for instance when the Provençal valse was danced[385] and the whirling round, raising their skirts, always revealed something pleasing to the sight, and I have seen many a man enraptured by it and heard men discussing it afterwards with excitement.

The fair ladies of Siena, at the commencement of the rebellion of their city and republic,[386] formed three bands of the loveliest and greatest ladies there ever were, each numbering upwards of a thousand, which in all made three thousand, one band clad in violet-coloured taffeta, another in white, the third in scarlet, all dressed like nymphs with very short skirts so that they completely showed their lovely thighs and calves,[387] and thus they paraded through the city before everybody, even the Lord Cardinal of Ferrara[388] and Lord de Thermes,[389] the two Lieutenant-generals of our King Henry,[390] all of them determined and swearing readiness to die for the republic and for France, and all prepared to put their hand to labour on the fortifications of the city, and indeed already bore faggots on their shoulders, which aroused everybody to enthusiasm. I give the story elsewhere, when speaking of warm-hearted women, for it relates to one of the most lovely acts ever performed by gallant ladies.

Here I shall confine myself to saying that I have heard a number of nobles and soldiers, both French and foreign, even some of the city itself, say that there never was so lovely a sight, because they were all great ladies, leading citizenesses of the said city, all vying one with another in loveliness, and as we all know, there is no lack of beauty among the ladies of Siena, for good looks are very common there. But if it was fine to see their fine countenances, it was equally fine to see and contemplate their lovely legs and their calves, in their nice stockings so well drawn and tight fitting, as the Sienese are so good at fashioning. And as they had their gowns cut very short, like nymphs, in order the more easily to march, this and the circumstance that their faces could be seen every day but not their legs or calves, tempted and heated the most chilled and mortified of men. There was *nous* indeed in the person who first thought of dressing a woman as a nymph, for thus she offers so many fine views and eye-fulls, for if the skirts are short and slashed at the sides as we can still see in the love antiquities of Rome, this all serves greatly to increase the lasciviousness of the sight.

But today what is it that makes the lovely ladies and girls of the Isle of Scio[391] lovable? Their beauty and their charm, of course, their sumptuous style of dress as well, but above all their very short skirts, which fully reveal their lovely legs and lovely calves and their neat, well shod feet.

Regarding all this, I recall that once at court a lady of very fine and lavish build, when once gazing at a magnificent lovely tapestry of the hunt in which Diana and all her band of virgin huntresses were very naïvely depicted, and though fully clothed showing their lovely feet and lovely legs, she had beside her one of her companions, a woman of very short, small stature, engaged in marvelling at the picture with her, and she said to her : 'Ah, child, if we all dressed like that, you would lose on the deal and not have much advantage left, for your huge pattens would give you away and you would never have sufficient grace in your gait, or be able to show your legs, as we tall women would, so you would have to hide and would never be able to come out. So thank our age and the long gowns fashionable today, which greatly flatter you and cover your legs so dexterously with your big, towering pattens a foot high that really look more like sledge-hammers than feet, for if a man were without weapon he would only have to cut off one of your legs and take it by the end and he could use the foot end, set in your huge patten, as a fine weapon to fight with.'

This lady had good reason to talk like that, for, if thus set in such huge pattens, the loveliest leg in the world loses all its beauty, especially as such a massive-soled boot contrives too great a deformity, for if a foot does not match the leg with lovely stocking and fine shape the whole is worth nothing at all. Whereby ladies who take such huge, clumsy pattens, thinking to embellish and improve their figures and thereby make themselves more lovable and presentable, at the same time rob their lovely legs and calves of their beauty, for those are worth quite as much in their natural state as any imitation tallness is.

Thus in ancient times a lovely foot embodied such lasciviousness that many circumspect and chaste Roman ladies, who needed to conceal their feet—as today too many do in Italy, in imitation of ancient times, making as much scruple about letting people see their feet as their faces, and conceal their feet under their long gowns, as much as they can, so they cannot be seen, and when walking bear themselves so restrainedly, so discreetly and soberly that their feet never show at all below their skirts.

That is good for those who are of prudish make-up or appearance, and do not wish to cause temptation, and we are obliged to them, but I rather think that if they but had the liberty they would show both foot and leg and other things too, and that what they want is to show their husbands by this excess of hypocrisy and this petty scrupulousness what well-behaved wives they are. But I need only refer you to facts.

I know a very gallant, estimable knight who because at Rheims during the coronation of Henri III he saw the lovely leg, drawn with a white silk stocking, of a certain lovely great lady who was widowed and tall, from under the grandstands[392] which were put up for the ladies to watch the coronation from, was so taken by her that from then on he felt quite broken-hearted with love, and what her face had not been able to accomplish her lovely leg and calf did, so that this lady with all her fine parts nearly caused the death of this estimable knight. I have known of other men of like temperament.

So, to wind up, as I have known many gallant courtier comrade of mine make his device, the showing of a lovely leg and lovely foot is very dangerous and prone to bewitch eyes lusting for love and I am surprised that many good writers, both our poets and others, have not written in praise of legs as they have of other parts of ladies' bodies.[393] For my part I would have written more, had I not been apprehensive lest because of excessive praise of those parts of the body people objected that I cared too little for the other parts. Besides, I have yet to write on other matters and so cannot spend so much time on one alone.

Whereby I conclude with this little declaration : 'For love of Heaven, Ladies, do not be so eager to make yourselves seem tall and to make yourselves out to be different, lest you diminish the loveliness of your legs when these are lovely, or at least those of some of you are, but you spoil their charm by those high pattens and high heels. I know you need them, but when you wear them to such excess you displease people more than you realise.'

After this essay, let him who will praise a lady's other beauties, as many a poet does, but a lovely leg and a well turned calf and a lovely foot are yet a great boon and have great power in the rule of love.

FOURTH ESSAY

On Married Women, Widows and Girls to ascertain which class of them is hotter in love than the others

ONE day in Madrid,[394] when I was at the Spanish court, engaged in the sort of conversation that one carries on in such places, she put a question to me : 'Which is the greater fire of love, that of a widow, that of a wife, or that of a young girl?' When I had given her my opinion she told me hers in the following words : 'It seems to me all the same that although by great fervour of their blood unmarried girls are inclined to love passionately, they nevertheless do certainly not love like married women or widows, because of the great experience in the matter that the latter have. That after all is only common sense, just as anybody born blind and so without sight from birth cannot crave for sight like somebody who has had sweet enjoyment of it, then lost it.' To which she added : 'And just as it is less difficult to abstain from a thing one has never tried than from what one has experienced and liked.' There you have the reasons advanced on the matter by that lady.

Now, among the questions in his *Filocopo*,[395] in the ninth book, in fact, the worthy and learned Boccaccio further says this : 'With which of the three, a married woman, a widow and a girl is it better to fall in love in order to bring one's desire to a happy result?' Boccaccio replies through the mouth of the Queen, whom he introduces saying that for all that it is a bad thing, and against God and conscience, to desire a married woman, who is not at all independent, but subject to her husband, this is easy to accomplish. But not with a girl or a widow.

Indeed, such love may prove dangerous, particularly since the more one blows a fire, the brighter it burns, otherwise it goes out. Indeed, all things wear away by use, except lust, which augments thereby. But a widow who has been a long time without such experience scarcely feels it any more and is no more concerned with it than if she had never been married. Indeed, she is more likely to be warmed by memories than new desires. While the virgin who does not know and has never experienced what it is, (except in imagination) has only a lukewarm desire for it. The married woman, however, being more heated than the others, often craves it, and also may sometimes be indignant with her husband for what he has said to her or for having beaten her, whereupon, anxious for vengeance (for there is none so vindictive as a woman, especially concerning this) she cuckolds him thoroughly and soothes her ruffled spirits thereby. Besides, one gets tired of always eating the same meat and even great princes and ladies often weary of good provender and delicacies and turn to other food. Further, with girls there is too much labour and time to be spent in order to overcome them and submit them to a man's will, and when they do love they do not know it. But in widows the former fire easily regains its strength and very quickly makes them crave what through long disuse they had forgotten, and then they are impatient to resume it and achieve it, regretful for all the time they have lost and those long nights spent chilly in their poorly-warmed widows' beds.

To these arguments advanced by the Queen the reply was made by a noble named Ferramonte. Leaving the married women aside, as very easy to overcome and without any waste of words to argue the contrary, he returned to the question of girls and widows, and maintained that a girl was stauncher in love than any widow, for she, having already tried the secrets of love, never loves with a firm love, but is hesitant about it. She is slow to get involved, she quickly changes one man for another and is unable to make up her mind with whom to form a union in order to achieve the greatest advantage and honour. And many a time, indeed, she may want neither of two men, but vacillates between them, so love never really does take root at all. Virgins are just the opposite to this, all such matters being so many unknowns to them. They thus tend to form one love relationship only and to this they devote all their thoughts, once they have carefully selected, and try to please the chosen sweetheart in everything, in the belief that it is a very great honour to be thus steadfast in one's love. Further, a virgin gets extremely ardent about things she has never seen, heard, or tried, and thus more than any woman of experience would, she tries to see, hear and try everything. Besides, the craving to see new things thoroughly masters her, she turns to experts, which merely increases her fire still more, and thus she comes to crave union with the man whom she has made lord of her thoughts. You have no such ardour in a widow, since she has already been through it all.

Now Boccaccio's Queen takes up the thread again and in order to say the final word on the matter, draws the conclusion that a widow is a hundred times more painstaking about the pleasure of love than a virgin, as the virgin would dearly like to preserve her virginity and maidenhood, since all her future good name is set in this. Further, virgins are timorous by nature, and by this fact little apt or skilled in finding the devices and conveniences which suit the circumstances needed for such doings. With widows this is not the case, for they are clearly very practised, hence bold and crafty in the art, since they have already given and lost what the virgin has yet to yield, so that they are in no fear of being examined and charged with showing signs of having lost their maidenhood, and they also know far better what secret ways there are to get whatever they want.

Another point is that a virgin is apprehensive of the initial assault on her virginity, since in some this is rather a troublesome and painful than a gentle, pleasant business, all of which widows do not fear, but, however brusque the man tackling them may be, are able to let the whole business proceed swimmingly. For love is a pleasure which is the contrary of many another, since often enough it can easily happen—a girl needs to recover a bit from the first shot, though thereafter the pleasure increases steadily, whereas since the first shot costs her

221

less, from having already experienced it so fully, the widow is a hundred times easier about it than a maid, who, having to yield that part which is very dear indeed to her, thinks it over a thousand times before she finally assents. All of which, the Queen concludes, means that it is better to have recourse to a widow than to a girl, since she is found easier to win and debauch.

Now, if we take Boccaccio's arguments and examine them, comb them through a little and discuss them (basing ourselves on statements I have known estimable nobles and ladies to have made on the subject, after considerable experience) I hold that one should be in no doubts but that anybody who wants to obtain quick enjoyment of love should turn to married women, unless they wish to give themselves a lot of trouble and use up a lot of time, the more so since, as Boccaccio observes, the more one pokes a fire, the hotter it gets. Thus it is worth your married woman, who gets so heated up with her husband that if he fails to have all that is needed to quench the conflagration which he starts up in his wife, she must needs draw on some other source or be burned up altogether. I knew a lady of good family, of a fairly good position too, and of good blood, who once remarked to her love, (who told it to me,) that all her life she had never been as keen on the act as people might say (and God knows they said enough) and that often enough she could very easily have done without it, had it not been that her husband stirred her up so with all his fidgetting with the fire, without being capable of sufficient stuff to quench the flames, which he made so big and so hot that she simply had to run to her lover for aid. Further, often enough she was not even satisfied by him, and would retire all alone to her closet or her bed and there all by herself work off her frenzy as best she could, either in the Lesbian way, or by some device or other, or else it went so far, she said, that had it not been for the disgrace of it she could have given herself to the first man she came upon in any nook of a ball-room, even of the stairs, so tortured was she by her attack of fever, like nothing less than the mares in Andalusia, which get so hot that when they cannot find a stallion to ride them and are unable anyhow else to satisfy themselves, they stick their parts out into the winds which blow there, so these beat down into them, and thus they get rid of their heat and fill themselves up. This gives rise to those so very swift horses which we see coming from those parts, just as if they retained something of the natural speed of their father, the wind. I rather think there is many a husband who would like very much his wife to find a wind like that to cool her down and make her heat pass off without going to seek out lovers and plant ugly horns on his head.

Now, there is this characteristic of womenfolk which I have just mentioned which is most peculiar, that of not burning unless the fire is first poked. One should not be surprised at it, for, as a Spanish lady once said : 'The more I want to get out of the heat the more my husband fans up my brasier.' And there is no doubt about it, they are quite capable of being utterly consumed in it, exactly as this Spanish lady suggested, since by what is said or by mere embracing and touching, not to speak of mutual attraction, they very easily let themselves go whenever they have the opportunity, without any respect for their husbands.

For, to tell the truth, what very frequently more prevents any girl or woman from indulging in love-making is the fear they have of blowing up their bellies without eating beans, which is something that married women do not fear at all, for if they swell, it is the poor husband who has done it all and bears the full responsibility. And as for the laws of honour which Boccaccio quotes, which forbid love-making, well, most women do not care a hoot for them, alleging as valid arguments that the laws of Nature must take precedence, and Nature never makes anything that is purposeless, and it was Nature gave them not only limbs, but also such noble parts they are meant to be used and put to some service, not to be left idly unemployed. Nature neither prohibits nor orders more here than in regard to any other bodily functions. Further they say (at least some of our ladies do) that the law of chastity is only for women who do not love at all and have not found a single estimable friend, for it would be very unseemly indeed, worthy

223

of vituperation, in fact, if such were to surrender their bodily chastity, as if they were mere courtesans. But ladies who do love and have made well-chosen friendships are not at all prohibited by the laws of honour from helping their male friends relieve the fires which consume them and giving them something capable of extinguishing them, and they maintain that giving life to a man who asks it is indeed well done, it is to be kind to them and not in the least wild or cruel, as Regnaud said *à propos*[396] of the disquisition of poor afflicted Genevieve.

Regarding which, I once knew a very estimable and great lady who, when one day her friend came upon her in her closet translating that stanza of the said Regnaud, *una donna deve dunque morire*—'A lady was thus to die'—into French lines as fine and well made as I ever knew (for I saw them subsequently) and he had asked her what she had just been writing: 'Here,' she said, 'is a translation which I have just made, which is equally a judgement on me and a decision taken to give you the satisfaction you crave, so it only remains for you to carry it out,' (which, after this perusal, was accomplished without delay). How much better a judgement that was than any which would have been given at the Tournelle Court,[397] for just as Ariosto supported Regnaud's words with his very excellent arguments, I assure you that she did not forget a single one, but translated and embodied every one, so well indeed that the translation was quite as stirring as the original. And thus she indicated to a friend like this that she wanted to give him life and not at all to be inexorable towards him, after which he certainly did not lose any time about obtaining it.

Why indeed, seeing that Nature has made her kind and tender-hearted, should not a lady make free use of the gifts with which Nature has endowed her, without our being thereby ungrateful or in any way girding against her or objecting? As did a lady of whom I heard who when one day she saw her husband walking and parading up and down in the palace hall could not refrain from saying to her lover: 'Look, there's our man walking up and down, doesn't he look a real cuckold! Would I not have been sinning against Nature, seeing she

224

designed him so and intended him to be a cuckold, if I had gone against her and failed to make him one?'

I have heard tell of another lady who complained of her husband who did not treat her well but spied jealously on her, suspecting that she was planting horns on his head. 'Isn't he kind!' she said to her lover, 'he thinks his fire is similar to mine, for I extinguish his in a jiffy, with no more than four or five drops of water, but in fact mine, which is much deeper, like a furnace, needs quite a lot of quenching, for we women are hydroscopic by nature, or like sand-pits, the more water we take in the more we want.'

And another lady put it much better, saying their privy part was of the nature of poultry which get the pip if they lack water and die if they cannot keep sipping. Likewise their part gets the pip and often dies if not frequently watered, though different water from well water is needed in that.

Another lady said that she was by nature like a good garden, the water which fell from heaven was not enough for her, if she was to be fruitful she needed some from her gardener's watering-can too.

Another lady used to say that she liked to resemble good business-men who know how to look after their land well, so never put it all in the hand of one bailiff to develop but put it under various hands, as one man could never cope with it all. Likewise she preferred to administer her c——— and develop that, and she felt all the better for it.

I heard of one estimable lady who had a very ugly lover and a very charming husband, so was well away, but an intimate friend one day remonstrated with her for not choosing a more handsome lover, whereupon she retorted: 'Don't you know that you need more than one worker to cultivate a bit of land, and that often enough the more handsome and finely made man is not the fittest for the job, but the more rustic and robust type is?'

Another lady whom I knew, who had a very ugly husband who was a most ungracious man, chose a lover just as ugly as he was, and when one of her friends asked why, said: ' 'Tis the better to get used to my husband.'

225

Another lady, one day discussing love-making, both her own and that of her friends, said : 'If women were always chaste, they would never know what the opposite was,' basing herself in this on Heliogabalus's opinion, when he said that half of one's life should be spent on virtues, the other half on vices, otherwise, if everything in a person were either good or bad, people would never have a notion what the opposite quality was, though the one often serves to temper the other. I have known great persons to approve that judgement, even regarding women. Thus the wife of the Emperor Sigismond, who was called Barbe,[398] said that it was just silly for the same person always to be chaste, and she much disapproved of her ladies and girls who stuck to that way of life, which she for her part greatly departed from. For her only thoughts were for festivities and dances, balls and love-making, and she ridiculed those who did not do the same, or who went into retreat and fasted to mortify their flesh. I leave it to you to decide if all was well at the court of that Emperor and Empress, I mean regarding those of either sex who liked love-making.

I have heard people speak of one very estimable lady and one who was famous, too, who, when she fell sick with love of one of her men, because of that great law of loyalty which husbands so stoutly advised and preached was loth to risk the dangers with which that little part between her legs threatened her, but instead burned and desiccated day after day, so that in no time she saw herself who had formerly been a fresh, plump woman, in good condition, become thin and dry and languishing, till when she looked in her mirror one day she suddenly realised that she was quite a different person. 'However could it be,' she said, 'that in my best years, all because of scruples and notions of honour about the craving of such a little spot of me, I have restrained such fire so exceedingly that I have thus gradually come to dry up, till I am consumed and aged and made ugly before my time, so I am like to lose the brightness of the beauty which made me prized, valued, loved? And in place of a lady with a lovely body have turned into a smoked carcase, or rather a mere skeleton, so I am likely to be banished from good company and laughed at, the mockery of everybody? No, I am not going to let that happen but will cure myself with the remedies which are in my power.' And thereupon, just as she said, so she did, giving herself with satisfaction both to herself and her lover and regained her fine flesh and became as lovely as she had been before, without the husband knowing what cure she had used, but attributing it all to the doctors, whom he thanked and greatly honoured for thus having restored her, as he thought, to his great advantage.

I have heard tell of another great lady of a fine character indeed, with a ready tongue too, who when she was sickly and one day her doctor told her that she would never be well unless she did so-and-so, she replied at once : 'Right come on, then.' So there and then she and the doctor had their pleasure together, by heart and by body. One day, she remarked to him : 'It is the talk everywhere that you do me, but that's all the same to me, since I am now in good health'—and she did not say 'do' but made free use of the gallant little word which begins with an *f*. 'And I'm going to do it as much as I can too, since my health depends on it,' she added.

These two ladies were not at all like that estimable lady of Pampeluna, whom I mentioned once before,[399] who is to be found in the Queen of Navarre's *Hundred Tales*.[400] When she was head over heels in love with Lord d'Avannes, she preferred to conceal her fire and store in her bosom, which was utterly consumed by it, for she chose rather to die than to sully her honour. But from what I have heard a number of estimable ladies and lords say about it, she was a foolish woman, most heedless of the salvation of her soul, since by doing this she caused her own death, which it was in her power to ward off, and for a mere trifle, too. For, after all, as an old French proverb has it :

> *Grass mown and c—— explored*
> *Damage little, soon restored.*

What indeed is it, when all is said and done? Once accomplished, can anybody possibly see the business? Does the lady walk any less erect? Can anything be distinguished? I mean of course when the deed is accomplished privately, between four walls, and nothing is seen of the act. I would like to see the great lady, among those I know, (for it is in them that love mainly resides—as that lady of Pampeluna put it, it needs a big wind to rattle a big door,) who ceased to walk head erect, in this court or elsewhere, and with as grand appearance as any Bradamante[401] or Marfise.[402] And what man would be so presumptuous as to ask a lady if she had just come from doing it? I assure you their husbands (at least some) would not dare utter a word to them, so well do they know how to dissemble and to maintain their haughty bearing. And if the husbands (those in question) should think of mentioning it or threatening them, with any outrage, by word or by deed, they are certainly lost, for even if hitherto they harboured no malice against them, now they at once become revengeful and return tit for tat. For there is an old proverb which says : 'If beat his wife a man begin, be sure her c—— at once will grin.' This means that it has hopes of a good meal, knowing the temperament of the mistress to whom it belongs, for as she cannot resort to other weapons for vengeance she makes use of that particular part, however carefully the husband tries to watch over it, to second her and be her great support.

For, the most frequent specific they know for attaining their end, is to complain to each other, or to their ladies-in-waiting and maids, winning them over to seek them out new lovers, if they have none, or, if they have, to bring them to the trysting place. Then the maids stand guard to see that neither husband nor anybody else surprises them. Now such ladies win over their maids and their women and corrupt them with money and presents and promises, and often enough some ladies even bargain and pact with them, to the effect that the maid is to get half the proceeds, or one visit out of three. But the worst of it is that very often the mistresses deceive their maids and take it all for themselves, with the excuse that their lover did not give them any more than a trifle, and that was not enough for them alone. Like that it is all pie in the sky for the poor maids and their women, although they stand watch and keep guard well. In all of which there is some measure of injustice and you may be sure that if the case were to

228

be debated with the arguments given on both sides, there would be a lot to discuss and to laugh at too, for after all, cheating them of their salary and covenanted portion is sheer robbery. There are other ladies who keep their pacts and promises very loyally, and do not knock anything off their women's share, in order to be well served and supported by them, behaving in this like sensible shopkeepers who let their foremen or their partners have their just share of the takings. Such ladies deserve to be very well treated, for having shown such gratitude for the trouble, the watches kept, the protection afforded. For, after all, the women do endanger themselves and risk a lot, as in one instance of my knowledge in which, while the girl was on watch with her mistress in her chamber with her lover having a good time, both of them very busy indeed, the majordomo turned up and tackled the girl sharply, asking her what she thought she was doing, she had rather have been inside with her mistress than pimping like that, on watch outside, doing a bad turn to her mistress's husband, of all of which he then said he would inform his master. But the lady in question won him over by another of her maids, in whom the man was in love, for, implored by her mistress, who also gave her a present, she promised the majordomo something that he wanted, and he was thereby pacified. Nevertheless, this lady never liked the man after that and harboured a malice against him, till, seizing the occasion when at last it turned up, she had her husband get rid of him altogether.

I know one lovely, estimable lady[403] who had a maid in whom she had placed her friendship, looking after her well, even permitting great familiarities, to the point that when sometimes she saw that this lady's husband was away from the house, either detained at court or on some long journey, she would often gaze at her mistress as she dressed her, wondering, for she was the loveliest and most delightful of ladies, till one day she said : 'Ah! Is he not a wretched fellow, this husband of yours, having so lovely a wife and leaving her alone so long at a time without visiting her? Is he not asking for you to cuckold him here and now? You ought to, were I as lovely as you are, I would do it to my husband, if he was absent for such long periods.' I leave it to you to imagine whether this maid's lady and mistress found that nut to her taste, and if she did not find a foot to fit her slipper, so she might make some use of so fine an instrument.

Now there are ladies who make such good use of the assistance of their maids to conceal their love affairs that the husbands do not notice anything, but actually place their lovers at their disposal, to be members of the household, as their gentlemen-in-waiting, which also serves as cover, so that if at any time the husband does find the man in his wife's room, he is of course only there to wait on her or on this or that young lady of hers, and under such pretext the ladies have an excellent method of playing their game without the husband's ever knowing anything about it.

I knew a very great prince who began paying court to a lady in the suite of a great princess, merely to find out the love-making secrets of her mistress, and get at them the more easily.

In the course of my life I have known many cases of this sort of thing, though not many who did it quite in the way one famous, estimable lady whom I knew did, who was fortunate enough to be served by three fine, gallant nobles, one after the other, who, when they left her service, came to wait on another very great lady, whereupon the first lady made a most pleasant remark, saying that she had so trained and shaped them, by such fine lessons and tricks, that when they came to serve this other, who was a great princess, they were better instructed and shaped, and to get as high as that a man needed first to serve those a little lower down, so as not to fall short higher up. For to reach the top of a flight of stairs one needs must start with the lower stairs, as we see in all crafts and fields of knowledge.

This was a very great honour to her, greater than that of one lady I knew, who was in the suite of a great lady who was married. When this great lady happened to be taken by surprise in her bedroom by her husband when she had just received a little scrap of paper from her lover, she was so well supported by this under-lady that the latter neatly took the note and without any hesitation and also without the husband's even noticing it, swallowed it whole in one piece and had he seen what was in it, he would certainly have treated his wife very badly. Now that was a very great service, and the great lady in question never forgot it.

I know many ladies however who came off badly for having put too much trust in their maids, and yet others who came off as badly through not putting their trust in them. I have heard the story told of one lovely, estimable lady who had taken and chosen a noble who was one of France's finest, most valiant and accomplished men in the art of giving pleasure and satisfaction by his delightful body. She would never trust one of her maids, but gave a rendezvous in a third place, and it was arranged that there should be only one bed in this room, so that her women would have to make their beds up in the ante-chamber, and as there was a trap-door for cats in the door which they had not thought about till just before the lovers were to meet, it was decided to stop this up with a board, so that if anybody should push the door, this board would make a clatter, which would warn the lovers to lie quiet and be on the look-out. One of the women, however, thought there was something fishy about all this. She was also vexed and had taken umbrage because her mistress mistrusted her (for previously her mistress had always shown most trust in her, on many an occasion confiding in her more than the others,) so when her mistress was in bed she decided to keep watch and listen at the door. She heard her mistress's voice, whispering away, but realized that this was not the bedtime reading with which, by the light of a candle, the better to build up the deceit, she had for the past few days been wont to amuse herself in bed. So the woman was now curious to find out all about it. And all at once there came a most fitting opportunity, for a young cat by chance came into the ante-room, where the women were. So she and her companions took it and thrust it through the cat-hole into her mistress's room, not of course without knocking down the board which sealed the hole, thereby making a clatter. The lover and his mistress were of course most upset and started up in bed, but when by the

231

gleam of their torch and the candle they saw that it was only a cat which had come in and knocked down the trap, without more concern they got back into bed, especially as it was late and everybody should by now be asleep—but without closing that cat-hole again, leaving it open, in fact, so that the cat could get out again, as they did not want to keep it shut up in the room with them all night. By this means that under-lady and her companions were able to see things enough which their mistress did, which afterwards they revealed to the husband, whence followed the death of the noble and the disgrace of the lady.

That is what scorn and mistrust of other people can bring about, as harmful as excessive trust in them, as when in a case I know one very great prince went to the length of taking all his wife's maids one by one and torturing them to make them confess all her lively doings and the services they rendered her in her love affairs. But that enquiry was however never carried through to the end, to avoid greater scandal. The first suggestion of it had come from a great lady whom I will not name, who had her knife in the other. Subsequently God punished her.

To come to the end of our married women, I will wind up by saying that there is nothing like your married woman to extract good profit, and without delay too, from her position, for married women know their business so well that the most subtle and most loftily titled of husbands are deceived by them. I have said enough about this in the chapter on cuckolds and married women, (where you will find some good stories,) without adding to it for the moment.

And so, following the order adopted by Boccaccio, our guide in this essay,[404] I come to unmarried girls, who one must admit without question are by their nature at the outset very timorous and loth to yield what they prize highly, also because of the incessant admonitions and counsellings made them by their mothers, their brothers, their fathers and other relations and their mistresses, all accompanied by very stern threats. So that even if they had all the desire in the world, they will mortify it as much as they can, fearing lest their disobedient bellies immediately show what has taken place—without which fear they would make many a good meal. But all unmarried girls have not such qualms, for some blind themselves to every consideration and rush boldly into it, their heads not lowered, but held very high indeed. In which they make a great mistake, as the disgrace of a girl when seduced is very great, and a thousand times more important to her than that of a married woman or a widow, for the girl who loses her great treasure thereby becomes an object of disgrace, of vilification, everybody points the finger of scorn at her and she loses any good marriage possibilities, though I have certainly known many such who have in the end found some boor who deliberately or in ignorance, with or without his eyes open (or even forced to it), has thrown himself between such a girl's legs and married her, for, as I have said elsewhere, stained though they are they are still very delightful.

I have known many men and girls who have gone through it, including one[405] who most disgracefully let herself go and get put in the family way by a well-known prince,[406] and without any concealment or sense of decency about her confinement either. When it was found out, all she would say was: 'How could I help it? I'm not to be blamed, it was not my fault, nor my little button's, it was just my sleepy lack of foresight, for, had I been crafty and cunning like most of my girl friends, who have done just as much as I have, or even worse, but who know how to cure their pregnancy and have an abortion, I would not be in this difficulty today, and nobody would have known.' Her girl friends were very angry indeed with her for saying this, and she was expelled from the band of maids of honour by her mistress, though it was said it had been she who had ordered her to obey the will of the prince in question, since she had an interest in him, and wanted to win his goodwill. Nevertheless after some time the girl did manage to find a good match and made a very wealthy wedding,[407] from which a handsome line has now sprung. There you see that, had this poor girl been as cunning as her companions or other girls, all of this would not have happened to her, for I have in all truth in my time seen girls who were quite as cunning and crafty in the matter as the most veteran of married women, even to the point of being very good and very clever pimps, not satisfied with what their own goods could bring them in, but hunting after the profits of those of others.

It was a maid of honour at the French court who was the author and producer of that delightful comedy entitled *Love's Paradise*, given between four walls, in the Bourbon Hall,[408] with none present but the participants in the plan, the men and the women, who were both actors and audience at once. Those who have heard the story of it told will guess what I am getting at. It was played by six characters, three men and three women, one was a prince with his own lady, who was a great person, though not too great. He certainly loved her dearly. The second was also a prince, and he acted his part with a great lady, who was of rich stuff. The third was a noble, who paired off with the maid-of-honour, whom he married after, for, gallant as she was, she insisted on playing her part as well as the others. After all, as a rule the author of a comedy does act one of the parts or at least recite the prologue, as this girl did, and unmarried though she was, she played her part very well, maybe better than the married women, for she had seen the world in other countries, and, as the Spanish has it, had been *rafinada en Segobia*, 'had her wits sharpened in Segovia,' which is a saying in that country, because the last touches are put to good cloth there.

I have heard much talk of many girls who, serving their mistresses as go-betweens, have come to want to have a nibble themselves. This results in such ladies often being their girls' slaves, from fear lest the girls expose them and publish their love-affairs abroad, as I have explained above. It was from an unmarried girl that one day I heard that it was great stupidity in girls to make their front passages a matter of honour, and if some were silly enough to have scruples about them, she was not going to be so foolish, as there was nothing disgraceful about it, the fashion by which one kept one's privy parts covered and secret put it all right, and any girl was a ninny, not fit to be alive, who did not know how to look after herself and have the enjoyment of love-making.

When a certain Spanish lady was under the impression that her daughter might be afraid of the rupture to take place in the bridal bed in the first night, she set herself to try to talk her out of her worries, it was nothing, she said, there was no pain about it, indeed, she would quite like to be in her daughter's place so she could demonstrate, so much better, what it was all about, when the girl replied: *Beso los manos, señora madre, da tal merced, que bien lo tomare yo por mi*—'Thank you very much, mother dear, for that kind offer, but I'll manage all right by myself.'

I have heard tell of a girl of very lofty lineage, whom when she helped herself to a little pleasure there was talk of marrying abroad, to a Spaniard. Then, one of her secret lovers, laughing, told her that he was very surprised that she who had so loved the rising sun was going to sail west where it drooped down (Spain being towards the west) but at once she replied: 'Yes, I have heard sailors who have navigated a lot say that sailing to the Levant is very pleasant and delightful, I have often navigated in those waters myself, by the compass which I carry on my person, but when I am in the west I shall still use it to go straight back again to where it rises.' Good interpreters will be able to explain this allegorical figure, they will tumble without my explaining it. Now, after such language, I ask you whether that girl had always been dutiful to Our Lady the Virgin?

There was another whom I have heard cited who when she had heard wonders told about the city of Venice and all its strange features, including the freedom which held there for all people, even for whores and courtesans, said to one of her friends: 'Ha! Good gracious me! If only we could transfer all our goods there by letter of credit, so we might lead that delightful, lucky courtesan's way of life, there's none other can touch it, even were we empresses of the whole world.' There's a nice, hearty desire for you! But it really is true, I doubt if any one wanted to lead that sort of life could be better off than they would in Venice.

I would say much the same of the wish expressed by a lady years ago, who when she had heard the story of a poor male slave who had escaped from the hands of the Turks, about all the torments and maltreatment to which he and all the other poor Christians, when they were held there were submitted—and this man told her quite enough, and described all manner of cruelties, it occurred to her to ask him what they did to the women. 'Alas, Madame,' he said, 'they so-and-so them so much they die of it.' 'Then, please God,' said she, 'I might some day die such a martyr's death!'

Three great ladies, one of them unmarried, were to my knowledge one day talking together, when they came to wishes. One said: 'I would like to have an apple tree which every year bore as many golden apples as a tree does natural fruit.' Another said: 'I would like such and such a meadow, to produce as many pearls and precious stones as there are flowers in a meadow.' The third, who was unmarried, said: 'I would like to have a dove-cot the holes in which were as good as that of so-and-so' (naming a certain lady, the favourite of such-and-such a King, whom I will not name,) 'though I would want my hole to be entered by more pigeons than hers.'

These ladies were not like a Spanish lady whose life is described in the *History of Spain* and who one day when the great Alfonzo, King of Aragon, was making his entry into Saragossa, threw herself down on her knees before him to crave justice. When the King said he would hear her case, she begged his ear in private, which he granted, and then she complained of her husband, saying that he slept with her thirty-two times, doing it both by day and by night, and never gave her any respite of pause or rest. The King then sent for the husband and learned that this was indeed true, the man thinking he should not fail his wife and that he was doing nothing wrong, since she was his wife. After that, the King called his Council together to hear about it, and then decided and ordered that the man should touch his wife only six times a day, though he added that he was bound to say that he marvelled greatly at the great heat and virility of this man and also at the great frigidity and continence of the wife, who seemed quite the contrary of the nature of all other women (so says the story) who go to their husbands with their hands clasped in prayer and to other men too to get enough, or else to lament if their men give other women what belongs to them.

A certain unmarried girl of good family was not at all like this wife. The day after her marriage, telling some of her girl friends the incidents of the past night, she said : 'What nonsense Is that all there is in it? Why, I used to hear some of you and other women talk about it and also heard so many fine, gallant men promising the moon and wonders. Heavens alive, my dears, that man,' (her husband, that is) 'who made himself out to be so hot and so deeply in love and such a stout fellow and fine jouster, why, he never got beyond four tilts at the ring with his lance, he was just like any ordinary man at a tournament, three for the ring, one for the ladies. What's more, in between them all there was more posturing than you could see yesterday at the grand ball.' You may conclude that since she complained it was too little, she wanted her round dozen. But everybody, of course, is not like that Spanish noble.

And here is how they make fun of their husbands. There was one, for instance, who at the very beginning of the first night of her marriage, just when her husband was about to tackle her, turned shy and difficult about it, till it occurred to him to tell her that if he took his big dagger the game would look very different and she really would have something to cry out about. Upon which, in fear of that bigger one with which he threatened her, she let him get to work at once. But the next day she was the one who was not afraid, not satisfied with the little one, she now wanted to know where that big one was with which he had threatened her the previous evening. Upon which the husband replied that he had not got a bigger one, he had merely been teasing her, she would have to be satisfied with the little equipment he had got. Then she said : 'Now is it nice to tease a poor simple girl like that?' I don't quite know whether to pronounce that girl naïve and silly, or a crafty and cunning one who had already had a taste of it. I leave the matter to the ecclesiastical court's expert assessors.

Bien plus estoit simple un' autre fille, laquelle s'estant plaincte à la justice que un gallant l'ayant prise par force, et luy enquis sur ce fait, il respondit: 'Messieurs, je m'en rap-

porte à elle s'il est vray, et si elle n'a pris mon cas et l'a mis de sa main propre dans le sien.—Ha! Messieurs, (dis la fille) il est bien vray cela, mais qu'il ne l'eust fait? car, amprés qu'il m'eut couchée et troussée, il me mit son cas roide et poinctu comme un baston contre le ventre, et m'en donnoit de si grands coups que j'eus peur qu'il me le perçast et m'y fist un trou. Dame! je luy pris alors et le mis dans le trou qui estoit tout fait.'[409] Si cette fille estoit simplette, ou le contrefaisoit, je m'en rapporte.

I will now tell two stories, of two married women who were as naïve as that girl was, or as crafty, as you please. It relates to a very great lady whom I knew, who was very lovely, and much desired. When one day a very great prince sought her for love-making, or rather, pleaded eloquently with her to let him, promising her very fine, very grand favours, with magnificent presents and wealth both for herself and her husband, she yielded without too much difficulty to all this most enticing temptation, yet all the same was not going to let him do it at once, not till, like a very naïve, young, newly wed bride who just did not know worldly ways, she had told her husband and asked his advice, yes or no. Without hesitation the husband said : 'Oh, no, no, my pet, by Christ, what is this you propose and speak to me of? A dastardly act which would never be mended either for you or for me !' 'Ah, yes, but, sir,' replied this lady, 'you will be such a big man and I such a big lady that nobody will be able to utter a word against us.' In the end, though the husband still refused to say yes, by dint of all this talk the lady now began to gain courage, and cunning too. She did not want to lose such an opportunity, and she took advantage of it with this prince and with others too, casting her stupid naïvety aside altogether. I heard the story from one who had it from the great prince himself. He had also heard it from the lady herself, whom he reproved, assuring her that in such matters one should never go to one's husband for advice, he had other sources in his court.

This lady was as simple, or more so, as another I heard of, to whom an estimable noble not only suggested love, when the husband was close at hand, but engaged with another lady, but also put his kestrel (or, to be more explicit, his tool) in her hands. She took hold of it and held it tight, then, turning to her husband, said : 'Husband, see what a lovely present this noble has made me, may I accept it, do please tell me.' Utterly aghast, the poor noble withdrew his kestrel so roughly that it caught on the corner of a diamond on her finger and this so rooted into his tool from one end to the other that he thought he had lost it altogether, and the injury was not without causing him great pain, even danger to his life, too, and he left the room rather quickly, watering the floor with his blood, which was dripping copiously. The husband, however, did not run after him to tackle him about what he had done, merely laughed heartily, both at his poor little wife's simplicity and the fine present offered her and also the way the noble was punished for it.

Now I must really tell the following rustic tale, because it is not at all bad. A country lass was being conducted with tabor and flutes and fine ceremonial to the church for her wedding, when by chance whom should she meet but her girlhood's sweetheart, so out loud she cried : 'Farewell, farewell, Pierre,' (that was his name,) 'you'll not do me any more now, my mother's marrying me.' She did not say 'do', either, but the proper word, in stark simplicity. The naïvety of that was quite equal to the regrets she seemed to feel for what was no more.

Since we are on country life, let us now turn to another. A lovely young girl had brought a load of wood to market to sell, and as usual was running the price up and up, as the bidders chimed in, till one shouted. 'And I'll add a good f——g.'

'Right you be,' cried the lass, 'you take I right here where there's witnesses.'

There you have girls and women who were very naïve, and such (and there are quite a lot of them) are very different from many others, a tremendous number, in fact, in high society, who are far more crafty and twisty and neither ask their husbands' advice or show them the presents they get.

I heard tell of a girl in Spain who on her first marriage night, while her husband was labouring wearisomely away to

239

make a breach in her fortifications, (and not without some trouble, either,) suddenly burst out laughing and said : 'My Lord, not for nothing are you a martyr, for I am a virgin, but as I'm patient enough, you'll be able to do it in time.' Here was one who, to balance the husbands who tease their wives, teased her husband, as indeed many a girl has cause to do on that night, even when they have found out all about it in advance, or learned from others, or pondered and pictured by themselves what that great moment of pleasure is going to be like, thinking it something very great and lasting.

There was a Spanish woman who on the morning after her wedding, recounting her husband's good points, named several, then went on, 'Except that he's poor at arithmetic, he doesn't know how to multiply.'

A girl of good situation and family (whom I knew and heard tell about it) on her wedding night, when everybody was eavesdropping, as is the custom, and her husband had made the first breach and though not asleep, was taking a little rest, and then asked her if she wanted some more, said nicely : 'As much as you like, sir.' You may imagine that at that reply the gallant husband was taken aback and scratched his head.

Girls who produce fine sayings like that so promptly after their wedding are certainly capable of giving their poor husbands a headache and making them wonder if they are really the first to dip their anchors in those waters, or will be the last to do so. For there can be no doubt but that the man who does not make such an effort that he almost kills himself to satisfy his wife will sooner or later have her making him wear horns. As the old French proverb put it :

> *If hubby does not fill her fair*
> *Be sure she'll find what lacks elsewhere*

Certainly, if a woman does get all she can take out of a man, it does get him down, that is to say, it kills him. There is indeed an old saw that a wife should not make her dear one give more than he is willing and should spare him as much as she can, unless he happens to be her husband, from whom she should suck the marrow of his bones. This is why the Spanish comment runs *que el primero pensamiento de la muger, luego es casada, es de embiudarse*—'the first thought of a woman when married is to widow herself.' This, as I hope to show elsewhere, does not fit everybody, but only refers to some women.

There are girls who, unable to retain their heat for any length of time, only yield readily to princes and high nobles, men most suited to stirring them up, both by their favours and their presents, and also in consideration of their kindnesses. For after all, everything in them is fine and perfect, even when they are fatuous, as I have known some to be. There are other girls who do not run after them, but mainly avoid them, rather because they have a name for being great boasters, long-tongued scandal-makers, little given to being discreet, so the girls prefer sensible, circumspect nobles, of whom however there are not many. But the girl who does find one and get him is most fortunate. However, to avoid all this trouble, they choose (at least some do) their gentlemen-in-waiting, some of whom are handsome, others not. Anyway, I have known some girls do this, and certainly they do not usually have to waste much time asking such servants, for, getting them up, as I have known many girls at court and elsewhere not to scruple to have their men-servants do, putting them to bed, undressing them, putting on and taking off their footwear and opening their shifts for them, it is impossible for it to be otherwise but that, seeing so many fine things in them, such men should have their appetites whetted, and so many girls get them involved in this way on purpose, so that after their eyes have played their part, the other parts of the body follow suit in turn.

I knew one girl of high society, lovely if ever there was one, who made her gentleman-in-waiting the companion of a great prince who was keeping her, and thought he was the only man fortunate enough to enjoy her, though all the time the valet kept in step with him. And she had made a very good choice too, for this gentleman-in-waiting was very handsome and very stalwart, so that in bed, or rather, on the job, one would have known nothing to choose between the two men. Indeed, in many fine points the gentleman-valet had the advantage of the prince, who knew nothing of this love-making or these intimacies till he had left her and married, so did not treat the valet at all badly, but was even delighted to see him, and when one day he came upon him out, merely said : 'Is it possible that this man was my rival? Yes, I can quite believe it, for apart from my high rank he is the better man of us two.' This valet had the same name as the prince. He was also a very good tailor, famous at court for taking girls' measurements, so that there was not a girl or woman he did not fit when they wanted some tailoring done for them. I do not know if he dressed them quite as thoroughly as he did his mistress, but I do know that they were not at all badly served by him.

I knew a girl of good family who, having a lackey who was fourteen, whom she had made her fool and entertainer, with all the fooling and the entertainments he gave her made little fuss about letting the man kiss her and fondle her and feel her, as intimately as if he had been a woman, and often in front of everybody, too, though people would all forgive it and say he was just a fool and such a delightful entertainer. I do not know if he went any further, but I do at least know that later, both when married and widowed and married again, she was a very shocking strumpet of a woman. So you may well imagine that she first lit her wick with that burning bit of coal, and so well that subsequently it never let her down in all her bigger affairs and high up conflagrations. I had observed this particular girl for a whole year, but when I saw her intimacies in her mother's presence,—and her mother had the reputation of being one of the most hypocritical and false prudes of her time—and saw she actually used to laugh about it and that her mind was quite at ease about it. I at once foresaw that the girl would be bound to proceed from these trifles to bigger things, and some day would be a very spicy morsel indeed. And how right I was, too.

I knew two sisters, of a very good Poitou family, both un-married, of whom there was a lot of queer talk, as there was also of a big Basque servant of their father's who, since it was held that he was a very good dancer, (and not only of his country jigs) was regularly allowed to take them to dances—taught them dancing, in fact. He certainly taught them all the dances right enough, including the strumpets' jig, by which they were nicely disgraced, though in spite of that they did not fail to get good husbands, because they were rich. For once you have money people do not mind anything, but will take whatever they get, even were it still hotter and more scorching. Later I came to know this Basque fellow, and he was certainly a decent soldier and of fine bearing, and he looked as if he had seen a bit of the work, too. He had been dismissed, to avoid scandal, and after that had become a guardsman in Lord di Strozzi's column.[410]

I also knew another eminent house, a great one too, the mistress of which made it her occupation to bring up estimable young ladies, including relations of her husband's and as this lady was very sickly and always under doctors and apothecaries, there was as a rule a lot of trouble there. To make matters worse, since unmarried girls are all prone to such ailments as anæmia, the ferret trouble, fevers and the rest, it happened that two of them fell sick of the tertian ague, and were put in charge of an apothecary for treatment. He certainly treated them all right, with his portable drugs and medicines, but the nicest of all was that he actually slept with one (the scoundrel). And this was dealing with such a lovely estimable, noble young lady of France, too, with whom a great king was most eminently satisfied, till this fine apothecary came along to fix her up like that. I knew the girl myself, and upon my word she deserved a different tackler from that. Later, as a matter of fact, she made a good marriage, and was taken to the altar as a virgin and even held to be one! In that, however, I conceive her to have been very cunning, for when she could not hold her water, she applied to that apothecary and he gave her antidotes for pregnancy, which is what girls are most afraid of, and there are some men so expert that they do give them drugs which very effectively prevent pregnancy, or, if they do become pregnant, cause the pregnacy to drain away so subtly and so discreetly that one could never even notice it, the girl feels no sign of it apart from some flatulence, as I heard of one girl who had formerly been brought up as a daughter of the late Queen of Navarre, Marguerite I. Either by accident or knowingly she became pregnant, but she was not worried. She found a first-rate apothecary who gave her a potion which brought away the fruit of it (and she was six months gone!) piece by piece, part by part, so easily, that she went about her business all the time and never felt any illness or pain, and then subsequently made a gallant marriage without her husband detecting any trace. What a skilled physician that was! And there are also remedies given to make a girl seem a virgin with maidenhead intact just as before (as I asserted in my chapter on cuckolds) and one I heard of an empiricist only the other day : namely, to take leeches and put them on the part, so they suck all the blood from it, till by their sucking they have caused and leave small embolisms, blisters full of blood, so that when, come the wedding night, the gallant husband proceeds to tackle them, he bursts those blisters, out of which the blood pours, making him all bloody, which is a great delight to both parties, and so, as the Italians say, *l'onor della citadella è salvo,* 'the honour of the citadel is saved.' I find this an excellent, sovereign remedy, if it is true. But if it is not good there are a hundred others which are better, such as these gentry the physicians and learned and expert apothecaries know so well how to invent and apply. This is why the gentry as a rule are so well off, so affluent, they know both how to wound and to repair, just like Pelus's lance in olden times.

I knew the apothecary I have just spoken of, and *en passant* really must tell this one about him, of when I saw him in Geneva, the first time I went to Italy,[411] because at that time that was the usual route for Frenchmen, through Switzerland and the Grisons, because of the wars. He called on me at my lodgings. I at once enquired what he was doing in that city, if he was there to doctor pretty girls, as he had done in France. He replied that he was there to do penitence. 'Do you mean to tell me?' I asked him, 'that you don't get such good mouthfuls here as you did at home?' Ah, *Monsieur*,' he replied, 'that is because God has now called me and I am illuminated with his spirit, and now have knowledge of his holy word.' 'Yes,' I said to him, 'and in the old days too you were religious and you certainly doctored both body and soul and preached and taught girls enough.' 'But, *Monsieur*,' he said, 'now I know the Lord better, than I did then, and no longer wish to sin.' I remain mum as to a number of other exchanges between us on the same subject, both serious and laughing, but the rascal certainly did enjoy that mouthful I speak of, and it was worthy of a more gallant man than he was. So it was well for him he quit that house in good time. He would soon have come to a bad end. Now let's leave it. Be he cursed, for the hatred and envy I feel about it, as Ronsard said of a physician who used to come night and morning really more to have a peep at his mistress's body and feel her bosom, her breasts, her belly, her thighs and her lovely arms, than to medicate her against the fever which possessed her—on which Ronsard made a most delightful sonnet, which is in the second book of his Love poems, [412] and begins:

> *Oh what hate and envy I do feel*
> *For the doctor who night and morning will appear*
> *Without a cause to palp her breasts and steal*
> *His hands all down the stomach of my dear . . .*

Just like him, I feel great jealousy for a physician who did just the same to a lovely and great lady whom I loved, but of whom I never had such intimacy, though I would rather have had her than a little kingdom all to myself. Such persons are undoubtedly in a key position regarding both girls and women and have a great handicap with them when they want to obtain them. I knew two doctors at court, one called Castellan, who was physician to the Queen Mother,[413] the other Lord Cabrian, doctor to de Nevers,[414] later in service with Ferdinand de Gonzago.[415] Both had their love affairs and by what was the talk, the greatest men at court would have sold their souls to the devil, so to speak, to have been able to compete with them.

One day I was talking, together with the late Baron de Vitaux,[416] with Lord Le Grand,[417] a great Paris physician, who was of good standing and well informed. He had come to see the Baron, who was ill from love-making. And we both put questions to the doctor on several points about dealings with the fair sex, and my faith he had some nice things to tell us, he told us a dozen stories which made our bristles rise, and went so deep that when it struck nine and he rose from his seat he said : 'Really, I am a sillier man than you two, who have kept me here two good hours gossiping with you two, and quite forgotten six or seven patients I must go and see.' And, bidding us good-day, he left us, after we had replied by saying : 'And you doctors, mark you, know how to have a good time, including you, sir, why, you have just spoken like a past-master.' But lowering his head, he replied : 'Upon my word, upon my word I have. Yes, yes, we do know how to get it and we have it, too, for we know secrets that nobody else does. But now that I am old I have bid Venus and her naughty boy farewell. Today I leave all that to you young fellows.'

There is another sort of people who in fact ruin the girls they are appointed to teach their letters and be their teachers. When they choose these men sink very low, for while giving the girls their lessons they are alone with them, either in the girls' room or in their study and I leave it to your imagination what opportunities they have there, and what suitable stories, fables and anecdotes they can tell the girls to put them on heat, and when they see them thirsty and hungry for it, how well they know how to seize the moment !

I knew a girl of very good family, a great family, I assure you, too, who was ruined and made a whore by having heard her schoolmaster tell her the history, or rather the fable, of Tiresias, who, since he had tried both one and the other sex, was by Jupiter and Juno elected judge in a dispute between the two of them, namely : who had and who felt the greatest pleasure in coitus and the venereal act, the man or the woman? The judge thus appointed brought the finding against Juno, saying that it was the woman, whereupon, annoyed at having been condemned, she took away his sight and made the poor judge blind.[418] One should not be astonished at the girl's being tempted by such a story, for having often heard, both from her girl-friends and from other women, that men were so keen on it and found such great pleasure in it, if Tiresias was right, women must be even keener still, and so it was up to her to have a try.

Really, was it necessary to give those girls such lessons and were there no other subjects? But their teachers will say that the girls ought to know everything, and that since they are studying, wherever they come upon passages and stories which call for explanation (or are self-explanatory) they ought to read them and construe them, without skipping and turning over pages. What great numbers of girl pupils have been ruined reading the story I have just told, and those about Biblis, Caunus[419] and many others like them set down in Ovid's *Metamorphoses*, not to speak of the *Art of Love* which he wrote, and an infinity of other lascivious fables and lubricious passages in other poets which have seen the light of day, French and Latin as well as Greek, Italian, and Spanish! Hence the Spanish saying : *de una mula que haze hin, y de una hija que habla latin, libera nos Domine*, 'of a whinnying mule and a Latin-talking girl, Good Lord, deliver us!'

And everybody knows that when their teachers choose to be bad and give their charges such lessons, they know well how to sauce them and pepper them up, till the shyest girl in the world would give way. Was not even St Augustine, reading the fourth book of the Aeneid, which contains the loves and death of Dido, stirred by compassion and saddened? I would like to have as many hundreds of crowns as there are girls, both in society and in nunneries, who have been stirred up and brought on heat and then deflowered by the reading of your *Amadis de Gaules*. I leave it to you what effect the Greek and Latin and other books have when commented and construed by the girls' teachers, crafty and corrupt foxes, compact of wickedness that they are in their secret chambers and with all their leisure.

In the *Life of St Louis*, in the history by Paolo Emili,[420] we read of a certain Marguerite, Countess of Flanders, sister of

Jeanne, daughter of the first Baudouin, Emperor of Greece,[421] who succeeded him, since, so history tells us, she had no children. In her early youth this Marguerite was given a teacher named Guillaume, a man of saintly life, a much respected man, who had already taken a number of priestly orders.[422] But that did not prevent his giving his pupil two children, who were christened Jean and Baudouin, all so secretly that few people were aware of it, though later they were legitimized by the Pope.[423] What a condemnation and what a teacher! Consult the history of it!

I knew a great lady at court, who was said to be the mistress of her reader and teacher. Indeed, it went so far that one day the King's fool, Chicot,[424] threw the fact in her face, publicly, in the presence of His Majesty and a large number of his courtiers, asking her if she was not ashamed to be kept (using that word) by such an ugly, villainous male as that man was, and why she had not had enough sense to choose a more handsome man. The company all set a-laughing and the lady in question a-weeping, as she thought it was the King who had prompted the fool, for he was wont to play such tricks.

There were other great ladies and great princesses I have known whose pleasure it was to spend whole days in their closets, dictating letters, (or pretending to) and having fine times with their secretaries, whom I also knew. And when they did not summon them to do this, having no reason to write a letter, they had them come and read to them to cloak it all, saying that it weakened their sight to read themselves. There is no excuse for these ladies or others who make such choices of men and behave so, they are much to be blamed, as also is their choice. They lack restraint, yet they have every liberty and opportunity to make whatever choice they pleased. But those poor girls who are the subjects and the slaves of their fathers and mothers, their relations, their guardians and mistresses, and are timid, are forced for their love-making to accept whatever rubbish there is that they find, without knowing whether it is cold or hot, roasted or boiled. And so it is that according to opportunity they mostly make use of the gentlemen-servants, their school teachers and tutors, those riding masters, lute players, violinists, dancing masters, painters, in a word, those from whom they learn the arts and crafts, or else from various religious instructors and friars, as Boccaccio or the Queen of Navarre in her *Tales* relate, and they also make use of pages such as I have known, lackeys and actors, two of whom I knew two girls at court to be in love with. Others again have their pleasure with poets, some of whom I have known to seduce lovely wives and lovely widows too, (for such ladies are very very fond of lavish flattery and this will often catch them)—in short, all those whomever they find handy and can catch. Lawyers who plead in the courts are also dangerous. That is why Boccaccio himself and others with him find that naïve girls are steadier in their loves and more reliable than married women and widows, for they are like people out on the water in a boat which has just capsized. Those who cannot swim at all snatch at the first branch they can and cling stubbornly to it till somebody comes to rescue them, others who can swim well leap straight into the water and swim stoutly till they reach the shore. Likewise girls, as soon as they get hold of a wooer, the first they pick on, cling to him and keep such a fast grip on him that they will not let go, but love him with great steadfastness, all from the anxiety caused by their lack of freedom and opportunity to get another when they choose. Whereas married women and widows, who know all the wiles of love and are experts, and have their freedom and the opportunity of swimming about in deep water without any danger, take the one they really like, and if they get vexed with a wooer or lose him, are soon enough able to find another one or two in his stead, for to them losing one usually means replacing with two. Further, the poor girls lack the means, and have not the presents to give, or the cash, to make a new catch of fresh men every day, for all they can offer their lovers are a few little favours, a lock of their hair, or tiny, seed pearls, a bracelet or a few little rings, or scarves, and other measly little presents which hardly cost anything. For, as I have seen, however great, of however good a family she may be or however rich an heiress, a girl is kept so short of funds, whether by her father and mothers, her brothers, her relations or her guardians, that she never has the means to dole out presents to her wooers and cannot be at all free with her purse strings, (unless it is that little front purse of hers,) and so they are *ipso facto* miserly, if only for this reason that they hardly have anything to dispense (for liberality consists in having means and depends entirely on that) whereas wives and widows can dispose of their means very freely, when they have any. And even when they do desire a man, and happen to fall head over heels in love and thus get caught, setting their heart on him, they would sell or give away everything, down to their very shift, to have him, just like greedy people and gourmands who when they crave some titbit simply have to try it, whatever it costs in the market. These poor girls are the same, and whether what they have set their heart on is good or bad, they have to have it.

I could give endless examples of their loves and their variety of tastes and the extraordinary ways in which they have known love, but there would be no end to it, and besides the stories would be worth nothing unless I named the persons by both Christian and surname, and that I would not do for anything in the world, for I have no wish to see them disgraced. Besides, I have sworn that in this book I would avoid any scandal, and I would not have myself open to reproach for any slander. But to give stories without the names does no harm, I leave it to anybody to guess who it concerns if they can, very often they will think it is one when it is really another.

Now just as one sees woods of such and such qualities, some for instance that burn quite green, like ash and young elm (and as quickly), while there are others that even if old, long since cut, and dry, (like old elm, and suchlike,) that will burn only with terrible difficulty, slowly, whereas others, by what is the usual nature of sere, old wood, when dry and old burn so briskly that they seem rather to be transformed straight away into ash than to burn, so is it with girls, wives and widows. Some, as soon as they are nicely green, mere saplings, ignite easily and burn so briskly that one would think they had imbibed love's heat and whorishness while still in their mothers'

250

wombs, (indeed, just as fair Lais did from that outstanding whore her mother, the lovely Timanda,) to such point that they do not even wait till maturity, (which may come at twelve or thirteen years,) to start love-making, but begin even earlier. Thus less than twelve years since there was a girl in Paris, the daughter of a cake-maker, who was found pregnant at the age of nine, so that when she began to have morning sickness, through her pregnancy, her father took her urine to the doctor. And he at once said she was pregnant. 'What?' cried the father, 'Sir, my daughter is only nine !'

Who was astonished but the physician. 'It's all the same,' he said, 'she's pregnant.'

And, after examining her more closely, he declared definitely that it was so. When they had got out of the girl with whom she had had dealings, the authorities punished the gallant with death for having had relations with her at such a tender age and put her in the family way so young. I am sorry to have had to give this instance and include it here, since it concerns a humble person, of low class, for I had resolved not to stain my paper with such little folk, only to write of big, eminent people. I have thus wandered a little outside my plan, but I may be excused, because of the rarity and unusualness of it, further since I know no such miracle happening in the case of our great ladies, whom I have certainly known at the age of nine, ten, twelve or thirteen years not only very easily to have borne and supported the male riding them, either in fornication or marriage, and I could give many an instance of their being deflowered at such an early age, without dying of it, or even swooning from pain, though quite possibly doing so from pleasure.

Concerning which, the story of a prince, now dead, a gallant and handsome man if ever there was one, comes to my mind. Complaining one day of the capaciousness of the privy parts of the girls and women he had had dealings with, he remarked that in the end he would be obliged to find mere infants, scarcely out of the cradle, in order not to feel such vagueness, as if right out to sea, as he did with the others, and thus to have more pleasure, swimming in a narrow creek. Had he said this to a great and estimable lady whom I know, she would have given him the same answer that she gave a famous noble when he made the same complaint to her. What she said was : 'I don't know who should complain most, whether you men, of our capaciousness and amplitude, or we women, of your minutenesses and diminutivenesses, your petty little baubles, because there is as much to be complained about in you as in us. For were you to have measures to match our capacities we should neither of us need to reproach each other.'

How right she was. And that is why one day at court a great lady, looking at the big statue of Hercules in the Fontainebleau fountain and studying it (together with the nobleman who was partnering her and holding her arm) remarked to him that though this Hercules was made very tall and stalwart, he was not quite as well proportioned in all his members as he should be, for the one in the middle was far too little, disproportionately small, not at all matching his vast colossus of a body. The noble in question rejoined that he found nothing to contradict in what she said, unless it was that we should conclude that in those ancient times the ladies did not have their parts as roomy as they were today.

A very great lady and princess,[425] hearing that certain nobles had christened a huge, vast-calibred cannon with her name, enquired why. One was found to reply : 'Why, Madame, just because it is of so much greater, wider calibre than any other.'

Yet, one must admit, they have sought cures enough and every day try new ones to make their doorways narrower and tighter, more difficult of entry, some using them, though others not. But nevertheless, once the road has been well trodden with frequent passage down it, by regular usage and union, or by the passage of babies, the openings are always much greater, vaster. Here I have rather lost my thread and got off the track, but since there all the same was a connection, no harm is done, but now back to the main road.

There are many other girls who soon lose the great sappiness and sensitivity they had when young, they mature and dry up, either through having very frigid parts to start with, that is when they become nubile (for there are such) or by being close pruned, so to speak, which is very necessary to some of them, for, as the Spanish saying puts its, *viñas e niñas son muy malas à guardar*, 'vines and girls need much watching,' if you are not going to have men on the road past or even local folk try them. And even when they begin to feel their button rise there are some who remain unmoved, whom even all the storms and gales of winter could not stir or wake up. There are yet others so stupid, so naïve, so crude and so ignorant that they just will not hear the word love mentioned, like one woman I heard of who made herself out so strict, of the reformed church, that when she heard a whore mentioned she swooned at once. And when this was told to a great prince in his wife's presence, he said : 'Then she had better not come here, for if she swoons just to hear whores mentioned, she would die on the spot in this place, she'd see so many.'

There are however girls who, once they begin to feel their heart a little, so easily tame to the business that they immediately eat out of your hand. Others however are so devout and conscience-ridden, fearsome of all our Sovereign Lord's commandments, that they are quick to reject any suggestion of love-making. Yet I have seen many a one of those pious, lord's-prayer-ing icon-guzzlers who under that hypocritical cover concealed the fires they were all the time incubating, so acting that the world saw nothing of it but thought they were most strict, not to say almost as good as saints. But many's the time they have deceived the world and the men in it, such as one great princess I heard of, (indeed, she was a queen, dead now,)[426] who when she wanted to assail any man with her love (for she was much given to so doing) always led off by talk about the love which we owed Our Lord, after which, out of the blue, she would switch over to earthly love and then to the love she felt for the man she was talking to, till in the end she got to the great point, or rather, the quintessence. And there you have the way our bigoted or sanctimonious womenfolk deceive us—that is, those of us who are rather simple and do not know their ways.

I have heard the story told, though I cannot vouch for it, that a year or two back, when there was a great public parade in a famous city, there was a woman seen, and nobody knew whether she was great or small, but she walked barefoot, as if in penance, whining away hard enough for a dozen of them—it was in Lent, and straight after the religious parade went off to join her love and dine off a haunch of lamb and a ham. However, the odour of the meats cooking reached the street, a crowd gathered, went up to investigate and—found the woman living on such a magnificent scale that she was there and then put under arrest and condemned to parade the city with her lamb joint, complete with spit, hung round her neck. Now was that not a good piece of work, punishing her in that way?

There are other ladies who are haughty and proud, who disdain heaven and earth, so to speak, who rebuff all men and any love proposal and send everybody flying. Yet one only needs to use a little patience and temporize with them a little, for with patience and time, you have them, and they are all humility, since it is in the very nature of arrogance of this sort, its supreme quality for a woman after having had her way and got very high to drop low and become very cheap. And I have even seen some of these haughty ones who after having greatly scorned love with anybody who spoke of it to them, came round to loving the men, even marrying in some cases men of quite humble situation, not their equals at all. Thus Love gets the better of them and punishes them for their overweening ways, delighting in infecting them more than others, for the triumph of it is then so much the greater when love overcomes that supreme haughtiness.

Years back I knew a girl at court so lofty and disdainful that whenever any able, gallant man approached her and attempted to make love to her, she responded so haughtily, in such refractious and arrogant terms (for she had a tongue!) that nobody ever tried again, and whenever anybody ever did tackle her and try to get down to it, she sent him off so refractiously, with very scornful words and gestures and expressions of her face, for she was very good at that. But at last love punished her, and she let one man have it so thoroughly that he put her in the family way about three weeks before her wedding. Yet this was with a man who was not a patch on all the other estimable nobles who had wanted to serve her. In this one must agree with Horace :[427] *sic placet Veneri*—'So please it Venus !' and such cases are that goddess's miracles.

Once at court it was a whim of mine to serve a lovely estimable girl, clever if ever there was one, of very good family, but haughty and very high-handed, and I was very deeply in love with her. So I decided to pay her attentions and bring her to her senses by addressing her as roughly as she answered me, for *meet surliness with surliness and a half*. This did not in the least outrage her, for by treating her like that I was really praising her very highly, and there is nothing so likely to soften the hard heart of a lady than praise, whether of her beauty and fine points or of her haughtiness. I even told her that all this suited her very well indeed, since she was so out of the ordinary, besides, whether married or unmarried anybody who made herself too intimate and accessible and did not maintain a lofty bearing, and haughty reputation for being haughty was not worthy of having attentions paid her at all, and because she was like that I tended to respect her the more, and never meant to call her anything but *my Triumph*. Which so pleased her that the next thing was her choosing to call me her *Haughty One*. I stuck to that method, and can boast that by it I had a share of her kindly graces, as much or more than any prince whatsoever at court, who wished to pay her attentions. But a very great favourite of the King's, who was a fine, brave nobleman indeed, robbed me of her, and by favour of the King married her. However, as long as she lived she and I were always very closely bound to one another, and I always had the greatest respect for her. I do not know if I shall be reproved for telling this story, for I admit it is said that no tale told about oneself is good, but the subject led me away, and besides, in this book I have told many others about myself, all sorts, but have usually concealed them.

There are also other girls who are of a cheerful temperament, and so gay, so excitable and so lively that they never have any other thought but laughing and passing their time frolicking, with never any other thought but their little excitements. I have known quite a number who would rather hear the violin, or dance, or jump, or run, than hear any talk of love, and some like hunting so much that one could sooner call them Diana's than Venus's maids. I once knew a fine gallant prince, (he is dead now,) who so fell head over heels in love with a girl, later married, that it was the end of him, 'for,' he said, 'whenever I try to tell her how I love her, all she can talk about is her dogs and hunting, so that I really would gladly be turned into a fine hound or other dog or have my soul enter the body of one, along Pythagorean lines, and have her decide to love me, and my soul be healed of its wound.' Later he gave her up, for he was not a good lackey and could not follow her and accompany her everywhere that her sportive moods, her pleasures and her frolics took her.

One should thus take note of one thing, namely, that such girls, after having ceased to be pullets and stopped scrabbling around (as we say of pullets,) and found their interest in frolicking, do like to try the bigger game, late though it may be. Such young people are indeed like little wolves, which are all prettiness, gentle and playful, so long as their hair is soft, but who when they get a little older become malicious and harmful. Such girls as I have just mentioned are exactly like that, and after they have had a good time and worked their imaginations off in their high jinks and youthful frolics, in hunting, in balls, in dancing, jumping, running and country dancing, upon my word, what do they want to do but come to the sweet ring dances of the Goddess of Love. In short, to wind up at last, there are hardly any girls, women or widows who sooner or later do not catch fire, in or out of season, like all kinds of wood, save the sort called *larix*, and they have nothing of that in them.

Now the *larix*, or larch, is a tree which never burns properly, never produces heat or flame or charcoal—as Julius Caesar found out when he was on his way back from Gaul. He had told the people of Piedmont to furnish provender and prepare camps on the main route of his forces, and they did as he ordered, all except those of a castle called *Larignum*, to which some rascally characters had retired, who had turned rebel and refused obedience. So Caesar had to turn back and besiege the place. Drawing in close to the stronghold, he saw it was fortified with nothing but a stockade, so he laughed and said he would soon have them. Whereupon he ordered fire to be put to the piles, and soon the flames rose so high that everybody expected ruin and destruction would result. But when the fire had burned itself out and there was no more flame, they were all most surprised, for they saw the stockade standing just as it had been before, complete, not burned at all or ruined, Caesar had to resort to other measures, namely, mining, after which the men inside at last parleyed and surrendered, when Caesar learned from them the virtues of the wood called *larix* from which this castle got its name of *Larignum*, being built and fortified with this timber.[428]

There are many fathers, mothers, relations and husbands who would like their daughters and their wives to have something of the nature of this wood, which burns so fiercely without suffering any mark or effect; their minds would be more at rest and they would not so often be on tenterhooks, nor would there be so many strumpets discovered or revelations of cuckolds. Yet we do not really want this, either one way or the other, for it would depopulate the world and, as somebody said (and a lady also remarked, whom I know) people would be like so many marble statues, devoid of pleasures and feelings. And Nature would be imperfect, whereas she is very perfection, and if we follow her as a good leader, we never need get on to the wrong road.

Now that is enough about girls, high time now that we spoke in turn of widows. Love with widows is good, both easy and profitable, since they enjoy complete liberty, and are in no way the slaves of fathers, mothers, brothers, relations or husbands, nor, what is more, of the courts. One can have a love affair with a widow as one pleases and sleep with her without being punished, as one is for sleeping with girls or wives. Even the Romans, who have given us most of the laws we have, never punished widows, neither by corporal punishment nor by fines, for making love. This I have from a great jurist, who quoted Papinian to me on the subject, and he too was a great lawyer. Treating of adultery, indeed, he says that if sometimes by error the disgraceful conduct of a girl or widow has been treated as adultery, that was an abuse of the word, while in another place he says that the heir has no right to call to book or otherwise check the widow of his predecessor because of her morals, unless during his lifetime the late husband had taken his wife to law about it, when the heir may carry on with the case, but may not otherwise sue her. And, true, in the whole of Roman law, one cannot find a single sanction applied to the widow, except if one remarries within a year of the husband's death, or without remarrying has a child after the eleventh month of the same year, the first year of widowhood being held to be controlled by the honour of her first marriage bed. There was also the law made by Heliogabalus, that a widow should not remarry within one year of the death of the husband, so that she should have ample opportunity to weep for him for a whole year and give due consideration to the taking of another husband. What thoughtfulness! There was good reasoning for you! But as to a widow's dowry, even were she to commit all the follies in the world with her body, the heir cannot deprive her of it, and the authority who gave me this alleged a sound reason, for if the heir, even if he had no other thought but for good, could institute a charge and start litigation to deprive the widow of what was her settlement, which would be to throw open the door to calumny and there would not be a widow (if with any property) who would escape calumnious persecution by their fine heirs.

According to all this, as I see it, Roman widows had ample opportunity and cause to enjoy themselves. And one should not be surprised if, as we see in his biography, in the time of Marcus Aurelius, as she followed her husband to the grave, one of them amid her greatest cries, sobs, sighs, weeping and lamentation, tightly clasped the hand of the man who supported her and led her, showing him thereby that she loved him and would marry him. And before the year was out she did so, though only by special dispensation (such as Pompey had when he married Caesar's daughter, a privilege not given to any but great men or women, as I have heard a great person declare.) So he married her, and so doing gained a fine picking, and while awaiting the event borrowed loaves from her oven to bake, as the saying goes. There you had a lady who did not mean to lose anything, but put herself in the market in most timely fashion, and yet by so doing lost none of her property or her endowment.

You see how well off Roman widows were, as indeed our French widows too still are, for by giving their hearts and their charming bodies pleasure they lose none of their rights, although the high courts have certainly discussed the matter many times. For instance, I know one great and rich prince of France, who carried on a lengthy lawsuit against his sister-in-law about her settlement, raising objections to her rather loose way of living while there was also some other fault, worse than these, that he also brought into it. But none the less she won the case, and her brother-in-law had to make her a substantial endowment and give her all that belonged to her, though at the same time the care of her son and daughter was taken from her. But that was because she remarried, which the judges and supreme senators do take into consideration, not allowing a wife who hastens to make a second marriage to have the care of the issue of the first one, although not long since, I knew of the case of two widows of fairly good blood who took their young daughters with them when they remarried, against the will of their brother-in-law and other relations. But then, they were greatly aided by the favours of the Prince who kept them. No law but a good c—— can set aside. But from now on I will keep off such subjects, as they are not my speciality, so that though I thought I was saying something sound, I might be saying nothing of any value, and I pass it all over to our great lawmakers.

Now, among our widows, we have some who like to seek the married state again and try their luck once more, just like your sailor who even after two or three or four shipwrecks still goes back to sea, or just as married women who, when in the family way swear and protest that they will never let it happen again, but no sooner have been churched than there they are once more pregnant at the first chance. Like a Spanish lady who, when in the family way, lit a candle at Our Lady of Montserrat church,[429] which by the virtues of our Lady of that name is of great aid in childbirth, yet in spite of that did not avoid a painful labour, and then swore she would never go through it all again, but was no sooner delivered than to the woman who handed her a lighted candle she said : *Serra esto cabillo para una otra vez*, 'Put this bit of candle away for next time.'

Others there are who do not wish to marry again, and of these there have been and still are many who, attaining widowhood in the prime of life, stay widows. We have seen the Queen Mother become widowed at the age of thirty-seven or thirty-eight,[430] and she has so remained ever since. And for all that she was beautiful, of great charm and most warm-hearted, she never contemplated a single man as possible match. But here I shall be told that even had she found anybody to match in greatness that great King Henry, the lord and husband of whom death had deprived her, she would have lost the government of the kingdom, which was worth more than a hundred husbands, and the maintenance of which was far better and more pleasant. However, there is nothing that love will not make us forget, and the Queen Mother is the more worthy of praise and remembrance in the temple of fame and immortality for having mastered and ruled herself and not done what another widowed queen did[431] who, unable to hold herself in, descended to marrying her majordomo, Lord de Rabaudange, which the King her son at first found very strange and embittering. Nevertheless, since she was his mother, he forgave and also pardoned this man Rabaudange for having married her, since by day, in public, the fellow still served as her majordomo, not to rob her of her greatness and majesty, while by night she made what she liked of him, making use of him, either as gentleman-in-waiting or as master, all of which the son left to their discretion and will, both of the one and the other. Yet you may imagine that it was really Rabaudange who ruled, for however great the person may be, when it comes to the point it is the superior partner who subjugates the other, by reason of the right of Nature and the human species in the matter. This story I have from the late Grand Cardinal of Lorraine,[432] who told it to King François II[433] at Poissy, when he made the eighteen knights of the Order of St Michael, (a very great number, quite unprecedented, till then,)[434] for among the company was a Lord de Rabaudange, then very aged, who had not been seen at court for a long time, indeed, not since certain earlier military expeditions, having retired after the death of Lord de Lautreq,[435] from melancholy and dejection, such as one often sees, for having lost a good master, whose captain of the guard he had been on the expedition to the Kingdom of Naples, where he died. And my Lord Cardinal also added that he thought this Lord de Rabaudange had come or was at least indirectly descended from that marriage of this other widowed Queen.

It is some time ago now that a lady of France married her page the moment she had raised him from pagehood, and after having remained a widow for some time.

Let us leave these little foibles of widows and speak of loftier, more sedate matters.

As Queen of France we once had Donna Isabella of Austria, who married King Charles IX,[436] and of her one can assert that she was altogether one of the best, the gentlest, the most sober-living and the most virtuous queens that ever reigned throughout the time of all the kings and queens of France that ever were. This I can say and so will everyone else with me who ever saw her or heard talk of her, and with very great truth, too and no offence to the others. She was indeed a very lovely princess, having as fine and delicate a complexion as any lady at her court, really delightful. She also had a very fine figure, if slightly on the small side. She was most circumspect in conduct, and also very genuine and very kind, and never did harm or hurt to any person whatsoever, nor ever offended anyone with the slightest word, and with it all she was more sedate, spare of words, and never spoke anything but her own Spanish.

She was very devout, too, without being at all demonstrative about it, never revealing her piety by any excessive, showy outward acts, never anything extreme, as I have seen in some of our lord's-prayer mongers. She just never missed the usual daily prayers and services, which she observed punctiliously, without copying any other fantastic forms or ceremonies. And yet, in truth, as I have heard some of her ladies relate, when she was withdrawn, in bed, hidden from all, her curtains tightly drawn, she was exaggerated in her piety, for she would remain kneeling in her shift in prayer for an hour or a half-hour on end, beating her breast and mortifying herself all the time, so great was her devotion. This had not been at all easy to observe till the king her spouse Charles died, but then, after she had gone to bed and all her women had withdrawn, there was one who slept in her chamber and, hearing her sighing, she decided to peep in through the curtains, and saw the Queen in that state, praying as I have said, and so doing nearly every evening, so that this lady-in-waiting, who was fairly intimate with her, one day took it upon herself to remonstrate with her, that in this way she was damaging her health. The Queen was then quite vexed with her for having found out and presumed to speak about it. Indeed, she was almost inclined to deny it, but finally ordered the lady-in-waiting not to breathe a word, and then desisted, for this one evening, only during the night to make up for it all, thinking her ladies-in-waiting would not notice. But they saw her and judged by the light of the mortar of wax which she always kept alight in the passage beside her bed, to read and pray sometimes during the night, whereas other princesses and queens kept theirs on a night table. Such prayers of course in no way resembled those of the hypocrites who just to make a show before other people pray in public, muttering away just to make themselves out to be pious and saintly.

Thus our Queen prayed for the soul of the King her husband, whom she regretted greatly, lamenting and bewailing, not like a lady who was wild and beside herself, out loud, scratching her cheeks and tearing at her hair, nor imitating the woman who was praised for her copious tears, but lamenting very softly, shedding her lovely, precious tears so tenderly, sighing so softly and in such a subdued fashion that one could really see her restraining her grief, so that the world should not think that she wanted to make a mere show of it (as I have known many ladies do) yet revealing what great mental anguish she did suffer. As a parallel, any flow of water which is dammed up contains more force than that which flows steadily. *A propos* of which it occurs to me that during the illness of her King her Lord and husband, when he lay on his sickbed and she came to see him, she would at once sit down close to him, not at his head as is usual, but a little aside, at a distance before him, and would remain there hardly speaking each to the other, but the whole time she was there would gaze at him, so fixedly that you might have thought she was cherishing him in her heart by the love she felt for him, and then one would see her shed such tender though covert tears that anybody who was not looking very closely would have noticed nothing, for she would wipe her swimming eyes as if blowing her nose, so that she moved the heart of every man present (for I saw it) to see her so distraught yet not reveal either her anguish or her love, or let the King perceive it. Her greatest concern during the King's illness was ever to go straightway after seeing him to pray for his health, although she was well aware of his amorous temperament and the fact that he had mistresses, some for show, some for pleasure. But she never once showed him a dismal countenance or said a harsh word to him, patiently bearing her little jealousy and the deprivation of love to which he subjected her. She was a most seemly and most dignified Queen to him, for these two were fire and water together, the King being hasty, all froth and go, while she was cool and exceedingly calm.

I have it from a reliable source that after being widowed there were certain of her more intimate ladies one of whom among the condolences she wanted to convey (for as you know in such a big band there is always one clumsy one) thinking to please her said : 'At least, Madame, had he left you a son instead of a daughter you would be the Queen Mother to the King today and your greatness would thereby be so much enlarged and confirmed.' 'Alas,' she replied, 'do not say such vexatious things. As if France had not enough misfortunes,

263

without my adding to them to ruin her completely. For if I had had a son, there would have been more divisions, troubles and seditions in a struggle to seize the administration and charge of the state during his infancy and minority and that would have given rise to more wars than ever before. For every man would have wanted to get something out of it, and make his pile, robbing the poor boy, as they tried to do with the late King my husband when he was small, had it not been for the Queen Mother and the loyal servants who opposed it. So that had I had a son I would have been wretched at being the cause of such dissensions, I would have felt guilty, for having conceived him, and would have been cursed by the people a thousand times, and their voice is the voice of God. That is why I praise my God and am grateful for the fruit he vouchsafed me, be it for better or worse.'

There you have the kind heart of that worthy princess, regarding the country in which she had made her home. I have heard it said that on St Bartholomew's Massacre night, of which she knew nothing, (and had not heard the slightest rumour of its preparation), she went to bed in her usual way and did not waken till morning, when, waking, she was informed of the fine drama that had been enacted. 'Alas,' she said at once, 'does my husband, the King, know of this?' 'Yes, Madame,' she was told, 'it is he who had it done.' 'Oh, Dear Lord!' she cried, 'what is this, and what counsellors have they been who gave him such advice? Dear God? I beg and crave you to be gracious and forgive him, for unless you take pity on him I fear greatly this crime will never be forgiven him.' And immediately she called for her prayer book and began to pray, her eyes streaming with tears.

Consider, please, the goodness and wisdom of this Queen, not to have approved of such an act, nor the manœuvre it embodied, for all that she of all people might have desired the total extermination of the Huguenot leader,[437] and all those of his faith, since they were opposed to everything that was hers, that she worshipped and honoured more than anything else in the world, while, on the other hand, she saw how greatly he disturbed the security of her husband the King her prince and husband, and further since the Emperor her father had surely told her, when she set out with him to come to France : 'My daughter,' he said, 'you are going to be Queen of a kingdom which is the loveliest, the most powerful and greatest there ever was in the world, and so I account you very fortunate. But you would be still more fortunate were you to have found it as flourishing as it once was, for you will find it greatly frittered away, a divided, wearied country, for though the King your husband holds a good part, the princes and lords of the other religion on the other hand also have a fair portion.'

She did indeed find it exactly as he said. Now that she was widowed, several persons (lords and ladies of the court) were of the opinion that when he returned from Poland the King[438] should marry her, especially as he was her brother-in-law. This he could indeed do by papal dispensation, for the Pope can do much in such matters, especially for the great, for considerations affecting the public weal arising therefrom. And there were indeed many reasons for concluding this marriage, which I leave to be deduced by the most eminent debaters, without my citing them. But among others there was the reason that this marriage would be a recognition of the great obligations of the King towards the Emperor, since he left Poland and returned, for one should be in no doubt that had the Emperor wished to put up the least obstacle in the world, he could never have left or made that journey and come from Poland to France in security. The Poles wished to keep him back, so that he had to leave without bidding them farewell, and the Germans were on the watch everywhere to seize him (as brave King Richard the Lion Heart of England[439] was, on his way back from the Holy Land, as we read in our chronicles), and they certainly would have taken him prisoner and held him to ransom and possibly worse, for they had a great spite against him because of that deed of St Bartholomew's night, at least the Protestants had. But, voluntarily and without ceremony, he confided himself completely in the Emperor, who received him very graciously and cordially and with very great honour, graciousness and intimacy, as if they had been brothers. And fêted him very honourably, and after his guest had spent some days with him, himself accompanied him one or two days out on his journey and gave him a very safe conduct through his lands, so that by his favour he reached Carinthia, thence the lands of Venice, and finally his own kingdom.

There you have the obligation of the King towards the Emperor, regarding which many people, as I have said, were of the view that King Henry III would discharge his debt if he would thus tighten the bonds of alliance. But at the time that he left for Poland he had seen already Lucia de Lorraine, otherwise known as Lady de Vaudemont, at Blasmont in Lorraine, one of the loveliest and most accomplished princesses of Christendom, on whom he had so ardently cast his eye that he was soon all afire, to such extent that on reaching Lyons again he despatched Lord de Guast[440] one of his great favourites (as indeed he well merited to be) to Lorraine, where he fixed and concluded the marriage contract between himself the King and her very easily and without much discussion, you can I am sure imagine, since it was an unsurpassable honour for both father[441] and daughter, the one thereby becoming father-in-law to the King of France, while his daughter became the Queen. Of her I shall speak elsewhere.

To come back to our little Queen again. She for a variety of reasons became vexed to stay any longer in France, one being that she had not received the recognition or satisfaction which she merited. Therefore she made up her mind to leave the country for ever and end her glorious days with the Emperor her father and the Empress her mother, and while she was there, the Catholic King[442] lost his Queen, Anne of Austria, sister-german of our Queen Isabella, whom he wished to marry. So he sent an envoy to ask the Empress, own sister of the Catholic King, to make the first moves towards this alliance. But even when asked the third time, and when the Empress her mother spoke to her of it, she refused to have anything to do with it, as excuse alleging the honoured ashes of her late husband the King, which she did not wish to outrage by making a second marriage, and further because of the too great consanguinity and close relationship between her and the

King. Whereupon the Empress and the King her brother desired to get a very learned and eloquent Jesuit to speak to her about it, and this Jesuit exhorted her and used all the arguments he could, not forgetting to bring forward all the great passages in holy writ and elsewhere which could serve this design. But she in turn confounded him by others just as fine and just as true, for since she had become a widow she had made a great study of holy writ. Finally, there was her determined decision, which was her most sacred defence, not to forget her husband by remarrying. So that this Jesuit gentleman came back empty-handed. But even so, urged by letters from the King of Spain, he returned to the charge again, not satisfied with the firm refusal of the widowed Queen. But now she was not prepared to waste any more time arguing with him, and she subjected him to such stern, threatening terms and told him outright that if he were to meddle and worry her any more, she would make him pay for it. She even went so far as to threaten him with a whipping in her kitchen. I have even heard more than this told of it, though do not know if it is true, namely, that when for the third time this Jesuit went back to her she did lose all patience and did have him punished for his effrontery, though all the same I do not believe it, for she was too fond of people of saintly life, like such as he.

There you have the great constancy and lovely steadfastness of that virtuous Queen, which in fact she maintained to the end of her days, when she joined the venerated bones of the King her husband when, having without cease venerated him with her regrets and her tears, and now unable to offer any more (for she exhausted a whole fountain of them,) she at last succumbed, dying so young that she could not have been more than thirty-five years old[443] when it happened. A loss, in truth, but too dear, for she might still have served as a model of virtue to the estimable ladies of all Christendom.

And, in truth, if she showed her love for the King her husband by her constancy, her virtuous continence and her unceasing regrets, she showed it still more regarding the Queen of Navarre,[444] her sister-in-law, for when she learned that this

K

Queen was living in very great extremity of poverty, reduced to a single castle at Auvergnac,[445] all but abandoned by most of her own folk and most of those whom in the past she had obliged, she at once sent a messenger to see her and offer her all her own means, to the point that in the end she gave her the half of her French revenues, sharing these with her as if she had been her own sister, and indeed it was said that that great Queen would have been reduced to great suffering had it not been for this great liberality of her kindly sister-in-law, for which the Queen of Navarre had great respect for her, loving her and honouring her so much that it was with difficulty that she could bear the news of her death with normal restraint, but through it was brought to her bed, and lay there three weeks, weeping and moaning, and never after ceased lamenting her and mourning for her, remembering her with words of such great praise that none more suitable could have been found to laud and immortalise her. I have also been told that Isabella of Austria wrote and published a lovely book concerning the word of the Lord and another book of reminiscences of what happened in France in her day. I do not know if this really is so, but so I have been assured, and also that this book has been seen in the hands of the Queen of Navarre, as having been sent her before Isabella's death, and that she made much of it and declared it to be a very fine work, and since such a divine oracle said so, one must needs give credence to the story.

Here you have in brief what I can relate of our good Queen Isabella, of her kindness, of her virtue, of her constancy and her continence, and of her loyal love for the King her husband. She was thus virtuous by her very nature. I have heard Lord de Lansac,[446] who was in Spain when she died, say that the Empress said to him : *El mejor de nosotros es muerto*, 'the best of us is dead.' It might seem that by such acts of hers this Queen had wished to imitate her mother, her great aunts and her aunts.

For the Empress her mother, although very lovely, and left a widow fairly young, never would remarry, but contained herself and still does so most discreetly in her widowhood and in great continence, having left Austria and Germany, the realm of her Empire, after the death of the Emperor her husband. She then went to Spain to join her brother, after he sent for her, begging her to come and assist him in the great burden of his affairs, as she did. She was a very wise and very clever princess. I have heard the late Henry II, who was a better connoisseur of people than anybody in his kingdom, say that in his opinion she was one of the most estimable and clever princesses in the world. When she went to Spain, after first crossing the Germanies she came to Italy and Genoa, where she took ship, and as it was winter, in the month of December, that she embarked, bad weather overtook them off Marseilles, where she was obliged to cast anchor. But she would not put into harbour, neither her ship nor any of her galleys, lest she cause offence or give rise to suspicion, and only went ashore once herself, to take a look at the city. She was seven or eight days there, waiting for fair weather. Her finest and most estimable act was that day when she left the galley on board which she usually slept, to attend matins and mass and communion in the Church of St Victor, with burning devotion, after which, her dinner having been been brought to the Abbey and prepared, she dined there, and after dinner she made conversation with some of her ladies and nobles and some gentlemen of Marseilles who brought her all the honour and reverence due so great a princess, since the King had ordered them in recognition of the excellent reception and great welcome she had shown him at Vienna, to receive her as if she were himself in person. Thus she was well noticed, particularly since she spoke to them very intimately, showing herself very forthcoming to them, more in the German or the French fashion, than in the Spanish. So they were very pleased indeed with her, as she was with them, after which she thought it seemly to write a letter to the King to thank him, and to tell him that these were as estimable a group of men as she had seen in any city. And she named some twenty in particular, such as Monsieur Castellan, known as the Lord of Altivity,[447] Captain of the Galleys (and he was well known for having married the lovely Chasteauneuf of the court and for killing the Grand Prior, he being killed with him, as I hope to relate elsewhere). It was his own wife who told me what I say, and she expatiated to me on the perfections of that great princess, how she enjoyed her stay at Marseilles, and how she admired it. And she did greatly enjoy strolling about there, but when evening came she did not fail to return to her galleon to sleep, so that if the weather should turn fair or a good wind spring up in the night, sail could be set at once, or simply because she did not wish to offend anybody. I was at court at the time when the news of her call at Marseilles was brought to the King, and he was most concerned as to whether she had been given the good reception which was due to her, and he desired. This princess is still alive and steadfast in her fine virtues, and from all I have been told has also much served the King her brother. She has latterly withdrawn into a nunnery of the order known as the *decalçadas* or the barefoot nuns, because they wear neither shoes nor stockings. It was founded by another Spanish princess, a sister of hers.[448]

This Princess of Spain has been a very lovely princess, of self-evident majesty, or she would not have been a Spanish princess, for there is no question but that a lovely exterior and fine grace always go with majesty, and above all in Spain. I was honoured by seeing her and talking to her fairly intimately when I was in Spain on my way back from Portugal. I had gone to make a first call and pay my respects to our Queen Isabella, and was conversing with her, and she was asking me for all sort of news of France and of Portugal, when somebody came in to tell the Queen that the Princess was approaching. At once she said to me : 'Please do not go, Monsieur de Bourdeille. You will now see a very lovely, very estimable princess. It will be a pleasure for you to see her. She will also be very pleased to see you and to ask you for news of the King, her son, since you have seen him.'

As she spoke, there was the Princess, whom I found very lovely indeed, to my taste, extremely well dressed, on her head a Spanish-style headdress of white crêpe, coming down very low in a point on to her nose, but otherwise attired in widow's weeds in Spanish style, for she wore silk almost as a rule. My eyes were at once fixed on her, examining her and admiring her, indeed, she so held my gaze that I was quite ravished, when the Queen called me over and told me that the Princess wished to have news of the King her son. I had indeed clearly heard her telling the Princess that she had with her a noble come from her brother the King, on his way home from Portugal.[449] Thus summoned, I approached her, and kissed the hem of her gown in the Spanish manner, when she received me very graciously and affectionately, and then proceeded to ask me for news of the King her son and what he was doing and how I thought he looked. For at this time there was talk of a desire to conclude a marriage between him and Princess Marguerite of France, the King's sister, now Queen of Navarre. I told her a great deal about this, for at the time I spoke Spanish as well or better than my own French. Among other enquiries, she made this one : whether this son of hers was handsome, and whom he resembled ? I told her that he was one of the finest princes of all Christendom, as indeed he was, and that he was the very image of her, with all her good looks, at which she gave a little smile, while the colour which suffused her cheeks showed her pleasure at what I had said.

After I had talked with her for a considerable time, the Queen was summoned to supper, and so the two sisters parted. Then, laughing, the Queen said : 'You made her very happy indeed, saying what you did about her son's being like her.' Then she asked me what I thought of her, did I not think her a very estimable woman, just as I had heard she was, adding : 'I think she would like to marry my brother the King here, and I should like it too.' All of which I of course related to the Queen Mother of the King, when I was back at court,[450] which was at the time at Arles in Provence. But she said that she was too much his senior and might have been his mother. I also added what I had been told in a reliable quarter in Spain : that she was firmly resolved not to marry again at all, since she could not marry the King of France, and thought of withdrawing from the world altogether. And indeed she had so firmly, so confidently, got that lofty match in her head that her head was full of it, and she really thought it would come

271

about, or else she would indeed retire to the nunnery I have mentioned to end her days, and indeed was already building there for her retirement. And so it was that for a long time she sustained herself with that hope and belief, preserving her widowhood very circumspectly, till she learned of the King's marriage to his niece. And then, all her hopes gone, she pronounced the following words, or words to this effect, as I was told : *Aunque la nieta sea por su verano mas moza, y menos cargada de amos que la tia, la hermosura de la tia, ya en su estio, toda hecha y formada por sus gentilles y fructifores anos, vale mas que todos los frutos que su edad florescida da esperanza a venir; porque la menor desdicha humana los hara caer y perder, ni mas ni menos que algunos arboles, los quales, en el verano, por sus lindos y blancos flores nos prometen linda fruta en el estio, y el menor viento que acade los lleva y abate, no quedando que las hojas. Ea! dunque pasase todo con la volumtad de Dios, con el qual desde agora me voy, no con otro, para siempre jamas, me casar.* 'Though the niece may be younger and less burdened with years than the aunt, the beauty of the aunt, already in full summer, fully formed and shaped by her seemly years, and bearing fruit, is worth more than all the fruits that the niece's age, now that of blossoming time, gives any hope of providing, for the slightest human mishap will tear that fruit off and send it to the ground, to be lost, just like any tree in the lovely Springtime which with its lovely white flowers promises fine, healthy fruit in Summer, but it needs only one wretched little wind to blow up to take them away, bring them down and efface them, leaving nothing but the leaves. But let it all be as God's will is, with whom I shall now go and marry him for ever, and none other.'

As she said, so did she, and led a good, saintly life, so that thus withdrawn from the world she left ladies both great and small a lovely model to imitate. There may be some who would say : 'Thank Heavens she cannot marry King Charles, for, had that been possible, she would soon have cast off the stern observances of widowhood and resumed the sweet usages of marriage.' That may well be assumed. But on the other hand one can also assume that the great desire she showed, to marry a great king, was a piece of ostentatiousness, both overweening in itself and very Spanish, revealing her great effrontery and a refusal to be in any way brought low, for, seeing her sister an Empress, which she could not be, she then wanted to rival her, and it was for that reason that she aspired to be Queen of the Kingdom of France, which is equal to any empire, if not superior to it, and since, though she could not really achieve it, at least she did attain it in the great craving of her ambition, as I have heard told of her. To sum up, if you ask me, this was one of the most gifted foreign princesses that I ever saw, even though she was open to blame for withdrawing from the world, which she did more from pique than real piety. But there you are, that is what she did, and her good and saintly end did at least show there was much holiness in her.

Her aunt, Queen Marie of Hungary,[451] withdrew from the world in the same way, but only when far advanced in years,[452] and that was both to retire from the world and to aid her brother the Emperor to serve God well.[453] That Queen was widowed when very young,[454] losing King Louis, her husband,[455] who was killed very young in a battle he fought against the Turks,[456] not so much for any cause as on the persuasion and pigheadedness of a cardinal who had great sway over him, and said that he should never lose faith in the power of God or in his just cause, and that even if there were only, so to speak, ten thousand Hungarians, as these were all good Christians and fighting for God's cause, they could defeat a hundred thousand Turks. Thus this cardinal egged him on and urged him so that he lost the battle, and when he tried to retreat was caught in a bog and drowned.

The same happened to the last king of Portugal, Sebastian,[457] who perished wretchedly when, though his forces were too small, he engaged the Moors[458] in battle, they being three times as strong as he was, and did so on the advocacy and preaching and stubborn advice of certain Jesuits, who made much to him of the powers of God who allegedly by his mere glance could destroy the whole world, even were this all to unite against him, which indeed is in itself a very sound reflection. However, one should never either thus count on or abuse God's greatness, for he has secrets which we do not know. Some have said that these Jesuits acted and spoke thus with the best of intentions, which may well be so, others say they had been won over and prompted by the King of Spain, thereby to bring that plucky young king to destruction, so the King of Spain might subdue the more easily what he did in the end subdue.[459] Whatever the truth, certainly both these errors resulted from these gentry venturing to direct armies without knowing the trade of soldiering.

This is why after the great disappointment of the expedition to Italy[460] the great Duke de Guise[461] often said : 'I am very fond of God's Church, but I shall never undertake any conquering expedition on the mere word and faith of a priest,' by which he meant to charge the Pope Caraffa, known as Paul IV,[462] who had not kept his promise, though made with great solemn words, or rather, he charged his brother the cardinal,[463] who had gone all the way to Rome to discuss matters and see how things stood and then very frivolously egged his brother on to it. One may assume that de Guise had it in fact from them both, for I have certainly been told that when more than once de Guise spoke in such terms in front of the Cardinal, thinking it was a stone out of his garden, the cardinal got very angry, though he held his anger in. I have digressed about this because one thing led to another.

Now to get back to our great Queen Marie, by that misfortune of the King her husband she became a widow while still very young and very beautiful too, as I have heard from several people who had seen her, and according to portraits I have seen which show her to be so, without a trait of ugliness or anything to find fault with, unless it was her large, pouting lips, in the Austrian fashion, which all the same does not come from the Austrian house, but that of Burgundy, as I have heard a lady of the court of those times declare, saying that on one occasion Queen Eleonora[464] on her way through Dijon on a pilgrimage to the Nunnery at Chartres, when there went to see the venerated tombs of her ancestors, the Dukes of Burgundy, and was anxious to have them opened as several kings have theirs. She then saw a number of them[465] so well preserved and so complete that she could recognise various features, among them their lips, whereupon she cried : 'Why, I always thought our lips came from the Austrian side, but from what I see now, they come from Marie of Burgundy, our ancestress, and from other ancestral Dukes of Burgundy. If I ever see my brother the Emperor I shall tell him this, indeed I must write and tell him.' This lady who was present assured me that she heard this and she said that the Queen made this remark with evident pleasure, and had reason to, for the house of Burgundy was quite equal to that of Austria, since it was descended from a son of France, Philippe the Bold, from whom they obtained great property, great liberality and pluck and sterling qualities of bravery. For in my opinion there never were four great dukes, one after the other, like those four dukes of Burgundy. I may often be reproached with exaggerating, but on the other hand I am easily to be excused, since I know nothing about fine writing.

So, our Queen Marie of Hungary was very lovely and charming, and very pleasant too, though she seemed rather manish, but she was none the worse at love for that, nor in warfare, which she made her main preoccupation. The Emperor, her brother, recognized her abilities and skill in the military art and sent to request her to join him and have conferred on her the responsibility which their Aunt Marguerite of Flanders[466] had had, the one who governed his Low Countries with as much gentleness, as the other had shown rigour. Thus as long as she lived King François was loth to wage war in her quarter, although the King of England egged him on to do so, for, he said, he did not want to displease that estimable princess, who had been so kind to France and who was yet so sensible, so virtuous and also unfortunate in her marriages, more so than her qualities deserved, the first union having been with King Charles VIII, who while she was still very young sent her back to her father,[467] the second with Jean, son of the King of Aragon, by whom she had a posthumous son[468] who died in early infancy, and the third with handsome Duke Philibert of Savoy, of whom she had no issue,[469] after all of which she made her motto : *Fortune infortunee, fors une.* 'Unfortunate fortune, excepting one'. She lies with her husband in that lovely convent of Brou, so sumptuous, near the town of Bourg en Bresse, which I have seen.[470]

So the Queen of Hungary was of great assistance to the Emperor, for he was all alone. True, he had Ferdinand, King of Rome, his brother, but Ferdinand had his hands full keeping even with great Sultan Suleiman. Morover, the Emperor also had the affairs of Italy on his hands, and Italy was then in great ferment,[471] also Germany, which was no better, because of the Great Turk, then Hungary and Spain, with that country rebelling[472] under de Chievres,[473] also the Indies and the Low Countries,[474] Barbary[475] and France, in short, almost half the world. He made this sister, whom he loved above all, Governor-General of all his Low Countries, where for twenty-two to twenty-three years[476] she served him so well that I do not know how he would have done without her. Thus he trusted her in all his business and administration, so much that when he himself was in Flanders he left all his affairs in those Low Countries to her, and the Council was held at her residence, under her. It is true that, clever as she was, she referred everything to him, and reported to him all that took place in Council, when he was not present, which pleased him greatly. She waged excellent wars there, sometimes through lieutenants, sometimes in person, always on horseback, like a grand Amazon.

It was she who first initiated the great firings of our France, and burned down lovely houses and castles, such as that of Follembray,[477] that lovely, pleasant mansion which our kings had had built for the pursuit and pleasure of hunting, which was an act which gravely vexed and annoyed our King, though in course of time he returned tit for tat, having his revenge on the lovely mansion at Bains,[478] which was held to be one of the wonders of the world, putting to shame (which is indeed fairly said, from what I have heard those who knew it in its great days say) the seven wonders of the world which were so famous in ancient times. It was there that she had fêted the Emperor Charles and all his court when his son, King Philippe, came from Spain to Flanders to see her, and the festivities which were then put on were so perfect, so outstanding, that at the time all the talk was of the *fiestas de Bains,* as the Spaniard called them. Thus though I recall what great shows were put on during the Bayonne expedition, what joustings, duels and pageants, what expenditure[479] was to be seen, it was all nothing compared with *las fiestas de Bains.* So said certain elderly Spanish nobles who had seen them, and I myself read about it all in a Spanish book specially written about them, and I can certainly assert that never was anything done or seen more lovely, in no way less pleasing than the great shows of Rome when they staged their one-time games, except for the gladiator combats and the wild animals. But apart from these the Bains festivities were the loveliest and most pleasing, more varied indeed and more all-embracing.

I would gladly describe them here from what I have seen in that Spanish book and learned from some men who were present, and also from Lady de Fontaine, known as the fair Torcy, at the time daughter of Queen Eleonora,[480] but I might well be reproached with being too great a digressor, so it will be for another occasion that I shall keep the titbit, for it is well worth while, though I will add that among the grand shows there was the following : she had a great fortress built of brick and this was attacked, defended and the siege relieved by six thousand foot soldiers of the old forces, with bombardment by thirty cannon, some attacking, some defending, with all the same ceremonies and manœuvres that are used in real warfare, and the siege lasted three and a half days, and never was anything seen so fine. The Emperor took special pleasure in it.

You may be sure that if this Queen played the magnificent, it was from her anxiety to make it clear to her brother that everything that she had from him or his Estates, all the allowances, all benefits coming from his conquests, were devoted to his fame and his pleasure. And the Emperor was duly gratified too and lauded her for this and was mightily pleased with the outlay she had made, above all that on his own chamber, the walls hung with a grand tapestry pageant, all in gold, silver and silk, depicting all his glorious conquests, his eminent enterprises, his war expeditions and the battles which he had engaged, waged and won, above all not forgetting the routing of Soliman before Vienna[481] and the capture of King François.[482] In a word, there was no detail that was not very fine indeed.

But his poor mansion ceased to glitter very soon thereafter, being completely pillaged, ruined, and razed to the ground. I have been told that when its mistress learned of the destruction she fell into such a state of distress, outrage and anger that it was a long time before she recovered. Also that going that way one day subsequently, she had a whim to see the ruins and gazed at them most piteously, her eyes swimming with tears, and swore that all France should repent this, and would feel her incendiary torches, for she would never rest till lovely Fontainebleau, which was made so much of, was also brought to the ground, and not one stone remained on another. And in all truth she did vent her rage most savagely on Picardy, which felt it badly, put to flames by her, and I do believe that had not a truce been concluded, her vengeance would have been very great indeed, for she had a stout and hard heart, one not easily softened, both on her side and ours she was considered to be a little too cruel. But women are like that, even the great ones, very given to vengeance when outraged.

From what people say, the Emperor loved her the more for these qualities. I have heard it related that when at Brussels he formally resigned and gave up the Low Countries, in a great hall in which he had called a general assembly of all the estates, after he had addressed this assembly and his son said all he wished, and also humbly thanked his sister Queen Marie who was seated next to him, she rose from her throne and, making her brother a profound curtsey, with majesty grave and grand and assured grace, addressed her own word to the assembly and said : 'My Lords, in the twenty-three years that it has pleased the Emperor my brother to give me the charge and administration of all his Low Countries, I have applied and brought to my task all that God, Nature and Fortune accorded me in the form of the means and grace to accomplish it all to the best of my ability. However, if there is in anything I have done any shortcoming, may I be pardoned, yet I think I have for my part never forgotten anything or spared anything that I should have brought to it. Nevertheless, if, I say, I have lacked in anything, I crave your forgiveness. But if any of you does not wish to do so, but is discontented with me, let me say that that is the least of my cares, seeing that my brother the Emperor is content, for my main wish and concern has throughout always been to please him.'

When she had delivered herself of this, she made another profound curtsey to the Emperor, then sat down again. I have been told that this speech was found just a little too overweening and bold, especially as it was a farewell speech on the occasion of handing over the rule and taking her leave of a people on whom she should rather have left a good impression, to ensure that they regretted her departure. But what did she care of that, when her only aim was to please and satisfy her brother, and from that moment to withdraw from the world altogether and keep her brother company in his religious retreat and at his prayers.

This story I heard from a gentleman in my brother's service who was in Brussels at the time, having gone there to pay the ransom for this brother of mine, who, capture at Hesdin,[483] had been prisoner five years at Lisle[484] in Flanders, and this emissary saw the whole of that ceremony and all the heart-rending farewell of the Emperor, and he told me that some of the nobles were secretly rather incensed by those bold words of the Queen's, though not so much so that they ventured do anything or show their resentment at all. For they knew quite well what a domineering lady they had to do with, and that, had anybody angered her when she was on the point of leaving, it might easily have produced some final stroke of violence. So there she was, relieved of it all, accompanying her brother to Spain, which she never left since, either she or Queen Eleonora her sister, dwelling there to her very grave : they died within one year of each other,[485] all three. The Emperor went first, as the senior, and the Queen of Hungary followed, the two sisters very circumspectly maintaining their widowhood. True, the Queen of Hungary was a widow longer than her sister, and she never remarried, while her sister did so twice, both in order to become Queen of France, (which was a fine morsel), and on the prayers and persuasion of the Emperor, to serve as very powerful bond for the assurance of peace and the public weal, though the substance of that bond did not hold very long. For after it was knotted, war followed as cruel as ever. But the poor princess could not help it, for she did all she could, although on that account the King her husband did not treat her any better for it, for he now roundly cursed the alliance, as I have heard said.

After the departure of the Queen of Hungary, there was no great princess with King Philippe (from now on the invested lord of these lands) other than Christina of Denmark, Duchess of Lorraine, his cousin-german, from then on known as 'Her Highness,'[486] but she kept him company loyally throughout his stay there and conducted his court very finely. For as I have certainly noticed on my own account, apart from discussions and statements I have heard among the greatest of men, any court of a king, prince, emperor or monarch, however great it be, is a poor thing unless supported and given standing either by the court of a queen or an empress or some great peeress and of a great number of ladies and eligible girls.

In my opinion this princess was one of the loveliest and also as accomplished a woman as I have ever seen. In countenance she was very pleasing, tall and very fine of speech, and above all she dressed very finely, so that in her time she gave our French ladies and her own too a model and an example of how to dress, a style which was known as *à la Lorraine,* as far as the headdress, the coiffure and the veil went, which was all very lovely on the ladies of our court, though admittedly they did not adopt it save for great festivities and shows, the better to be dressed, the more magnificent, all *à la Lorraine* in imitation of Her Highness. Above all she had the loveliest hands ever seen, so that I have heard them praised by the Queen Mother[487] and compared to her own. She was an excellent horsewoman, most dignified mounted, and she always rode astride too, in the way she had learned from Queen Marie,[488] her aunt. And I have heard it said that the Queen Mother learned it from her, for previously she used to ride side-saddle, which without question lacks the grace and dignity of riding astride. In this she really aimed at imitating her aunt the Queen, and never rode but Spanish horses, Turkish or Barbary steeds, and very fine Spanish jennets indeed, with an excellent canter, such as I saw her have at one time a dozen of, all very fine, nothing to choose between them. This aunt was very fond of her, and found her character just what she prized, both in the outdoor life she loved, hunting and so forth and in the virtues she knew her to possess. So, when she was married, she often went to Flanders to see her, as I have heard Lady de Fontaines[489] relate. But when she was widowed, particularly after her son[490] was taken from her, she left Lorraine incensed, for she was a woman of powerful emotions. She went to live with her uncle the Emperor and her aunts the Queens, who showed her a warm welcome.

The loss and absence of her son she found hard to bear, even though King Henry offered her all manner of excuses, alleging his desire to adopt him as son. She was however unable to be reconciled to this, and seeing Lord de La Brousse[491] made his tutor, replacing Lord de Montbardon (a very wise, estimable noble whom the Emperor had appointed, since he had long known his good qualities, having seen him as a French refugee) she found it all so distressing that one Maundy Thursday she went and sought out King Henry[492] in the grand hall at Nancy, where the whole court then was. And with very confident charm and that great beauty which made her still more admirable, she approached him, unabashed, maintaining all her own dignity, except that she made one profound curtsey, then with tears in her eyes reproached him with the wrong he was doing her, robbing her of her son, a thing so dear to her, more dear than anything else, and so pleaded with him, telling him that she had not deserved such harsh treatment, seeing the great place whence she had come, and further since she thought she had done nothing against him. And she said all this so well and with such fine grace and gave such good arguments and bewailed her lot so charmingly that the King, who was by nature anyway courteous to ladies, took great compassion on her, not merely the King, indeed, but all the peers, great and small, who were present.

The King, who was the greatest respecter of the fair sex there ever was in France, made an extremely estimable reply, not in a great flurry of words, or in the shape of a long harangue as Paradin alleges in his *History of France*. For it was not in the least his nature to be at all prolix, he never said very much, never was a very wordy man. Besides, there is no need, it is not even seemly, for a King in his speech to imitate a philosopher or great orator, and the briefest speech and most terse questions and answers are better and more fitting for him, as I have heard Lord de Pibrac[493] say whose teaching was excellent for its great sense of restraint. So whoever may read that harangue in Paradin which was made, or rather, said to be made, at that point by King Henry, will not believe a word of it, for, as I have heard several great people who were present say they heard no reply at all, nothing at all of what he said, none of his speech. But the truth certainly is that he consoled her very estimably and modestly for the grief of which she spoke, but said she had no reason to feel it so badly, since it was not from any personal animosity, but to assure her son's condition; that he wanted to have him at his side, keeping company with his own eldest son, taking his meals with him, living in every way the same life and enjoying the same position; and since he was of French extraction and the King himself was French, he could not be better brought up than at the court of France and among Frenchmen, where he had so many relatives and friends. And above all he did not forget to add that the house of Lorraine was more obliged to that of France than by mere Christianity, hinting at the obligation of the Duke of Lorraine towards Duke Charles of Burgundy,[494] who was killed at Nancy. So it was an irrefutable conclusion that without France he would have ruined both the Duke of Lorraine and the Duchy with him and made him the most wretched prince in the world, whence one could see to whom the house of Lorraine owed most, that of France or that of Burgundy. And thus he chid her gently and taunted her for leaning somewhat to that side, so that she might have influenced her son that way

too and brought him up in it. And this was what he had to safeguard against. And so he quoted to her the obligation which
the House of Lorraine owned the French, for having been so
assisted by them in the conquests of the Holy Land, of Jerusalem, of the kingdoms of Naples and Sicily. He also pointed
out that it was neither his nature nor his ambition to want to
get rid of the peers, but rather to aid them in all things when
they were in an unhappy position, as he had done the little
Queen of Scotland,[495] the Duke of Parma, and Germany, so
sorely hit that it would have fallen low without his aid. And by
the same kindness and generosity he aimed to take this young
Lorraine prince under his wing to bring him up in a higher
state than he had otherwise and make a son of him by marrying him to one of his daughters, and so she had no reason at
all to be sad.

But all these handsome words and fine arguments were
quite powerless to console her or persuade her to suffer her
grief with more patience. So, with another curtsey, still shedding precious tears, she withdrew to her chamber, the King
accompanying her all the way to the door, and the next day,
before he left, he went to call on her in her chamber and take
his leave of her, but without her gaining any more of what she
wanted. Thus, seeing her beloved son vanish from her sight,
to be taken to France, she on her part resolved to leave Lorraine and withdraw to Flanders to her Uncle the Emperor
(what a lovely title!) and her cousin (what an alliance, and
what titles too!) Which she did, and did not move from there
till peace had been concluded between the two Kings and the
King of Spain had gone overseas.

She exerted great influence in that peace-making, if she
was indeed not the main factor, for from what I have heard,
after having exhausted themselves in much difficult negotiation
at Cercan,[496] without the representatives of either side making
any progress or coming to any agreement, constantly at a loss
or off the track, like men hunting, she, either because she was
inspired with the divine spirit or by some good Christian zeal
in addition to her natural *nous*, undertook to conduct these important parleys and did so well that a result was achieved

which was most fortunate for the whole of Christianity. Thus nobody more suitable than she was could be found to move and settle that great stone in place, for she was a very clever woman and a well informed person if ever there was one, a lady of outstanding authority. There is no question about it, small, low-standing people are not as fitted to play this role as are the great. At the same time, the King her cousin had confidence in her and respected her and trusted her. He was very fond of her, and had great affection and love for her, for she raised the whole standing of his court, making it more brilliant. Without her, it would have been a very dull place. And yet, later, as I have understood, he did not give her proper recognition and did not treat her at all well regarding the lands which came to her as marriage settlement in the Duchy of Milan, when she married Duke Sforza[497] there, for I have been given to understand that he took some of them from her and in time also robbed her of part of the others.

I have been told that after the death of her son she was very displeased with de Guise and his brother, the Cardinal, charging them as much for having put the King up to it, from their own ambitious reasons of seeing their near cousin adopted as a son and married into the dynasty of France as because she had rejected de Guise's hand in marriage, when he proposed to her. She was haughty in the extreme and declared she would never marry the youngest of the family of which she had once married the eldest son, and because of that rejection de Guise had a grudge against her, though he really lost nothing in the marriage[498] which he did make soon after,[499] for that bride too was of a very illustrious family, a grand-daughter moreover of King Louis XII, who was one of the best, most courageous kings that ever bore the crown of France, and she was also, at the same time, the loveliest woman in all Christendom.

Regarding this I have been told that when these two lovely princesses first met, they were most curious about one another, staring hard at each other, front face, side face, neither able to see enough and find out enough about the other. I leave to your imagination what thoughts might be hunning in their lovely souls. Indeed, it was just like what we read took place just before that great battle fought in Africa between Scipio and Hannibal which brought the war between Rome and Carthage to an end. Before beginning it the two leaders met in a brief truce of arms of about two hours. When they came close one to another, they remained for some time rapt in contemplation of each other, each struck by the valourousness of the other, each so famed for his great deeds, all of which showed in their countenances, their bodies and their grand martial movements and gestures. And it was only when they had spent some time thus ravished in mutual contemplation that they began to parley, as Livy so well describes.[500] What a thing high quality is, admired despite all a man's hatred and animosity, just as was loveliness here in these two ladies and princesses, despite the jealousy each felt!

There is no question, their loveliness and fine graces could be said to be equal, unless perhaps Lady de Guise was a trifle the superior. But she was thus content to surpass her rival in this, though not in haughtiness or pride, for she was the gentlest, the best, the most unassuming and friendly princess that one could have seen though she had her own way too of being haughty and bold. Nature had made her so, both in her great stature, her gravity of bearing and her lovely majesty, so that seeing her one would have hesitated to approach her. But once one had approached her and spoken to her, one found nothing but gentleness, she was all candour and friendliness, which she had of her grandfather, a good father of his people, and also of the gentle air of France. But it is also very true that when necessary she well knew how to maintain and apply her grandeur and royal dignity. I hope to speak of her separately elsewhere.

The Lorraine princess on the contrary was excessively dignified and a little too overweening. I had occasion to have dealings with her a number of times because of the Queen of Scotland,[501] who, when she was widowed, visited Lorraine, where I happened to be.[502] You would at times have thought that the Princess of Lorraine really wanted to make herself out superior and greater in majesty than the Queen of Scotland, but she was a person of great cleverness and broadmindedness and never allowed anybody to succeed in gaining any advantage at all of her, although she was gentleness itself. The Lord Cardinal her uncle had in fact thoroughly warned and informed her of the other princess's temperament. Unable to shed her former superiority, she nevertheless did wish to modify her attitude towards the Queen Mother when they met. But it was one haughtiness capped by another, which was a haughtiness and a half, for when necessary the Queen Mother was the most haughty woman in the world, I have both seen her myself and heard several great men declare the same of her, particularly when it came to curbing the superior, overweening attitude of any person who might seem to want to be so, for she would humble them right down to the very centre of the earth. However, to Her Highness she did behave modestly, deferring to her considerably and honouring her, though all the time keeping a hand on the snaffle, now raising her arm high, now lowering it lest she forgot herself and said too much, though I did on two or three occasions hear her exclaim : 'This certainly is the haughtiest woman I ever saw !'

That was when she went to the coronation of the late King Charles IX at Rheims,[503] where she was invited. When she entered the city, she did not want to ride on horseback, because she was afraid that in this way she would not show her greatness or royal nature sufficiently, but entered in a very magnificent coach completely upholstered in black velvet (because of her widowhood) and drawn by four white Turkish horses,[504] the finest one could have found, harnessed all four abreast, as in a triumphal chariot. She sat by one door of the coach, very finely attired, all in black, in velvet gown, but on her head the white of mourning, her hair beautifully and most superbly and elegantly dressed and covered with a white starched coif. At the other door of the coach sat one of her daughters, the one who later became the Duchess of Bavaria,[505] while inside was the Princess of Macedonia, her lady-in-waiting. The Queen's wish was for her to enter the outer courtyard in that magnificent style. She herself stood at a window and then in a low voice cried : 'What an overweening woman !' Then, when the

Duchess had alighted and climbed the stairs, the Queen went alone to the centre of the hall to meet her, a little in front of everybody else, but going nearer to the door than to the centre point of the hall. And the Duchess was given a great welcome by the Queen, who at the time managed everything herself, because of the tender age of the King her son, bringing him up and having him do as she wished, greatly to Her Highness's credit. The whole court, both the great men and the little, felt much respect and admiration for the Duchess, and found her very lovely, although she was now getting on in years, and might have been a little beyond forty. But there was no change to be seen in her, and her autumn certainly surpassed the summer of many women. This princess was worthy of great respect for having been so beautiful and kept her widowhood to her grave, so inviolably and absolutely faultlessly revering her husband and his shade, and not concluding any third marriage.

She died one year after having learned the news that she had become Queen of Denmark, her country of origin, and that this Kingdom had descended to her, so that before dying she did see the title of *Highness* that she had borne so long changed into that of *Majesty*, though not to enjoy it long, about six months, to be precise. Yet it was an honour and good fortune to bear the title Majesty before she died, and all the same, so I have been told, she was resolute in her decision never to go to her kingdom, but to end her days in her Italian estate, at Tortonna.[506] And the local people never called her aught else but Milady of Tortonna (though it was not a handsome title, nor worthy of her), to which place she had withdrawn a very long time before she died, both because of certain vows she had taken at holy places and elsewhere and to be close to the waters of that part of the world, for she had begun to ail, being very gouty.

Her occupations there were very worthy, saintly and estimable, namely, praying, and distributing alms and charity on a grand scale to the poor, particularly to widows, among whom she gave a thought to poor Lady Castellana of Milan, whom we had seen at court wretchedly dragging out her days, without the aid of the Queen Mother, who had always done her some little kindness in a state of great poverty. She was a daughter of the Princess of Macedonia, issued from that great family. I saw her once, a most honourable woman, very aged. She had been Her Highness's tutor, and when Her Highness learned how impoverished the wretched Castellan had become, she sent for her, had her brought to see her, and treated her so well that she never more felt the neglect she had felt in France.

This is in short what I can say about that great princess and of how beautiful her most discreet conduct was, even when widowed. It is true that one could object that she had been married once before, with the Duke de Sforza, but he died very early, and their married life had not lasted a year. She was only fifteen or sixteen when widowed. And for this reason the Emperor, her uncle, married her to the Duke of Lorriane, to build up more and more alliances, but even so she was widowed in the flower of her years, without having had many years enjoyment of her fine marriage, and the years which remained to her, the finest and most valuable for love, she designated and spent on a retiring chaste widowhood.

While on this subject I should say something, in two words, about that lovely widow of years gone by, namely, Blanche de Montferrat,[507] may her name be honoured, of one of the ancient families of Italy, who became Duchess of Savoy, the loveliest and most perfect princess of her time, and one of the most discreet and sensible of women, who also taught and most discreetly managed the guardianship of her son[508] and administered his lands, as well as any lady and mother ever did who became widowed at the age of twenty-three.

She it was who received the little King Charles VIII so honourably when he visited her Kingdom of Naples and passed through all her lands, principally calling at the city of Turin, where she accorded him a triumphant entry,[509] at which she herself deigned to be present, riding in the procession grandly accoutred, showing what a great lady she felt herself to be. For she appeared on that occasion in magnificent state, dressed in a fine gown of *bouclé* cloth of gold, edged with large diamonds, rubies, sapphires, emeralds and other precious stones, her head garlanded with similar precious stones of great value. Round her neck she wore an outstanding necklace of very large oriental pearls of inestimable price, and bracelets of the same sort on her arms. She was mounted on a fine, superbly caparizoned white steed, and this was led by six gentlemen-in-waiting, attired in embroidered cloth of gold. At her heels came a large troop of girls, very richly, enticingly but decently clad in the Piedmontese style, which was a sight worth seeing, and behind them came a very large troop of nobles and knights of the country. Next in her suite came King Charles, under a magnificent baldaquin, to dismount at the castle, where he put up, and the Duchess of Savoy introduced her son who was very young,[510] to him at the door of the castle, before he entered. She then made him a very fine formal speech, presenting him with his lands and goods, from her part and that of her son, which the King accepted very graciously, thanking her profoundly and saying he was most obliged to her. Throughout the city were to be seen the shields of France and of Savoy, interlaced with a big love-knot, and their mottos, with the words : *Sanguinis arctus amor*—'the close bond of love'—as the Chronicle of Savoy tells us.[511]

I have heard some of our fathers and mothers who had it from theirs who saw it (for instance, the Lady Senechal of Poitu, my grandmother,[512] who was then a girl at court, and who confirmed it all) relate that the talk at the time was of nothing else but the beauty, the discretion and the wisdom of this Princess, and that all the courtiers and gallants of the court, when they returned to France from their journey, were for ever telling the maids-of-honour and the ladies of the court about her loveliness and her virtue, and they also made a point of telling the King, who seemed thereby to be wounded.

All the same, quite apart from that loveliness, he had real reason to be most fond of her, for she assisted him in every way that she could, and gave all her jewels, her pearls and her trinkets to lend him and deposit wherever he wished, which was a very great obligation indeed, for, as anyone will admit, ladies are very attached to their jewels, their rings and their trinkets. And they would certainly sooner lend or deposit some precious part of their own body than their treasury of jewellery —I speak of course of some, not of all. This was indeed a great kindness of hers, for, without that courtesy and further that of the Marquise de Montferrat, who was likewise a very estimable and very lovely lady, he would have been in an embarrassing situation and would have returned without money before he had more than half completed this journey, in worse case than the French bishop who went to the Council of Trent without cash and also without any Latin. Imagine setting sail like that, without any brass! But there is certainly a great difference between the two, for in the one case the situation was saved by a lovely generosity and great ambition which, convinced that his courageous heart should find nothing unsurmountable, turned a blind eye to all the inconveniences, but the other lacked both wit and ability, thereby sinning from ignorance and stupidity, had it not been that he trusted in finding what he needed once he got there.

In this account of that lovely entry which I have just given, it was the grand quality of this Princess's get-up which should be observed, for it was suggestive rather more of a married woman (one might say) than a widow. *A propos* of which the ladies at the time said that for so great a King she could to that extent do without mourning, although otherwise there was no need for any dispensation, and seeing that it is great persons who set the law in all this—and in those days widows, it was said, were neither so restricted or so restrained in their clothes as they have been for the past forty years. For instance, there was one great lady of my acquaintance who was very much in the good books of a certain King—indeed, provided him with his little pleasures—who though always dressed in silk, nevertheless did dress modestly, so she might the better cloak and mask her behaviour, and other widows of the court, anxious to imitate her, did the same. Yet she did not restrain herself too much, let alone to the point of austerity, but still dressed very nicely, lavishly indeed, but all in black and white, so that the effect was more a worldly one than that of a widow's restraint. Above all she always revealed her lovely bosom. I heard the Queen, mother of King Henry, at the coro-

nation and at the wedding of Henri III make the same observations, that the widows of the past did not pay so much attention to their clothes, their modesty or what they did, as they do
today, or as she had seen in the time of King François, who
liked his court to be free in every way. Widows even danced,
and were taken as partners as freely as the girls and married
women. The Queen Mother spoke about that point and said
that she had asked and ordered Lord de Vaudemont[513] to lend
the festivities distinction by partnering the Princess de Condé,[514]
which to please her, he did, and with her opened the great
ball. Those like me who were at the Coronation saw this and
will remember it well. There you have the liberties which
widows enjoyed at that time. Today this is forbidden them, as
sacrilegious, also because of the colours, for they dare not wear
anything else now but white and black, though they may wear
petticoats or under-skirts and stockings in grey, tan, violet or
blue. I have seen some who have been so free as to use red,
scarlet and chamois-colour, as in times gone by, for then they
could wear any colour as under-skirts and stockings, but not, I
have been told, have such colours in their gowns.

Thus this duchess, of whom we have just spoken, could certainly wear that gown of cloth of gold, for this was her mask
of rank and greatness, which befitted her and it was permissible for her to show her sovereignty and dignity as Duchess,
much indeed as our Countesses and Duchesses wear or may
wear ducal garments at ceremonies today. Today our widows
may not wear jewellery, save on the fingers, and carry a mirror
or two and books of hours in bindings and lovely belts, but
nothing on the head or the body, though of course plenty of pearls
round their necks and on their arms. But I can swear that I
have seen widows just as becoming in their black and white,
which are quite as attractive colours as some of the fantastic
hues married women and girls wear in France. That is enough
about that foreign widow, now I must say a little about our
own, for I wish to touch on our Queen Dowager[515] Louise of
Lorraine, wife of Henry III, recently deceased.[516]

It is both possible and right to praise this Queen highly, for
in her marriage she and the King her husband behaved so

sensibly, chastely and loyally that the knot by which she was bound to him always remained firm and unbreakable, and was never found loosened, even if her husband the King did like and take an occasional change, after the fashion of great men, who have their own frank liberties, and also notwithstanding that at the outset of their marriage, (that is, ten days after the wedding,) he did not exactly give her great occasion to be happy when he took from her the maids and young women who had always been with her, brought up with her since she was a girl, and whom she greatly missed. That certainly hurt her very much, especially regarding Lady de Changy, a very lovely and very estimable girl indeed, who certainly should not have been banished from her mistress's side and from the court too. It is most chagrining thus all at once to lose a good friend and *confidante*. I know that on one occasion one of her most intimate ladies was presumptuous enough to remonstrate, laughing and joking, that since she could not have a child by the King, nor ever would have, for many reasons which were talked of at the time,[517] she would do well to borrow one from some third, secret assistant, so as to get a son, so that if the King should happen to die, she might not remain devoid of authority, since in that event she could become the Queen-Mother and have the same rank and greatness as the Queen her mother-in-law.[518] But she vigorously rejected that ridiculous advice and took great umbrage too at the suggestion, and never after that did she like that lady who had advised her so to do, preferring to rest her greatness on her chastity and virtue rather than on any issue come of vice (though the advice, which is according to the Machiavellian teaching, is one which generally speaking is not at all to be rejected outright).

It is said that the third wife of King Louis XII, Queen Marie of England, did not do like her, for when she had become discontent and scornful because of the impotence of the King her husband, she did decide to try that device, taking as guide the Count of Angoulême, who later became King François I, then a handsome and very pleasing young peer, whom she always gave a good time, calling him 'my son-in-law'. Indeed, so he really was, for he had already married Lady Claude, the daughter of King Louis. And the Queen was genuinely attracted by him, as he, when he saw her, was with her in turn, so that it would have needed little enough to unite those two fires, had it not been for the late Lord de Grignaux,[519] an honourable and very sedate and sensible noble of Perigord, who had been Knight of Honour of Queen Anne, as we have seen[520] and at this time was still the Knight of Honour of Queen Marie. He saw that this business was going to come off and he reproved the Prince of Angoulême for the sin he was about to commit, and bitterly said to him : 'How now, by Holy Easter' (for such was his oath) 'what on earth do you think you are at? Don't you see that this woman, who is wily and subtle, wants to attract you to her merely so you will make her pregnant? And if she were to have a son, you would still be just Angoulême, never King of France, as you hope to be. The King her husband is getting on in years, and incapable now of giving her a son, but, if you meddle with her and connect with her, young and hot as you are, and she hot too, by Holy Easter! she'll take it at once and will make a son, and then you will be done! After that you would have to say: Farewell my share in the Kingdom of France. So for Heaven's sake do think twice about it.'

This Queen certainly wanted to practice and to try out that Spanish proverb and saying, which says that *nunca muger aguda murió sin herederos*, 'no sharp-witted woman ever died heirless', which means that if a woman's husband does not engender any, she resorts to the aid of a second to make them for her. The Duke of Angoulême had indeed contemplated it, but protested now that he was sensible and had given up the idea. But yet, tempted again and again by the caresses and wiles of the fair Englishwoman, he once again rushed at it, more than ever. What a thing love's fury is! All over a titbit of human flesh, for which a man pines away and gives up and loses kingdoms and empires, as history tells us again and again. In the end, seeing that this young man was going to ruin himself, and was still carrying on this love-making, de Grignaux told the Duchess of Angoulême, his mother,[521] and she

then reproved and rated him so soundly that he never went
back to it. Yet none the less it is said that just before and just
after her husband's death this Queen certainly did all she could
to be able to live and reign as Queen Mother. But the King
passed away too quickly, and did not leave her much time to
achieve what she wanted. Yet, even so, after he was gone she
spread the rumour day after day that she was pregnant, to the
point that, not really being so, it is said that she achieved a
swelling outwardly by gradually adding linen pads to her
belly, and that when her time was to come she had a baby
boy ready who would be given out as hers, but was really the
child of another woman who was pregnant at about the same
time, the child to be produced when at last she was allegedly
confined. But the Regent was a woman of Savoy, and hence
only too well aware of how boys are made. Seeing that things
were going too far, either for her interests or those of her son,
she had the Queen thoroughly examined by doctors and midwives, and when they saw all the wraps and linen padding she
was using, it was all revealed, and her plot failed, and she never
became Queen Mother, but was sent back to her own country.

There you have the difference between this Queen Marie and
our Queen Louise, who was so circumspect, chaste and virtuous, and never wanted to be Queen Mother at all, whether
genuinely or by false supposition. But had Queen Marie
brought off her trick, there would have been nothing else for
it, for nobody bothered and she would have taken many by
surprise. Wherein the present King owes his mother much and
should certainly love and honour her greatly for her part in
it, for had the other woman succeeded in it, and produced a
small son, instead of being the King he is the King would
have been no more than a petty regent in France, perhaps not
even that, and anyway that feeble title would have been no
guarantee against many more misfortunes and wars than he
has actually had.

I have heard some men, both religious persons and laymen,
give it as their considered opinion that our Queen would have
done better to have played the same trick, and France would
then not have known so much misfortune and ruin as she has

known and will know, and Christendom would have been in better case. I refer you to those bold and keen enough to express themselves on that head, to give their opinion, for we certainly have a matter of considerable importance to the state here, though not in my opinion one pleasing to God, to achieve which our Queen is much given (loving and worshipping God so powerfully that in order to serve him she was ever ready to forget her own interests). For, though she was a very lovely Princess (for the King had married her for her beauty and high quality) and young too, dainty and most lovable, her only thought was still for the service of God, for church-going, regular visiting of hospitals, nursing the sick, burying the dead, and she omitted none of the good, saintly works that saints and devout and good ladies, princesses and queens of past times of the primitive church, performed. After the death of the King her husband she continued to do just the same, using her time now to weep and regret him and pray for his soul, so that her life as widow was just like that of her life as wife. During her husband's life she was suspected of leaning rather to the side of the League, since, good Christian and Catholic lady though she was, she liked those who were on both the defensive and offensive for their faith and church. Yet she never did really like them, all the more since they killed her husband, though she sought no other revenge or punishment than it might please God to send, as indeed she begged all men, but above all our King, who was due to see justice done for that enormity done to a sacred person. Thus this princess lived in marriage, and thus she lived in widowhood too without reproach. At last she died, with a reputation that was lovely and most edifying, after a long wasting illness, hectic and emaciated, it was said, and without taking care of herself after having been too given up to melancholy. She achieved a death that was lovely and saintly, and before she passed away had her crown brought to her and placed it at the head of her bed beside her, so it should never leave her while she was alive, but she should be the crowned head so long as she was on earth.

She left one sister, the Duchess de Joyeuse,[522] who imitated her in her prudency and chastity of living, and she went into deep mourning and lamentation for her own husband, who was also a bold, valiant and accomplished lord. What is more, I have been told that when the present King was in a difficult situation, hard pressed at Dieppe,[523] when with forty thousand men Lord du Maine held him there besieged, caught as in a bag[524] had she been in the place of Lord de Chates,[525] in command in the city, she would have found excellent revenge for the death of her husband, not like the commander who, because of what he owed Lord de Joyeuse, need not have harboured him, she said; and subsequently she did not love him but hated him worse than the plague, unable to forgive such an error, though others think he did keep his faith and the loyalty he had sworn. But a woman offended, whether justly or not, will not be appeased, like this one, unable to love her King today, though even if she did belong to the League party, she greatly regretted the late King and wore mourning for him, and said that she and her husband owed him great obligations. Finally, she was a kind and wise princess, to be honoured for the grief she showed for a considerable time after the death of her husband, for in the end she did at last remarry, to the Duke of Luxembourg.[526] Since she had been married so young, was she to be consumed with love for the departed for ever?

Lady de Guise, Catherine of Cleves,[527] one of the three daughters of the Duke of Nevers (three princesses on whom one could not lavish sufficient praise, either, for their beauty or their virtuousness, and on whom I am writing a separate chapter), has with great dignity never forgotten the eternal absence of her lord and husband and still continues to do so. But then, what a husband that was! The *nonpareil* of this world. That was what she herself called him in some of the letters she wrote to those ladies who were her more intimate friends, whom she prized after her misfortunes, and by those fateful and sad words revealed the great grief which lacerated her soul.

Her sister-in-law, Lady de Montpensier,[528] (of whom I hope to speak elsewhere,) wept her husband too most copiously, and though she lost him when still very young, still both lovely and lovable for the many fine qualities of her soul and body, she never thought to remarry, even though she had been so very young when married to a husband who was already old, so that she only very slightly tasted the fruits of marriage. Yet she never would make up by a second marriage for the lack and deficit she had known.

I remember several princes, nobles and ladies often expressing their admiration of the Dowager Duchess de Condé, of the house of Longueville,[529] who would never remarry. She was one of the loveliest ladies of France, very desirable, and although left a widow very young, yet preferred her widowed state and never would remarry.

The Marquise de Rothelin her mother,[530] did likewise, and although she too was young and beautiful when widowed, she died a widow. There was no question about it, both the mother and the daughter were capable of setting a whole kingdom on fire with their eyes and their soft glances, and at the court of France they were considered to be the most pleasing and most attractive among the ladies. So one need have no doubts but that they set the hearts of many men on fire. But there was no talking of any proposal of marriage being considered by them. They both most loyally maintained the oath given their deceased husbands, they never married a second one.

I would never end, were I to cite all the princesses of the court of our Kings who stood out in this respect. It remains for me to praise them all elsewhere. So now I leave them and turn a little to a number of ladies who, though not princesses, were also of glorious breed, with souls as generous as theirs.

Lady de Randan, known as Fulvia Mirandola, of the great house of La Mirandola,[531] was widowed in the flower of her years, while still very lovely. She went into such profound mourning over her loss, that she never once ventured to look in her mirror, but denied the white crystal which so desired to see her lovely countenance, so that she should not be able to say what the lady said who broke her mirror and dedicated it to Venus with these lines in Latin![532]

> *Dico tibi Veneri speculum, quia cernere talem*
> *Qualis sum nolo, qualis eram nequeo,* that is :

'Venus, I dedicate my mirror to you, for as I now am I have

297

neither heart nor patience to look in it.' Lady de Randan did not scorn her mirror for this reason, for she was very lovely, but on account of the vow she had made to the memory of her husband, who had been one of the perfect nobles of France, and on whose account she abandoned the world altogether, never thereafter dressing in any way but with great austerity and devotion, wearing a veil, never showing her hair, with merely a simple kerchief about her head, and yet in all that indifference manifesting great loveliness. Thus Lord de Guise, recently deceased,[533] never called her by any other name but 'the nun', for she dressed and enveloped herself up just like one of them. And this he would say laughing with her and teasing her, for he was very fond of her and respected her greatly, just as she was very fond of him and all his family.

Lady de Carnavalet, widowed twice,[534] rejected Lord d'Espernon,[535] then known as Lord de La Valette junior, as third husband, just when he was coming greatly into favour, and was in love with her too (and she was certainly a very lovely widow and most charming). Unable to get from her what he would so much have liked, he eventually pressed a proposal to marry him. He even got the King to mention it to her three or four times. But she categorically refused to accept the married state again, for she had tried it twice, once with Count de Montravel, then with de Carnavalet. And when her most intimate friends, even I myself, then in attendance on her, protested to her what an error it was to reject such an eminent offer, which would have brought her to the very summit of greatness, (in worldly goods, riches, favour and every dignity,[536] seeing that it was La Valette, the King's greatest favourite, indeed, his shadow) she replied that these were not what constituted happiness for her, she was resolved to keep her full freedom and self-contentment, the memory of her husbands, (of whom she said she had had quite enough,) satisfied her.

Lady de Bourdeille, by origin of the illustrious and ancient house of Montberon[537] together with the counties of Perigord and the vicounties of Aunday, having become a widow at the age of thirty-seven or thirty-eight (and take it from me that in Guyenne, where she lived, there was not one to surpass her in her time in beauty, fine graces or loveliness of bearing, for she had one of the most beautiful, the tallest and most finely developed figures one could ever have seen, and if her body was lovely, so was her soul) and so a most desirable widow, was sought after and solicited in marriage by three great and wealthy princes, but replied to them all : 'I do not mean to be like many ladies, who declare they will never marry, and do so with such oaths that one would really think one could believe them, but it all comes to nothing. No, I really do say very definitely that so long as God and my flesh give me no other desires than I have at this moment and there is no change in me, I have said good-bye to marriage for ever.' And when another suitor remonstrated : 'What is this I hear, Madame, do you really mean to burn up green, in your finest years?' 'I do not quite know what you mean by that,' she replied to him, 'but so far alone in my bed, I have not been able to find any heat in me, it is a widow's bed as cold as ice. I admit, were I together with a second husband, I do not say that when I came close to his fire I should not catch light myself and burn, as you put it, yet, since cold is easier to bear than heat, I have made up my mind to be content as I am and refrain from a second marriage.' And, exactly as she said, she kept her word to the final moment, and has remained a widow for twelve years, without losing any bit of her loveliness, but continuously nurtured it and maintained it unblemished. This was most dutiful to the ashes of her husband and proof of how she had loved him when alive. It was also a great token to her sons to honour him always. And thus she died, still a widow.

The late Duke de Strozze[538] was one of those who had definitely sought her hand, but, great and related to the Queen Mother though he was,[539] with suitable apologies she declined. Now what a character that was, to be lovely, estimable and a very wealthy heir into the bargain, yet pass the remainder of her lovely days on lonely down (or wool), as isolated and as chill as an iceberg, and thus spend so many widowed nights ! Oh, how many women there are different from such a lady ! And yet there are also several like her, so many indeed that if I wished to cite them all I would never be done. And to our Christian ladies

I would like to add some pagan ones, like that lovely, sweet, kind Roman lady of times gone by, Martia, eldest daughter of Cato of Utica, the sister of Portia, who, after losing her husband, lamented him so persistently that when asked when her mourning would end, she replied : 'the very last day of my life !' And as she was lovely and very rich, she was more than once asked by others when she was going to marry again, 'That,' she would say, 'will be when I find the man who wishes to marry me for my virtues, not for my goods.[540] As we all know, she was both rich and lovely, and as virtuous, (if not doubly so,)—otherwise, she would not been a daughter of Cato, or a sister of Portia. But that was the silly answer she used to give those who waited on her and sought her hand, making them believe that they sought her for her goods, not her virtues, though she had quite sufficient of these. And in this way she easily got rid of her gallants and importuners.

St Hieronymus, in an epistle he made to a virgin named Principia, lauds a sweet Roman lady of his day whose name was Marcella, of good and great family, coming of a long line of consuls, proconsuls and praetors. Becoming a widow very young, she was much sought after, both for her youth and the antiquity of her line, and also for her lovely figure, which particularly affected the will of the men (so St Jerome Hieronymus says, in so many words, and mark what he says !) also on account of her gracious ways and behaviour. Among others who sought her hand was a great and wealthy Roman prince named Cerealis, who also came of a consular family, and he greatly wanted her to have him as second husband. Since he was somewhat getting on in years, he also promised her considerable property and gifts as marriage settlement. Even her mother, (whose name was Albina,) strongly counselled her to accept, and found the proposal good, certainly one not to be refused. But her reply was : 'Had I the desire to plunge into the waves again and brave the high seas of a second marriage, and not devote myself to chastity, I would rather it were with a husband than a genealogical table.' This suitor thought she had said this because of his age, so he replied that elderly men might live long whereas a younger man might die soon. But to this she replied : 'Yes, indeed, a young man may soon die. But an elderly man cannot possibly live long.' These words persuaded him to withdraw. I find this lady's utterance very sound, and certainly value it higher than did her sister Portia, who, after the death of her husband, decided to leave this life and commit suicide. And when all iron objects with which she might have killed herself had been taken away, she swallowed hot charcoal and burned her intestines away, saying that a lady of courage never lacked the means to kill herself. Hence it was that Martial wrote that clever epigram[541] of his, made especially, (and very finely) about this lady, saying that (according indeed to some philosophers, even Aristotle in his *Ethics*, where he speaks of fortitude or force) by killing herself she did not evince either particular courage or greatness of heart, nor did many others who have done the same, such as her husband, saying that to avoid a great misfortune they seized at a lesser one. (I am writing a separate essay about this.) Sufficient here to say that it would have been better had this lady used her time regretting her husband and thereby avenging his death, rather than kill herself, which served no good at all, being merely empty spite against herself, as I have heard some say when they critized her for it. However, I must say I cannot find praise enough for her or for all the other widowed ladies who have loved their husbands dead as much as they did alive. There indeed you have why St Paul praised them all so much and spoke well of them—a teaching he had from his great Master. Yet I must however say that I have learned from the most perspicacious and explicit people that lovely, young widows who find themselves in that state with their nature too, thus do connive against themselves and refuse to taste once more the sweet fruits of the second marriage which the laws of God and man, Nature, youth and beauty would allow them. Yet from a strange crankiness of temperament, being queer in the head they do abstain from what they crave, clinging to the vague, vain shades of their late husbands, which are like lost sentries of the world beyond, while away there in the Elysian Fields those husbands give not a care for them, even perhaps laugh at them. In the whole of this matter they should refer back to the remonstrances and the nice arguments which Anna offered her sister Dido, in the fourth book of the *Aeneid*,[542] and they are very fine indeed, for they teach a widow who is young and lovely not to be too subservient to a vow of widowhood, which after all is more a matter of form than of faith. It is not as if after their husband's decease they were content to crown them with lovely garlands of flowers or herbs, as was done in ancient times, (and girls still do today,) for such demonstration of affection would be fine, much to be praised, and would indeed last a time. For all one can really give them is a few fine words which soon evaporate, lost in the tomb as quickly as the body. So let widows who are lovely and young have some taste of this world, since they still really do belong to it, and let them leave religion and the rule of widowhood to old women.

Now that is enough about these widows who observe permanent Lent. Let us now talk of the others, that is, those who may have a hatred of the vows and the rigours of a second marriage, yet adapt themselves to it all and turn yet again to the sweet, pleasing god, Hymen. There are such as are too amorous by far of their suitors even while their husbands are still alive, thus have their mind set on them even before the husbands are gone, and already then plot with them what they will do. 'Ah,' they say, 'if only my husband were dead, we would do this and that, we would live in this way, we would have a good time in that, and so cleverly that nobody would ever suspect our former love-making, oh, what a lovely time we would have! At this very moment we would be on our way to Paris, to court, and we would agree on it all in such a way that nobody could harm us, you would apparently pay court to so-and-so and I to so-and-so, we should get this from the King and we should have that. We would then provide our children with tutors and guardians, we would not need to bother about their goods or their affairs, only our own, or we might even enjoy their property till they came of age. We would have property and that of my husband at least, we would lack nothing on that score, for I know where all the titles and deeds are' (and so on). 'In a word, who would be better off than we should?'

There you have the fine talk and plotting of these married women with their wooers before the time comes, though there are some women who only succeed in bringing their husbands to their death as far as wishful thinking, talk, hope, and expectation go, and are cheated of it, because their husbands do not die at all, while there are others who if their husbands are too slow about it, as quickly as they can hasten them on to their immortal dwelling. Of such our courts high and low have had and still have many cases daily before them, more than people realize. But the best of it all, the peak, is that they do not do what a lady of Spain did, who, when she was badly treated by her husband, killed him, and then killed herself after, first making the following epitaph, which she left on the table in her closet, written in her own hand:

> *Aqui jaze qui ha buscado una muger,*
> *Y con ella casado, no l'ha podido hazer muger.*
> *A las otras, no a mi, cera mi, deva contentamiento.*
> *Y por este, y so flaqueza y atrevimiento,*
> > *Yo lo he matado,*
> *Por le dar pena de su pecado:*
> *Y a my tan bien, por faita de my juyzio,*
> *Y por dar fin a la mal-adventura qu'yo avio.*

That is to say: 'Here lies one who sought a wife and was unable to swive her. He gave others in my vicinity satisfaction, but not me, and for that reason and for his pusillanimity and overweeningness I have killed him, to punish him for his sin, and then also put myself to death, for my lack of judgement, and to put an end to all the misfortunes I have known.'

The lady's name was Dona Magdalena de Soria, and some say she did well to kill her husband, for the cause he had given her, but she was very silly also to kill herself, as indeed she herself does admit, saying it was for lack of judgement that she killed herself. She would have done better by far to have given herself a good time after she had killed him, unless of course she was afraid of the law, afraid of being charged with murder, and for that reason preferred triumph by her own edict rather than let the edict of the magistrates have triumph over her. I assure you that there have been and still are women cleverer than that, women who play their game with such subtlety that you both have the husbands dead and them very much living and in clover too, with their gallant wooers, engaging not in such self-indulgence as Dona Magdalena but in sweet indulgence with their lovers.

There are other widows more circumspect, more virtuous, fonder of their husbands, and not at all cruel towards them, who do regret them and weep for them and lament them so greatly that to see them one would not think they would survive an hour of it. 'Oh, am I not the most wretched woman in the world!' they cry. 'Dear God, why do you not bring me to my death at this very moment, so I might follow close on my husband. No, I do not want to survive him, for what is there in the world to give me any relief now? Were it not for the little children he has left me as tokens, who still need some support, yes, I would indeed kill myself in this very instant. Cursed be the hour when I was born at all! If only I could see his ghost, or see him in a vision or in dreams, I would still be but too happy. Oh, dear heart! Oh, dear soul! Is it really impossible for me to follow you? Yes, I would follow you away out of this world altogether, if I had to do it myself! Oh, what thing can enable me to live, now that I have suffered the immeasurable loss of you, for were you alive I would have no other thought but to live, but now you are dead my only thought is to die. So is it now really better for me to die now, in thy love, in thy grace, in my own pride and satisfaction, than to drag out a life so vexatious and wretched and with nothing worthy of praise in it? Oh God! What pangs and torments, dear husband! the lack of you means to me, may I soon be delivered so I may see you and know such great delights again! Alas, he was so handsome, he was so lovable, he was so perfect in all things, he was so courageous, so valiant, he was a second Mars, a second Adonis, what is more, he was so kind to me, he loved me so, he treated me so well! In short, losing him, I have lost all my fortune!'

304

In this way do our weeping widows carry on and say a host of other things too after the death of their husbands, some in one fashion, some in another, some disguised in one way, others in another, yet always after the general pattern which I have just described. Some are vexed by Heaven, others curse our world. Some go into fainting fits, others pretend they are dead, some go into trances, others seem mad, crazy, out of their mind, unable to recognize anybody, refuse to utter a word. In short, I would never be at an end were I to think of detailing all their deceitful tricksome ways of demonstrating their grief and their disdain for the world. I am not speaking of all widows, but of some, of many, indeed, if not of most of them.

Those who console them, men or women, who have no axe to grind but are merely performing an everyday task, waste their breath and accomplish nothing. Some, however, when they notice that their suffering patient is not even making a good show of it, teach her how to do so, as did one great lady whom I know, who said to another, (it was her own daughter): 'Pretend to swoon, my dear! You don't make nearly enough effort.'

Now, just as any great flood, after having made a violent, short-lived effort breaking its banks, returns eventually to its bed—a river, for instance—so after all that play acting you will see these widows recover and return to their former state, regaining courage, gradually becoming cheerful and thinking of everyday things. Instead of those death's-heads they bore like painted sculptured masks on their shoulders, in place of those skull and crossbones looks and that graveyard atmosphere you will see them wearing painted medallions of their husbands round their necks, though these they will still deck out with death's heads and sewn-on seed-pearls for tears, whole pools of them. In short, all sorts of ornament, all so nicely disguised, however, that anybody seeing them might think them to be tokens of mourning for departed husbands, not what they are, worldly gewgaws. Then, at last, just as you see little birds leaving the nest unable to fly far at once, fluttering from branch to branch, gradually learning to do it properly, so these

305

widows, as they leave their deep, heart-broken mourning will still not appear completely in public the moment they abandon their signs of grief, but they free themselves little by little, till suddenly they cast off the mourning entirely and so to speak throw all their widow's weeds out onto the nettle-bed, and let love return to their heads more vigorously than ever before, and think of nothing but a second marriage or other bodily enjoyment. So, you see, their great frenzy does not last. They had far better have been a little more moderate in their grief.

I knew one very lovely lady who after the death of her husband was so heartbroken and tearful that she tore out her hair and scratched her cheeks and bosom, which she continued as long as she could, and when others remonstrated with her for the wrong she was doing her lovely countenance, she said : 'Oh, Dear Heaven, what is this you say to me? What would you have me do with my face?' Eight months later who but she was using Spanish white and Spanish rouge and powdering her hair, a great change indeed.

A propos of this I will give a fine example, which may serve to exemplify all this, of a lovely, estimable lady of Ephesus,[543] whom when she lost her husband her relations and friends simply could not console, but so upset was she that, all lamentation and tears, cries and complaints and sobbing, she followed him to the grave after the ceremony, when he had been lowered into the place where he was to rest, and despite all the company present she flung herself into the grave after him, swearing and protesting she would never be parted from him, but would starve to death there and end her days by the body of her husband. And indeed she did do this for two or three days. But it so happened that when a local man was executed for a crime committed in the town he was first hanged, then taken outside the town to the gibbet where by custom such executed persons were hung up for a time to serve as example, under the guard of a soldier, to see that they were not taken away. Well, the soldier who was put on guard over his body, having his ears pricked up when left alone there, caught the sound of a voice lamenting somewhere near at hand and when at last he tracked it down, found that it was in this tomb, and when he went down into the tomb, there discovered this lady, as lovely as sunlight, all tears and lamentations. He spoke to her and tried to find out what she was so upset about. Graciously, she told him. He made an attempt to console her. Failing in the first attempt, he went down to her again and again, and was so assiduous that in the end he did win her over and brought her back to her senses little by little, when he had her dry her eyes. Then she began to listen to reason. Indeed, she yielded to it so well that he twice had his pleasure of her, using the coffin of her husband as couch, after which the two agreed to marry. Having got so far, she let the soldier go up to resume watch over the hanged man, because he was responsible with his head for the body. But for all his good fortune in his enterprise and execution with the lady, the soldier's luck would have it that while he was having only too good a time with her, who should have come on the scene but the relations of the poor man dangling in the wind, to cut him down if there were no guard there, and, finding none, as they did, they quickly and speedily made off with him to bury him decently wherever they could and thus end the dishonour which so stained the family name. When the soldier saw the body was no longer to be seen anywhere, he ran in despair down to his lady, to tell her of his bad fortune, and that he was now doomed, as the law of that place ran that any soldier who went to sleep on duty and let a body be taken must substitute for it and be hanged himself, and that was his prospect now for what he had done. Seeing that now he in turn needed some sort of consolation from her, the lady, who had so far been consoled by the soldier, thereupon said : 'Don't you worry, only come and help me get my husband out of his coffin, and we'll hang his body up there in place of the other one.' No sooner said than done, except that, as the soldier remarked that the previous hanged man had had one ear cut off, she served her husband the same to make him the better resemble the other man. The following day the court authorities came out, but found nothing to complain of. And thus the lady of Ephesus saved her lover by a shocking, very villainous act done to her husband, though she had so wept and lamented him that one would never have expected that there was such a shocking end in store for him.

The first time I heard this story was from Lord d'Aurat,[544] who told it to stalwart Lord du Guast[545] and some other nobles when they were dining with him, and du Guast was very struck indeed with it, for there was never a celebrated man his equal for liking and appreciating a good story. And just after this, happening to attend the Queen Mother in her chamber, what did he see but a lovely young widow, freshly made and modelled, all tears, with veil down to the tip of her nose, really wretched and dejected, hardly saying a word to anyone. Lord du Guast immediately said : 'See her? Before the year's out, she'll be an Ephesian widow.' Which she was, not so basely, however, but she did marry a man of low estate much as du Guast had prophesied. I was also told the story of de Beau-Joyeux,[546] the Queen Mother's Gentleman of the Bed-Chamber and the best violinist in Christendom. Not only was he master of his art, and of music generally, his was also a very culti-vated mind, he was most knowledgeable, and above all he had a great stock of very fine stories and lovely tales, and was always to impart them to his most intimate friends and he now told some of his, for in his time he had both seen and himself enjoyed some fine love encounters, for with his supreme art and his fine, bold temperament, both excellent instruments for love-making, he could do a great deal. It was the Lord Marshal de Brissac who passed him on to the Queen Mother[547] when she was Regent, sending him from Piedmont with a very fine company of fiddlers, a complete orchestra, in fact. His name was Baltazarin, but later he changed it, and it was he who composed those lovely ballets which were constantly danced at court. He was a great friend of both Lord du Guast and myself, and we often chatted together and invariably told each other a good tale or two, especially of love-making and the tricks ladies get up to, and among others he once told us this story of the lady of Ephesus, which, as I have said, we had already heard from Lord d'Aurat, who said he had it from Lampridius,[548] and since then I have read it in the book on

Funerals,[549] (certainly a fine work) dedicated to the late Duke of Savoy.

Some may say I might have done without this digression. Yes, but I did want to mention my friend *à propos,* who often when he saw some of our tearful widows would remind me and say : 'There's another who'll be a lady of Ephesus, if she hasn't been already.' Admittedly, that was a very unusual tragi-comedy, most inhuman too, casting such a cruel slur on her husband.

She was not like a lady of our time, of whom I have heard, who when her husband died cut off his front or rather his middle parts, which she had formerly prized so much, and embalmed them, scenting them and odorifying them with perfumes and very highly-scented, musky powders, then encasing them in a silver-gilt casket, which she kept and preserved as something very precious. You may well imagine that she examined this relic from time to time, in eternal remembrance of the good times she had had. I do not know if this is true, but the story was told the King who retold it to several of his more intimate friends, and I have heard him say that in the St Bartholemew massacre Lord de Pleuviau was killed, who in his time had been a brave soldier, in the Tuscan war, under Lord de Soubise,[550] and in the civil war too, as he showed particularly at the battle of Jarnac,[551] where he commanded a regiment, and also the siege of Niort.[552] Well, after the act, the soldier who killed him told his wife, who was heartbroken, all tears and desolation, and also rich and beautiful, that if she would not marry him, he would kill her too, and treat her the same as her husband,[553] for at Niort it was war to the bitter end, all hand-to-hand fighting. To save her life, the poor woman, who was still lovely and young, was thus compelled to combine funeral and wedding. Yet she was to be forgiven, for could a frail, feeble little woman do aught else? It would have been equivalent to suicide had she thus abandoned her lovely bosom merely to the sword of a murderer. But 'the time is gone, fair shepherdess,' we have no more of those inspired, undauntable women we once had. Besides, our holy Christendom prohibits suicide, which serves our widows today as good excuse, for they say that were it not prohibited by God, they would do away with themselves, and in that way they wrap up their humbug.

In the same massacre another lady of very good family was widowed who was also very lovely and attractive, and though widowed but a moment before, she was taken by force by a noble whom I know well, and this left her so shocked and upset that for some time she was thought to have lost her reason altogether. Soon after, however, realizing that she was widowed on the right side of middle age, she gradually became worldly again and reassumed her natural vitality, forgetting the outrage and marrying again—and a marriage of love with an eminent man, too, in which she did very well.

I will further add the following : there was one woman widowed in the St Bartholemew massacre by the death of her husband, who was killed with the others. She was so upset that whenever she saw a wretched Catholic, even though he had not been in it, she was apt to faint, or she would at least stare at him in horror and hatred as if he were the plague. It was no use talking to her of going to Paris, or even within five miles of it, for neither her eyes nor her heart would bear the sight of the city—do I say sight, why, not even hearing of it could she abide. After two years, however, she brought herself to it and went to say *how-do-you-do* to that good city and look about it and go in her coach to the palace, but she would still sooner have done herself to death or cast herself into a fire than enter the *Rue de la Huchette*, where her husband had been killed. Just like a snake, which so loathes the shade of an ash-tree that it would rather risk its life and creep through the hot coals of a fire, Pliny says,[554] than venture into a shade so hateful to it. So that the late King, being present, (when he was Prince, it was)[555] said he had never seen a woman as wild with loss and grief as she was, adding that in the end somebody would have to stun her, like they do wild young falcons to hood them, and so train her. But after some time he remarked that she became quite tame enough all by herself, and let herself be hooded, bringing herself to it. And what did she do very soon after that? She could not see enough of Paris, was all excitement, parading about from one side of the city to the other, all ways, every way, without respect for any oath she had taken. And then trust her! One day, returning from a journey after eight months absence from court, I had just paid my respects to the King when I saw that self-same widow enter the hall of the Louvre Palace so togged out, so bedizened, in the company of all her women relations and friends, to display herself to the King, the Queen and all the court, and receive the first stage of the sacrament of marriage, that is, the bethrothal blessing, from the hands of the Bishop of Digne,[556] Grand Almoner of the Queen of Navarre. Who was taken aback but myself, though, from what she told me later, she was still more so, quite unexpectedly seeing me like that at her great betrothal gathering, staring and rolling my eyes ironically, as I did when I thought of all the airs she had put on and the oaths I had heard her make. And how she did stare at me, too, for I had myself courted her and wanted to marry her too, for she now thought, that was her impression, that I had come there and taken up that position expressly to be present on this particular occasion, to serve as both witness and judge and condemn her for what she was doing. And she said—swore it—that she would rather have paid ten thousand crowns not to have me present, pricking her conscience as I did.

I knew one great lady, a countess and a widow, of very high position, who did the same, for, though a staunch, unbending Huguenot, she agreed to marry a very estimable Catholic noble, but the misfortune was that before the wedding took place a pestilential fever seized her in Paris and so infected her that it caused her death, and when she was in high fever she lamented wildly, even saying: 'Alas, is it possible that in so large a city, where everything is known, there is not one doctor who could cure me, who would like to earn some money, for I would pay very well? It would not be so bad had my death come after my marriage and at least my husband had known how much I loved and honoured him.' (Sophonisba said otherwise, for she repented having become engaged before drinking poison). Well, with these words, and others in like sense, this countess turned over in bed and died. What a thing the frenzy of love is, thus mid-way across the oblivion-full Styx to recall those pleasures and fruits of love which she would so like at least to have tasted before she quit the garden.

Now, while these Huguenot ladies have done such things, I have certainly known Catholic ladies who have behaved in a similar fashion, and, after having threatened them and their religion with worse than hanging, married Huguenots. (If I decided to add them, I would never be done.) This shows that widows should be sensible and not cry out so loudly at the beginning of their widowhood, getting themselves worked up, all thunder and lightning and downpours of tears, merely later to make such exhibitions of themselves and appear foolish. Better say less and do more. But to this they say: 'Oh no, at the outset you have to be as determined as a murderess, and as impudent, self-confident enough in fact to swallow any disgrace. That only lasts a little time, it passes off, as soon as people have some other woman to gossip about they will leave me alone and pick on her.'[557]

In a little Spanish book I have read that Victoria Colonna,[558] daughter of the great Fabricio Colonna, and wife of that great Marquis de Pescayre[559] (*the nonpareil* of his time, Heaven alone knows) after the loss of her husband fell into such a desperate melancholy that it was impossible to think of anything that would console her, whenever anybody tried any method, old or new, she merely said: 'What do you wish to console me for? My husband's death? You are mistaken. He is not dead, for he is still very much alive and active in my soul. I feel him there every day and every night, coming to life again, stirring and reborn.' These would have been lovely words if, after some time, having bid him farewell, and sent him to walk on the far bank of the River Acheron, she had not married again, becoming the wife of the Abbé of Farfe,[560] who was certainly not to be compared with her great Marquis. I do not mean in blood, for de Farfe came of the noble Ursini line,[561] just as good, and as ancient as that of Avalos,[562] even more so. But the properties of these two men did not match at all, for Pescayre's estates were incomparable, while his value was inestimable, though the Abbé certainly gave great proof of his personal qualities too in the loyal and valiant way he worked for King François, though this was all a matter of little hidden, unsubstantial shifts, quite the opposite of the deeds of the other man, who had achieved great and well-known results, often by very outstanding victories. Further, the profession of arms of the other man, engaged in and trained in from an early age, and practised every day, could not but surpass greatly that of a man of the church, who had anyway adopted that career late in life. Not that I mean by this to say anything derogatory about a man once dedicated to God and his church who broke his vow and left that calling to turn to arms, for that would be to do wrong to so many a bold military leader who has taken that course.

Was not Caesar Borgia, Duke of Valentinois, first a cardinal, yet subsequently so great a military leader that that worthy teacher of Princes and great men, Machiavelli, took him as example, a rare model for all others of his ilk to follow and mould themselves on? We have seen the Marshal de Foix, who was a man of the church, once known as Protonotary de Foix, become a great military leader.[563] Marshal Strozze[564] was dedicated to the church, then, when the red bonnet was denied him, left his vestments and took up arms. Lord de Salvoison, of whom I have spoken[565] (who followed him closely, indeed, and would have accompanied him to war, had he been of as eminent a family and a relation of the Queen's) had also first followed the long-frocked profession. Yet what a great military leader he was! Had he lived longer, he would have surpassed everybody. Did not Marshal de Bellegarde,[566] long known as the Provost of Ours, once wear the mortar-board? The late Lord d'Anguien,[567] who fell in the battle of St Quentin, had been a Bishop, Lord de Chevallier de Bonnivet likewise.[568] And that gallant Lord de Martigues[569] had also been in the Church. In short, there are many others on whom I would rather not spend space. Though I must praise my own people, and not without good reason. My brother, Captain Bourdeille,[570] the former Rodomont of all Piedmont, had also been dedicated to the church, but, finding it was not his proper sphere, changed his long robes for shorter ones, in no time to become one of Piedmont's best military leaders and bravest men, marked down for a very elevated career too, had he not, alas, been killed at the age of twenty-five. In our day at our court we have seen many such, for instance, the young Lord of Clermont-Tallard,[571] whom I once saw Abbot of Bon-Port, but after he left the abbey won distinction in our armies and at court too, one of the gravest, most valorous and estimable men we have ever had, as he showed very clearly by his death, falling gloriously at La Rochelle,[572] the first time we entered the entrenchment. I could name a good thousand such, and I would never end. Lord de Louillelas,[573] known as 'The Young Prior' had once been Bishop of Tiays, but subsequently led a regiment and served the King most loyally and valiantly in Guyenne, under Marshal de Matignon.[574]

In short, I should never be through were I to name all such men, so for sake of brevity I remain silent, also from fear of having it imputed to me that I am too inclined to digress, though I have done so here much to the point, à propos of that Vittoria Colonna who married the Abbé. Had she not married him as her second marriage, she would have been better off with her own name and title of Vittoria—for having won a victory over herself, and also since, unable to find a second husband like her first, she would have shown herself content.

I knew many ladies who imitated that precedent. There was one[575] who married one of my uncles, the bravest, most valiant, most perfect of men of his time.[576] When he died, she married another[577] who was as like him as an ass is to Spanish steed, (my uncle of course being the steed.) There was another lady[578] I knew who married a Marshal of France who was a handsome, estimable valiant noble.[579] In a second marriage she switched to take a man who was the very opposite of him, who had also been in the church,[580] and of her it was said that when she went to court, after this second marriage, (she had not attended for twenty years,) she reassumed the name and title of her first husband, regarding which our royal courts and the high court too should take good note and pass a law, for I have known very many indeed to do the same, which shows far too little regard for the women's late husbands, to want to bear their name after they have they have gone, and since they have committed such an error they should pay the consequences. There was one widow whom I knew who when her husband died lamented him so heartbrokenly for about a year that she was expected to pass away herself at any moment. After a year, when the time came to go out of full mourning into half mourning, she said to one of her women : 'Pack this piece of crêpe away carefully, it may come in again another time,' then at once caught herself up : 'But whatever am I thinking of?' she said, ' I am dreaming. Rather die than go through all this again!' But when her mourning was over, she married a second husband, and one much inferior to the first, too. 'But,' (they say, these women) 'he was of as good a family as the first.' Yes, I admit, he was, but yet what of virtue and character? Are they not more to be valued than anything? And the best part of it as I see it is that when it is done they do not get far, for God provides for their being treated (and beaten too) just as thoroughly as they deserve. Then they are all repentance, but it is too late.

Such flighty ladies have some quirk or kink in their heads that we don't really know of, as a Spanish lady I heard of, who, wanting to marry again, and hearing somebody admonish her and ask what of the great love her husband had had for her, replied : *La muerto del marido y nuevo casamiento no han de romper el amor d'una casta muger,* that is : 'The death of a husband and a new marriage need not destroy a chaste woman's love.' Now fit those two contraries together, if you please.

When they wanted to remarry her, another Spanish lady said something even better : *Si hallo un marido bueno, no quiero tener el temor de pedelo; y si malo, que necessidad de del?:* 'If I get a good husband I do not want to live in fear of losing him, if a bad one, what use will he be to me?'

When a Roman matron named Valeria lost her husband and some of her women friends were trying to comfort her about her loss, she said : 'Of course, he is dead for you, but

315

within me he lives eternally.' The Marquis I have spoken of had borrowed such words from her. Such pronouncements of these estimable ladies are quite the opposite of what a slanderous Spaniard said : *que le jornada de la viudez d'una muger es d'un dia,* 'that the duration of the widowhood of a woman is one day.' A lady I will now tell of said something far worse. This was lady de Monnains, widow of the King's lieutenant[581] slaughtered at Bordeaux by the people, on account of the salt tax. When she was brought the news that her husband had been killed and treated as he was, she at once cried : 'Oh, my diamond, whatever has happened to that?' This was one she had given him when they married. It was priced at 1,200 crowns, and he always wore it on his finger. Thereby she made one wonder whom she went into mourning for—her husband, or her diamond?

Lady d'Estampes, greatly favoured by King François and for this reason little beloved by her husband, when another widow happened to come to see her to seek pity for her in her widowhood, said : 'Ah, my dear, you are too happy to be in such a condition, everybody who wants can't be' (as if she herself really wanted to be a widow.)

Widowhood suits some, not others. But what are we to say of widowed women who hide their new marriage and do not want it made known? I knew one who kept her re-marriage secret for more than seven or eight years,[582] and never did want to have it published or made known. People said that this was from the fear of her young son in which she went, one of the most valiant and estimable men too, lest he do her or her husband[583] an injury. But the moment he was killed in a skirmish of war, which crowned him with great fame, she let her marriage come to light and be published.

I have been told of a great lady who was a widow who afterwards, more than fifteen years since, married a very great prince and lord, but the world knows nothing of it and it is still not recognized, so secret and discreet has it been kept, and the talk is that the lord is afraid of his mother-in-law, who was very domineering to him and did not want him to marry her daughter because of his little sons.

I knew another very great lady who not long ago died after being married to a simple noble for some twenty years, without anybody's noticing it or even hearing it rumoured.

I have heard a lady of high quality and ancient line say that the late Lord Cardinal du Bellay, when both bishop and cardinal, married Lady de Chastillon,[584] and was her husband when he died, which she alleged à propos of something that Lord de Manne, Provencal, of the house of Cental, otherwise Bishop of Frejus,[585] once said, and he had followed the said Cardinal fifteen years at the court of Rome, and been one of his intimate protonotaries. They were talking of the Cardinal and she enquired whether he had never said, or confessed, that he had been married, and who was taken aback but Lord de Manne at such a question! (He is still alive, and will be able to say if I am lying, for I was present.) His reply was that he had never heard tell of such a marriage, either from the Cardinal or anybody else. 'Well, then let me tell you now,' she said, 'for there is nothing truer than that he was married, and really did die the husband of Lady de Chastillon.' I can assure you, I was most amused to see the expression of amazement on Lord de Manne's face, for he was a very conscientious, religious man, and thought he knew all his late master's secrets, but was thoroughly taken aback by that one, shocked too, because of the holy rank that the dead man had enjoyed.

This Lady de Chastillon was the widow of the late Lord de Chastillon, said to have tutored the little King Charles VIII together with Bourdillon,[586] Galiot[587] and Bonneval[588] who tutored the royal brood. He died at Ferrara, having been wounded in the siege of Ravenna, and taken there for treatment.[589] The lady in question was widowed very young and lovely, sedate and virtuous, so was chosen Lady-of-Honour to the late Queen of Navarre. This was the Queen who gave that fine piece of advice to the lady and great princess who is described in the Queen's *Hundred Tales*,[590] the one into whose bed a noble slipped one night through a trapdoor giving on to a room under the edge of the bed, and trying to take her, but only getting some fine scratches down his handsome face. And how when she

317

wished to complain to her brother, Lady de Chastillon made the objection that you will find in the *Tale,* together with the fine piece of advice, which is one of the loveliest and wisest, and most suitable for avoiding scandal that could be given, the leading high court chairman in Paris could not have done better, indicating moreover that this was a lady as wily and as subtle in such connivings as she was sensible and level-headed, so that there is no reason to doubt that she kept her marriage to her cardinal secret. My grandmother, the Lady Seneschal of Poitou, had her place after her death.[591] This was by choice of King François himself, who selected and appointed her, and actually sent a messenger all the way to her house to fetch her, and personally introduced her to the Queen his sister, since he knew her to be a very wise and very virtuous lady, so that he called her *our chevalier sans reproche,* though she was still not so subtle, so cunning or so wily in such a matter as the lady who preceded her, nor involved in a second marriage. And if you would know from whom the news came, it was the Queen of Navarre herself and Admiral de Bonnivet, as I have it from my late grandmother. Though, all the same, as I see it, the Queen was under no obligation to conceal her name, since the other was nohow her equal in chastity and left the room embarrassed, and despite the lovely, wise remonstrance this Lady of Honour, Lady de Chastillon made, the Queen insisted on divulging it, and whoever has read the story will find it was so. And I think that it was her alleged husband, the Lord Cardinal, one of the best spoken, most knowledgeable, eloquent, wise and discreet men of his day, who had taught her thus to discourse and remonstrate so well. This story might be rather shocking because of the holy, ecclesiastical eminence of the other party, but any who wishes to tell it should hide the name.

But if the story of this marriage was kept secret, that of the late Lord Cardinal de Chastillon was not,[592] for he himself divulged it and published it, without borrowing anybody else as trumpet, and died a married man, without giving up his long vestments and red bonnet. On the one hand he made the reformed faith the excuse, for he was a staunch adherent of that, and on the other the fact that he wanted to maintain his rank and not lose it (which he otherwise would not have done,) and enter the council, where he could have done much for his faith and his party, as indeed he would have been highly capable of doing, being a very able and a very great person.

I think that the Lord Cardinal du Bellay[593] might have done the same, for at the time he was inclined towards the faith and doctrines of Luther (much as the court of France too was somewhat influenced by them, for all new things please) but also because this wretched doctrine did give people, even ecclesiastical persons, rather a lot of liberty with regard to marriage.

Now let us stop talking about these persons in positions of honour, because of the great reverence we owe their rank and their position in the church. Now we ought to give some notice to our elderly widows, who remarry even if they have not six sound teeth in their jaws. It is not long since a lady, widowed for the third time, and in her eighty-fourth year, was married for the fourth time, to a noble in Guyenne who is of fairly high position. I do not know why she did this (for she was very wealthy and had also a considerable fortune in cash, which this noble was after) unless it was that she simply did not want to give in yet, but still wanted to frick in the laurels as Mademoiselle Sevin, the Queen of Navarre's female clown, put it.

I also knew a great lady who at the age of seventy-six was married again, and to a noble who was not at all of the first water. She lived a hundred years, and still kept going. In her time she had been one of the loveliest of women and, as people said, had made the fullest use of her delightful young body, in every sort of way, when still only a candidate for marriage, when married, and when a widow too.

Now there are two terrible female characters for you! They must both have been very hot by nature. I have indeed heard good expert bread-bakers say that an old oven is easier to heat than a new one, and once heated, holds its heat better and bakes a better loaf.

I do not know what their lovers and frequenters find so savoury about them, but I have certainly seen many bold and gallant fellows as keen on making love with elderly women as young, or even more so, and I have in fact been told that it is because of the advantages they get from such unions. I have indeed seen some who loved elderly women very hotly indeed, without getting anything from their purses, (except of course those in their bodies) and some years ago we even saw one great sovereign[594] who loved a great widowed lady who was well advanced in years[595] so much that he left his own wife and all other women, however lovely and young they were, just to sleep with her. But in this case he was quite right, for she was one of the loveliest and most delightful ladies one could ever have seen, and her winter was undoubtedly to be preferred to the spring, summer and autumn of others.[596] Among those who have had a lot to do with Italian courtesans, one has seen—and can still see—some who invariably select the most notorious and ancient of them, those who have bedraggled their skirts the most, finding greater charm, both bodily and spiritual, in them. This is why when sent for by Mark Antony to go and see him, the delightful Cleopatra was not grealy excited, for she was confident that, since she had been able to capture Julius Caesar and Cneius Pompeius, son of the great Pompey, when she was still only a slip of a girl and still did not really know what men were or her own business was, she would certainly handle this man, a mere coarse, crude soldier, very differently now that she was at the height of her intelligence and in the prime of life —as indeed she was. So, to tell the truth, if youth suits some for love-making, others find that maturity, with its refined intelligence, long experience, clever speech and extended practice are greater attractions.

There is an unsettled question about which I used once to ask doctors, of the man who asked if he was not likely to live longer because in all his life he had never known or touched an old woman—basing himself on the physicians' aphorism which runs *vetulam non cognovi*: 'I have never loved an old woman,' and other such sayings. The doctors I asked did, I must admit, give me another ancient proverb which ran that *an old thrashing-floor is good but not an old flail*. There were also others who said : *It's not the mount that matters but the rider*. Hence they say that in their experience they have known elderly women so hot and fiery that whenever they had dealings with a young man they drew out of him whatever they wanted, and would distil and suck all the moisture there was in him out of him, to moisten themselves the better—I mean of course those who are otherwise too dried up to make love, for lack of substance. The physicians I asked also gave me other reasons, but let those who want to know more about this ask for themselves.

I once saw an elderly widow, a great lady, who in less than four years wore down both a third husband and a young noble-man she had taken for lover. She simply made dust of them, not by knifing or poisoning them, but by the sheer attrition and distillation of their substance out from them. Yet, to look at the lady in question, one would never think her capable of it, for in public she was most pious, most whining and hypocritical, to the point of never even pulling on her shift in front of her women, lest they saw her naked, or making water in their presence. But, as a certain lady said of her own sort, she was finicky like that with her women, but not with her men and her gallants.

Yet what of that? Which now is the more defensible or per-missable to a woman, to have several husbands in her life (and there are many who have had three, four or five) or to have only one husband, but one, two or three lovers? For I have truly known some as restrained and loyal as that. About this matter I once heard a famous great lady say that she made no distinction between a lady who had several husbands and one who only had one or two lovers beside her husband, except to remark that the married woman's veil was a cloak to every-thing. But, she said, as far as sensuality and lust went, there was not a doubloon's difference between them. In this she was embodying the Spanish saying which runs : *algunas mugeres son de natura de anguilas en retener, y de lobas en excoger* : 'Some women are like eels when you want to keep them but like she-wolves if they want you,' since the eel is very slippery and difficult to hold, and the she-wolf always chooses the ugliest wolf.

It once happened to me at court, as I have related elsewhere, that a rather great lady, who had been married four times, came to tell me that she had just dined with her brother-in-law, and I should guess with whom, and she was quite brazen about it too, thinking nothing wrong. But I was rather spiteful. I laughed and replied : 'And who the devil would be the guesser who could guess that one? You have been married four times, and I leave it to a better man than myself to say what sort of brother-in-law you may have in mind.' Then she retorted : 'You are being malicious,' and told me who it was. 'Now that's the way to talk,' I said, 'not like just now.'

There was once a lady of Rome[597] who had had twenty-two husbands, one after the other, and likewise a man who had twenty-two wives. So to round off the party, these two both decided to marry again—each other. In the end it was the husband who survived the wife, for which he was so highly esteemed and honoured in Rome by everybody, for so fine a victory, that he was drawn through the city in a triumphal chariot, palm in hand, crowned with laurels. What a victory, what a triumph !

In the time of King Henry, his court included the Lord de Barbarzan, called the Holy Lover,[598] who married three times, one woman after another. His third wife was the daughter of Lady de Mounchy,[599] who was tutor to the Duchess of Lorraine,[600] and she was tougher than the two first, and beat them at it, for he died under her. And when he was lamented at court and she was disconsolate at her loss, Lord de Montpesat,[601] who had a neat turn of speech, jibed that instead of condoling with her, they should make much of her and praise her highly for the victory she had won over her husband, of whom it had been said that he was so vigorous and strong and had such guts that he had killed his first two wives by dint of what he did to them, and this third one, who had not gone under in the battle, but had come out victorious, should be praised and admired by the court, for so fine a victory over such a valiant, robust champion, and for so doing it was she who should be considered famous. What fame!

I have heard much the same said by a prince of France, that he made no distinction between a woman who had had four or five husbands and a whore who had three or four lovers, one after the other, except that one was coloured by marriage, the other not. Thus when a gallant man of my acquaintance married a woman who had already been married three times, another whom I know said frankly: 'Anyway, he's at least married a whore out of a brothel with a good name.' On my faith, these women who remarry are like miserly surgeons, who refuse to stitch up their poor wounded man's wounds properly, just to prolong the healing and earn a little more money. Thus there was a woman who said: 'No use halting half-way in one's career, one should finish it and go to the very end.'

I am amazed that these women, who even when well on in years, are so hot and hasty to remarry, do not save their honour by using some of those refrigerative remedies, those potions making for coolness, to rid themselves of their heat, but instead of being prepared to use them, resort to all that's the contrary, and maintain that such refrigerative drinks harm their insides. I have seen and read a little book of former times, in Italian, which though silly enough did at least include a number of prescriptions against lustfulness, as many as thirty-two but they were so silly that I simply would not recommend women to use them, or to subject their bodies to so much sheer vexation, which is why I have not included any of them here. Pliny however mentions one, used in ancient times by the Vestal virgins, and the ladies of Athens used it too during the festivities of Ceres, known as the *Thesmophoria*, to cool themselves and take away any hot desire for love-making, whereby they hoped to celebrate the feast in greater chastity. It consisted in poultices of the leaves of a tree called the *agnus castus*.[602] But you may well imagine that though during the festivities they mortified themselves thus, afterwards they certainly threw their poultices away.

I once saw a tree of that sort in Guyenne, at the house of a great, estimable and very lovely lady, who often used to show it to visitors who came to see it as a great rarity, and she would tell them about its effects. But the devil knows if I ever saw or heard of woman or lady ever picking a single branch, or making the smallest little poultice, not even the lady to whom that place and its tree belonged, though she need never have stinted using it. But then, it would have been a pity had she done so, for her husband would have been no better off. Indeed, it was better by far to let her manage things as Nature arranged it all, so lovely and so charming was she, and by so doing she produced a very fine family.

And, to tell the truth, such austere and chill receipts should be left to the poor nuns, who, for all their fasting and mortification of the flesh, poor dears, are often beset by the temptations of the flesh, and if they had the liberty would—at least, some of them—take a little refreshment like women of the world, and who often enough repent ever having repented, just like the courtesans of Rome. There is that delightful story of one that I could tell, who vowed to take the veil. Before she retired to a nunnery one of her lovers, a French noble, came to see her to say goodbye, since she was going to quit the world, and before she went begged her for some love, but when she granted it she said : *'Fate dunque presto, ch'adesso mi verrano cercar per far mi monaca, e menare al monasterio,* 'only do make it a quick one, they're coming at any moment to make me a nun and take me to the nunnery.' You may well imagine that she was quite willing to have this last go so she could say : *Tandem haec olim meminisse juvabit,* which in Latin means : 'After all, it'll do me good to have something to recall as the last time.' What repentance, indeed, and what a criticism of religion ! And when once they have been made nuns, at least the pretty ones (I of course mean some of them) I am sure they live more on repentance than on food either bodily or spiritual. There are some who know a cure for it, either by dispensation or the absolute liberty they practise with themselves, for here they are not treated as the Ancient Romans treated the vestal virgins when they committed an indiscretion, which was horrible, abominable. But they were pagans, all horrors and cruelties.

We Christians who follow our Christ in gentleness, should be as benign as he was, and just as he forgives us, so should we forgive. I must set down here the frightful way the Ancient Romans treated those virgins, but I would rather leave it on the tip of my pen.

Now let us leave these poor recluses, since, on my faith, once they are incarcerated there they endure enough trouble, as a Spanish lady once said, when she saw a very lovely, estimable girl being made to take the veil, *O tristezilla, g en que pecasteis, que tan presto vienes à penitencia, y seys metidæ en sepultura viva!* that is : O' you poor little dear, in which have you so sinned that you are so quickly come to penitence, to be buried alive?' And when she saw the nuns feasting her and showing her all manner of honour, she said : *Que todo le hedia, hasta el enciensa de la yglesia,* that is : 'that it all stank there, even the church incense.'

Concerning such virginial vows, Heliogabalus made a law[603] that no Roman virgin, not even a vestal, should be forced to virginity saying that women were too idiotic as far as their sex was concerned to be forced to promise what they could not guarantee. Hence the men who introduced hostels to bring up, educate and marry off poor girls performed a very charitable deed, both for enabling them to feel the sweet fruits of marriage and for turning them away from lechery. Thus, in Rabelais,[604] Panurge spent a lot of his money on concluding such marriages, even for old and ugly women, for more money had to be spent to them than on the lovely ones.

There is one question which I should like to see explained frankly and without any beating about the bush by some of the ladies who have made the trip, namely : when they marry a second time, how they behave concerning their remembrance of their first husbands? There is one rule in it : the latest of our loves and hatreds always make us forget the first ones, thus second marriages bury the first. As to which I will adduce a delightful example, though not one of highly situated or famous people, though none the less it should be quite authoritative, as it is said that knowledge and wisdom are often hidden in shabby, obscure places. Once a great lady of Poitou asked a peasant woman, one of her tenants, how many husbands she had known, and how she had found them. The woman made a little curtsey as they do there, and quite coolly said : 'I'll tell you, my Lady, I have, God be praised, had two husbands. One was called Guillaume. That was the first. The second was Colas. Guillaume was a good man, easy in his ways, he treated me very well, but God pardon Colas' soul for he was a wonder, he was, at it.' But she did not say just 'at it', but pronounced that little word which begins with *f* outright, without any disguising it or wrapping it up. Just notice, if you please, how that naughty woman prayed for the soul of the one who was a man of lust and very hot. And precisely for what, too, if you please? Because he did her well. And not a single prayer for the first one ! I rather imagine many of our frisky, fickle ladies are just the same, for, when it comes down to it, that is the main thing that concerns them, and so it is the man who plays the best game who is most loved, and they are always prone to imagine that their next husband may perhaps prove a wild one. Though often enough they are deceived, and do not find the new husband's shop has the goods they thought to find. or else, in some cases, it is all so feeble, so worn out and deteriorated, so flabby, frayed, limp and dangling that they regret ever having paid a penny for it, as I have known many an example I could quote. In Plutarch[605] we read that when Cleomenes married Agis's lovely wife Agiatis, after his death, as she was extremely lovely, he fell deeply in love with her. But in her he came upon the great grief that she felt for her first husband. He was so sorry for her that he was really rather pleased about this love which she felt for her first husband and the charming way in which she never forgot him, so many a time he would turn the conversation back to Agis and enquire about many things, incidents and delights, which they had known together. He did not have Agiatis with him long, for she died, which he greatly regretted. It is quite common for husbands thus to handle wives who were widowed.

I think it is time I wound up, or I never shall.

There are other ladies who say that they love their later husbands more than their first ones. 'Because,' some have told me, 'as a rule the first we marry by command of our kings and our queens, our mistresses, or by the compulsion of our fathers and mothers or our guardians, not by our own free will, whereas in our widowhood, when we are utterly free, we make our own choice, and only marry for our own sound, good pleasure, because we fall in love with them, and it really pleases us to marry them.' There is no doubt but that there is some reason in this, were it not that very often, as the old proverb says, *love-affairs which are begun by rings are ended by knives,* so indeed we see every day, with those cases and examples we have of women who when they have saved them from the law or the scaffold, from poverty, low estate, the depths, raising them up have expected their husbands would treat them well but find these beat and manhandle them and treat them very badly, even robbing them of life itself, which is God's punishment for having been too regardless of their first husbands, of whom they would say hanging was not good enough, yet who did treat them well. Not at all like one woman I heard of who on her wedding night, when her husband began to tackle her, set so a-weeping and a-sighing that she was two things at once, Summer and Winter. Her husband asked her what made her so wretched, and if he was not doing his duty well. She replied : 'Alas, you are doing it very well indeed, but I can't help recalling my husband and how he begged and prayed me never to remarry after his death, but to think of his little children and have a care for them. And alas, I can see only too clearly that you are soon going to give me some more. Oh, whatever shall I do? I do believe that if he can see me from where he is now he must be cursing me.' What a character, never to have thought of such things or been wise till too late ! But her husband soothed her and made her imagination slip in and out of her centre hole a number of times, and when she opened the bedroom window the following morning she sent any thought of her first husband flying, for there is an old proverb which runs that *the woman who buries her husband no longer makes any fuss about burying the next,* and another which says : *There's more show than sorrow in a woman that loses her husband.*

There was another widowed great lady whom I knew who was quite the opposite of this one, and did not weep at all, for on the first and second nights of her marriage she jousted so much with her second husband that they broke the bedstead and went right through it, although she had a sort of cancer on one breast. Despite her illness she did not miss out a single detail of her love-making. And after that she frequently held forth about the stupidity and incompetence of her first husband. And from what I have heard some men and women say, here you have something which is the last thing that husbands want from their wives (namely, to be told about the virtue and valour of their first husbands) as they are jealous of the poor deceased men, who seem thereby almost to come back to this world. However, the wives are allowed to say as much that's bad about the first husbands as they choose. This is why there are quite a large number of men who even ask for details, just as Cleomenes did, and (feeling themselves most vigorous and strong), make comparisons and interrogate their wives on their first husbands' powers and vigour in those delightful skirmishes, and some men and women have told me that to make their present husbands think they are the better men the ladies will sometimes let them believe their predecessors were mere apprentices, and this has good results. Others, however, assert just the contrary, that their first husbands were very fierce, which they do just to make their new husbands buck like asses under the cudgel.

Such widow wives would be good on the Isle of Scio, the loveliest and sweetest isle of the Levant, formerly a Genoese possession, but usurped thirty-five years since by the Turks,[606] a great pity and loss for Christendom. Well, on that island, so I am told by some Genoese merchants,[607] it is the custom that if a woman wishes to remain a widow and never remarry, the lord can compel her to pay a certain fee known as the *argomoniatico* which (if the ladies will excuse me) means *useless, retired c——*. Similarly, at Sparta, (so Plutarch tells us in the *Life of Lysander*,) those who never married or married too late or who married badly, were fined. I have asked some men of the Isle of Scio on what the custom could be based, and they replied that it was to ensure constant repopulation of the island. I must say that our France is in no likelihood of being depopulated or infertile because of our widows not remarrying, for I would say that there are more who remarry than do not, so they would pay no tax at all as 'useless, retired c——s'. For if not in marriage, then otherwise they certainly cultivate theirs and harvest from them too, as I hope to relate. Nor would some of our French girls pay any more than those of Scio where, peasant girls and town girls alike, if they lose their maidenhood before marrying and wish to go on with that trade, they are liable to pay a lump-sum tax of one ducat (which is very cheap indeed for permission to ply that trade all their lives). It is payable to the captain of the night watch, and entitles them to do as they wish without fear or danger, and these fees are the principal source of income of the charming captain.

These ladies and girls of Scio are quite the opposite of those who formerly dwelt there, who, from what Plutarch says in his *Opusculae*, were for seven hundred years so chaste that nobody ever remembered a married woman committing adultery there or a girl being deflowered outside marriage. Unbelievable miracle! You may take it from me that they are very different today.

Not that the Greeks did not always have a number of ceremonies which prompted free love-making. For instance, we can read of the custom of the Isle of Cyprus in times gone by in which it is said that the good lady Venus, patron of the island, brought in a law by which the local girls were to promenade the shore all round and earn their living by giving sailors who sailed by or put in the freedom of their bodies. Crews used to go ashore for that very purpose, and ships even turned aside from their true course to touch dry land there, and after taking their little refreshment with the girls used to pay them very well and go their way, some sad at leaving such beauties behind, and so the girls found husbands, some for better, some for worse, some low placed, some high, some great, some small, according to the beauty, the characteristics and the appeal of the girl.

Today none of the young ladies of Christendom would promenade like that, exposed to the wind and rain, the cold, the sun, and the heat, for the labour of it is too arduous and too exhausting for their tender, delicate skins and white bodies, but instead they have the men come and seek them out in sumptuous booths, amid lavish curtains, and there draw amorous, conjugal tribute from their lovers, and without paying any tax at all. I am not speaking here of the courtesans of Rome, who are liable to taxation, but of greater women than they are. So that most of the time, in fact, the fathers, mothers and brothers of some of the women there have no great trouble finding cash or paying to get married, since on the contrary it is very often they who give their families money and also improve their position in goods and public offices, ranks and dignities, as I have known in many a case. This was why Lycurgus ordained that virgin girls should be married without any cash settlement, because men should marry them for their virtue, not for money. Yet what virtuousness was that, when at the great public ceremonies they all sang and danced in public stark naked together with the lads, or wrestled in public? History tells us, indeed, that this was done in all decency, but one wonders what decency was there in such a state of affairs, with pretty girls showing themselves publicly? There was no decency in it at all, though certainly there was pleasure in the sight, particularly in the movements of their bodies in their dancing, and still more when they wrestled, and then when it came to falling on one another and, as the Latin puts it, *illa sub, ille super* and *ille sub, illa super,* that is, with the girl under, the lad on top, then *vice versa.*[608] Now tell me, how could all that be made out to be really decent? I don't think there is any chastity but would be destroyed by it, and that doing this in public with lesser liberties taken, in broad daylight, under cover of darkness in secret meetings great wrestlings and joustings must have followed. There is no question but that this was likely, seeing that the same Lycurgus[609] allowed those men who were handsome and inclined to borrow other men's wives to plough there as if it were rich, fine soil, and there was nothing reprehensible in a worn-out old man lending his pretty young wife to any gallant young man whom he chose, though Lycurgus did make the requisition that the wife should be allowed to select as partner the nearest relation of her husband (provided he pleased her) to couple with him, so that any children they might engender should at least be of the same blood and breed as the husband. The Jews had their law of the sister and brother-in-law,but our Christian legislation has straightened all that up, although admittedly our Holy Father has granted a great many dispensations, and for the most diverse reasons. In Spain it is all much done, though by dispensation.

Now let us talk a little, and in the most sober way that we can of certain other widows, and then we shall end. There is yet another kind of widow, for there are some who do not remarry at all, but avoid marriage as if it were the plague, as one told me, of a great family, a very clever woman indeed, whom I had asked whether she would offer her vows to the god Hymen again, replied : 'Now on your faith, would the convict or slave who had plied the sweep a long time, chained down, then at last recovered his liberty, not be very foolish and ill-advised if of his own free will he elected to submit himself to the rule of a savage Barbary pirate? Just so with me. After having been in the slavery of a husband, am I going to involve myself with another? What fate should I then deserve, seeing that otherwise, without any risk, I can give myself a good time?' Having asked another great lady, a relation of mine (for I do not wish to be harsh) if she had no desire to join with anybody in marriage, 'No cousin,' she replied, 'what I mean to do is just to join with somebody in enjoying myself,' though she used another verb with *con* to suggest that what she really meant was have her c—— enjoy anything else but another husband, following the old proverb which says that : *better fly to love than marriage*, as well as : *women are the mistresses everywhere*. That is good for an ancient proverb, for it is they who receive and are the queens everywhere (I mean the lovely ones).

I have heard of another woman whom a nobleman who was inclined to sound her as to marriage asked whether she did not want a husband, when she cried : 'Oh, don't speak to me of husbands, I shall never have another, but I've nothing against a lover.' 'Then if I cannot be your husband, may I be your lover?' said he, and she replied : 'Pay me attention and stick to it and some day you may be.'

A lovely estimable widow of about thirty, thinking one day to banter with an estimable nobleman, or, rather, thinking to attract him to make love to her, was about to mount her horse one day and had taken hold of the apron of her cloak, which had caught on something, when she turned to him : 'See what you have done to me, you rascal,' she said, 'you have torn me in front.' 'I really would be most sorry to have hurt that part,' said he 'for it is far too fine and too pretty a one.' 'And whatever do you know about it?' she said, 'you have never seen it.' 'Now, now,' replied the gentleman, 'are you going to deny that I have seen it a hundred times when you were a little girl and I could pull up your petticoats and have a good peep, as long as I liked?' 'Oh,' she said, 'then it was only a mere slip of a front, without any whiskers, who hadn't a notion what life was really like. Now she's grown a beard and is unrecognizable, you just would not know her.' 'Yet she's in the same place that she was then, she at least hasn't changed her position. I think I'll find her just where she was.' 'Yes,' she said, 'she is still in the same place, but my husband stirred her up quite a bit, and wore her, more than Diogenes did his barrel.' 'Maybe,' said the noble. 'But now what can she do without being stirred?' 'Just what a clock can,' said the lady, 'when it is not wound.' 'You had better look out,' said the noble, 'and see you don't suffer the same fate as those clocks of yours do if they are left too long without winding, because their springs rust up and then they are no use at all.' 'Comparisons,' said the lady, 'do not always completely fit, the springs of the clock you are thinking of are not given to rusting, they are always in good condition, wound or unwound, always ready for when winding time comes round again.' 'Well, then please God,' replied the noble, 'that when that time does come round, I may be the winder.' 'When that festive day does come,' said the lady, 'we won't spend it idle, my clock and I'll make it a working day. But God help the man I do not love as much as you.' And with double-meaning little shafts, which stabbed him to the heart, the lady kissed the noble heartily, and mounted her horse. 'Good-bye,' she said, 'and *au revoir et bon appétit!*' Misfortune however would have it that this estimable lady died only six weeks later. The noble in question thought he would die of a broken heart, for by that barbed repartee of hers and other things said previously, she had so raised his hopes that he was confident he had won her, as indeed I think he had. Accursed be the ill-luck of death, for this was one of the loveliest and most estimable women one could ever see, certainly worth sinning both venially and mortally for.

Another lovely widowed lady, when an estimable noble asked her whether she was not fasting and denying herself meat, as people did, she said she was not. 'Indeed, I had noticed,' said the gentleman, 'that you were not too scrupulous and ate meat in this season as in any other, both raw and cooked.' 'That was when my husband was alive,' she said, 'but my widowhood has reformed me and changed my way of life.' 'Take care,' said the noble, 'of fasting so much for when their appetite returns those who do so in excess find that their bowels have become so narrow and restricted as to be incommoding.' 'The gut in my body which you mean,' she said, 'is not so narrow or so starved that when my appetite for it comes back I shall not be able to satisfy it.'

I knew a great lady whose plumpness while a girl and later, after marriage, was all the talk. She happened to lose her husband, and so mourned him that she became as thin as a rake-handle, yet she did not desist at all from giving her heart its delight in another part, to the extent of calling in the assistance of a secretary of hers and some other men, even her cook, so it was said, though nevertheless all without recovering her plumpness, although the cook in question, who was a very fat, greasy man, should as I see it at least have larded her a bit. And so she took one and another of her gentlemen-in-waiting, all the time making herself out to be the primmest and chastest women in the whole court, with nothing but virtue on her lips, ever spiteful of tongue about all the other women, with fault to find in each. Just like that great lady of the Dauphiné, in the Queen of Navarre's *Hundred Tales*,[610] who was found by a noble who was head over heels in love with her sprawling on the greensward with a groom or muleteer on top of her. That cured the noble of his love-sickness all right.

I have been told of a very lovely woman at Naples who was reputed to have business with a Moor who was the ugliest man in the world, who was only her slave and groom, but her strange temperament resulted in her loving him.

In an old novel by Jean de Saintré, printed in the Gothic character,[611] I have read that he was brought up as a page by the late King Jean. By former custom, great men used to send their pages about with messages, as indeed some people still do today. But then they went anywhere across-country, on horseback, and I have even heard our fathers say that they were often sent on regular embassies, for by dispatching a page with a horse and a silver coin, one was quit and saved money. This little Jean de Saintré (for thus he was called for a long time) was much liked by his master, King Jean, for being so high-spirited, and he was often employed to take messages to the King's sister, who at the time was a widow (the book does not say whose widow). Well, after he had brought her a number of missives, she fell in love with him, and one day, finding him conveniently alone, she tackled him and began enquiring whether he did not love some lady of the court, and which one did he like best—a customary conversational gambit of many ladies when they wish to make the first move in love with anybody, as I have seen them do. This little Jean de Saintré who had never thought of anything less than making love, said : 'Not yet.' She then went on to mention a number of ladies at court and ask if he had his mind on them. 'Even less,' he said, till at last she came to expound to him the virtues and advantages of love. For in those older times it was just as it is today, some great ladies were much given to lechery and never satisfied with things as they were, and the more wily they were the better time that they had, and they gave their husbands a fine dance with their deceitfulness and follies. So this lady, seeing of what fine quality this young lad was, proceeded to tell him that she would like to find him a mistress who would love him well, only he would have to pay her attentions properly. And despite all the shame the lad felt about all this, she made him promise that he would keep it all a dead secret. Then at last she unburdened herself to him and said she herself wanted to be his lady and his love—for in those days the word *mistress* had not come into use. The young page was very surprised, and thought at first that she was making fun of him or wanted to trap him into being indiscreet, so as to have an excuse to have him thrashed, yet she at once proceeded to show him so many signs of the heat and conflagration of love that he knew it was no mockery at all, while she kept on repeating that she would look after him personally and make a great man of him. So in the end their love-making and delights lasted a long time, throughout his pagehood and after, till she was at last obliged to go on a long journey, when she put him in the care of a huge, corpulent abbé. And that is the story you can see in the *Tales of the world adventure*[612] of a personal servant of the Queen of Navarre's, where you will read how this abbé insulted Jean de Saintré, who was both bold and valiant, and how soon after he returned it with triple interest. It is a very fine story, and I take it from this source I mention.

So you see it is not a modern trend at all for ladies to love pages, even when they are as spotty as pheasants. What feminine crankiness, to like a lot of lovers but no husband! They do it of course from love of freedom, which is certainly a delightful thing, and they think that when they are out of the domination of their husbands they are in paradise, with a fine marriage settlement to administer and domestic affairs to look after. They it is who handle the money, everything passes through their hands, and rather than servants they are mistresses, choosing their own pleasures. And they do so among those who do what they want.

There are others who are unquestionably anxious not to make a second marriage, so as not to lose their greatness, dignities, property, wealth, ranks, good and favourable treatment, and such widows hold themselves in restraint for that reason. I have heard and known of several great ladies and princesses doing so who, from fear of not again finding the greatness they had before, which they want, and of losing their position, have never consented to remarry. On the other hand they allow themselves a lot of love-making, thus changing and transforming love into pure pleasure. Thereby they lose no rank, no footstool, neither their high seat or other position in the Queen's bedchamber or elsewhere. Have such not been happy indeed, enjoying their greatness and also climbing high and falling low all at the same time? No thought can there be of saying anything to them or reproving them for it, or all you get is scorn, denials, 'no, no and no,' they are all contradiction and spite.

I have heard it said of one widow lady, (I knew her, too,) who kept a certain estimable noble dangling for a very long time, all with the promise of ultimate marriage, but he was never prominent enough for her. Then her mistress, a great princess, chose to reprimand her for it. But, cunning and corrupt as she was, she replied : 'What is this, Madame? Are you proposing to prohibit all really estimable love-making? That would be too great an oppression.' One should know that by 'estimable love' she meant the most lascivious kind of lovemaking, that which is well compounded with spermatic compost, as indeed all love-making is which though maybe born pure, chaste, and estimable, later loses its maidenhood and by a certain touch of the philosophic stone is transformed and made indecent and lubricious.

The late Lord de Bussy,[613] the man of his time who told the best stories and was also good at it, seeing a widowed lady one day at court—a great lady, too—who still plied the trade of love-making, cried : 'What's this? Does that old mare still go to stud?' The lady was told what he had said, and she could have murdered him. When he heard of this he said : 'I know how I can soon make my peace and patch that up. Tell her, I beg you, that that was not at all what I said, what I said was *Does that filly still cast glad eyes at the nags?* For I am quite sure that she is not annoyed because I take her for a pleasure-loving dame, but because she thinks I said she was an elderly one, but as soon as she hears I really spoke of her as a *filly*, she will conclude that I still look upon her as quite young.' In this way

once she heard this satisfaction and obtained this verbal re-
habilitation, the lady was pacified, and renewed her friendly
relations with de Bussy, at which we did all have a hearty
laugh. All the same, this was all in vain, for people still accounted her a patched-up old mare, who despite her advancing
years still whinnied to the stallions.

This lady was not at all like another I have heard of, who,
after having being a boon companion when young, as she
advanced in years began to be godfearing and given to prayer
and fasting. When one estimable noble remonstrated and asked
why she kept so many vigils in church and so often fasted at
table and whether it was to overcome or dull the pricks of the
flesh. 'Alas,' she said, 'they are all over,' which she uttered as
pitiably as that powerful, lusty wrestler Milo of Croton did his
response when one day he went down into the arena among
the gladiators merely to look on, (for he had grown very old,)
and one of the troupe came to ask him if he would not like to
have a little bout as he did in the old days. Pitiably drawing
back his toga and baring his powerful arm and staring at his
muscles and sinews, he merely said : 'Alas, they are dead.'
Had that woman done the same and in a gesture like Milo's
drawn up her skirts, one would not have seen a privy part of
much value or so very tempting.

A similar gesture and similar words to de Bussy's were those
of a noble I know. Coming to court, from which he had been
absent for six months, he saw a lady on the way to the academy
which the late King had founded there. 'What's this?' he said,
'is there still an academy here? I was told it had been done
away with now.' 'Need you ask, seeing she's going,' replied
another. 'Her master is teaching her his philosophy in it, all
about perpetual motion.' True, indeed, however hard philosophers rack their brains to discover perpetual motion, there is
none more to be relied on than that which Venus teaches in her
school.

A lady of the world made a still better rejoinder to another
lady whose beauties were being greatly praised, the exception
however being made that she had very wooden eyes, with no
life in them, they never moved. 'I suppose,' said this other lady,

'all her attention is so set on moving the rest of her body, especially the middle bit, that she has no time for her eyes.'

Now, were I to wish to set down in writing all the smart replies and good stories I know which would illustrate this matter, I should never be done, and as I have other moves to make, I refrain, and will conclude together with Boccaccio, whom I have earlier quoted, and say that all women, unmarried, married and widowed, (or at least most of them,) lean to love-making. I have no intention of speaking of the common people, neither those of the fields nor of the towns, but of great ladies only, towards whom my pen flies. And to sum up, if one really asks my opinion, I would certainly say that apart from the risk and danger from husbands, there are none like married women, for being given to love-making and eager to get something out of it, since their husbands so heat them up that, just like a stove the fire of which is constantly well piled and poked, all they ask is the raw material, that is, water, firewood and coal, to maintain their heat constant. So anybody who wants to use the lamp had better keep it topped up with oil, though at the same time beware traitors and the ambushes set by those jealous husbands, in which even the wily are often caught.

It always behoves a man to proceed with as much circumspection and also as much boldness as he can and do like that great King Henry,[614] much given as he was to love and at the same time a great respecter of the ladies, discreet withal, hence a tremendous favourite, whom the ladies all accepted and whenever he changed beds and went to sleep in that of some other lady who was expecting him, he would, so I have it from a reliable source (even in his secret apartments at St Germain, Blois and Fontainebleau, with their little escape stairs and nooks and attics in his castles) would never go without having his favourite gentleman-of-the-bedchamber, a fellow named Griffon[615] it was, to walk in front with a boar lance and a torch, the King following with his big cloak or his nightgown wrapped well across his face and his sword ready tucked under his arm. And when he had got into bed with the lady, he would still keep his boar lance and his sword close to his head, and Griffon outside the well-closed door, sometimes with orders to keep watch, sometimes just to sleep there. If a great King took such care of himself (because there had been cases of men caught, both Kings and great princes, as for instance Alexander, Duke of Florence[616] in our time) I leave it to your imagination what lesser lovers had to do. Though there are some over-bold fellows who scorn any precaution, though they are also often caught.

I have heard it related that King François, when he had a certain very lovely lady whom he kept a long time[617] for mistress, and one day, in order to sleep with her at an unusual hour, went to see her unheralded as he could, and had the authority to do for he was the master and came to her door and knocked loudly, she, who at that moment had Baron de Bonnivet in bed with her, did not dare call out what the courtesans of Rome have their maids say : *Non si pùo, la signora è accompagnata,* 'Impossible, Madame has somebody with her.' It was a matter merely of deciding very quickly where the gallant might hide most safely. It so happened that it was summertime, and the hearth had been piled with fresh branches and greenery, in the French way. So she counselled and advised her lover to hide in the hearth as quickly as he could, just as he was, in only his shirt, among the leaves, since the weather was in his favour, as it was not Winter-time. Well, when the King had done his business with his lady, he wanted to make water, and, getting up, went to the hearth to do so, since there was no other convenience, and he had such great need that he watered that wretched lover more thoroughly than if anybody had tipped a bucket of water over him, just like a gardener with his watering-can and rose, in fact, all over him, even his face—in his eyes, up his nose, in his mouth—everywhere, in fact, a drop or two may have slipped down his gullet. I leave it to you to imagine what a state the nobleman was in, for he did not dare move. What patience and steadfastness, too ! When he had eased himself, the King said goodbye to his lady and left the room. She locked the door after him and then called her lover back into the bed, to take the chill out of him with her fire, and then had him put on a clean shirt. Once their great fright

was over, they even laughed at it all, though, had he been discovered, both he and she would have been in great danger. This
was the very same lady who when she was much in love with
Lord de Bonnivet but wanted the King to think the opposite,
one day said : 'Why, he's a fine figure of a man, de Bonnivet is,
thinking he's such a grand fellow. The more I tell him so, the
more he believes it, too ! I think he's very silly. But I just find
it entertaining to talk to him, for all the same he is very amusing and sometimes says such funny things, you just can't help
laughing when you're with him, he's so quick with an answer.'
Thereby she meant to make it clear to the King that all the
conversation she had with de Bonnivet had nothing at all to do
with really liking him, let alone making love with him, and
being false to the King. Oh, what a lot of ladies there are who
resort to such tricks to conceal the love-affairs they have with
other men ! They malign them and make public fun of them,
while behind the scenes they do nothing of the kind. Those
are among the tricks and deceits of love.

I knew a very great lady who when one day she saw her
daughter,[618] one of the loveliest in the world, eating her heart
out for love of a nobleman[619] against whom her brother was
very stomachy, one thing she said to her daughter was : 'Come,
my dear, do give up that man, he is so coarse and boorish and
so ugly, just like a village cake-maker.' The daughter burst
out laughing and applauded her mother's words, and said he
was indeed the image of a village cake-maker. But despite
his red baker's cap she loved him, though some time after,
about six months it was, she left him for another.

I have known several ladies who have threatened with worse
than hanging the women who make love with men of low
estate, such as their secretaries, their gentlemen of the bedchamber or other humbler men, and loathed such love-making
worse than poison, yet themselves indulged in it just as much,
even more, than the others did. All that is the ladies' *finesse*,
they will go so far in public as to attack their lovers fiercely,
insulting them and threatening them, while behind the scenes
they have a very frolicsome time with them. These women
have so many tricks, for, as the Spanish has it : *mucho sabe*

la zorra, pero sabe mas la dama enamorada—'bitches know a lot but ladies in love know more.'[1]

But for all that lady I speak of did to rob King François of his wits, she could never prevent a grain of sense remaining, as I can vouch, and *à propos* of this I recall how when once I had made an excursion to Chambord,[620] an elderly custodian who was there and had once been a personal servant of the King's gave me a great welcome, for since those days he had come to know my family at court and in the wars. So he insisted on showing me round personally, and when he took me to the King's bedchamber he showed me there a word of writing on the window frame. 'Look,' he said, 'My Lord, read that. If you have ever seen the handwriting of my master the King, there you have it!' Written in large letters were the words : *All women are fickle*. With me I had a very estimable, clever gentleman noble of Perigord, a friend of mine (Lord de Roche) and he at once remarked : 'Clearly some of those very ladies whom he loved most, and of whose faithfulness he was most sure, he must have found fickle, deceiving him, and was very upset and that was why he wrote those words.' The custodian, who heard us, said : 'And right you are, indeed, and no laughing matter, My Lords, for of all the ladies I ever saw or knew, there was not a single one who was not far more fickle than any of his dogs stag-hunting. But they always deceived him on the sly, for had they been found out, that would have been the end of them. There you have the womenfolk, they are never satisfied with their husbands or their lovers, whether great kings, princes and lords, but always have to have something fresh, and as such this great King had known and experienced them to be, after having seduced them himself and snatched them from the hands of their husbands, their mothers, their freedoms and their widowhoods.'

I both knew and was told of a lady[621] who was so much beloved by her prince[622] that because of his great love for her he

---

[1] Brantôme does not always translate perfectly. Spanish *zorra* means *vixen*, but the Spaniards use *vixen* to symbolize *whore*. Thus my translation of the word is a trifle more explicit than Brantôme's, who falls rather flat with mere 'renard' or 'fox' for *zorra*.

heaped all sorts of favours, benefits and grandeurs on her, to such an extent that there was nobody to compare with her. And yet she was so enamoured of a certain lord[623] that she would never break off with him, but when he himself remonstrated with her that the King would eventually bring them both down low, said : 'That's all one to me. If you leave me, I shall ruin myself just to ruin you. I would rather be called your whore than the King's mistress.' What character she had. But also what lust !

Among others, I also knew another great widowed lady who did just the same, for though a very great man almost worshipped her, she still had to have a number of other lesser lovers dangling round her, so she should never lose an hour's time and be at a loss, for one single one in such matters never can cope all the time, also since such is the rule of love, that a mistress is not tied to a certain given time or any single given person. Take for instance that lady in the Queen of Navarre's[624] *Hundred Tales* who had three lovers at once and was so clever that she was able to keep them all three going at the same time.

The fair Agnes,[625] beloved and worshipped by Charles VII, was suspected by him of having given him a daughter which he suspected was not really his and did not want to recognize. Thus : *Like mother, like daughter* is what the chroniclers say. Just the same with Anne de Boleyn,[626] wife of King Henry[627] of England, whom he had beheaded because she was not satisfied with him but committed adultery, and he had taken her for her loveliness too, and worshipped her.

I knew a lady who, when a very estimable noble had been her lover and then after some time left her, found herself discussing their past together. Wishing to appear a great gallant, the noble said : 'Well, and do you really think that you were my only mistress at the time? Would you be so very surprised if I told you that as well as you I had two others?' Quickly she replied : 'You are going to be even more astonished if you have hitherto thought you were my only lover, for I had no less than three others in reserve at the time.' There, you see, a good ship always needs two or three anchors to be well moored.

342

To wind up, long live love of women! And, as I once came across, written in her own hand, on the writing-pad of a very lovely and estimable lady who *hablaed* Spanish a little and understood it better : *Hembra o dama sin compagner, o esperanza sin trabajo, y navio sin timon, nunca pueden hazer cosa que sea buena,* that is : 'Never did a woman or lady without partner, hope without labour, or ship without rudder do anything worth while.' This proverb is alike equally fitting for wife, widow or unmarried girl, for none of them can achieve any good without the partnership of a man, nor is it any use thinking one can get them without a little trouble and labour, combined with brusqueness and firmness. All the same, the wife and the widow do not give a man as much trouble as the unmarried girl, for, as people say, it is easier and more simple a matter to conquer and get down somebody who has already been conquered and put on her back than one who never has, and it does not require nearly so much effort to use a path which has already been cleared and well trodden than that which has never been cut or trodden, two comparisons which I call on travellers and fighting men to endorse. Thus it is with girls, and there are indeed some so headstrong, those who have constantly refused to marry, still living with their parents, and if you ask them why, they say : 'That's how it is, that is my temperament.' Just as Cybele, Juno, Venus, Thetis, Veres and other heavenly goddesses all despised the title virgin—all save Pallas, that is, who was born direct of Jupiter's brain, which merely goes to show that virginity is merely a conception of the brain. So if you ask our girls who never marry (or, if they do, then it is as late as possible, when they are already getting on in years) why they do not marry, they will say : 'Because I do not want to, because that is my temperament and how I see things.'

At the court of our kings we saw some such in the days of King François. The Lady Regent[628] had a daughter who was lovely and estimable, Poupincourt[629] her name was, who never married at all and died a virgin just as she was born, at the age of sixty years, for she was very circumspect indeed. La Brelaudière died a girl,[630] with maidenhood intact, at the age of eighty, the one, I mean, who was tutor to the Duchess of An-goulême[631] when she was a girl.

I knew the daughter of a very great, very eminent family[632] who was seventy and had never consented to marry, though she did not fail to make love. And those who chose to excuse her for not marrying said that she was not suitable for wife, as she had no privy parts at all, only one little hole through which she made water. Heaven knows however that she still found something good enough for having quite a lot of fun elsewhere. What a fine excuse that was!

Lady de Charansonnet of Savoy[633] latterly died a virgin at Tours, and was buried with chaplet and white virginal gown with all solemnity and great ceremony, accompanied to the grave by a vast concourse of people, at the age of forty-five or even more. And you may rest assured this was not for lack of suitors, for she was one of the loveliest and most estimable and discreet girls of the court, whom I have known to reject the hand of very fine and very great suitors.

My sister, Lady de Bourdeille,[634] at court one of the Queen's ladies-in-waiting, has likewise rejected a number of fine offers and has never consented to marry, nor ever will, so resolved and stubborn is she about living and dying a virgin at a good age. And so far—and she is getting on in years now—she has stuck to it.

Lady de Certan,[635] another of the Queen's ladies-in-waiting, and Lady Surgières, the clever one at court,[636] also known as Minerva, and many another.

I recall the *Infanta* of Portugal,[637] daughter of the late Queen Eleonora,[638] as being of the same mind, and she died a virgin at the age of sixty or more years. This was not in default of greatness, for she was great in every way, nor from lack of property, for she had a great deal, even in France, where Lord Gourgues,[639] Treasure-General, had arranged her affairs well, nor was it in default of gifts of nature, for I saw her at Lis-bon,[640] at the age of forty-five, and she was then a very lovely and pleasant girl, with charming manners and dignity, most gentle and pleasant, worthy of having a husband like her in every-thing, so courteous she was, specially to us Frenchmen. I can freely assert this, having had the honour of talking with her frequently and intimately. When the late Grand Prior of Lorraine[641] led his galleys from the Levant, intending to go to Scotland, during the time of little King François,[642] and called at Lisbon and stayed there a few days,[643] he called on her and then saw her every day. She gave him a very courteous welcome and found much pleasure in his company, and made him many lovely presents. Among other things, she gave him a chain for his crucifix which was all diamonds and rubies and large pearls, all very finely and lavishly worked, which might have been worth between four and five thousand crowns and went three times round his neck. I am sure it was worth that much, for he could always pawn it for a thousand, as he did once at London, when we were on our way back from Scotland, though the moment we set foot in France he sent a messenger back to redeem it, for he prized it because of the attention of that lady, who had greatly caught his imagination and still held it. And you may take it that she loved him no less, and would willingly have broken her virginal bond for him (in marriage, be it understood, for she was a very circumspect and virtuous princess). And I will say even more—had it not been for the disorders which began in France, her brothers would have invited him to Portugal and kept him there. He himself had wanted to go back there with his galleys, on the same route, to see this princess again and suggest marriage, and I assure you it would not have been a mistake at all, for he came of as good a line as she did, descended from great kings though she was, and apart from that he was one of the really handsome, charming, estimable, indeed, best princes of Christendom. Her brothers, especially the two elder, for they were the spokesmen for them all and captained the ship, I saw when he spoke to them of it, telling them of his voyage and the pleasure and the favours, they had accorded him and they were most anxious that he should make the journey again and visit her once more, and advised him to aim at that, for the Pope would at once have given ecclesiastical dispensation, and had it not been, as I say, for those disorders in France, he would have done so and emerged, as I see it, to his honour and satisfaction.

The said princess liked him very much, and spoke very warmly of him to me, and regretted him greatly and interrogated me much about his death, as if her heart had been engaged, which is easy enough in such circumstances for a man who is at all perspicacious to recognize.

I have been told, by a very clever person, I can't say whether a virgin or not (she may well have tried love), why some girls are so slow to marry. They say it is *proper mollitiem*, and the word *mollities* is to mean that they are too soft, that is, too much in love with themselves and too anxious to mollycoddle themselves and find their pleasure with themselves alone, or with others like them, in the Lesbian way, and take their pleasure only with girls, thinking, and indeed being firmly convinced that with a man they would never get so much pleasure, and so are satisfied with their own delights and tasty pleasures, without bothering about any men or dealings with them, let alone marriages.

Such girls, thus remaining virgins, untouched by man, would formerly in Rome have been most honoured and highly privileged, to the point that the law had no power even to sentence them to death, so that we read that when during the triumvirate there was a Roman senator among those proscribed who was condemned to die, with all his family, when one of his daughters, a very lovely, sweet girl, was brought to the scaffold, she was found not to be of ripe age, and still a virgin, and the executioner had to deflower her and devirginize her himself on the scaffold, so that thus polluted he could at last apply the steel. The Emperor Tiberius took special delight in thus having lovely girls and virgins publicly deflowered and then executed which was certainly a very vile form of cruelty.

So the vestals were most honoured and respected, as much for their virginity as for their religion, but if they did happen in the very least to sin with their bodies they were punished a hundred times more rigorously than if they had not been so carefully guarded by the sacred fire, for such were buried alive in frightful torment. One reads of a man named Albinus,[644] a Roman, who happened to come upon a number of vestals outside Rome on their way somewhere, and told his wife and children to get out of their coach, to take up the vestals and convey them. And in this way they gained such authority that very often they entrusted go-betweens to negotiate between the people of Rome and the knights, whenever they came to blows. On the advice of the Christians, the Emperor Theodosius expelled them from Rome, when the Romans deputed a man named Symmachus[645] to intercede for their return with their goods, rents and other sources of income, which were great, especially as daily they distributed such a great amount of charity that they never allowed any Roman or even an alien passing through the city to beg for alms, so great was their kindness to the poor. But in spite of this the Emperor Theodosius would never let them return. They were called vestals from the word *vesta* meaning fire, which for all its flickering and leaping and flaming, like a virgin, never produces seed nor receives any. They spent thirty years thus virgins, after which they might marry, but rarely was any of them happy when she left the order, any more than our nuns are when they take off and put aside the veil. They were all greatly given to pomp, superbly dressed, and the poet Prudentius describes them very well, as rather like the canonesses of Mons in Hainault and Remirement in Lorraine today, who may marry. However, this poet, Prudentius,[646] also attacks them fiercely for riding about in the city in such very luxurious coaches and going to the amphitheatres so dressed up to see the gladiators and other warriors and wild animals too, fight there to the death, as if they found great pleasure in thus seeing men kill each other and shed blood, so that he begs the Emperor to do away with blood-thirsty combats and other such disgraceful spectacles. These vestals should certainly never have gone to see such games, though they could always say that since they did not enjoy the other pleasant games that other women played they might as well have some pleasure from those.

As for the condition of many widows, there are also many who make love like these girls, as I have known some to do, and others who prefer to have frolics with men in secret, and do whatever they want to, which they could not when in a subordinate position in marriage. Hence when one sees some widows remain so a long time, one should not praise them quite so readily as one might till one knows what sort of life they lead, but only when one knows this can one praise or despise them, for a woman, when she wants to give herself what is called a free rein, can be frightfully crafty and easily sell a man down the river if he does not take good care, and being so crafty they are so good at bewitching and dazzling the eyes and thoughts of a man so that he can never after really know what they are really doing, for one can so easily take one to be such a modest woman, so discreet, so well-behaved, who is really going to be no more than a good whore, and play her game so neatly and so covertly that nobody knows a thing.

I knew a great lady who remained a widow for more than forty years, achieving the reputation of being the most seemly lady of those parts or at court, yet *sotto coverto* (in secret) she was a thoroughpaced tart, and had plied that trade nicely for twenty-five years, first as girl, then as married woman and finally as widow, and all so skilfully and subtly that when at last she did die, at the age of seventy, still nobody had spotted it. She got her money's worth out of her part as well as a woman ever did. Once, when a young widow, she happened to fall in love with a young nobleman, and as she could not get him in her net in any other way, on Innocent's Day,[647] taking advantage of the old custom, she went to his bedroom with some birch twigs early in the morning ostensibly to give it to him for not being up, but of course it was the nobleman who gave it to her, and without much difficulty, though he did not use twigs. She did many others too.

I knew another widow who kept her widowhood fifty years, living loosely all the time, but all most decently and modestly, making love with quite a number of men, at various times. At last, when one whom she had loved for twelve years, and had had a boy by secretly, happened to die, without any scruples she flatly denied that she had ever had anything to do with him. Does that not point to the need for that caution I spoke of regarding widows—that one needs to know how they lived and died before one pronounces on them? But I shall never end. Let us wind up.

I know very well that many people may object that I have omitted many a fine retort and anecdote which would have improved and ennobled my subject. I grant it, but if I tried them all I should never have seen daylight. But I shall be most obliged to anybody who cares to take the trouble to do better.

And so, dear ladies, I end, and forgive me if I have said anything which offends you. I was not born or brought up to offend or displease. If I speak of some women, it need not include all, and of those I speak only under concealed names, or giving none at all. I conceal them so well that nobody is ever going to guess who they are, and none can be disgraced except because somebody suspects, not from any indications of mine.

I think and fear I may here have retold several anecdotes and tales that I have told before in my other essays. If so I beg those who are kind enough to read them, all to forgive me, for I do not pretend to be a great essayist or to have a good enough memory to recall every detail. The great person Plutarch often repeats himself in his works. Anybody who may care to print my books will only need a good editor to put it all right.

FIFTH ESSAY

On the love-making of some elderly women and on how some of them are more given to love-making than others, and how this can be seen from several examples, without naming or disgracing anybody

SEEING that earlier on I spoke of elderly ladies who love riding, I decided to write the present essay. So I begin, by saying that one day, when at the court of Spain, in conversation with a lady, who though very estimable and lovely, was somewhat advanced in years, she said that no lovely lady, or only a rare one, ever allows herself to become old from the waist down.

I at once asked how exactly she meant, whether this was through the loveliness of the body below the waist (that this in itself was in no way diminished by age) or was it that desire and appetite for the pleasures of the flesh never came to be extinguished or cooled off lower down. She replied that she meant both one thing and the other, 'for as far as the promptings of the flesh go,' she said, 'one must not imagine that one gets rid of those till death comes, though it may seem that age would like to repugn them.' But every lovely woman is very fond of herself and that love of herself is not at all for her, but for others, a woman is not at all like Narcissus, the fatuous fellow, who so liked himself and loved himself that he abhorred any other sort of love-making.

A lovely woman's character is indeed quite different from that as I have heard one very lovely lady say who was fond of herself and much loved to get being by herself, all alone, in her bed, stark naked, and there contemplate herself in all

350

manner of poses and admire herself and watch herself with lustful thoughts, cursing the fact that she had taken vows to one man only, who, she told herself, was not worthy of so lovely a body, (meaning of course her husband,) and who was far from being her equal. This went on till at last she got so heated by such contemplation and such sights that she bade her chastity and her married vow farewell and made love with a new suitor.

There you see how beauty can kindle the fires and the flames of a lady, who then, so they shall not be wasted, passes them on to whatever men she chooses, whether husband or wooers. And thus one form of love leads to another. Further, if a woman is thus lovely and a man comes along and woos her and she does not object him outright, you may be sure her skirts will soon be up. Indeed Lais said that a woman only needs to part her lips and make one conciliatory reply to a wooer and her heart is gone and opens up to him.

Further, once she takes pleasure in them or allows a man to praise her loveliness, her charms and her sweetness, as we courtiers have made a practice of doing as the first stage in laying siege to her, a lovely, estimable lady never rejects the praise given her, and however long it may take, if we persist in our wooing, we have her.

There is another thing, no lovely woman who has once tried the love game ever unlearns it, she always finds it very agreeable and pleasant to go on with it, exactly as we are very vexed to give it up, once we have grown accustomed to good meat, and the older one gets the better it is for one's constitution, say the doctors. Likewise the older a woman gets, the more eager is she for the fine meat she has grown used to, and just as her upper mouth gets to like the taste of it, so does her lower mouth, and that sort of gourmandize is never forgotten and is never tired of as the years pass on, except indeed if affected by a long illness or something else out of the ordinary, the physicians say, so that even if for some time she is vexed, in the end it is nevertheless resumed.

It is further said that all activities are decreased or diminished by age, which robs people of their ability to perform any of them except the act of Venus, which by its nature is performed very gently, without distress or any hard labour, and in a fine, soft bed, very much at one's ease. I am speaking of the women, not men, for their share in it is all the work and labour. This is why it is that a man who is accustomed to that pleasure will soon give it up, even though to his own detriment, but, whatever her age, a woman is just like an oven, which accepts whatever is put into it, of course, I mean if anybody wants to do the putting. But there's no mare so old, if she wants to go to it and be poked that can't find some rascally rider. Besides even if an elderly lady is unable to make love properly and come to a finish as she did in her young years, she always has the cash and the means to get whatever she wants at market price, and fine goods too, I am told. But any high quality goods make holes in the purse (contrary to Heliogabalus's opinion, for the more he bought dear meats the cheaper he found them,[648]) all except Venus's goods, which, the more they cost, the more they please, because of the great longing one gets to make the goods, that is the act which one has purchased, come up to scratch, so that whatever ability one has one exploits trebly, even a hundredfold, if one can.

This is what a Spanish courtesan told two fine Spanish knights when they called on her at the same time and quarrelled over her, went straight out of her house, drew their swords and began to fight. Sticking her head out of the window she shouted down : 'Gentlemen, it's with gold and silver, not cold steel, that my favours are to be had.'

So it is that any love well purchased is good. Many ladies and knights who have made such deals can tell you that. For me to give examples of the many ladies who have burned with the passion in their old age as much as in their youth, or who have assuaged, or rather maintained their fires by further husbands and fresh lovers, would be very superfluous, since I have already given a number elsewhere. Yet I will give a few here, fitting ones, for the subject demands it.

J'ay ouy parler d'une grande dame, qui rencontroit le mot aussi bien que dame de son temps, laquelle, voyant un jour un jeune gentilhomme qui avoit les mains tres-blanches, elle luy demanda ce qu'il faisoit pour les avoir telles. Il respondit, en riant et gaussant, que le plus souvent qu'il pouvoit il les frottoit de sperme. 'Voilà, dit-elle, donc un malheur pour moy, car il y a plus de soixante ans que j'en lave mon cas (le nommant tout à trac), il est aussi noir que le premier jour; et si je le lave encore tous les jours.'

I have been told of a lady rather advanced in years who wanted to remarry, and one day asked the advice of a doctor about it, saying she wished to consult him because she was very moist and full of ill humours which had begun when she was widowed, and had been with her ever since, and added that this had never worried her while her husband was alive, because by the assiduous efforts they made together those humours were constantly dried up and used. The doctor, who was a merry fellow, and also wanted to please his patients, advised her to remarry and in that way expel those humours of hers, adding that it was better to be dry than moist. The lady followed his advice, and, elderly as she was, found it very good, though I must say it was with a new husband and lover who appreciated her as much for the love of hard cash as for any pleasure he got from her. Yet there are many elderly ladies with whom one certainly has as much enjoyment and can perform as well, if not better than with younger ones. This is because they are more knowledgeable in the art of how to do it and so they give their lovers more zest. When getting on in years the courtesans of Rome and Italy adduce the maxim that *old hens make better soup than young ones.*

Horace mentions an old woman[649] who when at it moved and fidgeted in such a way, so violently and unrestrainedly that not only did she shake the bed, she shook the whole house. There was a nice old lady for you! The Latins called such moving and fidgeting *subare a sue,* 'being boar-hot.'

Of the Emperor Caligula[650] we read that of all the wives he had he preferred Cesonnia, not so much for her good looks or her resplendency in middle age, for she was beginning to get on in years, as for her great lustfulness and lecherousness (and for the vigour in applying it which the years and much practice had brought). She left all the other wives far behind, although

353

they were younger than she was. As a rule he took her with him on his military expeditions, dressed and armed like a man, riding astride too, at his side, and would often even exhibit her stark naked to his friends, to show all the tricks of lissomness and lust she could contrive.

One must admit that age had not reduced this woman in what was lovely and lustful, since Caligula loved her so. Nevertheless, despite all the great love he had for her, very often when he embraced her and touched her lovely throat, so bloodthirsty was he that he could not refrain from exclaiming : 'What a lovely throat, and all mine too, to have slit if I like.' Alas, at last the poor woman was indeed thus killed at his orders by a thrust of a centurion's sword, while her daughter was stoned and broken to death against a wall, which also must have been by the foul work of her father.

It is also said of Julia, step-mother of the Emperor Caracalla,[651] that one day when almost by negligence she was half naked and Caracalla saw her without ceremony, he cried: 'Oh, how gladly I would, if only I might,' to which she at once replied: 'You are welcome. Did you not know that you are the Emperor, you make the laws, you don't obey them?' Upon which good reply and readiness he coupled with her and married her.

Very similar was the answer given to one of our three last Kings, which one I will not say.[652] He had been smitten by a very lovely estimable lady and fell in love with her, and after a first few little hints of this to her, one day proposed to her in so many words through the medium of an estimable and very able noble whom I know, who, when he took the missive to her, did his best to persuade her to say yes. Being no fool, she defended herself as best she could, with various good arguments which she could well put forward, without leaving out the great one, or rather, the little one, of her honour. Well, the upshot was that after considerable discussion the noble at last asked her for a definite answer. What, after all, was he to say to the king. And at last, after some apparently distracted reflection, she suddenly brought out : 'What am I to say? What else but that I am well aware that no refusal ever profited the man or the woman who made it to either king or sovereign, for, that as a rule, making use of his power, he is in a better position to take and order than to request and plead for anything.'

Satisfied with this reply, the noble took it forthwith to the King, who seized opportunity by the forelock and went straight to the lady's chamber, where without much struggle she was put on her back. This I think was a spirited reply by which to indicate a desire to have dealings with her sovereign. As one might put it, though it is not a good thing to play about or be at loggerheads with one's King, it is worth while finding a way out that never hurts, and women are always clever and reliable about finding that.

To go back to Julia, step-mother of that Emperor, she must have been a whore to love and take as husband the man who so soon before had killed her son.[653] Yes, she really was a whore, and a debased one too. But of course it was a great thing to become Empress, and for that honour could well go by the board. Although well advanced in years, this Julia was much loved by her husband, for despite her age she had lost nothing of her beauty, for she was both very lovely and very sprightly, as witness that reply of hers which raised her so very high.

Philippe Maria, the third Duke of Milan, as second wife took Beatricina, widow of the late Facino Cane, when she was quite old,[654] but she brought him four hundred thousand crowns, not to speak of furniture, rings and jewels all amounting to a high price, and those wiped out the years. And yet her husband suspected her of going on the loose with others,[655] and for that reason had her executed. So see whether advancing years made her lose a taste for the love-game. You may assume that the great practice she had made of it merely added to her desires.

Constance, Queen of Sicily, who from youth upwards, all her life had not budged from a cloistered chastity, a vestal bottomed woman if ever there was one, came out into the lay world, emancipating herself, at the age of fifty, and not beautiful at all, indeed, she was quite decrepit, but nevertheless she wanted to assay the sweets of the flesh and she married, and at the age of fifty-two became pregnant,[655] and took it into her head to have her confinement in public, in the meadows outside Palermo, where she had a marquee and tent specially erected, so nobody should question that she herself had indeed borne fruit, all one of the great miracles ever seen since St Elizabeth, though the *History of Naples* assures us that the child was generally assumed to be somebody else's. Nevertheless, she was a great character. But then, people like that, born out of wedlock, are essentially robust, as a great man once remarked to me, and as the proverb has it,

> *Bastards do deeds of mighty worth*
> *By reason of their contrary birth.*

I knew an abbess of Tarascon, sister of Lady d'Usez, of the Tallard family,[657] who put aside the veil when over fifty and married the great Chanay, who was a leading musician at court.

Many other nuns have done the same, either in wedlock or out of it, to try the taste of the flesh at that very ripe age. And if such as they are do this, what is to be expected of our courtly ladies, so accustomed to love-making from their tender years? Should old age prevent them from tasting or sometimes even consuming a nice little piece of what they have for so long been used to? What otherwise would be the purpose of so many fine restorative broths and potages made either with ambergris or some other carminative in them, comforting drugs to warm and tone up their aged, chilly stomachs? Nor should one doubt but that such compounds, by restoring and building up a debilitated inside make for a further little process under the padding, warming them internally and causing venereal heats such that afterwards they really do need expelling by cohabitation and copulation, the most sovereign remedy there can be and the most ordinary too, without any resort such as would otherwise be made to a physician. And ask the physicians if I am not right. And what is best for them is that as they are well on in years and on the verge of fifty they no longer need fear pregnancy, so have complete, ample liberty to have their fun and gather all their arrears of pleasure, which some quite likely have not taken up purely from fear of her traitorous belly's possible swelling. Hence there are quite a number who give themselves a better time love-making after fifty than before that age. And I have heard of many a lady great and small who was of such temperament. Indeed, I will go further, I have actually myself known many and heard them talk of it, many a time saying how they wished they were fifty, so they would be unable to get pregnant and so be better able to make love, without any fear of disgrace. So why ever, once they are over fifty, should they refrain?

You might say that some even after they are dead have some measure of movement and sensation in their flesh, so I ought to tell a tale, and indeed shall do so. I used to have a younger brother, known as Captain Bourdeille,[658] one of the bold and valiant military leaders of his time. I must say this of him, even though he was my brother, and without any derogation from the praise I give him, for the individual combats he sustained in the wars and elsewhere are proof enough of it, for he was the nobleman of France who was most handy with his weapons. Hence in Piedmont he was known as one of the Rodomonts of that country. He was killed in the final attack at the storming of Hesdin.[659]

Now, he had been dedicated by his father and mother to letters, so at the age of eighteen was sent to Italy to study. There he made Ferrara his centre, because Lady Renée of France, then Duchess of Ferrara, was very fond of my mother, so she took him in to apply himself to his studies, for there was a university there. But as he was neither born for it nor adaptable to it, he made hardly any progress, but rather amused himself in courting and making love, till he fell head over heels in love with a widowed Frenchwoman in the Duchess's service known as Lady de La Roche, and had his pleasure of her, and they were both very fond one of the other. Then, seeing him ill fitted for letters, my father sent for him and he had to come back home.

Loving him as she did, and afraid of faring badly, because of her strong leanings towards Lutheranism,[660] then in fashion, Lady de La Roche begged my brother to take her to France with him, to the court of the Queen of Navarre, where she had previously served, the Queen having given her to Lady Renée when she married and left for Italy.

My brother, being young and utterly thoughtless, and also very fond of this mistress of his, took her with him all the way to Paris, where the Queen was at the time, and the Queen was very pleased to see her, as she had been the wittiest of her women, who told the best tales. She was indeed a lovely widow, gifted in every way.

After spending a few days with my grandmother and my mother, then at the Court, my brother turned back, to go to see my father. And in the end, thoroughly fed up with scholarly work, and seeing how ill fitted for such study he was, he left them and went off at once to the wars in Piedmont and Parma, where he acquitted himself with much honour. He continued at this for five or six months, without coming home, at the end of which time he came to see my mother, who was then at court with the Queen of Navarre, the court then being at Pau, and he paid his respects to the Queen as she was on her way back from evening service. She, certainly the finest princess in the world, then welcomed him warmly and, taking him by the hand, walked with him in the church precincts for quite an hour or two, asking him all sorts of things about the wars in Piedmont and Italy, and many other things, to all of which my brother replied so well that she was very pleased (for he was a good talker) both with his mind and his body, as he was also a very handsome noble, then twenty-four years old. At last, after having talked with him for quite a time, for it was the nature and temperament of that honoured princess never to miss any good conversation or such a meeting with an estimable man, passing from one thing to another, as they walked up and down, suddenly stopped my rascal of a brother over the tomb of Lady de La Roche, who had died three months previously. Then, taking his hand, she said : 'Cousin' (for that was what she called him, seeing that a d'Albret daughter had married into our Bourdeille family, though I don't put on any airs on that account, nor does it make me more ambitious) 'cannot you feel something moving under you and under your feet?' 'No, Madame,' he replied. 'But think a bit, cousin,' she replied. My brother said : 'Madame, I have thought, but I can feel nothing moving, I am treading on solid enough ground.' 'Then,' said the Queen, not keeping him in suspense any longer, 'let me tell you, you are standing over the tomb and the body of poor Lady de La Roche, who is buried beneath you and whom you so loved. And as souls feel after our death, one cannot doubt but that this estimable girl, so recently deceased, was moved as soon as you were on her. And if you did not feel it because of the thickness of the masonry, one should still have no doubts but that she felt you and moved. And as it is a pious act to think of those who have passed on, particularly of those one has loved, I beg you to say a *Pater noster* and an *Ave Maria* and a *De profundis* for her. And sprinkle her with holy water. You will then acquire the name of a very faithful lover and a good Christian. So now I will leave you to it, and be gone.'

And off she went. My brother did not fail to do what she said. Then he went to see her, and she scolded him a little, for she was a great observer of the niceties of life and very gracious in that respect. Such indeed was the outlook of that kindly princess, who saw such things more from sheer sweetness of character, and to set an example, than because actually she believed it all, if you ask me.

That cultured thoughtfulness recalls to me the epitaph of a courtesan buried at the church of *Nostra Dama del Popole,* with this inscription : *Quaeso, viator, ne me diutius calcatum amplium calces,* 'Please, passer-by, don't ride me any more, I've had more of it than most women.'

Now, to conclude, it would not be surprising if that Spanish lady had got this sentiment from beautiful ladies who were loved a lot, loved a lot themselves and still love and like praise, even though they are scarcely any longer what they were. Yet it is the greatest pleasure you can give them, which they like the most, when you tell them that they are just the same as they always were, they have not changed a bit or grown any older, and above all they are not ageing from the waist down.

I have been told of a very lovely and estimable lady who one day said to her knight : 'I know not but that old age may bring me some greater disability' (for she was fifty-five) 'but, God be praised, I never made love as well as I do now, nor did I ever have so much pleasure out of it, so that if things go on like this till I am very old, I shan't complain at all of old age or time past.'

Now, as for love and sexual desire, I have given enough examples here and elsewhere without dragging the matter out any more. Let us now pass to the other maxim, concerning that loveliness of the lovely woman which age does not diminish from the waist down.

And indeed, *à propos* of that, this Spanish lady adduced various good arguments, with charming instances in which she made comparison between such lovely ladies and those superb old buildings which once were built, the ruins of which are still so grand, as one sees in Rome, in the proud antiquities there, the ruins of those lovely palaces, those superb amphitheatres and those great baths, which still clearly show what they once were and are the wonder and awe of the whole world. For their ruins remain a marvel which amazes, seeing that as one can often see in the architechtural work undertaken by our best architects and masons, that lovely buildings have been built on them, showing that the foundations are better and finer than new ones would be, so that wherever architects find old ruins and foundations, they immediately build on them rather than on new ones.

I have also often seen fine galleys and ships built by reconstruction work on old frames and keels which had lain idle in some harbour for a long time, but are worth quite as much as those made and carpentered all anew, of fresh timber from the forest.

Further, this Spanish lady asked if one did not often see the tops of tall towers carried away, stripped, dilapidated by winds, storms, and thunder, while the lower part remained sound and whole? For it is invariably those upper parts that the tempests attack, one also sees gales wear and erode rocks from the top down and erode the upper part more than the lower. Just like that, many lovely ladies lose the glow and loveliness of their beautiful faces by many misfortunes, either by cold or by heat, or sunshine or moon, while others, far worse in fact, ruin themselves altogether by the many creams they apply, thinking to improve their looks, whereas the lower

360

parts have no cream applied, nothing but natural spermatics, yet there no effect of rain or wind, sunshine or moonshine is felt.

If those parts are affected by heat, the ladies know well enough how to protect or rather how to refresh them, and the same applies to the cold, in a variety of ways. There is so much inconvenience and so much trouble spent on preserving the upper beauty, but even when you see a lovely woman lose in countenance, one should nevertheless not conclude that any thing down below has deteriorated, and there is any hint there of less beauty and soundness, or that it is a bad thing to build on them.

I have heard the story told of a great lady who had been very lovely and much given to making love, that one of her former suitors once lost sight of her for four years, because of a journey he had had to take. When he came back he found the lovely face he had left very changed, and this so repulsed him and so cooled him off that he made no more approaches at all to her or any attempt to renew their past pleasures. She took due note of all this, but contrived for him to have to go to see her when she was in bed, and when he had come, she said : 'I am well aware, my dear so-and-so, that you scorn me because age has changed my looks, but wait a moment, you look at this,' (and she laid bare the lower half of her body) 'and see if any-thing has changed here. If my face has misled you, this need not.'

Gazing at her, the nobleman found she was indeed as lovely and sound as ever, and at once his appetite returned, and he at once made a nice meal of the meat he had thought must be getting mouldy and spoiled. 'There,' said the lady, 'there, sir, see how mistaken you were. Another time, do not pay such heed to our deceptive faces, for the rest of our bodies does not always re-semble them. A lesson I have taught you !'

A lady in like condition, having thus lost her good looks, was so angry, so indignant with herself, that she would never again look in her mirror, saying it was unworthy of her. She had her women do her hair for her and to make up for it merely looked at her lower parts in the glass, taking as much pleasure from contemplating them as she had previously done from her face.

I have heard of another lady who, when she slept with her lover in daytime, covered her face with a fine white Holland kerchief, from fear lest, seeing her face, her upper part should cool him off and, giving him a distaste for her, make the gun below misfire—for there could be no hint how old she was from the parts below. *A propos* of which, there was one very estimable lady I heard of who had a nice response. Asked one day by her husband why the hairs down below were not as white and hoary as those of her head : 'Ah !' she cried, 'that wretched treacherous thing who makes all the madness never feels it at all or takes it in. He just makes my other parts, including my head, feel it, so it never changes itself, it is always the same and just as energetic, in just the same mood. In particular, it is always as hot as ever, always as sound and always has the same good appetite, not at all like my other limbs, which have all their share of ills, which is why my head is white and hoary.'

She was right in this, for that part of the body certainly does engender aches and ills and goutinesses, without the gay little fellow down in the middle feeling a thing. But doctors say it is through being hot there that ladies become hoary-headed above. Anyway, this is why lovely ladies never age at both ends at once.

I have been told and assured by men who had had much experience of women, including courtesans, that they have hardly ever seen a lovely woman aged in that part, for all their lower and middle parts, including their thighs and legs, were always fine in every respect, and their will and inclination to love-making remained unchanged. I have even been told by a number of husbands that they found their 'old ladies' (as they called them) as fine below in desire, in friskiness, in beauty as they ever were—and as ready for it too, the only part of them that had changed was their face, and they liked sleeping with them as much as in their youth.

For that matter, what a lot of men there are who even prefer an elderly woman for mounting to a young one, just as there are many men who prefer old horses, either for riding all day on serious business or for exercising and sport, for old horses have been so well taught in their youth that in their old age you will find nothing to complain of in them, they are so beautifully trained and have also kept up their skill.

In the Royal stables I once saw the horse known as *le Quadragant,* trained in King Henry's day. He was over twenty-two, but, old though he was, he functioned excellently and had forgotten nothing, so well indeed that he still gave his King and any who saw him handled, very great satisfaction.

I have seen a big charger named *Le Gonzague,* of the Mantuan breeding-stud, in like form, a horse which was the contemporary of *le Quadragant.*

I have also seen *Le Moreau superbe,* who was used as stud stallion. It was Lord Marco Antonio, in charge of the Royal stud at Meun[661] who one day when I happened to pass that way demonstrated him to me, high-stepping and jumping and wheeling as well as when M. Carnavale,[662] his previous owner first trained him, when the late de Longueville offered £3,000 for him,[663] but King Charles[664] refused and took the animal for himself, with compensation indeed.

I could cite many another, but would never be done, and refer you to the valiant grooms who have seen many such horses.

When encamped at Amiens,[665] the late King Henry,[666] for the day of the battle chose a fine, very powerful but also very old charger named *Le Bay de la paix.* That horse died of a fever at Amiens, so expert horse doctors say, who found it very peculiar.

The late Lord de Guise[667] sent to his stud at Esclairon[668] for *le Bay Sanson,* kept there as stud stallion, to ride in the battle of Dreux and the horse served him very well there.

In the first wars,[669] the late monarch[670] took twenty-two horses at Meun,[671] which had been kept there as stallions, for use in his wars, and distributed them among the lords who were with him, reserving some for himself. Among these good d'Avaret[672] acquired a charger which the Lord Constable had given King Henry, which he called *le Compère,*[673] and aged though it was, there never was a better horse, and its master took it to some fine encounters in which it served him well. Captain Bourdet had *Le Turc,* the horse on whose back the late King

Henry received his mortal wound[674] from the Duke of Savoy.[675] This horse was named *Le Malheureux*, 'Unlucky,' and was already so called when given to the King, which was a very bad omen for him. But that horse had never been so good in its youth as it was in its age, and its master, who was one of the most valiant gentlemen of France, brought the best out of it. In short, among so very many of these stallions one never saw a single case of use preventing them from serving their masters, their monarch or their cause. Indeed, there are old horses which never give in. Hence the proverb : *good horses never grow old*.

Just like that are many of the ladies, who in their old age are quite the equal of others in their youth and give as much pleasure too, through having been very well trained and prepared in their youth. And one must admit that those are lessons it is hard to forget, and what surpasses everything is that they are inclined to be most big-hearted and generous in the giving, whereby to keep their knights and riders, who take more money and want bigger fees for riding an old mount than a young one, which is the opposite of grooms, who do not charge so much for looking after a trained horse as a young mare which needs breaking in, which is only common sense.

There is one question I have known to be put touching elderly ladies, namely, wherein lies the greater triumph, in seducing an elderly lady and having one's pleasure of her, or a young one. The answer usually given is that the wildness and heat of youth are in themselves quite seduceable enough and easy to love, but the sedateness and coolness which old age seems to bring are less easy to seduce, so that whoever achieves trimphs there is the more worthy of esteem.

Thus that notorious courtesan Lais used to boast and make much of the fact that the philosophers were more frequent pupils in her academy than any other younger and foolish men.[676] In the same way, Flora was proud to see great Roman senators at her door rather than silly young knights.[677] Hence it seems true that it is a great triumph when in favour of pleasure and love's satisfaction one overcomes the sedateness liable to be found in elderly folk. I refer you to those who have tried.

Some men say that a broken-in mount is more pleasing to ride than a wild one, which is unable to trot-job steadily for a long time. What is more, what delight and what extreme mental satisfaction one can have when seeing the entry into the ballroom, or the Queen's apartments, or a church, or any other grand assembly, of an elderly lady of great quality and what the Italians call *alta guisa*, (haughty bearing, that is,) particularly if it is a Lady-in-waiting of the Queen's or of some other Princess, or the governess of some Royal daughter, or any great lady given in charge of her to keep her discreet in behaviour, and seen to look so prim, so chaste, so virtuous, that the whole world is sure she is so, because of her years, yet one can have reason to reflect and perhaps even to whisper to some reliable friend and confidant : 'Just look at her, how sage and grave she is, how disdainful and frigid she looks, too, so one would not think she could make a single dew-drop quiver—yet, my dear fellow, just think, when I lie in her bed and clasp her there is not a weathercock in the world that twitches or veers so much or so nimbly as her loins and buttocks do.'

If you ask my opinion, any man who has known that does indeed feel pleased with himself. Oh, how many such ladies have I not known in our circles who aped the sedate, the prim, even the censorious, yet were most loose and venereal when they came to it, more often too to be brought to love-making than any of your young ones, who are far too unsophisticated and afraid of the duel. Is it not said that there is never such hunting as that of old vixens that want to feed their young.

We read that in times gone by many Roman emperors found great pleasure in seducing and so forth those great and honoured ladies of antiquity as much for the pleasure and satisfaction of it, (of which there can be no question,) as for the triumph and distinction they can feel for having seduced them and trodden them, just as in my own day I have known many a ruler, prince and noble who felt very triumphant and had great spiritual satisfaction from doing the same.

Julius Caesar and Octavius [678] his successor were very hot on such conquests, as I have remarked previously, and after them comes Caligula,[679] who would invite the most distinguished ladies of Rome to his banquets, together with their husbands, and would then stare at them and examine them so unswervingly, even taking their chins and tipping back their heads, if any felt ashamed and looked down, either so they might feel they were honourable ladies, of repute, or to pretend to be so and most prim and chaste (and there can really have been few enough such in days of those dissolute emperors). But if they happened to please the Emperor they had to be content and pretend to be so and remain satisfied with appearances, (and I have known many lords and ladies play this game). Then, whether undemonstratively or demonstratively, Caligula would take them from their husbands, leave the dining-room and take them to another room, where he had whatever pleasure it was his whim from them. After this he would bring them back, to resume their place, and then in all detail, to the whole company, praise their fine points and whatever peculiarities were concealed. And if any of them had any blemish, any ugly point or defect, he would make no effort to conceal it, but describe it and publish it, without disguising a single detail.

Nero, which was even worse, insisted on seeing his mother's body when she died, examining her closely, handling all her parts, praising this and saying shocking things of that.[680] I have heard the same said of some great Christian rulers, said to have been just as inquisitive about their dead mothers.

What I have related above was not all what Caligula did, for he even told about all the motions of these mistresses of the moment, their way of experiencing their sex, everything, in fact, that they did with their bodies and the expression on their faces throughout the act, and especially of those who had been sedate and modest, or at table had pretended so to be. For if when on their backs they did not want to do whatever it was his whim to have them do, one need have no doubt but that this monster threatened them with death, only afterwards thus to disgrace them as he pleased, and make them the general laughing-stock of all the other poor ladies who had thought these were really chaste and well behaved, (as some may indeed have been,) and not just hypocritical, pretending to be *donne da ben,* decent women, but now blatantly exposed and shown to be good, ribald tarts, though it was not a bad thing for him to expose those who tried to conceal what they really were. And what was the best was that, as I say, these were all great ladies, such as the wives of consuls and dictators, of pretorians and quaestors, senators, of censors, knights and other men of very great position and dignity, as we might say, the Queens of our Christendom of today, to whom are to be compared, since consuls ruled the whole world, the princesses of the world, great and small, the duchesses great and little, the marquises and the lesser marquises, the countesses and the little countesses, the baronesses and the knightesses and other ladies of great rank and fine breed. So that we need have no doubt but that, if several emperors and kings could treat great ladies as Caligula did, they would. But they are Christians, with the fear of God ever in their minds, they are governed by his holy commandments and their own consciences, their sense of honour, and also the way other men, not speak of the ladies' husbands, would look upon it, for no decent heart today would stand such tyranny, whereby we see that our Christian kings are much to be valued and praised, for winning the love of lovely ladies rather by gentleness and affection than by force and harshness, whereby the winning is all the lovelier.

I have been told of two great princes[681] who found great pleasure in thus revealing the beauties, charms and peculiarities of their ladies, also their deformities, blemishes and defects, together with their little tricks, movements and lusts, not in public, however, as Caligula did, but in private, with their great intimates. Now that was a fine misuse of the sweet bodies of those poor ladies, indeed, who thought they were doing right in their frolics, to please their lovers, only later to be described to others and laughed about.

Now to go back again to our comparison; just as one sees fine ancient buildings built on better foundations and of better stones and other material than others, so that their loveliness and fame is longer-lived, so are ladies' bodies so well made and of such fine composition and so impregnated with loveliness that one clearly sees time affect them less than it does others, not undermining them at all.

We read of Artaxerxes[682] that among all his wives the one he loved best was Astasia, who was very old, yet still very lovely, and she had formerly been the concubine of his late brother Darius. His son so fell in love with her, so beautiful was she notwithstanding her age, that he asked his father if he might share her, as well as part of the Kingdom. From jealous reluctance to have his son share that delectable morsel with him, the father then made her Sun Priestess, since those who achieve that position in Persia are dedicated to chastity.

In the History of Naples[683] we read that Ladislaus the Hungarian, who was also King of Naples, paid court to the Duchess Maria, wife of the late Rammondelo de Balzo, at Tarento, and after several sallies and skirmishes, in agreement with her children took her and, though she was well on in years,[684] married her, and took her with him to Naples, where she was known as Queen Marie and much beloved and cherished by him.

I saw the Duchess of Valentinois[685] at the age of seventy[686] as lovely of features, as fresh and as lovable as at the age of thirty. She was indeed much beloved and courted by one of the great and valorous kings of her time. This I can say frankly, without any wrong done to the loveliness of that lady, for any lady who is loved by a great King knows that this is a token of the perfection so abundant in her, by which she brought him to love her. So loveliness, which is a gift of heaven, should never be reserved to the demi-gods. I saw that lady, six months before she died, still so lovely that I think even the heart of a rock would have been stirred by her, and despite the fact that some time before this she had broken a leg on the paving of Orleans she walked and rode horseback as dexterously and featly as she had ever done. Her horse had slipped and fallen, and from the ills and pains she endured one would have thought her countenance would be changed, but nothing less than this, for her beauty, her grace, her majesty, her fine bearing remained just as they had always been. And apart from all this she was of tremendous whiteness, and that without any creams, though it is admittedly alleged that every morning she used to take broths of drinkable gold and other drugs which I do not know as a good physician or clever apothecary might. I believe that had that lady lived another hundred years she would not have aged, whether in her face, so finely drawn, or the parts of her body covered and concealed, of such fine constitution and regularity was she. It is a pity that the soil now covers that lovely body!

I saw the Marquise de Rothelin,[687] mother of the Dowager Duchess de Condé[688] and the late Duke de Langueville,[689] and she was of a loveliness utterly unblemished by either time or age, but remained as flourishing as she had ever been, save that towards the end her complexion became a trifle florid. But on the other hand her lovely eyes, unmatched in the world, (which her gracious daughter inherited,) never changed and were as apt to wound a man's heart as ever.

I saw Lady de La Bourdisière, who by her second husband became the Lady Marshal d'Aumont,[690] as lovely in her old age that one would have thought her still very young, so that her five daughters, who were all beautiful, never outmatched her. Indeed, had the choice been open to one, any man would have passed the daughters by in favour of their mother, yet she had had a great number of children. But she was a great one to look after herself, and mortally afraid of night damp and moonlight, avoiding them as much as ever she could, but the creams which were then commonly used she would have none of.

What is more, I saw Lady de Mareuil,[691] mother of the Marquise de Mézières,[692] at the age of one hundred, at which she died, as alert, as fresh and as lovely and sound as she had been at fifty. Now that had been a very lovely woman indeed in her youth.

Her daughter, this Marquise de Mézières,[693] was the same, and died like her mother, unblemished, though twenty years her junior, and beginning to stoop a little. She was the aunt of Lady de Bourdeille,[694] the wife of my eldest brother, who was like her, for although she was over fifty-three and had had fourteen children one would have said, (as one heard from those better able to pronounce, having seen her,) that the four daughters who remained with her were her sisters. Similarly can one see various Winter and late season crops equalling those of summer and keep too, and be sound and tasty, even more so.

Lady l'Amiral de Bryon,[695] and her daughter, Lady de Barbezieux,[696] were also very lovely in old age.

Recently I was told that lovely Paule de Toulouse,[697] who used to be so famous, is as lovely as ever, although she is eighty, she is not a bit changed, neither her fine figure nor her handsome countenance.

I saw Lady Comte, wife of the President of the High Court of Bordeaux,[698] just the same and at the same age, most charming and desirable, lovely in many ways, and I could name so many others, were it not that I should never finish.

A young knight was talking to an elderly lady, who in spite of her years was still lovely, when she made this rejoinder: 'However can you say that to me in my complines?' thereby, using the term complines, meaning to suggest her age and the decline of her best days and approach of night. The knight replied : 'Your evensong is worth more and is more lovely and more charming than the matins of any other lady that there is.' A charming way of putting it.

When another man spoke of love to an elderly lady and she remonstrated about her decayed beauty, though it was not too much decayed, he replied with the proverb : *A las visperas se conoce la fiesta*, 'it's when you come to evensong that you know whether the holiday's been good.'

Today too, one can see Lady de Nemours,[699] once, in her April, the beauty of the world, challenging time, though this wipes everything away. I—and those who have seen her as I have—can assert her to have been the loveliest of women in her youth in all Christendom. I once saw her dance, as I have said elsewhere, she and the Queen of Scotland together,[700] without any other ladies, by a sudden impulse, so that all the gentlemen and ladies present who saw them dancing might judge which of them bore the crown for beauty, and, so said one man, one might have declared it to be that double sun which Pliny records as having once amazed the world. Lady de Nemours, at the time Lady de Guise,[701] though not a Queen herself, as her partner was, offered the more opulent figure and, if I may say so without offending the Queen of Scotland, she also had a graver and more striking dignity. But she was a grand-daughter of that great King, father of the people,[702] whom she resembled in many features of her face, as I have seen her depicted in the closet of the Queen of Navarre, which made it amply clear which King that was.

I think I was the first to call her 'the grand-daughter of the King, Father of the people' and this was at Lyons[703] when the King returned from Poland. I frequently called her that, as she honoured me by finding it a good title and liking to hear me utter it. There was no question about it, she was a true grand-daughter of that great King, and particularly in kindness and in beauty, for she was kindness itself,[704] and one can find few, or none, who could say she had ever done them a hurt or displeasure, favoured too as she was by her time and by having as husband the Duke de Guise, who stood so high in France. So two very great qualities of excellence combined in this lady, namely, kindness and beauty, and she has cultivated them both to the present, and because of them has married two estimable husbands, two men the like of which could with difficulty have been found. And were yet another man who was worthy of her to be found and she were willing to accept him as third husband, she could still do so, so lovely is she still.

Further, in Italy the ladies of Ferrara are held to be fine, tasty morsels, whence the proverb *pota ferraresa*, just like *cazzo mantuan*.[1] A *propos* of which, a great prince of that land, who was once laying siege to a lovely, great princess of our France, was being lauded at court for his fine qualities, his valour and his good points, the late d'O., then Captain of the Scots Guards, capped it all by saying : 'Your forget his best point, he was a Mantuan *cazzo.*'

I once heard something similar, that the Duke of Mantua,[705] known because he was very hunchbacked, as *Gobbo*,[706] aspired to marry the sister of the Emperor Maximilian, when it was re-

---

[1] *Ferraran crocks and pans,* but the words of course have a double sense.—A.B.

ported to her about his hump, and, so it is said, she replied : 'No matter if the bell's a bit out of shape, so long as the clapper's sound,' meaning of course that same *cazzo mantuan*. Others say she did not actually say it, being too demure and well trained,[707] but others said it for her.

To go back again to that Ferraran princess,[708] I saw her at the wedding of the late Lord de Joyeuse,[709] where she was dressed in an Italian style cloak, held up to one side over the arm in the Siena manner, but there was still not any lady could outdo her, not a man who did not say : 'This lovely Princess cannot better herself, she is so beautiful. And it is easy to see that that lovely countenance covers and conceals other great beauties and parts which we do not see anything of, just as when we see the lovely, superb façade of a handsome building it is easy to judge that inside there are lovely rooms and anterooms, wardrobes, nooks and crannies.'

Quite recently she displayed her beauty in other places too and this in her late-season, even for Spain, at the wedding of the Duke and Duchess of Savoy,[710] where the wonder of her and her beauty and all her fine qualities were engraved in every mind for all time. Were the wings of my pen strong and broad enough to carry it up to high heaven, I should fly there, but they are too feeble, so I shall come back to her again elsewhere. So much, however, to state that she was a very lovely woman in her Spring, her Summer and her Autumn and even in her Winter, although she had so many worries and children.[711]

The worst is that the Italians, scornful of a woman who has had a lot of children, call her a *scrofa*, that is, a sow, whereas women who bring forth handsome, valiant, warm-hearted children, as that Princess did, are to be praised and should not be called that, but *blessed by God*.

I might cry : 'What remarkable worldly fickleness it is that the thing which is lightest and most inconstant, that is, a lovely woman, should be resistant to time.' That is not my own pronouncement, far from me to say such a thing, for I greatly value the constancy of some women, they are not all fickle, it is from another man I have taken that exclamation.

I would further gladly cite foreign ladies, as well as our own French ones, who are lovely in their Autumn and Winter, but I will only put in two of these.

One is Queen Elizabeth of England, at present reigning, and, I am told, as lovely as ever, and if this is so, I hold her to be a lovely Princess indeed, for I saw her in her Summer and her Autumn. As for her Winter, even if she has not quite reached it yet, she is drawing very near, for it is a long time since I saw her. The first time I saw her, I know how old she was said to be then.[1] I think that what has kept her beautiful so long is that she has never married or borne the burden of marriage, which is very onerous, especially when a woman produces several children. This Queen is worthy of all manner of praise, save for the death of that brave, lovely, rare Queen of Scotland,[712] and that was a grave blot on her virtues.

The other Princess and foreign lady is the Marquise de Douast, Donna Maria d'Aragon,[713] who when I saw her was a very lovely lady in her late season, and I will relate the circumstances as briefly as I possibly can. When King Henry[714] died, Pope Paul IV (Caraffa)[715] followed him one month later, and the college of cardinals had to meet to elect another. Among others who went from France was the Cardinal de Guise.[716] He travelled by sea to Rome with the King's galleys, the commander of which was the Grand Prior of France,[717] brother of the Cardinal who, as a good brother, took him there with a fleet of sixteen galleys. They made such good progress, with such favourable following winds, that they reached Civita Vecchia in two days and nights, and thence they travelled to Rome. And when they got there and the Grand Prior found that the arrangements were not yet complete for the new election, (indeed, it took three months more) and his galleys were lying idle in port, he decided to go as far as Naples to look at that city and while away the time. Well, when he got there, the Viceroy, who at the time was the Duke d'Alcala,[718] received him as if he had been a king. Even before he came into harbour he saluted the city with a fine salvo which lasted some time, an

---

[1] She was in fact 28 years old at the time. It was in 1561 that Brantôme saw her.—A.B.

honour which was returned him by the city and all its castles, so that during the salvo one would have thought it was real thunder. Then, keeping his galleys hove to in battle formation, some distance out, he sent Lord de l'Estrange of Languedoc[719] ashore in a small boat, (a most skilful and estimable lord, very well spoken), to go to the Viceroy, not to disturb him, but, (seeing that though we were nicely at peace we had only just emerged from a state of mutual war) to ask permission to enter the port, to see the city and visit the tombs of his ancestors buried there, and sprinkle them with Holy Water and pray for their souls.

The Viceroy granted this most graciously. So the Grand Prior proceeded into port and began another salvo, as fine and furious as the first, both using the light cannon of the sixteen galleys and other guns, and also batteries of harquebuses, so that there was a complete blaze of firing, after which he advanced grandly into the harbour, striking still more standards, streamers, and crimson taffeta ribbons and also his own flag of damask and with all the galley-slaves clad in crimson velvet, and the soldiers of his guard the same, with cloaks covered in silver-thread embroidery, captained by Geoffrey, a Provençal, a bold and valorous captain too, so that our French galleys were found very fine, trim and beautifully decked out, especially *la Realle*, which was above reproach, for that Prince was most munificent and generous in every way.

So, having entered harbour in such fine array, he landed and all the rest of us with him, where the Viceroy had ordered horses and coaches to await us to pick us up and take us into the city. And indeed, we found one hundred horses—hacks, nags, stallions, Spanish steeds, Arabs and others—each more beautiful than the last, caparisoned in embroidered velvet, some with gold, some with silver thread. Whoever wished to ride took a horse, while those who so preferred entered a coach, for there were also about twenty of the finest and most luxurious coaches, finely harnessed, drawn by the loveliest draught horses one could wish to see. There were also many great princes and lords present, some belonging to the Kingdom of Naples, some from Spain, who welcomed the Grand Prior on behalf of the Viceroy with great honour. He mounted a Spanish steed, the finest animal I had seen for a long time. Subsequently the Viceroy made him a present of it. It handled very well, too, curvetting very finely, to use the language of the time. As the Grand Prior was a very fine horseman, as good as he was a mariner, he made a fine sight mounted on this and brought the best out of the animal, with very fine style, for he was one of the most comely princes of the day and one of the most pleasant, most accomplished, also very tall and upstanding and agile with it, which is rare in such great men. So he was now conducted by all these lords and other nobles to the Viceroy, who was awaiting him and showed him all possible honours, housing him in his own palace and feasting him sumptuously both him and his suite. He could well do so, since this visit brought him twenty-thousand crowns.

Together with him, we were a good two hundred nobles, galley captains and others. We were lodged in the homes of most of the great lords of Naples, and very finely, too. First thing in the morning we found well-trained grooms awaiting on us, to learn our wishes and where we would like to go, and if we wished for a mount or a coach, our wish was fulfilled at once, off they went to find the mounts we required, so fine, so rich and so superb that a King would have been satisfied, and then out we went and filled in our day as pleased each of us. In short, we could not complain of not having all the pleasures and delights in Naples that we wished, and I need not add that there was all that, for never did I see a city fuller of every kind of amenity, all it lacked was free, homely, frank conversation with ladies of honour and good name, for there were enough of the others. To which, as far as that goes, the Marquise de Gouast made much amends, for love of whom I make this essay, the soul of courtesy and sound dignity as she was, and having heard tell of all the fine qualities of our Lord the Grand Prior and of the greatness of his line, when she saw him process through the city on horseback and recognized him, one day sent a very estimable and well-born noble to him to say that, had her sex and the customs of her land allowed her to call on him, she would very gladly have done so to offer him all she had, as all the great lords of the Kingdom had done, but she begged him to accept her apologies, while offering him her mansions, her castles, and all she had.

My Lord the Grand Prior, who was as courteous a man, thanked her profoundly, as befitted him, and sent her a message that he would call to kiss her hands immediately after dinner, which he did not fail to do, together with all of us with him as his suite. We found the Marquise in her hall together with her two daughters, Donna Antonina,[720] and Donna Hieronyma or Donna Joanna[721] (I cannot quite say, I have forgotten which name it was) with many lovely ladies and unmarried girls, all finely attired and with charm, so that apart from our courts of France and Spain I must say that nowhere else have I seen a finer bevy of ladies.

The Marquise greeted us in French fashion and received the Grand Prior with very great honour, and he returned this, though more humbly, *con mas gran societgo*, 'with the greatest solemnity,' as the Spanish has it. On this occasion their conversation was of commonplaces. Some of us, who knew Italian and Spanish, engaged the other ladies in conversation and found them very estimable and gallant, and also fine conversationalists.

When we left, as the Marquise had now learned that the Grand Prior proposed to spend a fortnight there, she said to him : 'My Lord, whenever you are at a loose end and have nothing else to entertain you, do come here, whenever you please, you will greatly honour me and you will be as welcome as in the house of your mother. Pray without hesitation make yourself as at home in mine as you would in hers. I have the fortune of being liked and visited as much as any lady by estimable and lovely ladies of the kingdom and this city, and since your youth and virtue show that you enjoy the conversation of estimable ladies, I shall ask them to come to see me more frequently than they usually do, to provide you and all this flower of the French nobility who are with you with companionship. Here are my two daughters, and though they are not so accomplished as one might desire, I will ask them to provide you with company in the French style, such as laughing, dancing, playing and chatting freely, as you do at the court of France. I would gladly offer my own company too, but that it would vex a young prince, handsome and estimable as you are, to entertain an elderly, superannuated, vexatious and hardly lovable person like myself, for old age and youth hardly match together.'

The Grand Prior at once took up her words and indicated to her that old age had in no way stolen on her, and he could not let that one pass, but her Autumn was finer by far than all the Springs and Summers that had ever been in that hall. Indeed, it was so, she was still a very lovely and very charming lady, indeed, more so than her two daughters, lovely and young as they were, though at the time she was well on the wrong side of fifty. This double reply which the Grand Prior made the Marquise pleased her greatly, as we could see from her smiling countenance, her speech and her bearing.

We left the mansion most edified by that lovely lady, and especially the Grand Prior, who was immediately quite taken by her, as he told us. So one should not be astonished that this lovely, estimable lady and her lovely bevy of ladies should invite the Grand Prior to her house every day, and if we were not there after dinner, we would be in the evening. The Grand Prior selected the elder daughter to be his lady, although he really preferred the mother, but this he did *per adumbrar la cosa*, to cloak the matter. There was much jousting, with the Grand Prior bearing off the prize and there were many ballets and much dancing. In short, that fine company were the cause that, although the Grand Prior had not intended to stay at Naples more than a fortnight, we were there six weeks without once finding it tedious, for we had all found mistresses too, just as our general had. Indeed, we would have stayed on longer, had not a courier arrived from the King his master, bringing news of the war begun in Scotland, so that he was obliged to move his galleys from East to West, though this was not till eight months later.

So we had to abandon those delightful pleasures and leave the lovely, charming city of Naples. It was indeed not without great grief and regret that our Lord General and all of us

377

with him departed, distressed to leave a place where we had enjoyed ourselves so much.

Six years or more later, we went to the aid of Malta.[722] I happened to be at Naples,[723] and made enquiries as to whether the Marquise was still alive. I was told that she was, and was in town. At once I made a point of calling, and was immediately recognized by an aged butler of the mansion, who went to tell my Lady that I wished to kiss her hands. Recalling my name, Bourdeille, she had me go up to her chamber and see her. I found her bedridden, because of a touch of erysipelas on one cheek. I assure you, she made me very welcome. I found her very little changed, and still so lovely that she could have made a man commit mortal sin, in intent at least, if not in deed.

She made much enquiry of me for news of the late Grand Prior, showing great concern, since she had been told that he had died of poisoning,[724] and cursing a hundredfold the miscreant who had done it. I told her it was not true, she should dispel that idea from her mind, and assured her that he had died of a pleurodynia caught at the battle of Dreux, where he had fought all day like a Caesar, and in the evening, getting very heated in the fighting in the last charge, and perspiring, had retired from the field when it was cold enough to split rocks, and so fell sick. The illness got a hold on him and he died of it a month or six weeks later.

By what she said and her manner she showed that she grieved him greatly. You should observe that, two or three years prior to this, he had sent two galleys cruising under Captain Beaulieu, one of his juniors in the fleet, and he had flown the flag of the Queen of Scotland, which had never been seen in Levantine waters, and was not even known there, so that they were most astonished to see it, for there could have been no thought of sailing under the French flag, because of the alliance with the Turks. The Grand Prior had charged Captain Beaulieu to land at Naples and in his name call on the Marquise and her daughters, to all three of whom he sent many presents, all the latest fashions of the court and the galleries of the Palais de Justice,[725] in Paris and in France, for the Lord Grand Prior was liberality and munificence personified.

And Captain Beaulieu had punctiliously accomplished all this, and been very well received, and was himself rewarded with a fine present.

The Marquise felt so grateful for the presents made her and for remembering her as he had done that she told me so again and again, assuring me that she loved him even more than before. For love of him she was also gracious to a Gascon noble, serving on the Grand Prior's galleys at the time, who when we left was very ill and stayed behind. He was then very lucky indeed, for, when he turned to this lady in his unhappy condition, she had him cared for at once and he recovered, and she then took him into her service, to be in charge of the garrison at one of her castles, and in addition to giving him that appointment she arranged for his marriage to a rich woman.

None of us had had the least idea what had happened to him and had believed him dead, but when we made that visit to Malta we had with us a noble who was his younger brother, who, one day, without special intent, mentioned to me that one principal reason for his being on the expedition was to seek news of a brother of his who had been with the Grand Prior and had been left behind in Naples, mortally ill, more than six years previously, after which there had been no needs. I then recalled the case and made enquiries for news of him of men of the Marquise's household, and they told me how lucky he had been, which I at once reported to his younger brother, who was most grateful to me, and went with me to call on my lady, where he learned more, after which he went to see his brother.

Now there was a lovely sense of responsibility, all based on the mere memories of us which she had, as I say. And after this discovery she made me even more welcome and entertained me much about times gone by and many other things which all made me find her company very lively and very delightful, for she was a wonderful, most elegant conversationalist. Time and again she begged me not to take any other lodging or board than hers, but I would never hear of planting myself on her, for it has never been my nature to be importunate or a beggar, but during the seven or eight days we were there, I went to see her every day, and was well received, and her chamber was always open to me without any difficulty. When I bade her good-bye, she gave me some letters of introduction to her son the Marquis de Pescayre,[726] at the time a general in the Spanish army. In addition, she made me promise that on my return I would call to see her at once, and then not put up anywhere but at her house.

It was indeed a great misfortune for me that the galleys which took us back did not set us ashore till we reached Terracina, whence we made our way to Rome, and I was quite unable then to go back to see her, so I decided I would go on to the war in Hungary, but when we reached Venice we learned of the death of the Grand Sultan Suleiman.[727] It was then that I cursed my bad luck a hundred times for not having returned forthwith to Naples, where I could have passed my time very well, and quite possibly by the intervention of my Lady the Marquise would have found good fortune there, by marriage or otherwise, for she did me the kindness of being very fond of me.

I think my wretched fate must have been against it, and insisted on bringing me back to France,[728] to be forever wretched, and where good luck never once showed me its fair face, except indeed in the outward appearance and fine show of being esteemed a man of gallantry and much honour. But not a hint of means or rank, however, such as some of my comrades, even others of much lower origin than I am, acquired, including some who would have been happy to have had a good word put in for them at any court or in any royal chamber of king or queen, or any other such place of public gathering, while at the sovereign's side, or whispering it in his ear, yet now I see them as inflated as pumpkins, much advanced, though I do not bother about them or account them any greater than I am, or envy them a bit, no, not a nail's breadth, for it all.

For, as far as I myself go, I am able to put into practice the proverb which our Saviour Jesus Christ offered with his own lips: *that no man can be a prophet in his own country.* Perhaps, had I followed foreign princes as well as my own and sought where to wield my sword among them as I did for these, I should now be as loaded with goods and dignities as I am with aches and years. Patience! If it is my fate, and I myself to blame, I curse that fortune of mine, but if it is through my princes, then the devil take them all, if he has not done so already.

There, this is the end of my story of that honoured lady. She died greatly renowned for having been a very lovely and very estimable lady, and for having left behind her a fine, ample line, such men as the Lord Marquis her eldest son, Don Juan, Don Carlos, and Don Caesar d'Avalos, all of whom I have seen, and spoken of elsewhere,[729] and the daughters took after their brothers. And here I end my main theme.

SIXTH ESSAY

On its not being seemly to speak badly of estimable ladies although they do have love affairs and on the great trouble that slandering them about their conduct has caused

THERE is one point to be noted about these lovely estimable ladies who have love affairs but who, however much frolicking they allow themselves, do not wish to be insulted or disgraced by what anybody says. If anybody does insult them, they are clever at getting their revenge, sooner or later. In short, they like making love, but not having it talked about. And indeed, it is not very nice, disgracing an estimable lady, or exposing her, for whatever is it do with the people generally if certain ladies and their lovers too do find satisfaction in it?

Our French courts, some of them, particularly recent ones, have been very given to tittle-tattling about these estimable ladies, and I have known moments when there was not one gallant man who did not invent some slander against these ladies, or at least tell some true story. In which there is much to be blamed, for one should never offend the honour of ladies, above all not of great ladies, I speak as much of those men who have their pleasures from love-making as of those who are unable to taste the venison at all and for that reason decry it.

Recent Royal courts, as I have just said, have been much given to such slanders and libels, very different from the courts of our other monarchs, who preceded them, with the exception of that of King Louis XI, that fine wash-out, of whom it is said that most of the time he shared the same platter with a number of nobles who were his intimates, and with others too,

382

in fact, everybody, all very dirty, and the man who could tell him the best and most salty tale of light-o'-loves was the most popular and pampered,[730] nor did he himself ever spare his efforts to furnish material for tales, also collecting them assiduously and always wanted to know what had happened, after which he would tell other people, publicly, too. That man was indeed a great disgrace.

He had a very evil opinion of womenfolk and did not believe a single one was chaste. When he invited the King of England[731] to festivities in Paris and was taken at his word he at once repented and found an excuse to break the engagement. 'Oh! by God's Easter,' was what he said, 'I don't want that man here, he would find some pampered juicy little morsel here with whom he would fall in love and she would make him want to stay on longer and come more often than would ever suit me.'

On the other hand he had a very high opinion of his wife, who was circumspect and virtuous,[732] though it was he who made her so because, if ever there was such a prince, he was a tetchy and suspicious one, and would soon have had any rivals slaughtered. And when he died, he ordered his son to love and respect his mother greatly though not to let her rule him, 'not because she is not very discreet and chaste,' he said, 'but because she is more of a Burgundian than a French-woman.'[733] Another thing is that he only loved her in order to get heirs, and once he had some,[734] hardly ever touched her again. He kept her at Amboise Castle living as a simple lady, quite humbly, as poorly dressed as a mere girl, and there he left her, with a tiny court, to occupy herself praying, while he careered about, having a fine time. However, the way in which the ladies were the common court dish, I will leave it to you to imagine, seeing that he had so low an opinion of them, not that he in any way grudged them such looseness, or in any way wished to restrict their games, as I have seen some Kings do. Yet his principal pleasure remained teasing them, till the women felt themselves so hemmed in by slanders that they were often not able to cock their cruppers as freely as they would have liked. Altogether, whorishness was the rule in his time, since the King himself and the nobles of his court so engaged in it. Another thing is that it was open to everybody to vie with everybody else mocking, whether publicly or privately, and see who told the best tales of their lechery and wriggling (as he would call it) and looseness. True, the name of the great ladies was kept cloaked, and these were judged solely by appearances and conjecture. I believe they had a better time than many whom I knew in the late King's time, who scolded and censured and repressed them excessively. This is what I have heard some old men say of that fine King.

Now, King Charles VIII, his son, who followed him, was not of such character, for of him it is said that he was the soberest and most decently spoken King ever seen, one who never offended man or woman with a single word. So I leave it to you to suppose whether the lovely ladies of his reign who indulged in pleasures did not have a good time. Further, he was very fond of the ladies and paid them great attentions, even too much attention, for, coming back from his visit to Naples very victorious and triumphant, he took such pleasure in serving them, fondling them and giving them so many delights at Lyons[735] by the fine combats and tournaments which he staged for love of them that he forgot all about his own folk left behind in that other Kingdom and allowed them to lose both cities and Kingdom, except for some castles, which still held out while calling on him to relieve them. It is also said that it was the ladies who were the cause of his death, for through too much indulgence with them despite his feeble constitution, he wore himself out and became so debilitated that his death was hastened.[736]

King Louis XII was very respectful to the ladies, for, as I have said elsewhere, he allowed all the ribald men of his Kingdom, such as the schoolmen and the corporations of lawyers at the high court, to say whatever they liked about anybody, except about the Queen his consort and her ladies and maids, although in his time[737] he was a boon companion and loved the ladies as much as anybody else. In this, though not in being evil-tongued, or arrogant, or boastful, he took after his ancestor Louis of Orleans[738] for that quality cost that King his life, for when one day he boasted out loud, at a banquet attended by Duke Jean of Burgundy his cousin, that he had a collection of portraits of the loveliest ladies he had enjoyed in his closet, Duke Jean happened to come in, and the first lady whose portrait he saw, the very first to catch his eye, was his own noble lady spouse, considered at the time to be very lovely. Marguerite was her name, and she was a daughter of Albert of Bavaria, Count of Hainault and Zeeland. Who was taken aback? The good husband, and you may well imagine what he said to himself! 'You've grown horns,' he thought, 'my dear fellow!'

But, giving no hint of the flea that was biting him, he hid it all and harboured his vengeance, till he fell out with King Louis about the Regency and administration of the Kingdom, and with this to disguise the real reason, and not his wife, had him assassinated at the Porte Babette[739] of Paris, after first dealing with his wife[740] (poison, you may imagine!) and with the heifer in calf gone, married as second wife the daughter of Louis, third Duke of Bourbon.[741] And may have moved from frying-pan to fire, for such folk given to horn-wearing change bedroom and timing in vain, they always grow new appendages.

However, this Duke acted very soundly in having revenge for the adultery without disgracing either his wife or himself, a very discreet piece of deception indeed. Further I have been told by a very great military leader that there are three things a discreet man should never blazon abroad if wounded by them, but hold his peace, and prefer to invent some other reason for a duel and vengeance, unless the case were so obvious and self-evident to many people that it could not be concealed. One instance is when one man is reproached by another with being a cuckold and his wife everybody's tart, the second when a man is charged with buggery and sodomy, and the third, when it is set about that he is a coward, and made a wretched flight from a single-combat or from the battlefield. These three things, this great captain said, are very disgracing if one announces that one is duelling about them, and often when one thinks one is clearing one's name one is merely making a worse advertisement than ever, for once the matter is noised abroad there is great disgrace, and the more it is poked the worse it stinks, exactly like any filth when one stirs it. That is why if one can keep mum about one's honour it is best to do so and conjure and try some new reason for getting one's own way about the real matter, and such insults should never be made the reason for any dispute or conflict or duel before one is forced to it. I could give many examples of that but it would be inconvenient because it would drag out my essay too long.

This is why Duke Jean was very wise to dissemble and hide his horns and find some other ostensible reason to have his revenge on his cousin who has disgraced him. But still his cousin made fun of him and noised it about, and there can be no doubt but that this mockery and the disgrace did not so much touch his heart as his career, and it was this brought him to taking the clever and very wise public step which he did.

Now to get back to my subject : King François, who was very fond of the ladies, (although, as I have said elsewhere, he was convinced that they are most changeable and fickle),[742] never would have any slandering of them at his court, but insisted on their being accorded great honour and respect. I once heard it said that one Lent, when he was at Meudon near Paris, there was a noble of his suite named Busambourg, from Xaintonge,[743] who, when he was serving the King with meat, which was in his charge, the King told him he was to take the remainder—as is sometimes done at court—to the ladies of that little band whom I prefer not to name for fear of shocking. This noble then chose to tittle-tattle to his fellow courtiers and company about these ladies not being satisfied with raw meat in Lent, they had to have some cooked too, and, what was more, demanded a platter-full. The ladies overheard this, and at once complained to the King, and he was so furious that he ordered the archers of his household guard without delay to take Busambourg out and string him up, but by chance the poor fellow learned in time (from one of his friends) which way the wind was blowing, and, slipping away, made good his escape, but had he been caught he would certainly have been hanged, despite being a noble of good origin, so enraged was the King on this occasion, quite beyond reasoning with. I have the story from an honourable person who was present. It was also on that occasion that the King laid it down that any man who assailed the honour of any of the ladies would without fail be hanged.

A little earlier, when Pope Paul III, of the Farnese family, had come to Nice[744] and the King called on him with all his court, his lords and ladies,[745] there were certain of the latter who were not among the ugliest who went to kiss the Pope's slipper, upon which a certain noble chose to say that they had gone to implore His Holiness's dispensation without disgrace whenever and as much as they pleased to taste raw flesh. The King heard of this and it was a good thing that nobleman too made his escape, or he would have been hanged, both out of reverence for the Pope and respect for the ladies.

Those nobles were not so fortunate in their encounters or rather, their talk, as the late Lord d'Albany.[746] When Pope Clement came to Marseilles[747] to marry his niece to the Duke of Orleans,[748] there were three ladies, lovely, estimable widows, who because of the pangs, the distress and the melancholy caused by the absence of their husbands and the cessation of any pleasure from them, had sunk so low and were so debilitated, so sickly and ailing that they requested d'Albany, who as a relation had the good ear of the Pope, to beg him for dispensation for all three 'to eat meat on the prohibited days'. D'Albany said he would do this for them, and one day brought them very privily to the Pope's residence, at the same time telling the King all about what he proposed to do. Lord d'Albany led off at the interview and, speaking in Italian, in rather a low voice, so the ladies might not hear him, said: 'Holy Father, here are three widowed ladies, who as you see are lovely and very estimable, and on account of their feelings of reverence for their deceased husbands and love of the children whom they have had by them, will not for anything in the world hear of making a second marriage, for that would wrong their husbands and their children, but, as sometimes they are tempted by the prickings of the flesh, they most humbly request Your Holiness, may they have dealings with men out of wedlock, and whenever they are ever so tempted?' 'What's that?' cried the Pope. 'Cousin! That would be against God's commandments. I cannot possibly give that dispensation!' 'Well, anyway, here they are, Holy Father,' said the Duke. 'Perhaps you could kindly hear what they have to say.'

One of the three ladies now spoke up and said: 'Holy Father, we begged Lord d'Albany to put the very humble request of us three before you and plead our weakness and constitutional debility.' 'My daughters,' said the Pope, 'the request is quite unarguable. It is utterly opposed to the commandments of God.'

Not knowing what d'Albany had said to him, the widows replied: 'Holy Father, at least give us leave three times a year, without disgrace. 'What's that?' cried the Pope, 'allow you the *peccato il di lussuria*—the sin of the flesh three times a year? I should be condemning myself. No, no, it is quite out of my power.'

Then, realizing that there was some trickery and mockery in it, and that Lord d'Albany had played a smart trick on them, they said: 'But that is not at all what we meant, Holy Father. We were only asking if we might take meat on the prohibited days.'

Whereupon the Duke d'Albany said to them: 'But, ladies, I understood you to say raw meat.'

The Pope immediately grasped the point and, beginning to smile, said: 'Cousin, you have made these estimable ladies blush, the Queen will be most annoyed when she hears of it,' though, when she did learn of it, as a matter of fact she merely found it 'a good one'. And later the King and the Pope also had a good laugh together, after which, giving the three ladies his blessing, the Pope granted what they wanted, and they went their ways very satisfied.

I was told the names of these three ladies, they were Lady de Chateaubriand or de Canaples, Lady de Châtillon, and the Lady Bailiff of Caen, all three most estimable persons. I have the story from elderly courtiers.[749]

Lady d'Uzès[750] did much better when Pope Paul III came to

Nice to see King François.[751] She was then Lady du Bellay.[752] From her youth up she had always been of a sprightly turn of mind and quick in repartee,[753] and one day, when she knelt before His Holiness, she begged him for three things—one, to be granted absolution because when she was a mere child, serving the Lady Regent, she lost her scissors at her work and made a vow to a bogus saint to do it with him if she found her scissors, though she did not really do anything because she did not know where his holy body lay. The second request was for the Pope to grant her a pardon for having taken one of her pillows into the privy passage beside her bed and there having wiped her behind and her front part too with it when Pope Clement came to Marseilles and she was still unmarried (a Tallard by name) so that when His Holiness later lay his worthy head and countenance and mouth on the pillow, through it he kissed her. The third was for him to excommunicate Lord de Tays,[754] because she loved him and he did not love her at all, and he was an accursed man and anybody who when loved did not love at all was excommunicable. Astounded at her requests, the Pope asked the King who exactly this woman was, then learned what a wag she always was and then had a very hearty laugh indeed with the King. I do not find it at all a matter for astonishment that later she became a Huguenot and made much mock of the popes, for she had begun to do that so early, though at that time she had always been found unimpeachable, so enchanting was she with her sprightly tongue and repartee.

One should not however assume that this great King was so prim and proper with regard to the ladies that he did not enjoy the good tales told him, though without scandal or slandering anyone, or that he did not tell some of his own too, or, great King though he was, and highly privileged, he did not want any ordinary person to enjoy the same privileges that he did. Some have assured me that it was a great concern of his that no estimable noble of his court should be without a mistress, and if any man did not acquire one he adjudged him a silly boob, and often enough would ask some of them for their mistresses's names and promise to look after them and say a good word for them, so kindly, so personal was he. Often, too, when he saw them deep in discussion with their mistresses, he would go up to them and ask what fine things they were talking about together, and if he disapproved, he would correct them and suggest suitable subjects. With his great intimates he was never miserly or mean about telling and sharing his own tales, and I once heard him produce a delightful one, something which happened to him (and he later told), all about a lovely young lady who joined the court. As this young person did not know the usages, she was easily guided by whatever the great men said, particularly if it was the King. Well, one day when he chose to plant his fully unfurled standard in her keep, she, who had heard and had already also noticed that whenever anybody gave anything to the King or took anything from him or had any dealings with him, it was the rule first to kiss him or rather his hand, for taking whatever it was and having touched it, she without more ado did the same. That is to say, when he approached her she most humbly planted a kiss on his hand, then took his standard herself and with the greatest humility, planted that in her keep, then coolly asked him how he wished her to serve him, as a chaste lady of standing should or as one well used to doing it. One need not doubt that he chose the latter method, because in that way she would be more agreeable to him than in the role of a mere modest girl, and then he found that she had certainly lost no time at court, neither regarding the preliminaries or the postludes, or anything else. After the operation, she made him a deep curtsey and thanked him humbly for the honour he had done her, saying she was really not worthy of it, but would he kindly always keep her husband's advancement in mind? I have been told the lady's name, too. Later she was far from being such a ninny as she was at that time, but turned into a very wily and smart lady. The King was not miserly with the story, either, but passed it on to several ears.

This monarch was most anxious always to know about the love affairs of his ladies and gentlemen, above all of their actual joustings, even of any fine airs the ladies might assume when at those frolics, the positions they adopted, the expressions on their faces, the words they used. And when told, he would first roar with laughter, then prohibit anybody from spreading the news and the scandal, but recommend a still tongue and observance of honour. He was well assisted in all this by that very great, very magnificent and very great-hearted gentleman, the Cardinal of Lorraine.[755] I have a right to call him very great-hearted, for in his time he had not his equal. His largesse, his gifts, his favours, but above all else his charity to the poor, became a byword. He regularly wore a large game-bag which the gentleman-servant who looked after his petty cash filled without fail every morning with three or four hundred crowns, and whenever he came upon a poor man, in went his hand, and whatever came into hand he would draw out, without thinking twice of examining it, and give it away. It was of him that a poor blind man spoke when in the street the man begged for alms and as was the Cardinal's custom he stuck in his hand and tossed a large handful of gold across to the man. 'Either you are Jesus Christ or the Cardinal of Lorraine,' said the beggar. And if he was a great and charitable alms-giver in this way to beggars, he was just as liberal to other people, but above all towards the ladies, whom he used to catch very easily by that bait. For in those days there was not so much money about as there is today, so the ladies were greedier for it, as they were for gew-gaws and jewellery.

I have heard the tale told how whenever a lovely girl or a new lady who was lovely, arrived at court, he approached her immediately and to win her told her that he would like to break her in himself. Is breaker-in the word? For, if you ask me, he never had as much trouble exactly breaking in as he would have had with a really raw filly. However, it was generally recognized in those days that it was a rare lady or girl indeed resident at court, or fresh arrival, who was not seduced or caught by the covering and the largesse of Milord the Cardinal. And rarely or never did any maid or wife leave that court still decent. But at the same time you would have found their coffers and their huge wardrobes fuller then of gowns and petticoats of cloth of gold or silver, or of silk, than those of our Queens and great princesses of today. I have had proof of this myself, having seen two or three who gained all that by their front part, for their fathers, mothers and husbands could never have given them so much.

Some may say I might well have omitted reporting this of that great cardinal, because of the honour due his robes and his most reverend state. But that was how the King liked it and took pleasure in it, and provided there is no malice in what he does, a man is dispensed of all other concerns, to serve his King, including making love and other things, as well as going to the wars, going hunting, going to dances, to pageantry and other events. Besides, he was a man of flesh and blood like any other, and also possessed great virtues and fine qualities which blotted out that trifling imperfection, if making love is to be called an imperfection at all.

I have heard the tale told of him about the respect due to the ladies. He showed it by instinct very largely, but forgot it, though not without cause, with regard to Donna Beatrix of Portugal, Duchess of Savoy.[756] When once on the road in Piedmont, on his way to Rome to serve the King his master, he called on the Duke and Duchess. After due exchange of small talk with the Duke, he left him to go to the Duchess in her chamber, to pay his respects. He went up to her, and she, who was arrogance itself, held out her hand to be kissed. The affront made the Lord Cardinal a trifle tetchy. He drew her closer, intending to plant a kiss straight on her lips. But she fell back. Then he lost patience and, pressing still closer, grabbed hold of her head and despite her will, kissed her two or three times. And though she cried out and protested in Portuguese and Spanish, alike, she had to put up with it.

'What's this?' he cried. 'Am I to be treated in this manner and fashion? I well and truly kiss my mistress the Queen, who is the greatest Queen in the world, and am I then not going to kiss you, who are only a dirty little Duchess? I'd like you to know that I have slept with many a lady quite as lovely and of quite as good family as you are.'

Perhaps he was quite right in this, and the Duchess was wrong to behave so haughtily towards a prince of so great a line, particularly when he was a cardinal, for that is a very great ecclesiastical rank, with which the greatest princes of

Christendom are not to be compared. But the Lord Cardinal was also wrong to respond so uncouthly, though it must have been very vexatious to so noble and warm-hearted a man, (whatever his calling,) to suffer such a rebuff.

Cardinal de Granvelle[757] made Count d'Egmont[758] feel this keenly, as well as others whom I leave on the tip of my pen, for to tell of them would be to confuse my essay too greatly, so I resume the thread of the late King Henry II, he who was so respectful to the ladies, whom he served with such great marks of respect and who had a great dislike of any who slandered them. For the point is : when a King serves such-and-such ladies of such-and-such a standing and of such-and-such a temperament, it is not at all seemly for his court suite to open their mouths to say bad things about it. Further, the Queen Mother kept a firm hand on things, to support her ladies and maids, and make any who slandered or libelled them feel it, whenever they were discovered, especially if she had been no more spared in the gossiping than her ladies. But she was not so much concerned about herself as the other ladies, since, she said, she felt pure and clean in soul and conscience, which were eloquent enough of her condition, and as a rule she just laughed at and mocked those libellous, slanderous scribblers. 'Let them sweat and labour, it is all for nothing,' she said. Though whenever she found them out, she did make them feel it.

It was the fortune of the elder Limeuil girl[759] at the very outset, when she came first to court, to make a libel (for she both talked and wrote well) on the whole court, though one which if all the same displeasing, was not really scandalous. You may rest assured, however, that the Queen gave her a very thorough whipping, her and two of her friends who were in it with her, and had she not had the honour of being a relation of the Queen's, because of the Turennes[760] being allied to the house of Burgundy,[761] she would have punished very ignominiously indeed, by the express orders of the King, who had a peculiar adversion from such writings.

I recall how once Lord de Matha,[762] a fine, valiant noble whom the King was very fond of, and who was a relation of

Lady de Valentinois, and as a rule had some frivolous dispute or other with the ladies and the maids (such a madcap was he!) one day quarrelled with one of the Queen's ladies, when another, whose name was big Meray,[763] thought to stand up for her friend, whereupon he made the blunt rejoinder: 'Oh, I'm not quarrelling with you, Meray, a big whackable draught mare like you!'

And indeed, Lady Meray was the biggest girl or woman I ever saw. She complained straightaway to the Queen that Matha had called her a mare and said she was whackable, and the Queen was so furious that despite all the string-pulling of his relation Lady de Valentinois, Matha had to go away from the court for some days, and even a month after his return could not enter the chamber where the Queen and her maids were.

Lord de Gersay[764] did even worse with regard to one of the Queen's maids against whom he had a grudge, and took his revenge. Nor was he lacking in eloquence, he had a sharp and quick tongue, especially when slandering, at which he was a dab hand. But slandering was then prohibited. One day after dinner when this maid-of-honour was in the Queen's chamber with her friends and the nobles (and it was the custom then not to sit otherwise than on the floor if the Queen was present) this lord took a ram's c—— from the pages and lackeys (they were playing with it in the back yard, it was a very big one and nicely distended) and, lying down next this girl, slipped it up between her petticoat and her gown so nicely that she did not notice till when the Queen rose from her chair to go to her closet, the girl (whom I will not name) of course got up too, and when she stood up to face the Queen so squeezed the furry hairy ram's parts against herself that she let out six or seven little squawks, so that you might have thought she was trying to amuse the company. For wasn't that girl astonished. So was the Queen, because the thing was clearly to be seen, nicely in place, without any hiding it. '*Notre-dame!*' cried the Queen, 'and whatever have you got there, my dear? And what did you mean to do with that?'

Blushing, almost in tears, the poor girl began to say she

did not know what it was, somebody who wanted to do her a bad turn had played a dirty trick on her, she thought it must be de Gersay. Once he had seen the fun begin and how the girl started, de Gersay had slipped out. He was sent for, but he refused to come, as he saw the Queen was angry, though nevertheless he stoutly denied he had done it. For some days he kept out of the way of the Queen's rage and out of the way of the King too, and had he not, together with Fontaine-Guerin,[765] been one of the great favourites of the Dauphin,[766] he would have been in serious trouble, though nothing could be proved against him, merely conjectured. At the same time, the King and his courtiers and several ladies could not help laughing, though they dared not show their amusement, seeing the Queen's annoyance, for if ever there was a lady who knew how to curb people and take it out of them, it was she.

An estimable noble and a maid of the court one day, after being very fond of one another, came to hate each other and quarrel, to such a point that in the Queen's chamber the girl suddenly said out loud : 'Let me be, or I'll tell what you said.' The noble, who had secretly told her something about a very great lady, fearing ill might befall him, and at best he would be banished from court, concealing his anxiety replied (for he was very quick in his responses) : 'If you tell what I told you, I will tell what I did to you.'

Who was taken aback but the girl! However, all she said was : 'But what did you do to me?'

He replied : 'What did I say to you?'

To which the girl's rejoinder was : 'I know very well what you said,' whereupon he said : 'And I know very well what I did.'

The girl insisted that she could prove what he had said and he said he could still better prove what he had done to her.

At last, after both having spent quite enough time on such back-chat ding-dong, to and fro, all in the same spirit, they were separated by the gentlemen and ladies present, although they were all getting great amusement from it.

The dispute then reached the Queen's ears, and she was very angry about it, and immediately insisted on knowing exactly what she had been told and what he had done to her. But as

o   395

they now both saw that there might be serious consequences, they decided to make it up together, and both went to the Queen and told her that all their squabbling had been merely a game, that this noble had not told her anything, nor had he done anything to her. In this way they satisfied the Queen, though nevertheless she did reprove and rate the noble soundly, particularly saying that his language had been too disgraceful. This gentleman swore to me twenty times that had the girl not made it up with him and had she revealed what he had told her (which would have had serious consequences) he would certainly have insisted that he had done what he said he had done to her, and risk her being examined to find out if she really was no longer a virgin and that it was indeed as he said, he had deflowered her. 'Yes,' I replied to him, 'but supposing they had examined her and found she was after all a virgin, you would have been lost, and it might have cost you your life.' 'Oh, God's death,' he replied, 'that is what I would most of all have liked, to have had her examined, I have no fears that I would have risked my life, I am sure I was right, because I knew very well who did deflower her, I knew another had been in her and not myself which was just what made me so angry, and if she had been found broached and trodden she would have been ruined, I would be avenged and she disgraced, and I would not have had to marry her and then get rid of her as best I could.' There, you see what risks poor maids and women run, deserving it or not.

There was one of very high origin[767] whom I knew who indeed did become pregnant by a very great and gallant prince,[768] though it was said that it was under promise of marriage, though afterwards the contrary came out. King Henry was the first to know, and he was extremely annoyed, for to some extent she belonged to him. However, without making any great noise or scandal, in the evening at dancing he wanted to lead her in the route of *La Torche* dance,[769] and others, in which, with her figure, which was very lovely, she could show her skill and dexterity better than anybody ever did before, and she had dressed so well on this particular day that there was not the slightest sign of her pregnancy, so that even the King, who kept his eyes fixed on her, could not tell whether she really was pregnant, and remarked to a very great intimate of his : 'Those fellows are most malicious and misguided to go and concoct this story about that poor girl being pregnant, I never saw her more charming. Those wicked slanderers who set the story about lied, and grossly, too.'

Thus this kindly prince exonerated that lovely, estimable girl and said the same to the Queen when he slept with her that night. But the Queen did not trust his opinion and the following morning had the girl examined in her presence, when she was found to be six months pregnant, which she confessed to the Queen, telling her that she had done it under promise of marriage. Nevertheless, the King, who was all kindness had it all kept as secret as possible, not to disgrace the girl, though the Queen was very angry. However, they smuggled her off to her nearest relations, where she was brought to bed of a fine son,[770] though the boy was unfortunate in that his alleged father[771] could never be persuaded to recognize him. The case dragged on a long time, but the mother failed to get anywhere with it.

Now, King Henry was as fond of good stories as his predecessors had been, but he would not have the ladies disgraced or their affairs disclosed, so that when he himself, who was of an amorous disposition, went to see any lady, he did so with as much concealment and cloaking as possible, so she should be free from suspicion and disgrace. And if some of his mistresses were revealed, this was not by his fault or consent, but rather the lady's, as for instance in the case of one I was told of, Flamin her name was, a Scotswoman,[772] of good family, who, when pregnant by the King[773] certainly did not keep mum but declared most boldly in her Scotch French that she had done her best, but luck would have it that she was in the family way by the King and she felt most honoured and happy about it. And she also added that Royal blood must have something very suave and be a more soothing liquor than any other, she felt so well on it, 'not to speak of all the nice presents you get of it.'

The son she then had was the late Grand Prior of France, latterly killed at Marseilles,[774] which was a very great pity, for he was a very estimable, very fine and valiant lord, which he clearly showed at his death. He was moreover a kindly man, the least tyrannical governor of his age or since, and Provence could certainly vouch for it that although he was a very fine and generous lord, he was a very knidly man and not an extortioner.

It was the view of that lady, like others I have heard of, that sleeping with a King was not disgracing, it was only those who gave themselves to lesser men who were tarts, not those who let great kings and gallant nobles have what they wanted, just like that Amazon queen[775] I mentioned who travelled three hundred leagues to be put in the family way by Alexander and have progeny by him, though it is also said that they are all really the same.

After King Henry came King François II, whose reign was so short that slanderers had no time to get themselves set for telling tales against the ladies, though, had he reigned a long time, one should still not believe that he would have allowed it at his court, for he was a King of very good and frank character, and not at all a lover of slander, in addition being very respectful to the ladies and esteeming them greatly. In addition there were his wife,[776] the Queen, the Queen Mother,[777] and his uncles,[778] all of whom were sternly opposed to babblers and tongue-waggers. I recall how once, when he was at St Germain-en-Laye, in August or September it was, it occurred to him to go out one evening to watch the deer mating in the lovely St Germain forest. And with him he took the princes closest to him and a number of great ladies, married and unmarried, whose names I could quote. And somebody insisted on gossipping about it, saying it did not say much for the character or chastity of a wife to go and watch such love-making and rutting of animals, especially as venereal desires were thereby exacerbated, seeing such things as examples, to such point that even if they did wish to remain unaffected, water and saliva came to their abdominal mouths and after that the only way to put it right was more saliva or sperm. The King heard of this and so did the princes and ladies who had gone with him, and I can assure you that had that particular noble not decamped immediately he would have been in a poor way. Indeed, he never again appeared at court till the King was dead and his reign over.

There were many defamatory libels against the men then administering the Kingdom, but none that so pricked or outraged as a lampoon entitled *The Tiger* (imitating the first epithet that Cicero levelled against Catilina),[779] as this spoke of the love-making of a very great and lovely lady and a great noble who was her near relative.[780] Had the gallant author of that been caught,[781] even if he had had a hundred lives, they would all have been forfeit, for the great, men and women together, were so indignant that they felt quite heartbroken.

This King, François II, was not so given to love-making as his predecessors had been, indeed, it would have been very wrong for him to have been, for he had for wife the loveliest and most charming woman in the whole world. And the man who has such a wife does not go roving as others do, or he is very wretched, and the man who does not rove is never very concerned to slander the ladies, or even speak well of them, except of his own. This is a maxim I heard a very estimable person utter, though I did see him fail to keep it several times.

He was followed by King Charles IX, who because of his tender years did not at first concern himself with the ladies, but merely thought of how to spend his time in the games of youth. Nevertheless, the late Lord de Sipierre,[782] who was his tutor, and in my opinion and that of anyone else the most estimable and delightful gentleman of his age and the most courteous and deferential to the ladies, so well instructed the King his master and pupil that he was as kind to the ladies as the Kings who had preceded him. For never, when big as when little, did he see a lady, however much in a hurry might he be, whether standing or running, on foot or on horseback, but he would at once salute her and very respectfully take off his cap. When he reached the love-making, he did to my knowledge serve a number of estimable ladies and girls, but with as much honour and respect as the greatest nobleman of his court could have shown. Nevertheless, during his reign the great lampooners did begin to come into fashion, among them even certain very gallant gentlemen of the court, whom I will not name, in most outrageous fashion maligning the ladies, all together and individually too, even some of the greatest. Some of these men thereby had serious disputes about this and found themselves in a poor position, not though because they admitted it, for they would deny everything. They would indeed have been punished, had they admitted it, and their King would have seen that they paid dearly for it, for they attacked ladies who were too great for this. Other ladies too put a good face on it and put up with countless libels which were going the rounds and endless insults which they swallowed like milk, never daring make any response. Otherwise the men's lives would have been at stake. In all this I was often amazed at people like that who let people slander them, many of them, indeed, to their very faces. For though they were reputed valiant men they would cheerfully suffer such petty affronts without uttering a word.

I can recall a libel made against a very great widowed lady, lovely and most estimable, who wished to marry a young, handsome, very great prince. There were some men whom I know well who were against the marriage and to dissuade the prince made a libel[783] of the most disgraceful I have ever seen about her, comparing her to five or six great whores of antiquity, notorious ones, most lubricious, and saying she was worse than any of them. The very men who wrote this handed it to him, telling him, however, that it came from others, and had been given to them. When the prince saw it he denied it and uttered countless insults at the cost of those who had written it. They suffered all this without a word, though they were men brave and valiant enough. But it really did make the prince wonder, for the libel was most precise about a number of details. Yet in spite of it, two years later that same marriage was concluded.

The King was so warm-hearted and kind that he would in no way encourage such people to have their little jokes in secret. Very fond of them himself, he nevertheless did not want the common run of people to be indulged with them, saying that he did not wish his court, which was the most noble and distinguished in great and lovely ladies in the whole world, and as such famed, to be abused or scorned because of the tongue of such anecdote-tellers and gallants. He said one could talk like that about the courtesans of Rome, of Venice or any other place, but not of the court of France and that even if folk were allowed to do what they liked they need not be permitted to talk about it as they liked.

This is how this King showed his respect for the ladies, which was so great that I happen to know that in his latter days, when an attempt was made to give him a bad impression of certain very great and very lovely and estimable ladies, as having been involved in certain matters of very great moment which concerned him, he absolutely refused to believe a word of it all, but made them as welcome as ever and died in their good graces and watered by the copious tears which they shed over his corpse. And they certainly had good cause thus to grieve him, later, when King Henry III succeeded him, for when he came back to France from Poland, and certain evil reports were made to him, he failed to esteem those same ladies as highly as they had hitherto been esteemed,[784] and became very critical indeed of them and some others whom I could name, though he did not thereby gain any greater affection, indeed, I am not sure that it did not rather do him harm and cause his evil fortune, not to say his ruin. I could give a number of details, but prefer to pass them over, except to say that one should realize that women are very revengeful creatures, and however long they may have to wait, get what they want. Quite the contrary of the vengeance of some men, which is very ardent at the outset and hot for realization, but by temporization and delay is soon cooled off and comes to nothing. That is why with a man one should take care at the outset and leave it to time to parry the blows. But fury in a woman lasts and to the very end temporization does not diminish it. I do not say this is true of all women, but there are few exceptions.

Some women have argued that we should forgive the King for the war he waged against the ladies by his criticism of them, that it was only done to curb and correct vice, as if mere correction was of any use here, seeing that it is in women's character that the more you forbid a thing, the hotter they are for it, and it is quite useless keeping an eye on them, for my experience has shown me that nothing you may do will divert them from the chosen path.

I know very well that there are some ladies whom this monarch loved with great respect and paid attention to most honourably, especially one very great and lovely princess,[785] whom he fell so deeply in love with before going to Poland, that after he became King he resolved to marry her, although she was already married to a great, fine prince, but one who was rebellious against him and had taken refuge in a foreign land[786] to rally men and make war on him. But when he came back to France the lady died in childbed. Death alone prevented that marriage, for he was set on it, and would have married her by favour and dispensation of the Pope, who would not have refused him, as he was so great a King, and for several other particular reasons, which you can imagine.

There were others too to whom this King made love, to bring them down. I could mention one great lady[787] on whom he avenged himself because of the displeasures her husband had done him. Having no means of catching the husband, he avenged himself on the wife, posting what he had done in the presence of several people, though this was a sweet vengeance indeed, since instead of putting the woman to death, he put her to life.

I know one lady whom he made love to because she led too gay a life and also because she did him a disservice. Without much trouble on his part to persuade her, she gave him a rendezvous in a garden, which he made a point of attending, but then would not touch her in any way, (so some say, though he certainly did), merely made an exhibit of her as if she were an object with a price, then banished her from his court in disgrace.

He always wanted to know how his men and women lived, and was very anxious to find out their underlying wishes. It is said that sometimes he would tell some of his more intimate friends about the good luck he had had. Very fortunate men those intimates of his were, for the crumbs from the table of such great Kings cannot fail to be very good. The ladies, to my knowledge, were very wary of him, and he himself used to scold them for it, or ask the Queen Mother to do so, who was always very ready, but not because she liked slander, as I have shown above by the little examples I give. But what else could she do, when these tales touched the ladies and their honour to the quick?

This King had, as I saw, from his youth been accustomed to hearing tales about the ladies. I have even told him one or two myself, and he told some too, though very much on the sly, lest the Queen Mother heard. For she greatly disliked his telling anybody but herself, so as to keep him under her thumb, and as he came of age and gained his freedom she would not lose control over him. And so he knew as well how the ladies of his court and kingdom lived as if he had had dealings with them all himself, even the great ones, and if there were any but recently come to court, he would approach them very courteously and decently and then tell them such stories that they were secretly astounded and wondered wherever he had learned it all from, though of course they rejected and denied it all. This indeed was his pastime, while he tirelessly applied his mind to other, greater things, so loftily that he has been said to have been the greatest king France had known for the past hundred years, as indeed I wrote elsewhere in a chapter specially dedicated to him.[788] So I will say no more about that, especially as it might be objected that I am too copious in examples of his life in this respect, and I should have to say more than I really know about it. Yes, I do know a great number of stories and some priceless ones too, but I have no intention of displaying the news of the court or the rest of the world either, and also as I could not modify or wrap up my tales sufficiently to be sure of preventing scandal.

Now, there are various kinds of slanderers of the ladies. Some slander some of them because they have been annoyed by them in some way, although they are the chastest in the world, and instead of the fair, pure angels they are make them out to be foul demons of evil living. Like an estimable noble whom I saw and knew who, because of a slight displeasure which a very estimable and circumspect lady caused him, slandered her very nastily, giving rise to a fine dispute. And he said : 'I am well aware that I am wrong and I do not question that this lady is most chaste and virtuous, but whichever of them offends me, the least in the world, even if she is as chaste and pure-living as the Virgin Mary, since I am unable to get the better of her in any of the ways I would a man, I shall say worse than hanging of her.'

God, however, can be annoyed by this.

There are other slanderers who, loving the ladies, but unable to impinge on their chastity, from sheer pique, speak of them as if they were prostitutes. Indeed, they do worse, they will even noise it abroad that they have had what they wanted of them but, having found out and observed them to be far too loose living, have given them up. I have known many such at our courts. There are others much the same who when the ladies for good reason give up their lovers and favourites of the bed, follow closely all their frivolities and ficklenesses and are disgusted to see other men take their place, and so piqued and heartbroken as lovers themselves, will so paint and slander those poor women as defies description, going so far as to describe in detail all the lewd little things they once did together and any markings they have on their naked bodies, all to lend verisimilitude to their tales.

There are others who, piqued because the ladies let other men have it but not them, slander them outrageously and have them watched, spied on and followed, all in order to be able to give more substance to what they allege about them.

In other cases, jealous for no other reason but the above, the ladies will slander those men they love the most, merely because they don't see half enough of them. There you have one of the great effects of jealousy. And such slanderers are really not so much to be condemned as one might think, for this should be laid at the door of love and jealousy, which are brother and sister of one birth.

There are other slanderers who are so born and inured to slandering that they would even slander themselves, in default of anybody else. Now would you expect the ladies' honour to be spared on their lips? At our courts I have seen many a one who, fearing to talk about other men, lest these lay hands on them, turn to running down the poor ladies, who have no other revenge but their tears, their grief and words of protest. All the same, I have known many men who came off badly for so doing, for there were relations, brothers, friends, wooers, even husbands, who made many a man repent of this and chew and swallow his own words. But were I to wish to tell of all the sorts of slanderers of the ladies which are to be found, I should never be done.

There is a view of love which I have known several men to hold, namely, that a secret love-affair is worthless, it must be at least a little plain, if not to everybody, at least to one's most intimate friends. And if one cannot tell everybody about it, at least it should become self-evident, either by demonstration or by badges or other favours sported, or in chivalric deeds, such as tilting at the ring, winning at jousting in tournaments, in pageantry, in single-handed combats at the barricade or in real ones in the wars, for such public satisfaction is very great in itself. True enough, what use would it be to a great military leader to have achieved some fine, outstanding feat of warfare, then keep quiet about it and have nobody know? I think it would be most galling. It must be the same men say, with lovers who have a well-placed mistress, and Lord de Nemours, that outstanding leader and paragon of all knighthood, was of that mind, for if ever prince, lord or noble was fortunate in love-affairs, it was he. He found no pleasure at all in concealing them from his more intimate friends, though all the same he did keep some of his affairs so secret from many men that it was not at all easy to guess what had happened.

As far as married ladies go, revealing is indeed a very risky business, but unmarried girls and marriageable widows, no, for the feasibility of future marriage colours it all and lends a pretext.

I knew one very estimable noble at court[789] who was paying his attentions to a very great lady,[790] when one day, in a party with his comrades, there was talk of the devices of their mistresses (and they were all challenging each other to guess each other's), this lord was resolute in not revealing his. He even went so far as to contrive another, belonging to a different person altogether, and so deceived them all, though among them there was a great prince who took him on oath and did nevertheless suspect his secret love-affair, yet with all his companions still got no more out of him, though really within himself this lord was now cursing his fate a hundred times for having thus been persuaded not to tell, like the others, what good fortune he had had, for it is so much easier to tell of one's good fortune than one's bad fortune.

There was another man I knew, a very gallant knight[791] indeed, who both by signs and words and in other ways let fall the name of a mistress which he should have kept quiet about, and was nearly killed at the hand of an assassin because of it. But another time, for something else, he did not escape, and so did subsequently pay for it with his life.

I was at the court in the time of King François II, when the Count of St Agnan married the Bourdaisière girl[792] at Fontainebleau. The following day, the bridegroom came to the King's bedchamber, and everybody began teasing him, as was customary, and there was one very fine great lord who asked him how many laps he had completed. The bridegroom replied : five. It so happened that among those present was an estimable noble, a secretary, who was the great favourite of a very great princess whom I will not name, and he said that was not so very good going, seeing he was on such a lovely road and it was such fine weather.

The great lord said to him : 'Ha ! God's death ! I'd like to know what your bag would be !'

The secretary replied : 'And why shouldn't you? Heavens, I knocked up a round dozen in twenty-four hours and the loveliest mound it was too about here, or anywhere else in France !'

Who was taken aback but the lord in question, for in this way he had found out something he had long suspected. And since he was deeply in love with that princess, he was very piqued to have hunted that place so long and never taken anything, while the other man had had such good luck and

made such a good bag. But for the moment this prince concealed his thoughts. But later, having banked his fury, he would
have paid it all back covertly but hotly, had it not been for a
circumstance which I will not mention. All the same he always harboured a grudge against this other lord. And had
that secretary been more sensible, he would not thus have
boasted of his hunting, but would have kept it very secret,
lucky as he was too, to have the whole business cleared up so
nicely.

What would you say of a noble of renown who just because of a little slight his mistress once showed him was so inconsiderate as to show her husband her painting which she
had given him and he wore round his neck? Which took the
husband much by surprise and greatly diminished his affection for his wife, though she did her best to put a good face on it.

But a man I know, a great lord, was much more in the
wrong who, out of spite because of a trick his mistress played on
him one day, went gambling and diced away the portrait she
had given him, and to one of his soldiers, for he was in general
command of the infantry. She found this out and thought she
would burst from mortification, and was very vexed indeed.
The Queen Mother[793] learned of this and reprimanded him, because it really was too inconsiderate thus to risk losing the
portrait of a lovely, estimable lady at dice. But the noble
attempted to put a good face on it by declaring that he had
reserved the parchment inside the casket, it was only the casket he had gambled on, as it was of gold and precious stones.
I have often seen the lord and lady in question have a nice
tussle about that and I have sometimes had a really good laugh
over it. Here let me say one thing: there are ladies,
and I have seen some myself, who in their love-affairs like to
be bullied, threatened, even nagged, and yield to that sort of
treatment more than to gentleness, just as there are some forts
which one takes by force, others by gentle means, but in spite
of that they never like being insulted or slandered as whores.
Very often words hurt more than deeds.

Scylla never would forgive the city of Athens till he had
brought it down in ruins, not for its obstinacy in resisting him,

but simply because of the inhabitants who shouted insults from inside the walls and badly insulted his wife, Metella.[794]

In some parts of the world which I will not name the soldiers skirmishing or at sieges of towns fling the honour of each other's sovereign princesses in each other's faces, one crying : 'Yours is a great skittle player !' and then 'Yours knows how to knock 'em down all right,' and it has been for words like those quite as much as for any other reason that princesses have often egged on their men to commit atrocities.

I have heard it said that the principal thing which enraged the Queen of Hungary[795] and prompted her to spread arson in Picardy and other parts of France[796] was the readiness of certain long-tongued insolent fellows on all occasions to chatter about her love affairs and all the year round sing a lewd ditty, all about 'the runnel of the Queen of Hungary,'[797] though it was so clear that this was only the work of some coarse countryman soldier of fortune.

Cato could never bear Caesar ever since that day, when the Senate was debating the Catiline conspiracy and Caesar was under suspicion, present at the sitting, a little note was brought secretly to him in which Servilia, Cato's sister, was giving him an assignation for them to sleep together. Cato was suspicious as to what it was, and also sure that Caesar had been hand in glove with Catilina, and now he cried out loud and insisted on the Senate's knowing what missive had been brought. Thus forced, Caesar showed the note and it was of course a frightful disgrace for Cato's sister.[798] I leave it to your imagination whether despite the pretence he made of hating Caesar on account of the Republic, Cato could help hating him because of that disgraceful note. Yet that was in no way Caesar's fault, and he had no other course but to disclose the note when it had been brought him in the Senate-house, or his life would have been at stake. But I do not believe Servilia was at all annoyed about it, and in fact those two did not break off their love affair at all, from which indeed was born Brutus, of whom Caesar was said to be the father, though Brutus certainly made Caesar an ill return for having engendered him.

Now, by yielding to great men ladies do risk a great deal, and if they gain favours and greatness and money, they certainly pay a good price for them all.

I have heard a story told about one lovely lady, estimable and of excellent family, though not so great as a certain great lord who was very much in love with her—one day this lord came upon her alone with her women in her chamber, seated on her bed, and after a few exchanges of words, in which he proposed love to her, he began to embrace her and then by gentle pressure got her down on her bed, after which followed the main assault, which she suffered with slight and courteous resistance, then said : 'It is a great pity you great lords cannot refrain from using your powers and taking liberties with us inferiors to you, but at least, were you but as given to silence as you are to freedom of speech, you would be so much the more desirable and forgivable. So, my Lord, can I request you to keep secret what you have done and preserve my honour?'

Those are the usual terms in which ladies of inferior rank reason with their superiors : 'Sir, at least please take care of my honour!'

Others say : 'If you breathe a word of this, sir, I am lost, for Heaven's sake preserve my honour!'

Others say : 'Only please, not a word, sir, to anybody, so that my honour may be safe, then I shall not worry at all,' as if to argue that one can make love as much as one likes in secret, so long as the world knows nothing about it they do not think themselves disgraced.

The greatest and most superb ladies will say to gallants inferior to them : 'Only take care not to breathe a word, not to a single person, otherwise you risk your life, I'd have you sewn in a sack and thrown into the river, or have you stuck like a pig.' That's the sort of thing they say. Indeed, there is not a single lady, whatever her quality, who wants to be disgraced or exposed in the slightest by men's lips, and yet you will find some so foolish, or so frenzied or carried away by love, that without the menfolk breathing a word against them, they will slander themselves. As, for instance, not so very long since, a very lovely and estimable lady, one of standing too, had a great prince fall very deeply in love with her. He then came to enjoy her, and when he gave her a very fine, costly bracelet with their initals quite clearly engraved on it, she was so foolish as to wear the thing every day, next her skin, above the elbow. Then came the day when her husband slept with her and happened to notice it, then examined it and found evidence enough in it to get rid of her by a violent death. What an ill-advised woman !

Years back I knew a very great sovereign[799] who had had a mistress for three years who was one of the most lovely at court,[800] when he was obliged to go away on an expedition of conquest, but just before going suddenly fell deeply in love with a princess,[801] who was very lovely and estimable, if ever there was one. And to make it quite clear to her that he had left his former mistress for her, and intended to honour and serve her completely, without any more thought for the memory of the other, before leaving he gave her all sorts of tokens, jewels, rings, portraits, bracelets and all the other dainty things which the other woman had given him, and when she saw some of these, she thought she would burst from the outrage of it, nor did she keep it entirely to herself, but found it her pleasure to disgrace the other woman, even if so doing she also disgraced herself. I believe that had that princess not died soon after this, the prince, when he returned from his journey, would have married her.

I knew another prince, though not so great,[802] who during his first marriage and his widowhood, came to love a very lovely, estimable girl of distinguished family,[803] to whom, during their love-making, he gave many fine presents—caskets, rings, jewellery and many other lovely trifles, among others a very fine, sumptuous mirror with his portrait in it. Now, later, the prince came to marry a very lovely and very estimable, well known princess,[804] who made him lose his taste for his earlier mistress, though there was nothing to choose between them in beauty.[805] And this princess so pleaded with and so implored her husband that he sent to his first mistress to request the return of all the loveliest things he had given her. This demand cut that lady to the quick, but yet she was so big hearted and so lofty, though not a princess, (although of one of the best families of France,) that she sent him back all the finest and most exquisite things, including the lovely mirror with the painting of the prince. But before she sent it, to improve on it, she took pen and ink and drew in a fine pair of horns, growing right out of the middle of his forehead, and, as she handed it to the noble who came to fetch the things she said: 'Here, my friend, take this to your master and tell him I am returning it all exactly as he gave it to me, and have taken nothing away and added nothing, unless he himself has touched anything up since. And tell the lovely princess his wife who so pleaded with him to ask of me what he had given me, that if such-and-such a well-known prince' (naming him, of course,) 'had done the same to her mother and had taken away what he gave her as love gift or token in order to sleep with her so often, she would be as poor of trinkets and jewel-lery as the smallest little maid-of-honour at court, (for her head is now so richly laden at the cost of that so-and-so, and of the privy parts of her mother too), and would now have to go out into the garden every morning to get something to prink herself with, instead of that jewellery. And now, what-ever she does with the daub with the horns, she's welcome to it.'

Anybody who knew that girl would vouch for me that she was just the one to do such a thing. Anyway, she told me all about it herself, and she was most outspoken too. However, the princess must have felt bad enough about it, both on account of her huband and of this woman, by feeling so dis-graced, and she blamed him, saying it was all his fault, for having so scorned and outraged that poor lady, who had really fully earned those presents by the sweat of her body.

The girl in question, being one of the loveliest and most charming girls of her time, despite having given her body to the prince in question, was not long finding a very wealthy man as husband, though he was not of such good family[806] as she was. And the day came when they threw in each other's faces the way they had honoured each other by marrying, she saying she was of such good family and he replying that he had done more for her than she had for him, because he had dishonoured himself to restore her honour, meaning to suggest by this that as she had lost her honour as a girl he had restored it by making her his wife.

I have heard the tale told, and had it from a reliable source, that when King François I left Lady de Chateaubriand,[807] his favourite mistress, to take the Duchess of d'Estampes,[808] who was born Lady Helly, whom the Queen Regent had taken into her household as maid-of-honour (and produced for King François when he came to Bordeaux[809] on his way back from Spain, when he took her as his mistress and abandoned Lady de Chateaubriand, all rather as one nail drives out another,) Lady d'Estampes begged the King to take back from Lady de Chateaubriand all the loveliest jewels he had given her, not on account of their price or value, for at that time pearls and precious stones were not so much sought after as they were to be later, but from love of the fine mottoes engraved or cut in them, all the work of the Queen of Navarre, who composed them, for she was a great master at that.[810] King François granted this request and said he would do as she wished, which he did. But when he sent a noble to her to request the return, Lady de Chateaubriand at once pretended to be ill and told the messenger he should come back in three days' time, and he would have what he asked for. Meanwhile, from sheer pique, she sent for a goldsmith and had him melt it all down, without the least respect for the fine things engraved on it, and when the noble returned, she gave him all the trinkets transformed into so many bars of gold. 'Go,' she said, 'now take these bars to the King and tell him that since it pleased him to take back what he had so generously given me, I return it all, and send him these bars of gold. And as for the mottoes that were once engraved on it, all that I have so well imprinted and embodied in my thoughts, and hold them so dear, that I could not let anybody else dispose of them, enjoy them or have pleasure from them but myself.'

When the King had received the bars and the lady's message together, all he said was: 'Take it all back again to her.

412

What I asked for was not the money value, for I would have given her twice that, I wanted the things for love of what was engraved on them. But as she has destroyed that in this way, I certainly do not want the mere gold, and I return it to her. In what she has done she has shown more pluck and more greatness of heart than I would ever have thought a woman could show.' But when spited and thus scorned the heart of a generous woman does do great things.

These princes who ask for presents back do not do as once did the Duchess de Nevers, of the Bourbon family,[811] daughter of the Duke de Montpensier, who in her day was a very sensible, very virtuous and lovely princess, held for such in both France and Spain, where she had been brought up for a time together with Queen Elizabeth of France, was the goblet-tender who poured out her wine for her,[812] for the Queen was waited on by her ladies and maids, each with her task, like us gentlemen round our Kings. This princess was married to the Count d'Eu, eldest son of the Duke de Nevers, and she was worthy of him, as he was indeed of her, for he was one of the handsome, charming princes of his day, and so he was liked and sought after by all that was lovely and estimable at court, and among others by one who had been such a one too, and with it was also very wily and clever. One day he happened to take to his wife and put on her finger a very lovely ring, with a diamond worth from fifteen hundred to two thousand crowns, which the Queen of Spain had given him when he left. When the Prince had seen that his mistress praised it very much and showed a desire to crave it, he gave it her forthwith, as he was very big-hearted and liberal, but told her he had won it at tennis. She certainly did not say no, and regarded it as an intimate gift and from love of him always wore it, so that the Duchess de Nevers (whom her fine husband had assured that he had lost it at tennis or else that it was pawned) happened to see it on the finger of that girl, whom she well knew to be her husband's mistress. She was so discreet and had such self-control that she did no more than change colour and gnaw at her pique inwardly, without giving any other sign, but looking the other way and never mentioning

413

it either to her husband or his mistress. In which she was much to be praised, for not having been malicious or backbiting and having disgraced the girl, as many another whom I know would have delighted in doing, to the general delight, giving them all food for tittle-tattle and slander.

You see there how very necessary and very good moderation in such matters is, and also that there can be good or bad fortune in it as in other things, for there are ladies who will not permit the slightest infringement of their good name, you only need to touch it with the tip of your little finger and they are disgraced, slandered, libelled everywhere.

There are others who venture across the sweet waters of Venus under full sail and bathe and swim stark naked in them, indulging their bodies and making their way steadily to the gardens and temple of Venus or Cyprus and take their pleasures there as they please, and no matter what is said of them, they might just not have been born at all. Thus fortune favours some and is unfavourable to others in the course of slandering, as I have known many an example in my time, and as there are still cases.

In the days of King Charles IV there was a libel made at Fontainebleau which was very nasty and disgraceful and did not spare either the princesses or the great ladies or any others. And if the author of that had really been known, he would have fared badly indeed.

At Blois too, when the marriage of the Queen of Navarre to the King her husband was agreed on,[813] another slander was made, just as scandalous, against a very great lady, and the author could not be discovered. But there were many plucky valiant nobles who were slandered, who all put a bold face on it and uttered many denials. There were so many others, that neither in that reign nor that of Henry III did one see anything else, and there was one that was very scandalous indeed made in the form of a song, to the tune of a *courante* danced at court at the time, and this was sung by the pages and the servants, bass and treble together.

In the time of King Henry III there was much worse, for a nobleman whom I have heard named (and whom I knew)

414

one day made his mistress the present of a book of paintings in which there were thirty-two great and lesser ladies of the court depicted stark naked, lying down and frolicking with their lovers, also depicted naked. There were some who had two or three at once, some more, some less, and these thirty-two ladies represented nothing less than the twenty-seven poses of the Aretin pictures, all different one from another. The characters were so well drawn in the flesh that one could imagine them talking and doing it, some undressed, naked, others in the clothes they were usually seen in. The men the same. In a word, the book was so interestingly painted and contrived, that it was talked about everywhere, and it cost eight or nine hundred crowns a copy and was illuminated throughout.

A book of pictures just like that I mentioned above was made in Rome in the days of the recently deceased Pope Sixtus, as I mention elsewhere.[1]

This lady showed it and then lent it one day to a woman friend and great intimate of hers, who was much liked and a very close friend of a great lady depicted in the book, one of the most prominent and highest situated of them all, and, as was only to be expected, she had told her about it. This lady, being one of those women who liked to see everything, desired to have a look, together with a great lady who was a cousin of hers, whom she was very fond of, and invited to have the feast of this book, and who was also in one of the pictures. The examination was made with great eagerness and thoroughness, sheet by sheet, without skipping one, so that they spent two good hours on it after dinner, but instead of being annoyed or vexed by it all, what did they do but laugh at it and marvel at the pictures and keep on turning back on them, thoroughly enjoying all their sensuous, lubricious meanings, till the two of them came to kissing each other with pigeon kisses and embracing and going further still, for they had anyway, the two of them, already been well used to this sort of play.

These two ladies were bolder and more plucky and persis-

[1] This paragraph in the Mérimée edition is placed several pages earlier, but clearly has by accident been misplaced from this position.—A.B.

tent than one of whom I was told, who, one day seeing this book together with two others of her friends, was so delighted and possessed with such a frenzy of love-desire and such a wish to imitate those lascivious pictures that she could not get beyond the fourth sheet, and at the fifth fell in a dead faint. What a shocking fainting-fit! Just the opposite of that of Octavia, Julius Caesar's sister, who when one day she heard Virgil recite the three lines which he wrote about her dead son Marcellus[814] (and she gave him three thousand crowns merely for those three) suddenly swooned. What a thing love is, love of another sort!

I have heard tell—this was when I was at court—that when he was well on in years a famous great prince,[815] who after the death of his wife had lived continently in widowhood, as his great piety inclined him to do, suddenly conceived the idea of marrying a second time, to a very lovely, virtuous young princess. And as, since he was widowed, he had for ten years not touched a woman, and was afraid he might have forgotten how to do it (as if that were a craft one forgot!) and so have a bad setback on his first married night, and be able to do nothing worth while, he thought he had better have a trial. So for money he acquired the services of a lovely young girl, a virgin just like the wife he was to marry, and it is also related that he had one chosen who was not unlike his future wife to look at. His luck was so good that he demonstrated quite well that he had not yet forgotten his old lessons, and the trial came off so well that, much emboldened and very pleased with himself, he turned to storm his wife's fort too, and there too brought off a fine victory and earned his renown. That trial was a more fortunate one than that of a noble I have been told of, who was very young and rather a ninny, but whose father nevertheless wanted him to marry. This young noble wanted to make a trial beforehand, to find out if he would be a proper companion for his wife, and so some months beforehand he selected a pretty prostitute whom he had come every afternoon to his father's game park, for it was summer-time. And there, in the freshness of green trees and a fountain, he frolicked and enjoyed himself with his girl, whom he got quite

416

excited about, till he was sure no man could do that devilry to his wife better than he would. But ill luck would have it that on his wedding night, when he wanted to unite with his wife, he could not do anything. And was he not surprised! He cursed his traitorous member for missing fire. In fact, he cursed the place where he was altogether, then, gaining courage, he said to his wife: 'My dear, I just can't understand it, why, every day in my father's game-park I'm all frenzy' (and he told her of his exploits). 'Let's go to sleep now,' he said, 'I know what we'll do, tomorrow after dinner I'll take you to the game-park, then you'll see something very different.'

And so he did, and his wife had a very good time. Ever after that saying was current at court: 'If I could only get you in my father's game-park, you'd see what I can do!'

You may be sure that together with the fauns and other lusty fellows who rule the woods, Master Priapus, god of Gardens,[816] there aided all good boon companions and favoured all their acts and achievements.

However, all trials are not the same, nor do they always come off, for, as far as love is concerned, I have seen and heard tell of many a good champion failing to remember his lessons and repeat the evidence so carefully mugged up in advance. For some are either too ardent or too cold, so that moods of iciness and heat can take them by surprise, others are lost in ecstasy to have such a sovereign prize in their arms, others become over-anxious, some are suddenly limp without any idea of why, while really they have got tied foreskins.

In short, there can be so many unforeseeable obstacles that suddenly intervene that were I to wish to tell them all I should be a very long time finishing. I refer you to the many men who have been married or have been adventurers in love, who will be able to tell you a hundred times more than I can. Such trials are good for men, but not for women. For instance, I have heard the story of a mother and lady of quality who, greatly prizing a daughter she had, an only child, had promised her in marriage to an estimable noble, but before she would let the marriage take place, from fear lest the girl would never stand that arduous initial effort, (since the noble in question was very robustly built and of great proportions,) first had her try it a dozen times with a young page whom she had, who was rather big for his years, saying that it was only the first opening up that was vexatious and that by starting at the beginning rather gently, with something small, she would take the bigger one more easily, as by all appearances did happen.

That trial was still more seemly and less shocking than one of which I was told once in Italy, of a father who had married his son while he was still only a young fool, to a very lovely girl to whom, such a ninny was he, the lad was unable to do anything either the first or the second night of his marriage.

And when the father asked both son and daughter-in-law how they were getting on connubially, and if they had triumphed, they both replied that they had done *niente*—'nothing.' But when the father asked his son what he had tried to do, the lad said he did not even know what he was supposed to do.

Sur quoy il prit son fils par une main et la nore par une autre, et les mena tous deux en une chambre, et leur dit: 'Or je vous veux doncques monstrer comme il faut faire.' Et fit coucher sa nore sur un bout du lit, et luy fait bien eslargir les jambes; et puis dit à son fils: 'Or voy comment je fais'; et dit à sa nore: 'Ne bougez, non importe! il n'y a point de mal.' Et en mettant son membre bien arboré dedans, dit: 'Advise bien comme je fais, et comme je dis, Dentros fuero! dentros fuero.'[1] *Et repliqua souvent ces deux mots en s'advançant dedans et resulant, non pourtant tout dehors. Et ainsy, apès ces frequentes agitations et parolles* dentro *et* fuero, *quand ce vint à la consommation, il se mit à dire brusquement et viste:* 'Dentro, dentro, dentro, dentro!' *jusqu'à ce qu'il eust faict. Au diable le mot de* fuero!

Et par ainsy, pensant faire du magister, il fut tout à plat adultere de sa nore, laquelle, ou qu'elle fist de la niaise, ou, pour mieux dire, de la fine, s'en trouva très-bien pour ce coup voir pour d'autres que luy donna le fils et le pere, et tout possible pour luy mieux apprendre sa leçon, laquelle il ne luy

[1] Pour *dentro* (dedans), *fuero* (dehors).

418

voulut pas apprendre à demy ni à moictie, mais a perfection.
àussy toute leçon ne vaut rien autrement.

I have heard many a lover and adventurer some very fortunate, talk and tell tales of having seen many ladies swoon
completely when in the sweet throes of love's pleasure, though
they all nevertheless recovered consciousness afterwards without any difficulty, and these men alleged that many women
when they reached the high point would cry : 'Oh ! Oh ! I am
dying !' I think they must find it a very sweet death.

There are others who roll their eyes up in such ecstasies, as
if they were really going to pass away, and become completely
immobile and insensitive.

Others I have heard of who go rigid and so tense in every
fibre and sinew and artery and limb that they bring on cramps,
indeed, there was one I heard of who was so given to such
cramps that nothing could cure them.

Others make their bones creak as if one were manipulating
them for some sort of dislocation.

I have heard of one woman, in this matter of swooning
away, that once when her lover was handling her on a chest,
as she came to the sweet culmination so fainted away that she
slipped and fell behind the chest and the tapestried wall, and
while she was struggling to get free and her lover was helping
her, a company of people came into the room and thus caught
her looking like a forked tree and had time to get a glimpse
of all she had, which was however all very lovely. She tried to
put a good face on it by saying that so-and-so had been playing
about with her and pushed her behind the chest, as if to suggest that of course she would never love him.

Ceste dame courut bien plus grande fortune qu'une que
j'ay ouy dire, laquelle, ainsi que son amy la tenoit embrassée
et investie sur le bord de son lit, quand ce vint sur la douce
fin, qu'il eut achevé, et que par trop il s'estendoit, il avoit par
cas des escarpins neufs qui avoient la semelle glissante, et,
s'appuyant sur des carreaux plombés dont la chambre estoit
pavée, qui sont fort subjects à faire glisser, il vint à se couler
et glisser si bien sans se pouvoir arrester, que du pourpoinct,
qu'il avoit tout recouvert de clinquant, il en escorcha de telle

façon le ventre, la motte, le cas et les cuisses de sa maistresse, que vous eussiez dit que les griffes d'un chat y avoneit passé; ce qui cuisoit si fort la dame qu'elle en fit un grand cri et ne s'en put engarder. Mais le meilleur fut que la dame, parce que c'estoit en été et faisoit grand chaud, s'estoit mise en appareil un peu plus lubrique les autres fois, car elle n'avoit que sa chemise bien blanche et un manteau de satin blanc dessus, et les calleçons à part; si bien que le gentilhomme, après avoir faict sa glissade, fit precisement l'arrest du nez, de la bouche et du menton sur le cas de sa maistresse, qui venoit fraischement d'estre barbouillé de son bouillon, que par deux fois desjà il luy avoit versé dedans et emply si fort qu'il en estoit sorti et regorgé sur les bords, dont par ainsi se barbouilla le nez, et bouche et moustaches, que vous eussiez dit qu'il venoit de frais de savonner sa barbe; dont la dame, oubliant son mal et son esgratigneure, s'en mit si fort à rire qu'elle luy dit: 'Vous estes un beau fils, car vous avez bien lavé et nettoyé vostre barbe, d'autre chose pourtant que de savon de Naples.' La dame en fit le conte a une sienne compaigne, et le gentilhomme a un sien compaignon. Voylà comment on l'a sceu, pour avoir esté redict à d'autres: car le conte estoit bon et propre à faire rire.

And one should not be under any illusions that when gathered together in private the ladies tell each other stories, quite as good as ours and exchange tales about their love-making, including the most secret things, and then roar with laughter and make fun of their gallants whenever they make a mistake or do anything ridiculous or silly. Indeed, they go one better, for they steal each other's lovers, sometimes not so much because of love as to draw their secrets from them and find out all the covert tricks they have been up to with their friends, and take advantage of the knowledge either to fan their flames or for revenge or to make war on each other in their private deliberations, when they are together.

Now that is enough on the matter under discussion. I would very much like, I must say, several tongues in this France of ours to be castigated for their slanders and made to behave like those of Spain, where for fear of his life a man would not dare sully the honour of any lady of greatness and renown, however slightly. Indeed, there they are so honoured that if they are met anywhere at all and somebody, however softly, merely calls : *Lugar à la damas,* 'Make way for the ladies !' everybody bows and offers them every honour and reverence. In the presence of ladies any unseemly language whatsoever is prohibited.

When the Empress, the consort of the Emperor Charles,[817] made her entry into Toledo, I heard that the Marquis de la Villana,[818] one of the great lords of Spain, thought himself in great trouble because he spoke threateningly to an *alguazil* (constable) who told him to move on, and such threats should never be uttered in the presence of the Empress, whereas were it in the presence of the Emperor, it would not have mattered so much.

When the Duke de Feria[819] was in Flanders, and the two Queens Eleonora[820] and Maria,[821] were going through the country, followed by their ladies and maids, and he happened to start arguing with another Spanish knight near his mistress, both very nearly paid with their lives, more for having done something so scandalous in the presence of the Queens and Empresses than for any other reason.

Similarly, at Madrid, when Queen Isabelle of France[822] was passing through the city Don Carlos d'Avalos[823] would have been executed there and then had he not slipped quickly into a church there which serves as refuge for the destitute, and he was afterwards obliged to flee from Spain in disguise, then was banished for life and confined in the most wretched island of all Italy, Lipari.

Even the fools, who have such privilege of speech, pay for it if they offend the ladies, as once happened to one called Legat whom I knew. One day our Queen Isabella of France[824] was discussing and talking of residences in Madrid and Valladolid[825] and saying how nice, how delightful they were, when quite innocently she said she would have liked those two places to be so close that she could touch one with one foot and one with the other, straddling her legs as she spoke, when this fool, who heard this, interjected : 'And I would like to be in the lovely middle *con un carrajo de borrico, para encar-*

gar y plantar la raya,' (with a donkey cart to mark out the ditch.) He got a good whipping in the kitchen for that, and indeed ought never have said such a thing, for that was one of the loveliest, most charming and most estimable Queens that Spain ever knew. She was certainly worth being thus desired, but not by that man, only by men a hundred thousand times of better quality than he was.

In my opinion these slanderous gentry who talk against the ladies would really like to know and enjoy the privilege and freedom of the vintagers in the Neapolitan countryside during the grape harvest, for while they are gathering the grapes they are allowed to say whatever they like and insult people passing by on the road how they choose. And you do indeed see them shouting and yelling after people, halloing them without sparing anybody, of whatever estate they happen to be, great or medium or small. And the pleasure in it is that they do not spare the ladies either, not even the princesses or other great ladies, whoever they may be, so that in my day I both heard and saw several ladies, for the sheer pleasure of it, arranging to go out into the countryside ostensibly for some need, but really specially to wander along the lanes and hear the vintagers' loose talk and all the endless salty, lubricious turns of speech they produced as they assailed them about all the lewdness and lubricity they indulged in with their husbands and lovers, even throwing in their faces their making love with their coachmen and pages and lackeys and even the grooms out riding with them. And, what is more, they would freely ask the ladies for the courtesy of their company and say they would tackle them and treat them a lot better than any other men. And all this was done most outspokenly, without masking their language in the least. The ladies' great pleasure in it was to have a good laugh and then egg the men escorting them to make some reply and try to best the peasants. Once the grape harvest is over, the peasants have finished with such language till the following year, or they would be seized at once and condignly punished.

I am told this custom still holds, and there are many in France would like it to be observed at some season or other,

422

just so people might have the pleasure of slandering, (which men here so like doing) with impunity.

Now, to wind up : the ladies should enjoy universal respect, as also should their love affairs and the favours which they keep secret. This is, now we are talking of this, why Aretin used to say that the tongues which lovers give each other are not used so much for direct enjoyment or the mere pleasure got from that act, of joining their tongues together, as for signing to each other to keep the secrets of their school, though there are always some imprudent husbands so loose and lewd in their speech that the things they do with their wives are not enough for them, they must needs make them known and publish them to their friends and make stories about them. It is for this reason that I have known wives to conceive a mortal hatred for their husbands and many a time withhold the pleasure which they used to give them, just so as not to be so disgraced, even though it was about what was done in wedlock.

Du Bellay the poet, in his Latin poems : *Tombs,* which are very lovely, wrote one about a dog which I think worth quoting here, for it concerns our subject. It runs :

> *Latratu fures escepi; mutus amantes,*
> *Sic placui domino, sic placui domine,*

that is : 'By barking I chased away burglars, by being silent I welcomed lovers, thus I pleased my master, thus my mistress.'

If one should so love animals for being secret-keepers, what should one do about men who hold their tongues? If we are to take the opinion of a certain courtesan on that subject (she was one of the most celebrated of times gone-by, and most accomplished at her profession)—that is, I mean, if we take Lamia's opinion—(can we?)—here is what she said : what a woman likes most of all in her lover is when he is discreetly spoken and close about what he does, for above all a woman dislikes a braggart who boasts of what he has not done and fails to do what he undertakes. The last clause is to be understood in two senses.

Further she said that even if she was one, a woman never

liked being pronounced a whore and so labelled. It is also said of Lamia that she never made fun of a man, nor did any man ever make fun of her or slander her. A lady like that, so knowledgeable in love matters, could well give a lesson to some people.

There, that is enough on this subject. Somebody more eloquent than myself might have made it larger or better, but that is precisely why I surrender my weapons, including my pen.

SEVENTH ESSAY

On lovely estimable ladies liking brave men and brave men liking courageous ladies

THOUGH themselves by nature cowardly and timorous, there never was a lovely, estimable lady who did not like bold, valiant men, bravery is so effective with the ladies that they always like it. That is merely having one's opposite love one, despite one's nature. Is it indeed not the case that Venus, formerly goddess of beauty, who was all grace and discretion, when up in the heavens and at Jupiter's court, finding some delightful, handsome lover, to cuckold her worthy husband Vulcan, never even thought of choosing one of the more dainty, nimbly-frimby kind, of whom there were many, but selected and fell in love with the god Mars, divinity of armies and of all forms of courage, and this despite the fact that he was a most foul fellow, all sweaty from the wars, whence he came, blackened by gunpowder and as filthy as could be, smelling more of the fighting man than a court darling, and in addition more often than not all bloodstained when he came home from battles and slept with her, without any attempt to clean up or perfume himself.

The generous, lovely Queen Penthesilea, when acquainted by his frame with the valour and brave deeds of Hector, of great prowess and those marvellous feats of arms against the Greeks outside Troy,[826] so fell in love with him at the mere news of it that (from a desire to have heirs, that is daughters, by so valiant a knight to inherit her kingdom) went to Troy to seek him out. When she beheld him she gazed at him in wonder and did all she could to be pleasing to him, not solely by the

425

weapons which she herself wielded, but also by her beauty, which was very rare. And Hector then never made one sortie against his enemies without her going with him, she was always beside him, where the fighting was hottest, and it is related that many times she accomplished such deeds of prowess that she made Hector marvel so that he stood often suddenly stock still in the middle of the fiercest combat, as if ravished, and would go a little aside the better to see to contemplate that grand queen fighting so valiantly. From this the world may imagine what their love-making was like and what they achieved in this, for it does indeed give cause for astonishment. Yet nevertheless their pleasure was not to last long, for in order the more to please her lover, she regularly took such fighting risks that in the end she was killed in the fiercest and most cruel confusion of battle, though there are all the same some who maintain that she never saw Hector at all, that he was dead before she arrived, and that when she got there and learned of his death she fell into such melancholy and depression for having lost the boon of seeing him (whom she had so desired and had pursued from so distant a land) that she flung herself deliberately into the most bloody of battles and thus died because she did not wish to live, now that she had been unable to see the brave creature whom of all men she had chosen to love.

The same did Thalestrida,[827] another Queen of the Amazons, who crossed a great country and covered I do not know how many leagues to reach Alexander the Great,[828] soliciting a favour of him (or doing whatever in those good old days people did do to get their ends) and, since she had heard of his fame as such a man, succeeded in sleeping with him to have progeny of such great, generous blood, which Alexander gladly granted.[829] Indeed, he would have been very spoiled and disillusioned had he not done so, for this particular Queen was as lovely as she was brave. Quintus Curtius,[830] Orosus[831] and Justinian[832] say so. It is related that she came to find Alexander with a suite of three hundred ladies-in-waiting, all extremely featly and charming, all armed, too, and to the teeth. And she curtseyed to Alexander, who then welcomed her with very great honour, and she spent thirteen days and thirteen nights with him, and accommodated all his whims and pleasures, constantly assuring him the while that if she had a daughter, she would keep her as a very precious treasure, but if on the contrary she had a son by this act, she would send the boy to him, because of the extreme destestation she had of the male sex in the matter of ruling the Amazons or in any way giving them orders, for by the laws enacted among them they killed their husbands. One may surmise that the other ladies great and smaller with her did just the same, and had themselves covered by Alexander's other captains and men-at-arms, for in this matter they could not but do what the lady who led them did.

The lovely virgin Camilla, beautiful and warm-hearted, who served her mistress Diana faithfully through the forests and woods in her hunting, when she got rumour of the valour of Turnus and those dealings of his with another valiant man, Aeneas, who caused him trouble, she made her choice, and came to seek him out, accompanied by no more than three very estimable and lovely companions, whom she had chosen as her great friends and faithful confidantes (also, you may surmise, as her *tribades*, for doing the fricarelle with her). And for the sake of honour, she made use of them everywhere, as Virgil tells us in his *Aeneid*,[833] and one was called Arinella, the virgin and brave one,[834] the second Tulla,[835] and the third Tarpeia,[836] skilled with brandishing the pike or dart (in two different ways, you may surmise) and all three Italians.[837] so, with her lovely little band (as we say, little and good) Camilla came to find Turnus, with whom she performed lovely feats of arms, attacking so often and mixed with the savage Trojans that she was killed, much to the regret of Turnus, who honoured her greatly, both for her beauty and for her fond assistance. This is how those lovely, courageous ladies sought out brave, valiant men and aided them in their wars and combats.

What planted such ardent fires of love in the bosom of poor Dido,[838] but the courage which she sensed in her Aeneas—if we are to credit Virgil? For when she had begged him to tell her all about the wars, the desolation and the destruction of Troy, and he had done so, (though to his great mortification, renewing such sorrows, but not forgetting his acts of courage,) Dido took keen note of it all and thought hard about it, then, proclaiming her love for Aeneas to her sister Anna, the most engrossing and striking words she said to her were : 'Oh, sister, what visitor is this who has come to me ! What grace he has, and what glorious courage and valour he does show, in arms and pluck ! I do truly believe he comes of divine stock, for lowborn hearts are cowardly by nature."

Such were her words, and in my opinion she conceived her love for him as much because she herself was bold and warm-hearted and so her instinct was to love her like, as from any wish to make use of him and have him assist her in what she wanted. However, the wretch deceived her and left her most cravenly, which was a turn he should never have served that estimable lady who had given him her heart and her love, especially seeing that he was, as I say, a foreigner and pro-scribed.

Boccaccio, in his book of *Famous Unfortunates*[839] tells the tale of a Countess of Forli named Romilda who when she lost her husband, had her lands and her property all taken by Caucan, king of the Avars. He took everything from her, so that she was reduced to retiring with her children to the castle of Forli, where he besieged her. But one day, when he went up closer to it, to reconnoitre, Romilda happened to be on the top of one of the towers and saw him and contemplated him for some time. And, seeing him so handsome, in the prime of life, moun-ted on a fine horse and all accoutred with fine equipment, and accomplishing such fine military exploits and not sparing himself any more than he did the least of his men, she immedi-ately fell passionately in love with him. And, casting off the mourning she was wearing for her husband and all the cares of her castle and the siege, she sent a messenger out to him to say that if he would take her for wife, she would surrender that stronghold the moment the wedding was celebrated. King Caucan took her at her word. And when the promised day came, she dressed superbly in her loveliest duchess's robes, which made her so much lovelier, for she was very beautiful. And when she had reached the King's camp, to consummate

the marriage, so he might not be reproached with not having
kept faith, he spent the whole night trying to satisfy the burning Duchess. Then, the following morning, when he got up,
he called twelve of his Avar soldiers whom he accounted his
toughest and strongest lads and handed Romilda over to them
to take their pleasure of, one after the other, and they then
spent a night so doing to the best of their ability, till day came
round again, when Caucan summoned her to him, and after
reproving her sternly for her lust and insulting her greatly, he
then had her impaled through her privy parts, by which she
died. Indeed a cruel and barbarous act, thus to treat so lovely
and estimable a lady, instead of giving her recognition and recompensing her and treating her with every courtesy because
of the good opinion she had had of his greatness of heart, his
valour and his grand courage, for all of which she had loved
him. This was an example, however, which some ladies today
should glance at, for there are indeed brave men of that sort
who became so inured to killing and to the harsh handling and
clashing of steel, that sometimes it is their mood to use their
weapons against the ladies. All men however are not of such
temperament, for when a number of estimable ladies do them
the honour of loving them and having a high opinion of their
valour, they leave their fury and frenzy behind them in camp
and when at court or in a bedchamber adapt themselves to
gentleness and decency and the courtesies.

In his *Tragic Tales*[840] Brandel relates one which is the loveliest
story I ever read. It is about a Duchess of Savoy, who one day,
as she was leaving the city of Turin, heard a Spanish pilgrim
who was on her way to Loretto for a vow she had taken, cry
out in admiration of her beauty and say quite loudly that if a
lovely, perfect lady were married to her brother, Duke Mendozza, who was so handsome so fine and so valiant, one would
really be able to say that the handsomest couple in the world
had come together. At once—for she understood Spanish very
well—she took these words much to heart, and love was engraved there, so that merely by something thus overheard she
so fell in love with the Duke of Mendozza that she was never
content till she had connived a supposed pilgrimage to St

James of Compostella to see this lover she had so unexpectedly found. Having come to Spain, she took the road which led to the mansion of the Duke of Mendozza and then had a fair opportunity to satisfy her sight with the lovely person she had chosen, for the sister of the Duke, who went with the Duchess, had warned her brother in advance of the noble visitor he was to expect. So he did not fail to go out to meet her, well clad, mounted on a fine Spanish steed, so doughty and so charming with it that the Duchess was really delighted with the report she had first heard, and marvelled at him both because he was so handsome and because of the glorious way in which he made manifest all the valour there was in him, which she was keenly aware of, together with the other virtues and accomplishments and fine points in him, which at once presaged the trouble they would some day cause her, as indeed later they did, very gravely, in the false accusation that Count Pancallier made against her chastity. However, for all that she took him to be a doughty and valiant soldier, in love he was a great coward, for he behaved with such frigidity and respect towards her that he did not utter a single word of love, which was what she was really most interested in, the reason, indeed, why she had made this journey at all, and so, piqued by such chill respectfulness, which was really great all-round cowardice in love-making, she left him the very next day, far from as satisfied as she would have liked to be.

Here you see how sometimes the ladies love men bold in love-making as well as fighting, not that they would like the men to be bold-mannered or arrogant, impudent or brash, as I have known some to be, for there has to be a medium in such things.

I know some who have lost many a good opportunity because of such respectfulness, and I could tell some good stories about it, too, were I not afraid of wandering too far away from my subject, though I do count on giving some, and so will tell the following one.

Years ago I heard the tale of a lady, one of the most lovely in the world, who in just the same way as above had heard that a certain prince was very bold and valiant,[841] and even while quite young had engaged in great feats of arms and come through victorious, and above all had won two great, outstanding battles against his enemies, so she felt a great longing to see him, and to do so made the journey to the province where he was at the time residing, all under a pretext into which I will not go. The main thing is that she made this journey. For what will a bold and loving heart not do? Thus she was able to see him and take a good look at him, for he travelled out a long way to meet her, and treated her with all possible honour and respect, as he should so lovely and great-hearted a princess. Even too much, some said, for the same happened as with the Duke de Mendozza and the Duchess of Savoy. Such show of respect merely breeds discontent and pique, and the upshot in this case was that she parted from him far less pleased than she came. It might have been waste of time for him and she might not have proved at all what he wanted, but it would surely not have been a bad thing to try, but very fair, and more to his credit.

What indeed is a bold, expansive spirit worth, if it does not show in every way, as much in love-making as in arms? For arms and love are really comrades, they go together and share each other's sentiments. As the poet says :[842]

> *Lovers also wage their wars*
> *Cupid has weapons just like Mars.*

Ronsard indeed made a fine sonnet about it in the first book of his love poems.[843]

Now, turning to the eagerness that the ladies show to see and to love great-hearted, valiant men, I once heard Queen Elizabeth of England, the reigning monarch there, tell a story about how one day, when she was at supper, with the Grand Prior of France of the house of Lorraine,[844] now Lord d'Anville, and also Lord de Montmorency and the Constable,[845] as guests, in the course of conversation she had begun to sing the praises of the late King Henry II, saying what a bold, valiant, warmhearted man he was and she used the words 'most martial' and said he had shown this in all he did, and had he not died so early, because of his martial qualities she had been resolved to go to see him in his Kingdom, and had had her galleons made ready to travel to France, so she might join hands with him for the faith and peace. 'In short,' she added, 'it was one of my great desires to see him, and I think he would not have said no, for it is my nature to love valiant men, and I grudge death's taking away so fine a King, especially before I set eyes on him.'

This same Queen, some time later, having heard the Duke de Nemours[846] spoken of as very fine and valorous, put keen questions about him to the late Lord de Randan,[847] when King François II sent that noble to Scotland[848] to conclude a treaty of peace outside Leith, which was besieged. And when de Randan had told her a lot about the Duke and gone into much detail about all his great and magnificent qualities and his valour, he could see in her countenance—and de Randan was a past master at love as much as at arms, a spark of love or affection, and also detected in her speech a great craving to see the Duke. So, not wishing to halt half-way, once such progress had been made, he tried to ascertain whether, supposing the Duke were to come to see her, he would be welcome, whereupon Elizabeth assured him that he would, from all of which de Randan concluded that they might come, all with a view to marriage.

So when he got back from this embassy to the court of England, he reported the whole conversation to the King and the Duke de Nemours, when the King persuaded the Duke, indeed, instructed him to take it up, which he did at once, extremely delighted at the thought that he might attain so fine a kingdom by marrying so lovely, so virtuous and estimable a queen.

To conclude, the irons were put in the fire, with the King providing generous funds, and the Duke made very great preparations, equipping himself most superbly and grandly in clothing, horses and arms, in short, in all fine things, omitting nothing (for I saw it all) so he might present himself to that lovely princess, above all not forgetting to take with him the flower of the youth of the French court, all so grandly equipped that Greffier the fool set the word going round about it that this was indeed *beans' blossom time*, suggesting it was all youthful folly, for the old lines run *beans' blossom time, young fools' prime.*

Meanwhile, Lord de Lignerolles,[849] a very able and keen-witted noble, at the time a great favourite of his master, the Duke de Nemours, was despatched to see the Queen, and he returned with a fine, very respectable reply which made the Duke happy to speed up the preparations for the visit. And I remember clearly that at court the marriage was considered as good as concluded, but we suddenly had to take notice that it was all off, and after such great, vain, useless expense, too.

I can no more tell than any other Frenchman could why all this fell through, unless to suggest that perhaps other love interests[850] had a greater hold on Queen Elizabeth's heart and absorbed her attention more, for the Duke de Nemours was in every way so accomplished and so skilled in arms and the other arts that any lady might have been expected to snatch at him, as indeed I saw some of the primmest and most chaste do, breaking their virginal vows on his account.

In the *Hundred Tales*[851] of Marguerite, Queen of Navarre, we have a very fine story of that lady of Milan who gave a rendezvous to the late de Bonnivet,[852] who was later Admiral of France, then arranged for her chamber-maids to make a clatter with swords on the stairs in depth of the night just as de Bonnivet was getting into bed, which they did magnificently, just as she ordered them, while she herself pretended to be alarmed and terrified, saying it must be her brothers-in-law, they must have noticed something, now she was ruined, he should hide under the bed or behind the tapestries. But de Bonnivet was not the man to be frightened, he just wrapped his cape round his arm and took his sword and cried : 'What sort of brothers do you think they are who can frighten or touch me? Why, they'll take fright at the mere sight of my sword-point.'

He opened the door, slipped out, and was just about to charge down the stairs, when he saw it was only those women clattering away. They were very frightened, and confessed everything, so de Bonnivet consigned them to hell and went back into the bedroom. Closing the door carefully, he found

433

his lady all laughter, flinging her arms round his neck and assuring him it was just a practical joke she was playing on him, and had he been afraid, or not shown the courage that he did, he would never have slept with her, after which, since he appeared to be reassured and satisfied, she put her arms round him and drew him into bed with her. No need to ask what they did all night, for she was one of the lovely ladies of Milan, one of whom he would not easily have obtained such an opportunity.

I knew one fine noble, who went to bed in Rome with a charming Roman lady in the husband's absence, when she gave him a similar scare, having one of her women burst into the bedroom to tell them that her husband was on his way back from the country. She pretended to be aghast and begged the noble to hide in a closet, or she would be lost. 'No, no,' said he, 'not for anything in the world will I hide, and if he does come in, he's a dead man!' But when he sprang for his sword, the lady burst out laughing, and confessed that it had all been to test him and find out what he would do if her husband did want to cause trouble, and whether he would defend her.

I knew a very lovely lady[853] who suddenly left a lover of hers because she concluded he was not plucky, and instead took another, of different stuff, a man greatly feared because of his sword-play, for he was one of the best swordsmen of the day.

I have heard elderly folk tell the story of a lady at court who was the mistress of the late Lord de Lorge,[854] who in his young days had been one of the most valiant and celebrated infantry commanders of his day. She had heard a great deal about his great courage, and one day when King François arranged a lion fight in the courtyard, she wanted to get proof of what she had heard about him, and so dropped one of her gloves into the lions' pen, which put them all in a rage. Then she asked Lord de Lorge to go in and get it for her, if he loved her as much as he said. Without turning a hair he wrapped his cape round his forearm, took his sword in the other hand, and coolly entered the lions' den to get the glove, in which his luck was so good that by facing the lions boldly all the time and

434

keeping his sword pointed at them, he made sure that they did not dare attack him. And when he had recovered the glove, he went back to his mistress and handed it to her, for which she and all present admired him and his courage greatly. But it is said that de Lorge was so indignant for thus making him her amusement that he then left her. It is even said that his indignation was so great that he threw the glove in her face, for he would much rather she had ordered him a hundred times to tackle a battalion of infantry, which he had so well learned to accomplish, not fight wild animals, in which he saw no glory.

I would as soon have the trick played by a lady on her lover who, when he made love to her and assured her that there was nothing so risky he would not do it for her, just to take him at his word said : 'If you love me so much, and are as brave as you say, stick your dagger in your arm for love of me.'

The man loved her so desperately that he drew his dagger and was about to stick himself, when I grabbed his arm and took the dagger away and persuaded him that it would be very foolish indeed to give anybody such a proof of love or courage. I will not name the lady, but the noble in question was the late Lord de Clermont-Tallard the elder,[855] the one who was killed in the battle of Moncontour, one of the bravest and most valiant of France's nobles, as he showed in his death, when he was in command of a company of men-at-arms. I was very fond of him and had great respect for him.

I have been told that the same happened to the late Lord de Genlis,[856] who fell in Germany leading the Huguenot forces during the third civil war, for one day when he was down by the Loire[857] with his mistress, she dropped her handkerchief into the water, a costly, fine piece of work, and did it on purpose too, merely to ask him to go in and recover it for her. Since he could swim no better than a stone he tried to get out of it, but she reproached him with being a cowardly lover who lacked pluck, whereupon without another word he plunged in and in his efforts to get that handkerchief would have been drowned had he not been fished out by another.

In my opinion such women are merely trying to get rid of

435

their lovers in a nice way, since they perhaps bore them. But it would be far better for them to give them some fine tokens and request them for love of them to wear these in honourable fields of war and there give proof of their courage and egg them on thus to go to the wars, but not do such silly things as I have just related. I could tell such stories endlessly.

I recall that when in the first civil war[858] we went to besiege Rouen, Lady de Piennes,[859] one of the estimable maids-of-honour of the court, doubting that the late Lord de Gergeay had been valiant enough to have killed the late Baron d'Ingrande in single combat, (for d'Ingrande was one of the most valiant nobles of court) to test his pluck gave him a favour made from a scarf, for him to wear on his hat. And when they came to reconnoitre the fortress of St Catherine, he attacked a troop of horse emerging from the city so courageously and dauntily that while fighting bravely he received a pistol bullet in the head and was killed outright. Whereby the young lady in question had proof of his bravery, and, had he not lost his life achieving this, she would have married him. Thus because she questioned his courage and wondered whether he really had killed the baron in question, (indeed, she had doubted it) she thought she wanted this proof. There is no doubt but that there are many such doughty men, and the ladies egg them on to it still more, and if they are wearied of fighting and un-interested, excite them and warm them up to it.

We had a fine example in Fair Agnes[860] who, when she saw King Charles VII in love with her (and, soft and weak-willed as he was, careless of his kingdom, thinking of nothing else but making love to her) she one day told him that while she was still a young girl an astrologer had foretold that she would be loved and waited on by one of the most valiant and courage-ous kings of all Christendom, and that when the King did her the honour of loving her she at first thought he must be that valorous king who had been prophesied for her, but seeing him so soft-natured and so indifferent to his duties, she had come to see that she was really mistaken, and her courage-ous king was not this one, but the King of England, who was achieving such fine feats of arms. 'So,' she said to the King,

'I am going to seek him out, for it is he whom the astrologer had in mind.'

These words so went to the King's heart that he began to weep, and then, gradually gaining courage, left his hunting and his gardens and got the bit between his teeth so well that by good fortune and valour combined he finally chased the English out of the kingdom.

Bertrand du Guesclin, when he married his wife, previously Lady Tiphaine;[861] went all out to satisfy her and left war-making, which he had so much practised hitherto, gaining great fame and glory. But she had reproached him about it and remonstarted with him that before his marriage he was on all lips for his great deeds, but from then on she was to be reproached for the break in his life and it was a great disgrace to her and her husband for him to have become a tame man. And she never stopped nagging, till she had restored his initial courage and sent him back to the wars, where he then did better than before. Here you see a case of an estimable lady putting the honour of her husband before her night pleasures, and there is no question about it, our own wives, even at our side, would not continue to love and cherish us, were we not brave and valiant, but when we come back from the wars after the accomplishment of some fine, handsome deed, they really do love us and take us warmly to their bosoms and find love best.

The fourth daughter of the Count of Provence,[862] the father-in-law of St Louis, who was the consort of Charles, Count of Anjou, brother of the same King,[863] grew impatient at being merely a simple Provençal and Angevin countess and being the only one of the sisters who was a mere 'lady', only a countess (for two of her sisters were queens and the third was an empress) never desisted till she had implored, urged and importuned her husband into fighting for a kingdom. And the two together became so pushing that Pope Urbanus made them King and Queen of the Two Sicilies. They then went together to Rome with a fleet of thirty galleys, to be crowned in great magnificence, by His Holiness, with the title of King and Queen of Jerusalem and Naples, which he conquered later,[864] as much by valorous fighting as by the means which his wife provided, selling all her rings and jewels to find the costs of the expedition. After which they reigned in reasonable peace, and a long time,[865] in the kingdom they had conquered.

A long time after that Isabel de Lorraine,[866] one of their granddaughters, a descendant both of them and their collaterals, did the same without her husband René, for he was a prisoner, in the hands of Charles, Duke of Burgundy,[867] while she, wise too and of great heart and pluck, was Princess of Sicily and Naples, having inherited the kingdom together with her husband, assembled an army of thirty thousand men and led it herself and conquered the Kingdom and seized the city of Naples.[868] I could name very many other ladies who greatly served their husbands in this fashion, when, great of heart and ambitious, they urged their husbands and egged them on to be great and acquire goods and eminence and riches. And that indeed is the finest and most honourable way to acquire them, at the point of the sword.

I have known many in our France and at our courts who were almost more prompted by their wives than by their will, and undertook and achieved great things. But I have also known many women who, thinking only of their own pet pleasures, hindered their men-folk and kept them at their side, preventing their accomplishing fine deeds and loth for them to find pleasure in anything but the game of Venus, so eager for it were they. I could tell many a tale, but that would be to spread myself too much on this subject, which is unquestionably finer (touching virtue as it does) than the other, which touches on vice. And it is more satisfactory to hear of these ladies who urged their husbands to fine deeds. I am not speaking solely of married women, but of many others too who for a mere little favour have made their wooers do many things they would not otherwise have done. For what satisfaction is it for them, how much greater the ambition and flush of the heart if when one is at war one can tell oneself that one is much beloved by one's mistress and what radiant countenance, what lovely gestures, what beautiful glances of her eyes, what embraces, what pleasures, what favours one can then hope to receive from her, if one achieves a fine deed for love of her.

Among other reproaches that Scipio made Massinissa when, bleeding almost all over, he married Sophonisba,[869] was that it was not seemly to think of the ladies and of love when one was at war. I hope he will forgive me if I say that as far as I go I think there is no satisfaction nor anything to give a man courage and ambition to do well to be compared to the ladies, I was in it all myself in years gone by, and as I see it, all men who take part in combat are the same, and you may ask them, for I believe they share my opinion, all of them, and that when they are on a fine military expedition and hotly pressed by the enemy their heart grows greater, doubles, in fact, when they think of their ladies, of the favours they sport, and of the caresses and warm welcome they stand to get from them, if they come through alive, while, should they happen to fall in battle, how the ladies will regret their decease. In short, by the love of their ladies and by thinking of them, all men's undertakings are simple and easy, all their combats are tournaments, and every death is a triumph.

I recall that at the battle of Dreux[870] the late Lord des Bordes,[871] a fine, gentle knight if ever there was one in his time, lieutenant of Lord de Nevers,[872] formerly known as the Count d'Eu (also a very distinguished man) when ordered to charge and break up a battalion of infantry marching in the van under the command of the late Duke de Guise the Great,[873] and the actual signal for the charge was given, at once spurred his steed, a Turkish grey, and was fortified by sporting a fine favour which his mistress had given him, (I do not name her, but she was one of the lovely, estimable and great maids-of-honour at court), and as he galloped off he cried out boldly that he was going to fight bravely for love of his mistress or else die a glorious death. In which he did not fail, for, breaking through the first six ranks, at the seventh he was dragged to the ground and died. Now tell me, did that lady not make good use of her lovely favour, and was she afterwards to reproach herself for having given it him?

Lord de Bussy was the young man who knew how to make

as fine a use of the favours of his mistresses as any young man of his day, particularly those of some ladies whom I know who were worth more combats, military exploits, sword-strokes than fair Angelica ever was of those of the paladins or knights of former times, whether Christian or Saracen. But I have often heard him say[874] that in the numerous single combats and battles and general engagements in which he took part, or undertook (and there were many of them) it was never so much to serve his sovereign or make a career as for the sheer glory of pleasing his lady. There is no doubt but that he was right, for all the careers in the world are not worth so much as the love and good will of a lovely and estimable lady and mistress.

Indeed, for what did so many brave knight errants of the Round Table and so many valorous paladins of France of times past undertake so many wars and distant voyages and go on so many fine expeditions, if not for the love of the lovely ladies whom they served, or wished to serve? I refer you to the paladins of France, our Rolands, our Renauds, our Ogiers, our Olivers, our Yvons, our Richards and an infinity of others. For that was a great age and most fortunate, for, if these men did something fine for the love of their ladies, their ladies were never ungracious and always found ways of well recompensing them when they met again, at rendezvous given in the forests and woods, beside fountains or in glorious meadows. There you had the great reward for valour which all these men craved of the ladies.

Now I have a question to put : why is it that women so adore such brave men that, as I said at the outset, their courage acquires that virtue and force by which it makes its opposite love it? In any case, it is a natural inclination that prompts the ladies to love great-heartedness, which is indubitably a hundred times more to be loved than cowardice, just as any virtue is more lovable than vice.

Some of the ladies who love such valorous men do so because it seems to them that just as they are bold and handy at arms and the martial profession, so they must be at that of Venus. This of course does apply to some men. Some men are indeed good in both ways, as Julius Caesar, most valiant man in the world once was, and many another doughty fellow whom I have known, but do not name. And such men have a vigour and charm quite different from your rustic or from other men of other callings. Hence one bout with such fellows is to them worth four with others—here I speak of ladies who are moderately sensual, not those who are excessively so, for they prefer quantity. But though the rule does apply sometimes, in some men, that is, and according to the temperament of certain women, it fails in others, for there are valiant men who are so frayed by all the trappings and the great efforts of war-making that when it comes to the requirements of the gentler game they are incapable of doing any more and so are unable to satisfy their wives, while there are other women, indeed, there are many of them, who would rather have a good practitioner of the craft of Venus, well formed and fresh, than four of those Martial ones, worn-out as they are.

I have known many members of the fair sex of that temperament, for after all, they say, one cannot do more than pass one's time well and extract the essential, without distinction of persons. A valiant soldier is fine and looks good in battle, but he does not know how to do a thing in bed (so these ladies say). A fine, well-developed, well rested gentleman-servant is worth quite as much as any noble who is fatigued, however fine and valiant he may be.

I refer here to those who have tried both activities and do so daily, for the noble's loins, however gallant and hearty he may be, are broken and debilitated by the armour they have worn, and cannot possibly furnish the requirements of love as can those who have never known strain or fatigue.

There are other ladies who like doughty men, either as husbands or as lovers, the better to fight and stand up for their honour and chastity, should any slanderer say things to their disadvantage. I have seen several such at court, where years ago I knew a most lovely great lady,[875] whom I will not name, who because she was much subjected to slandering left a favourite lover of hers forthwith because she found him soft and lacking in vigour to challenge and take her part, and took on another who was a very uncouth fellow, but bold and valiant, who bore his lady's honour by the point of his sword, and to whom nobody dared face up.

I have known many ladies like that, who always preferred to have a valiant man for escort and defence, which is very good and very often most useful to them. But they should then take care not to be fickle and love any other man, once they have put themselves under such men's dominion, for if men of this sort notice the least hint of their little frolics and tergiversations they cut up very rough and bully them most savagely, both their mistresses and their mistresses' lovers. I have seen a good few cases of this in my life.

So there you see, you have ladies who prefer to be possessed by such bold, uncouth fellows, but need to be very bold them· selves and also very true to them, or else so secretive in their doings that nothing ever leaks out. Unless of course what they choose to do is merely to arrange protection as do the courtesans of Italy and Rome who each likes to have her bully, or *bravo*, as it is called in Italian, to defend and keep her, but in the arrangement with them always stipulate that they are going to have other liaisons and their bully is not to say a word.

That is all very fine as far it applies to Roman courtesans and their bullies, but not when it applies to the gallant nobles of our country, or anywhere else, for that matter. But if an estimable lady does wish to be supported in her steadfastness and constancy, it is up to her lover, if she is in the slightest danger in the world, either to life or honour, from any malicious talk, to make no spare of his life in her maintenance and defence. Thus, it is that at our court I have known more than one to make a slanderer shut up at once, when he came to running down their mistresses and ladies, whom by the obligation of chivalry as well as by law we are supposed to be champions to in their afflictions, as bold Renaud did for fair Genevieve in Scotland[876] or the Duke de Mendozza for that lovely Duchess I have told about[877] or, as we read in our chronicles, the Duke of Carouge for his own wife in the time of King Charles VI. I could give countless other examples, both in older times and the present, among such as I have seen myself at our court. But I should never be done.

Other ladies I have known who have left cowardly men, despite the circumstances that they were very wealthy, to turn and love or marry nobles who so to speak, had only their sword and their cloak, but who were valorous and great-hearted, and by dint of valour and great-heartedness could hope to achieve greatness and high position, even though it is not always the most valorous who achieve these things. In which indeed they are wronged, for very often one sees the cowardly and pusillanimous achieve these things. But at the same time their elevation never shows to advantage in them as it does in the case of men of real valour.

Now, I should never be done if I proposed to relate all the various causes and reasons why the ladies thus love men who are great of heart. I am quite sure that if I wished to fill out this essay with innumerable proofs and examples, I could make a whole book of it, but as I do not wish to spend my time on one subject only, rather to vary it, and to deal with several different topics, I will be content with having said what I have already, although many people may object that this one in particular really was worth supporting with a number of ex-amples and lengthy proofs, when they would be sure to be clever and say : 'He has forgotten that story, and he has for-gotten this.' I know, indeed, I may know more such tales than they could tell, and tales most elevated by origin and most secret, too, but I have no intention of publishing them all or giving all the names I could.

That is why I keep silent. Nevertheless, before I bring it all to an end, I will make the following passing observation : just as the ladies love men who are valiant and bold in fighting, they also love those who are valiant and bold in love-making, nor will the man who is cowardly and excessively respectful in those matters ever succeed in them. Not that the ladies want them so over-arrogant, bold and overweening that they grapple with them and force them down on to their backs, but they do ask for a measure of boldness in their moderation, or moderation in their boldness, for unless they are she-wolves they are not going to do the seeking nor will they be indifferent. They do however know so well how to prompt the appetite and desire and they do attract so nicely to the skirmishing that the man who does not seize the occasion when ripe and get to grips, without respect of majesty or greatness, scruple or conscience or fear or any other consideration, really is a fool and lacks heart, and merits being abandoned for ever by good fortune.

I know two estimable nobles who were comrades,[878] for whose sake two most estimable ladies (and far from ladies of lesser quality, too) once arranged in Paris to go for a stroll in a park, and when they got there the two parted company, each going with her own suitor up a separate path, all so deeply overgrown with lovely vines that the daylight scarcely penetrated and the freshness was most delightful. Now one of the two nobles was bold, and realized that his outing had not been arranged only for a stroll in the fresh air. This he could tell merely from the countenance of his lady, which he saw to be burning with fire and with quite a different desire from that of picking the muscat grapes of the pergola, and also by the heated, spicy, wild things she let fall, and he did not miss the chance, but, taking her quickly and without any respect, lay her down on a little bed of greenery and turf, and had his pleasure delightfully, without her doing any more than murmur: 'Oh dear God! What are you about? Aren't you the wildest, strangest man in the world! Oh! but what if somebody came along, whatever should we say? Oh, dear Lord! Get off me. . . . !' But without turning a hair this noble continued the operation so resolutely that when he had finished with her he was very satisfied, as indeed she was too, so that when they had now walked three or four times round the paths, they set to work to have a second match. Then, emerging from their nook into another pergola, at the other end of this they found the other noble and the other lady, still strolling exactly as they had left them at the outset. Whereupon the lady who was satisfied remarked to the noble who was satisfied: 'It looks to me as if so-and-so has been a bit of a fool and only entertained his lady with words, it has been all talk and walk.' Then, when all four came together, the two ladies began to discuss how they had each got on, when the one who was satisfied said she had got on very well, thank you, for the moment she could not conceive of feeling better, while the unsatisfied one said that she had had to do with the biggest fool and the most cowardly lover she had ever seen. And to crown it the two nobles saw them laughing together, crying as they walked : 'Oh, the fool ! Oh, the coward, Oh Mr Respectful !' Whereupon the satisfied noble remarked to his friend : 'See, our ladies are talking about you and lambasting you, and you will find that you were too respectful and too soft,' which the other admitted. But there was now no more time, no more forelock left to be taken. However, having recognized his error, in a short time this other mended things by another method which I could easily tell you.

I knew two great princes, brothers,[879] both very well constituted and accomplished, who loved two ladies, (though one was bigger than the other in every way), and happened to be in the bedchamber of the big one, who just then was keeping to her bed at the time,[880] and each withdrew to one corner to entertain his lady. One entertained the big one with every possible token of respect and much hard-kissing, all profoundly honourable, with respectful talk, and never a hint of drawing really close to her, let alone storming the castle crags. Without any talk or show of ceremony, the other brother took his lady to a window embrasure and there, with a sudden gesture ripping her drawers, which were tight laced, open (for he was very strong) let her feel that he was by no means a lover in the Spanish style, with eyes alone or smirking features or words, but by the true and most fitting act a lover could desire. And having achieved his prize-taking, he left the room. But as he went he remarked, loudly enough for his lady to hear : 'Brother, if you don't follow my methods, you'll get nowhere. I tell you, you can be as bold and courageous as you like elsewhere, but if you don't show pluck in this place your honour's gone, this is nowhere to be respectful, this is where you see your lady awaiting you.' And with this he left his brother, who nevertheless still refrained, leaving it to another time, not that the lady valued him any the more for this or on the other hand ascribed any excessive frigidity in love to him, or lack of courage or physical inability, for he had shown sufficient elsewhere, both in war and love-making.

One Shrove Tuesday the late Queen Mother[881] had a very fine farce enacted in Italian, in the Rheims Mansion[882] in Paris, that Captain of Galleons Cornelio Fiesco had written. The whole court was present, both men and women, and many other folk too, from the city. Among other scenes there was one in which a young man spent the night hidden in the bed-chamber of a very lovely lady whom he did not even touch. When he told his friend about his 'good luck', the other asked : *Qui avete fatto?* 'What did you do?' He replied : *Niente!* 'Nothing,' whereupon his friend said : 'What a coward, what a sap! You did nothing? *Che maldita sia la tua poltronezza!* 'A curse on your cowardice !'

The same evening, after the play was over, we were in the Queen's bedchamber discussing the piece, and I asked a very lovely and estimable lady, whom I will not name, what she had found fine in the play, what pleased her most. Most ingenuously she said : 'What I thought nicest was what that young man's friend, Lucio, I mean, said to the one who had not done anything : *Ah poltronazzo! non havete fatto niente! che maldita sia la tua poltronezza!'*

As you see, this lady agreed with the friend who threw Lucio's cowardice in his face, she did not in the least value Lucio for being soft and weak, and she and I went on to a very frank discussion of the mistakes made by not seizing the moment when weather and wind are favourable, as any good navigator does. So I think I must also tell the following story and include it here among the others, which are more grave, because it is so delightful and ridiculous.

It is like this : I once heard an estimable noble, a friend of mine, relate that a lady of his country, who had on various occasions shown a gentleman-in-waiting of hers great familiarity and intimacy, all pointing to this end, the man in question, who was no fool at all, finding his mistress one summer day half asleep in bed without a stitch on and on her side, turning away from the passage by the bed, was tempted by her great beauty and her very suitable posture, in which it was so easy to take advantage of the moment and take her, since she was on the very edge of the bed, crept quietly up and accomplished it. When she looked quickly around she saw it was this gentleman-in-waiting of hers, whom anyway she desired, so, caught in the embrace of love as she was, she made no attempt to break free or escape or free herself from his grasp, no, not in the least, merely turned her head back and, keeping very still so as not to lose anything, said : 'Well, Mr Simpleton, whoever made you so plucky as to put it in?' Most courteously the gentleman-in-waiting replied : 'Madame, am I to take it out?' 'That is not what I asked, Mr Simpleton,' the lady replied. 'I asked who made you so plucky as to put it in?' But the gentleman-in-waiting still repeated : 'Madame, shall I take it out, if you say so, I will.' But she only repeated her question : 'Still not what I ask you, Mr Simpleton,' and so on. The two of them continued this repeated exchange of question and answer three or four times, without in the least desisting from the task in hand, till it was accomplished. Whereby the lady felt better off than had she ordered her gallant to 'take it out', as he suggested, so that she was well served by insisting on an answer to her first question—as the gallant for his part was by his reiterated reply. After that they had many a bout, to the tune of the same litany, for the proverb tells us that *it is only the first ovenful or the first pint that's dear*. Now there was a fine bold gentleman-servant for you! To such bold fellows one should make the Italian rejoinder : *A bravo cazzo mai non manca favor,* 'a bold so-and-so never lacks opportunity.'

Now you see clearly that there are many who are bold, courageous and valiant, both in arms and in love, others who are so in arms but not in love, yet others bold in love, not in arms, like that wretched Paris who was plucky enough and valiant enough to ravish Helen from her poor cuckold of a husband Menelaus and sleep with her, but not to fight with him against Troy.

Here you also have the reason why the ladies do not like old men or those who are getting on that way, since they are very timid in love-making and shy to ask, not that they do not have desires as great as the young ones, indeed, they may even be greater, but they lack the powers. Which is what a Spanish lady once said: Old men are like many people who, when they see monarchs in their grandeur, sovereignty and authority, greatly long to be like them, but never dare undertake anything against them, with the thought of dispossessing them of the kingdoms and taking their place. And she added: *Y a penas es nascido el deseo, quando se muero luego,* that is: 'The desire is hardly born before it dies again.' So it is with old men—when they see lovely women they desire them greatly, but they dare not attack, *'porque los viejos,'* she said, *'naturalmente son temerosos; y amor y temor no se caben en un sabo,'* that is: 'for old men are timid by nature and love and timidity never go together in the same bag.' They are indeed right to be hesitant, for they lack the weapons of both offence and defence, not like the young, who have youth and beauty. For, as the poet says: 'Nothing is unseemly in youth, whatever it does.' Another saying is that there's nothing pleasant in the spectacle of an elderly soldier or an elderly lover.

Now this is enough said on this matter, whereof I wind up and will say no more, except to add another subject which rather tends to border on this one, which is this: just as the ladies love bold, valiant, big-hearted men, men too love stout-hearted, warm-hearted women. And just as any warm-hearted, plucky man is more pleasing and more to be admired than another, so likewise with every distinguished, warm-hearted and brave lady. Not that I mean to suggest that the lady should do what a man does, nor play the soldier like a man, as I have known some to do or heard of it, who rode horse like a man, carried a pistol at their saddle-bow and fired with it and made war like a man.

I might in particular mention one lady[883] who during the League wars did this. Such disguising is a denial of their sex. Apart from not being pleasing, or at all decorous, it is more to be prohibited and more prejudicious than most people realize; thus one saw that gracious maid of Orleans come to an ill end, at her trial greatly condemned for so living, and her appearance being part cause of her fate and death. This is why I am against and have a poor opinion of such mannish ways. Yet I do like and approve of a lady who shows pluck and bravery, when in adversity or great need, with a fine feminine vigour which closely resembles that of the masculine heart. Without going to the great-hearted ladies of Rome or Sparta in times gone by, who in this exceeded all others (they are manifested enough and that is clear before our eyes) I would like to write of new cases, in our own age.

As the first, and in my opinion the finest instances that I know, we have those estimable and brave ladies of Siena, at the time of the uprising of their city against the unbearable yoke of the imperial forces, for when a regular defence corps had been organized, and the ladies had been ignored as unsuitable for fighting like the men, they wished to go one better and saw that they could do more than merely toil at their domestic chores by day and by night, and really take on their share of the burden, and they formed three companies.[884] And so, in January, on St Anthony's Day, these three companies, complete with drums and banners in the main square (which is indeed lovely) made their public appearance. The lady who led the finest, largest and most outstanding company of the city was Signora Forteguerra, clad in violet, with banner and company all in the same colour, and the motto: *Purche sia il vero,* 'Provided it be true'. And all these ladies were clad like nymphs, in short tunics, which revealed and displayed their lovely calves. The second company was led by Signora Piccolomini, clad in scarlet, with the company and banner of the same colour, and a white cross with the motto: *Purche non la butto* 'Provided I do not lay it low'. The third was that of Signora Livia Fausta, clad in white, with her company and banner in white, with a palm as device and the motto: *Purch'io l'habbia.* 'Provided I have it.' And following these three ladies were a good three thousand ladies of the nobility, bourgeoisie and others, all equally lovely, all well attired in their robes and complete uniforms of satin or taffeta, damask or other silken materials, all resolved to live or die for liberty. And on her shoulder each bore a faggot, for the fortifications which were being constructed and they cried: *'France! France!'* The King's representatives, the Cardinal of Ferrara[885] and Lord de

449

Termes,[886] were delighted by the sight, so rare and so lovely, and had eyes for nothing else but to gaze and marvel and contemplate and praise those lovely, estimable ladies. And indeed I heard some ladies and men present remark, never was so goodly a sight seen before. And God knows, fair ladies are not lacking in that city, they are in abundance, one does not have to pick and choose there.

The men who anyway were very keen on their liberty were still more stirred by this lovely enterprise and anxious not to lag behind their ladies, to such point that everybody, nobles, peers, bourgeois, merchants, artisans, rich and poor alike were eager and hurried to the fortifications to join with these lovely virtuous, estimable ladies, and all vied with each other in the work. Not merely laymen, but also ecclesiastical persons put their backs into it, and when they all returned, the men separately, and the women too all together, in parade order, they followed in procession to the square adjoining the Prince's Palace, holding hands, to salute the image of the Virgin Mary, patron of the city, while they sang a number of hymns and canticles in praise of her, to a very sweet tune, all in part singing, till to some extent from sheer emotion, to some extent from relief, tears streamed from all eyes, and after receiving the benediction from the Most Reverend Cardinal of Ferrara, they all retired to their homes, men and women alike all resolved to do better in future.

That godfearing performance of the ladies of Siena recalls to me (not as comparison) a profane but lovely occasion which took place in Rome in the days of the Punic War. One finds it described in Livy.[887] This was a solemn procession made by three times nine, that is twenty-seven young Roman girls, all of them virgins, attired in rather long robes (history does not record the colours) who, when the solemn parade was over, took up their positions in a public place where before the crowds they danced a dance in which, standing one behind the other, they gave each other a length of cord, dancing round as they did so, with much nimble foot work to the beat of the song which they sang. That was a very lovely sight to see, as much for the beauty of the lovely girls as their great charm, their fine style in dancing, and the dainty movements of their feet, for it certainly is pleasing to see dainty feet move when they are the feet of pretty virgins and the girls know how to move them in neat, harmonious rhythm. I have my own vivid conception of what that dance must have been like, and it has recalled one I saw the girls of my own homeland dance in my young days, a dance called *the girdle*, in which the girls took off their girdles and kept passing them one to another over their heads, then intermixed and interlaced them between their legs, leaping nimbly over them, all the time forming and dispersing figures by their dancing, with little leaps, following one another round, without ever losing the beat of the song or the instrument leading them. It was indeed a very pleasant sight, for those leaps, interweavings, dispersals, waving of girdles and the grace of the girls themselves all together had in it an indefinable element of delicate sensuousness such that it surprised me that in our day that dance has not been practised at our courts, because the drawers that girls wear at court are very becoming, and the dance enables one easily to see the loveliness of leg and pick out which girl has her garment drawn up the best and uses her limbs most gracefully. It is a dance better seen than described in writing.

To get back to our Siena ladies, (Ah, you lovely, plucky ladies! you should never have passed away, any more than your praise which will last as long as the world itself!) Nor should that lovely, charming girl of your city have ever died who one day, during your siege, seeing her brother bedridden with sickness and in no condition to go on sentry duty, softly let him lie in his bed while she slipped out of the room and took his weapons and accoutrements, and then, her brother's very image, reported for the watch and was taken for her brother, nobody in the darkness seeing who it really was. So is it said, that no love is as strong as the love of a brother and therefore in such a need no pains should be spared to manifest the finest warmth of heart, wherever it may be. I think that the corporal who was in charge that night of the platoon which included that lovely girl must when he learned of the deed have been very annoyed at not having better distinguished who

451

it was, so he might have sung her praises without delay or even exempted her from duty or purely so he might have contemplated her beauty, her charms and her military bearing, for one need have no doubt that she was at great pains to imitate it all.

No doubt about it, that fine deed cannot be overpraised, even though performed for so deserving an object as her brother. The same was done by gentle Richardet,[888] but for other reasons, for he had overheard his sister Bradamante talking about the beauties of that lovely Spanish princess and her vain loves and desires, and after she had gone to bed took her weapons and fine skirts and disguised himself as his sister, so alike were they in face and beauty, and then, in this shape, drew from that lovely princess what her sex had denied his sister, for doing which he would have paid dearly, had it not been for the protection of Roger, who thought he was his Bradamante (his mistress) and saved him from death.

Now I have heard Lord de La Chapelle des Ursins[889] relate that when he was in Italy he reported that so fine deed of the ladies of Siena to the late King Henry,[890] and he found it so fine that with tears in his eyes he swore that if ever the day should come when God granted him peace or a truce with the Emperor,[891] he would go in his galleys to the Tuscan Sea and thence to Siena, to see that city which had such pride in itself and its cause, and thank it for that outstanding act of initiative, but above all to see those lovely estimable ladies and tend them his special thanks. I believe he would certainly have done so, for he honoured all lovely, estimable ladies greatly. As it was, he wrote to them, principally to the three leaders, the most estimable letters of thanks that ever were, with offers which pleased and stimulated them still more. Alas, only a little time after that he had his truce, but in the meantime the city had been taken, as I have described elsewhere, which was an incalculable loss for France, losing so noble and so precious an ally which, recalling its origin and sensible of this wished to be joined to us again and part of us. For it is said [892] that these stalwart Sienese came of the people of France who in Gaulish days were known as the Senones, which we today retain in the name Sens. Further they still have a French temperament, for they are hotheaded, lively, quick and eager, as we are. The ladies, likewise, exhibit all the gentle and gracious and intimate qualities of the French.

In an old chronicle which I have quoted elsewhere[893] I have read that King Charles VIII, on the occasion of his visit to Naples passed through Siena, and was there welcomed with so magnificent and triumphant an entry into the city that it surpassed all other welcomes that he had in the whole of Italy. The welcome went so far as the greatest mark of honour and submission to him all the gates of the city were lifted off their hinges and laid down and so remained, the city open and free to all who chose to come or go for the length of his stay, and were only put back after he had gone. I leave it to you to imagine if the King, all his court and his army did not have good reason to love and honour Siena (as indeed they had always done and say everything possible good of it. The quarters accorded him and everybody were also very pleasing, and it was all any man's life was worth to show any disrespect, though nobody of any significance even wanted to. Oh, glorious Sienese, may you live long! Please God you may once again be ours in every sense, as you may well still be anyway in heart and soul, for the rule of the King of France is much more gentle than that of any Duke of Florence, and further, blood speaks true. And were we but neighbours, instead of being far apart, and combined together, who knows what we could not achieve?

The leading ladies of Pavia too, when besieged by King François, under the leadership of the Countess Hipolita de Malespina, their general,[894] also set to work carrying the hod, shovelling soil and repairing the ramparts, a real challenge to the soldiery.

A similar deed to that of these ladies of Siena which I have just related I saw some of the ladies of Rochelle accomplish during the siege of their city. As I recall, on the first Sunday of Lent,[895] during that siege, our Lord General[896] sent to summon Lord de La Noue to parley and come and discuss things with him[897] and report on the negotiations with which he was charged by the city. The story of it all is lengthy and strange, and I hope to set it down elsewhere. Lord de la Noue did not fail to respond, while Lord de Strozze was delivered to the city as hostage for him,[898] and there was a truce for that day and the following. The moment the truce was concluded, just as quickly as we could emerge from our entrenchments, a great crowd of the citizens of la Rochelle appeared on the ramparts and what was more, with them were about a hundred ladies, including some of the leading citizens' wives, most wealthy and most lovely. They were all dressed in white, from head to foot, all in fine white Holland, a pretty sight, and they were dressed so because of the strengthening of the city ramparts on which they toiled, shovelling earth and carrying it in hods, for other clothing would have been soiled, but these white garments could all be laundered in lye-water. They also stood out so much more from the others in those white garments. We were most ravished at the sight of those lovely ladies, and I can assure you that many men found more pleasure in this than anything else, the ladies too wanted to show themselves to us, and were not stingy about the sight either, for with lovely grace of movement they set themselves on the edge of the ramparts, very well worth the watching and desiring. We were very curious to know exactly who they all were, and were told that they were a company of ladies who had sworn on oath and thus banded together sworn to work on the fortifications and do their city this service, as they certainly did, to the point indeed that the more virile and robust among them also carried weapons. Indeed, I have been told that there was one who, having more than once repulsed her enemies with a pike, now cherishes that weapon as a sacred relic, and would not give it up, nor even sell it for a large sum of money, so dearly does she hold it.

I have heard some old Rhodes commanders relate, (and have myself read too in an old book)[899] that when Rhodes was beseiged by the Sultan Suleiman, the lovely girls and ladies of the city did not spare their exquisite complexions or their tender, delicate bodies, but bore a goodly share of the toils and labours of the siege, to the point of aiding the defence against the more fierce and menacing attacks, courageously assisting the knights and soldiers to hold out. Oh, fair ladies of Rhodes, your name and your fame have never faded and you never deserved to come under the dominion of barbarians!

In the time of King François I the city of St Riquier in Picardy was beset and attacked[900] by a Flemish noble named Dorin, one of Lord de Ru's standard-bearers, accompanied by one hundred armed, mounted men and two thousand foot soldiers, with some artillery. In the city there were no more than one hundred foot soldiers, which was very little. And the city would have been taken, had it not been that the ladies of the town appeared on the walls, armed too with boiling oil and boiling water and rocks and bravely repulsed their enemies, though these did all they could to break in. What is more, two of these ladies captured two standards from the attackers and bore them away with them from the ramparts into the city. In the end the assailants were obliged to withdraw from the breach which they had made in the ramparts and retire and eventually depart altogether, a victory which became famous throughout France, Flanders and Burgundy. Some time later, when King François came that way, he wanted to see those ladies, and praised and thanked them.

The ladies of Peronne did the same when that town was besieged by the Count of Nassau,[901] who aided the brave soldiers inside in just the same way and were much respected, praised and thanked by their King for it.

The women of Sancerre in the recent civil wars and the siege of the town were distinguished and praised for the fine deeds which they accomplished in all manner of ways.

During the recent wars of the League, the ladies of Vitré served their town in the same way when besieged by Lord de Mercoeur. The ladies of Vitré are very lovely and at any time always very finely dressed, yet they did not spare their beauty, but showed themselves to be virile and brave. And there is no question but that such great-hearted, manly acts, in such a cause, are as much to be valued in women as in men.

Just the same too were the charming ladies of Carthage in olden times. When they saw their husbands, brothers, fathers, and other relatives and soldiers cease firing at their enemies through lack of cords to their bows, these having all been worn out by so much firing throughout a long siege, the stocks of hemp, linen, flax, even silk, or anything else to make new ones having run out, conceived the idea, merciless to the crown of their beauty, of cutting off their lovely tresses of their own fair hair, and with their own hands, white and delicate as they were, spinning new bowstrings and supplying their fighting men, and you may imagine with what new vigour and courage the men could now bend their bows and shoot and fight, wielding such lovely tokens of their womenfolk.

We have read in the history of Naples[902] that that great military leader Sforza,[903] under the rule of Queen Jeanne II, when captured by the husband of the Queen, Jacques,[904] and put in close confinement, would doubtless have been decapitated, had his sister Marguerite not taken up arms and gone to war, and she did so well, all by herself, that she captured four of the leading Neapolitan nobles, then sent a message to the King that whatever he did to her brother she would do to them. So that he was forced to give in and let her brother go, safe and sound.[905] Oh, brave, great-hearted sister, hardly typical of her sex!

I have in mind certain sisters and female relations who, had they done something of the sort some time ago, might have saved a brave brother of theirs, who was lost for want of such aid and assistance as that.

Now I would like to leave these ladies of war-like, great-hearted prompting. Let us instead turn to some special examples, and for the finest specimen of the ancient world I can think of none other but Zenobia,[906] to represent them all. After her husband's death she saw no sense, like many, in wasting time on weeping and regrets, but devoted herself to securing the empire in the name of her children and making war on the Emperor Aurelian, who was then ruling, and the Romans, and gave them much trouble for eight years, till, going into the field of battle against him, she was conquered and taken prisoner and brought before him. When she was asked how she had dared make war on an emperor, her only reply was: 'Now I really do know you are the Emperor, be cause you have defeated me,' while he was so delighted to have done so and felt so uplifted by it, that he decided to make it a Roman triumph. With very great pomp and magnificence he had Zenobia march through the city in front of his trimuphant chariot, very grandly attired and decorated with such great wealth of pearls and precious stones, with heavy ornaments and golden chains, that they hampered movements, fettering her feet and her hands. This was done to mark that he brought her to Rome a captive and a slave. And so great was the weight of all her jewellery and those chains that she bore that more than once in the course of the progress she was obliged to halt, to rest. Unquestionably this was a great and marvellous event, since though conquered and made prisoner it was she who now dictated to the triumphing conqueror, making him pause and wait till she had got her breath! It was also great and estimable courtesy on the Emperor's part to let her have this pause and rest, bearing with her weakness, and not forcing her to hurry and drive herself on more than she could, so that one does not quite know what to praise the more, the decency of the Emperor, or the Queen's behaviour, for she may well have been deliberately acting a part, and was not so much tired or worn out as desirous of some show of greatness, to demonstrate to the world that even in the twilight of her good fortune she was going to gather in some harvest, as she had in its morning, thus making the great Emperor grant her this much by waiting for her slow, solemn progress. She secured great attention and admiration, both from the men and the ladies, some of whom would have given much to be like her, for, according to what those who wrote about her tell us, she was one of the loveliest of women. She was of handsome, tall, robust stature, with a very fine carriage, and graceful and dignified withal, and also had a very handsome and most pleasing countenance, with very bright black eyes. Among other fine points, those who describe her give her very fine, white teeth and a lively intelligence. She was very modest, sincere and gracious when needed, of fine speech, her voice clear, for she had regularly issued orders to her soldiers and frequently harangued them. I certainly think she must have been a pretty sight indeed, finely and superbly attired in her feminine robes, not her martial uniform, for when dressed all in white the sex always shows to advantage. It is to be presumed therefrom that the Emperor expressly did not wish to display her in his triumph otherwise than in her lovely feminine form, which would the better set her off and by reason of her perfections and her beauty make her a more pleasing sight for the crowds. Further, since she was so lovely, it is to be presumed that the Emperor had already sampled her, had enjoyment of her and was still having it, so that if he had conquered her in one sense of the word, he (or she, for both are true,) had also conquered in the other sense too. What astonished me is that since this Zenobia was so lovely, the Emperor did not take her and keep her as one of his courtesans, or that with his permission or that of the Senate she did not open an establishment for love or whoredom, as Flora did, by the labours of her body and shaking of her bed to get rich and accumulate great property and means, for to that establishment would have come all the greatest men of Rome to the envy of all others, for after all, so it seems to me, there is no satisfaction or delight to be compared with treading royalty and leadership and having one's enjoyment of a lovely queen, princess or peeress. I refer you to men who have done such things and achieved such lovely needs. Further, in that way this Queen Zenobia would have become wealthy by the purses of those great men, as did Flora, who would accept none but the great in her establishment.[907] Would it not have been better for Zenobia to have led such a life, in luxury, magnificence, profit and renown, than to sink to the want and misery to which she did, for she would have had to earn a starvation living by spinning together with common women, had not the Senate, in view of her former greatness, at last taken pity on her and appointed a small pension together with the grant of some small properties in land and other holdings, known for a long time as the Zenobian holdings. For there is no gainsaying it, poverty is a great evil, and anybody who can in any way whatsoever avoid it does well, as a man I know once declared. You see here how Zenobia failed to continue as courageous at the end of her career as she should, and that one should always persist in whatever one does. It is said that she had had a triumphal chariot built, the most magnificent ever seen in Rome, and in the days when she was really prosperous used to boast and say that this was for her Roman triumph, so overweeningly did she think she would conquer the Rome Empire. But all these plans went wrong, for when the Emperor defeated her, he took that chariot for himself and he it was rode in triumph in it, while she trudged on foot, so that he made more of a spectacle and triumph of her than if he had conquered a powerful King. Then say that the victory one gains over a lady, however achieved, is not great and very dazzling!

Similarly Augustus wanted to triumph over Cleopatra, but he did not manage it well. She forestalled him[908] in the way that Paulus Aemilius meant when he answered Persaeus, who when captive begged for mercy, to which Paulus Aemilius said Persaeus should have arranged for that in advance, meaning that he should have committed suicide.

I have been told that the late King Henry II never wanted anything so much as to make the Queen of Hungary[909] prisoner, not to treat her badly, though by all the razing to the ground of buildings in France she had given him good reason, but to have the glory of holding that great Queen prisoner and seeing how she would bear herself in captivity, if she would be as bold and haughty then as at the head of her armies. For, after all, there is nothing so superb or bold as a lovely, fine, great lady, when she wants and has courage, as that lady had, taking great pleasure in the name the Spanish soldiers had given her, for just as they called the Emperor her brother 'the father of his soldiers,' so they called her *la madre,* just as Victoria, or Victorina,[910] formerly, in the days of the Romans, was called the *Camp Mother* by the forces. There is no question about it, if an eminent and lovely lady undertakes a military responsibility, she brings a great deal to it, and stimulates the men greatly, just as in our civil wars I saw the Queen Mother,[911] who very frequently visited the forces, and encouraged them and gave them great confidence, or as today her grand-daughter, the Infanta Isabella,[912] does in Flanders, heading the army, showing her soldiers a valorous figure, so that without her and her lovely pleasing presence, Flanders, so everybody says, would never hold. And her aunt, the Queen of Hungary, never was her match in beauty, valour, great-heartedness or charms.

In our histories of France[913] we read how much the mere presence of the great-hearted Countess de Montfort[914] meant when she was in the siege of Hannebont,[915] for though her soldiers were courageous and valorous and had fought and come through many an attack and done so well as any in the world, they were beginning to lose heart and to want to surrender. But she addressed them so effectively and encouraged them with such fine, courageous words that they hung on, waiting for the longed-for assistance, which did arrive, in the nick of time, and relieve the city. Indeed, she did better, for when her enemies were engaged in an attack and she saw that their tents were all empty she mounted her charger and with fifty other good riders made a sally and brought such panic and fire into the enemy camp, that Charles de Blois thought he had been betrayed and called off the attack at once. About this I will tell the following little tale :

During the recent League wars the late Duke de Condé, who died quite recently,[916] sent to require of Lady de Bourdeille,[917] then a widow of forty years of age and very lovely, six or seven of the richer men of her land, who had withdrawn by her side in her castle at Mathas.[918] She rejected the demand outright, and said she was never a traitor and would not give up those poor men who had taken refuge with her. He sent a final message that if she did not give them up he would teach her to obey him. She replied (for I was with her, to support her) that since he did not know how to obey she would find it very strange if he thought to teach others, but when he obeyed his King, she would obey him, but otherwise, however much he might threaten, she was afraid neither of his guns or his investment, she was descended from the Countess de Montfort,[919] from whom her family had inherited that place, as she had her courage, and she was determined to hold the castle so stoutly that he would never take it, she would make her name as renowned there as her ancestress, the Countess, had hers at

Hannebont.[920] The Duke pondered this reply for some time, and for some days did not utter any more threats. However, had he not been killed, he would have attacked the castle, though she was ready, in heart and resolve and men and everything else, to give him a warm reception and I think he might have been put to shame.

In his book *On War*,[921] Machiavelli relates that Catherine, Countess of Forli, was besieged in her castle by Cesare Borgia, assisted by the French army, and though in the end defeated, resisted valiantly. The cause of that loss was that this place was too well furnished with keeps and strong places into which the men could retire, so that when Borgia invested it, Jean de Casala, whom the Countess had taken to support her and be in command, left the breach and withdrew with his men into a keep, a fault which enabled Borgia to take the place. And our author tells us that by this a great disservice was done the great-hearted pluck and the reputation of that brave Countess, who had been standing out against an army which the King of Naples and Duke of Milan had not dared withstand. But though the issue was unfortunate, she nevertheless emerged with the flying colours she deserved, and was the subject of many songs and poems in Italy in praise of her. This is a passage which is worthy of study by any who engage in fortifying houses and think of building a large number of keeps, castles, bastions and other strong points.

To return to our subject, in past times we have had many princesses and great ladies in our country who have given fine proof of their prowess, as did Paula, daughter of the Count de Penthievre,[922] who was besieged at Roye[923] by the Count de Charollois,[924] and there showed herself to be so courageous and great-hearted that when the town had fallen, the Count accorded her all the honours of war, and had her taken to Compiègne under strong guard, to be sure that she came to no harm, and honoured her greatly for her valour, and was also very furious against her husband, whom he charged with having wanted to encompass her death by charms with figurines and candles and sorcery.

Richilda, the only daughter and heir of Mons in Hainault,

wife of Baudouin VI, Count of Flanders,[925] did all she could against her brother-in-law, Robert le Frison, appointed guardian of Flanders' children, to rob him of the charge and acquire it, which she tried to achieve with the aid of Philippe, King of France,[926] and risked two battles. In the first[927] she was captured, as was also her enemy Robert, after which they were exchanged, when she ventured the second engagement, in which she also failed, and was routed as far as Mons, losing her son Arnulphe[928] in the battle.

Isabelle of France,[929] daughter of King Philippe le Bel and wife of King Edward II, Duke of Guyenne, fell into the bad books of her husband the King by reason of the malicious reports of Hugh Spencer,[930] and was thus compelled to retire to France with her son Edward.[931] Later she went back to England with her relation Baron Hainault[932] and an army which she led there,[933] by which means she took her husband prisoner, delivering him into the hands of those who were to bring him to an ill end,[934] which she herself was also fated to know, when because of her love-making with Lord Mortimer[935] she was imprisoned in a castle by her son, dying in captivity.[936] She it was who gave the English cause without reason to quarrel with France. Yet what lack of gratitude it was in a son thus to forget a great boon and for so small a matter treat his mother so! I call it a small matter because it was so natural a thing to do, and since it was unfortunate too, for having lived with soldiers (and she had indeed been used to living a man's life with them in the field, in tents and hutments,) she could not help some day doing the same behind the bed-curtains, as one so often sees.

I would take as example our Queen Leonora, Duchess of Guyenne,[937] who accompanied her husband the King[938] overseas, in the holy war.[939] By having so much dealing with military men and soldiers she in the end became too careless of her honour, till she had dealings with the Saracens,[940] on account of which the King repudiated her,[941] which cost us a great deal.[942] You may well suppose that she became curious to know whether her boon companions were as great champions when hidden from the eye as they were in the open field, though it is also possible that by temperament she liked doughty men, one form of valour attracting the other,[943] just as with virtue, for it was an eternal truth that was pronounced when it said that virtue is like thunder, it penetrates anything.

This Queen Leonora was not the only one in that crusade who accompanied the King her husband,[944] for before her, with her and after her there have been several other princesses and great ladies who have donned the crusaders' cross, but not on their legs, which they opened and straddled very wide, so that some stayed out there altogether and others came back very great strumpets, for, with such a multitude of men under arms, under cover of visiting the Holy Sepulchre they carried on a great trade of love-making, since, as I have said before, arms and love fit well together, both activities having much in common, much similarity of mood.

Such ladies however, are nonetheless worthy of our respect for loving the men and treating them as they do, not as the Amazons of old did, who, for all that they called themselves daughters of Venus, broke away from their husbands, declaring marriage to be real slavery, though they were always eager enough with other men, in order to beget daughters, for male children they had put to death.

Jean Nauclerus[945] in his *Cosmography*[946] tells us that in 1123 A.D., after the death of Libussa, Queen of Bohemia, who had the city of Prague enclosed in walls, and greatly abhorred the dominion of men, there was one of her maids-of-honour who had great courage. Vlaska was her name, and she so inspired the girls and ladies of the country and instilled them with the ideal of liberty and disgusted them so greatly with male dominion, that each of them killed her husband or brother or parent or a neighbour, so that in no time they were the mistresses of the country. Then, taking the men's weapons, they made such good use of them and became as bold and dexterous as the Amazons were, and won many victories. But later, by the negotiations and subtleties of one Prvislav,[1] the husband of Libussa, a man whom she had raised from the class of vil-

[1] The legendary husband of Libussa, whom Brantôme miscalls Thibusse, was not really Prvislav but Premysl. The name of the Queen herself and her maid-of-honour I venture to correct.—A.B.

lein, they were defeated and put to death. This was divine punishment for the enormity of that act which they committed by thus losing human nature. These ladies might well have shown how brave they were by some other courageous, virile acts, not by such cruelty, as we have seen in so many Empresses, Queens and other princesses and great ladies, by acts of nobility in the government and administration of their lands, and by other works, of which history offers examples enough, without my telling of them, for the ambition to dominate, reign and rule is planted in women's souls as much as in those of the men, and they are just as greedy for power.

I will however now mention one who was not so tainted, that was Victoria Colonna, wife of the Marquis de Pescayre.[947] I read a Spanish book[948] about her which said that when the Marquis heard the fine offer of the King of Naples made him by Hieronymus Mouron[949] on behalf of the Pope (as I have already related) if he would enter into an alliance with him, she, learning of it from her husband himself (who did not hide any of even his most private business affairs from her, neither great nor small) wrote to him (being very outspoken) and said he should remember the valour and virtue she had always shown, and that he himself had given it great praise and such renown that she was greater in glory and fortune than the greatest Kings on earth, and she wound up by saying that honour was gained 'not by the greatness of Kingdoms or great estates, nor by lofty, fine-sounding titles, but by unblemished faith and limpid virtue, and such honour would be ever praised and go down to our descendants, but there was no rank so lofty that it could not be conquered or ruined by the betrayal committed when faith was broken, and that for reasons of his love of faith she had no desire to be the wife of a King, merely that of a military leader who not only in battle, by his valorous hand, but in peacetime too by his great honour and unvanquished spirit, was able to conquer kings, great princes and military leaders and triumph over them and rule them.' That woman spoke with great courage and virtue, and truth and all, for it is very wretched to rule by vice, but to defy kingdoms and monarchs by virtue is glorious.

Fulvia, wife of P. Claudius (and in second marriage of Mark Antony) showed little interest in domestic affairs, but applied herself to great things, to handling state business, till she was said to rule emperors. Thus Cleopatra had reason to be very grateful to her and obliged to her for having so well taught and disciplined Mark Antony to obey and to submit to superior will.[950]

Of that great French prince Charles Martel we read that he never would assume or bear the title of King, which he might have done, but preferred to be a ruler and director of Kings.

Let us talk of some of our ladies. During the League wars we had Lady de Montpensier, sister of the late Duke de Guise.[951] She was a great statesman and quite considerably responsible, by her ingenuity and in person, for the building up of the alliance. Well, when this was on a firm footing at last, she was one day playing cards for forfeits (she was very fond of a game) when somebody remarked that she should shuffle the cards better, whereupon in front of a lot of people she said : 'I've shuffled them so well they couldn't be more shuffled nor will they ever be unshuffled again.' That would have been fine, had her people not lost their lives, though even those losses did not make her lose heart, she merely vowed vengeance. Indeed, when the news reached her, at Paris, instead of staying indoors weeping, like most women would have done, she left the mansion with her brother's children, and, holding them by the hand, walked through the streets, showing everybody her grief, stirring them up by her tears and moans and exhortations, all and sundry, to take up arms and rise in rage, and insult the dynasty and the image of the King, as people saw (and I hope to tell before I die) denying him any loyalty, but on the contrary swearing sheer rebellion, from which later the King's assassination followed,[952] regarding which one should be clear that it was those men and women who counselled it that were guilty of it. There is no question, the heart of a sister losing such brothers could not possibly have swallowed such a poison-ous draught without avenging the murder.

I have heard it related that after she had thus instigated the people of Paris to such hatred and insurrection, she set off to find the Prince of Parma and seek assistance from him to avenge the deed, travelling by such tremendous lengthy, post-horse relays that her coach was at last held up, the horses absolutely worn out, because of the mud in the depths of Picardy, unable to put one foot before the other and go forward or back, so worn out and exhausted were they. A very estimable noble of those parts who was of the reformed faith then happened to come that way and though she was well disguised, dressed differently and travelling under an assumed name, he recognized her, but, turning a blind eye to the steps that she had undertaken against men true to his faith and to her hatred for them, with the utmost courtesy addressed her and said : 'Madame I have no doubts about who you are. I am at your service. I see you are in poor condition. Do me the honour of coming to my house, which is near at hand, to dry your clothes and rest. I will provide you with the best I can. Have no fears, for though I am of the reformed faith, and you have so greatly detested us, I could not possibly leave you here without offering you the courtesy you certainly need.' She could not well reject such an offer, but gladly accepted. After he had fitted her out with all she needed, she resumed her journey, with this noble seeing her two leagues on the road, when she pressed on with her errand. And from what I have been told of that war, she recognized the courtesy of that noble by many return courtesies. There were many who were astonished that she should ever have trusted him, he being a Huguenot, but good gracious, necessity can do wonders, and seeing in him so estimable a man of such decent, frank address, she judged him likely to behave with decency.

When, after the death of her sons,[953] her mother,[954] Lady de Nemours, was taken prisoner, one need not ask whether she was not filled with anguish by such unbearable losses, to such point that, although by nature a lady of very gentle, even temperament, not to be roused up without very good reason, she uttered countless imprecations at the King's expense, cursing him roundly, (for what does one not say and threaten when in the throes of such loss and sorrow?) till she began commonly referring to the King as 'that tyrant'. Then, suddenly coming to herself again, she cried : 'Alas, what is that I said ? A tyrant ? No, no, I will not call him that, but kind and merciful monarch, if he brings death to me too, as well as to my children, and thus relieves me from my wretchedness and brings me to the blessing of the Almighty.' And then, silencing her cries and speech, as if thinking better of it, all she kept uttering was : 'Oh, my children, my children !' constantly repeating the words, with copious weeping such as would have softened a heart of stone. Alas, good reason indeed had she thus to lament and weep for them, for they were so fine, so kind-hearted, so virtuous and so valorous, and especially the great Duke de Guise, a true eldest son, a veritable paragon of the greatest value and nobility of heart. Indeed, she loved her children with such spontaneous love that when one day I had talk with a great lady of the court of the Duchess de Nemours, she told me that she was the most fortunate princess in the world, for many reasons which she gave, except the one thing, that she loved her sons far too much, for she had loved her children so intensely that the maternal apprehension on their account, lest ill befall them, had normally clouded her peace of mind, so she regularly lived in a state of unrest and anxiety, so you may imagine how deeply she felt the pangs, the bitternesses and the heart-stabbings which the death of those two sons caused, not to speak of her alarm for the safety of the other,[955] who was somewhere near Lyons, and the Duke de Nemours himself being a prisoner,[956] which was how she was not touched at all by her own imprisonment, or fear of death, as I have related.

When she was removed from the castle of Blois to be taken to that of Amboise, for stricter confinement, as she passed in through the doorway she looked up and turned her head towards the portrait of King Louis XII, her grandfather, in stone, mounted on a horse with fine martial grace, and paused a moment, gazing at it, then, with a lovely, self-confident expression on her face, which never left her said aloud to the many people gathered there : 'Were the man depicted there alive, he would never allow his grand-daughter to be thus

467

brought to this place, to be a prisoner, treated in this way. Then she continued on her way without another word. You may well imagine how she prayed inwardly to the shade of that great-hearted ancestor, to grant her just vengeance for her imprisonment, exactly as those who conspired the death of Caesar once did who, when on the way to commit the deed, turned to the statue of Pompey and in a low voice implored and invoked the shade of his power, once so great, to bring to a fortunate conclusion the enterprise they had undertaken. It may even be that in like manner the invocation of this Princess served to speed the death of the King[957] who had thus outraged her. A great-hearted lady who nurses vindictiveness is much to be feared.

I recall that when her late husband the Duke de Guise[958] received the wound which killed him, she happened at the time to be at his headquarters in the field, having come there to see him a few days previously. When he entered their apartment, wounded,[959] she met him at the door, distracted and tearful. Greeting him, she cried : 'Is it feasible that the wretch who did this and he who had it done' (no doubt thinking of the Admiral)[960] 'shall remain unpunished? God, if you are just, as you should be, avenge this ! . . . Otherwise . . .'

But before she could complete the sentence, her husband had taken her up and he said : 'Dear wife, do not use words which offend God ! If it is he who for my sins has brought me here, let his will be done, and his name be praised, while if the blow comes from another quarter, may revenge be reserved to God, for he will bring it about, without your aid.'

Nevertheless when he was gone, she pursued that revenge so ardently that the man who killed him was eventually torn apart by four horses,[961] while the man allegedly responsible for the doing of it was killed some years later,[962] as I hope to relate in the right place, all by reason of the instructions which she gave her son,[963] which I saw with my own eyes, and the advice and eggings on with which she fed him from early youth, till vengeance was accomplished.

The counsel and exhortations of wives and great-hearted mothers can do much in this, *à propos* of which I recall that when, touring his kingdom, King Charles IX came to Bordeaux, the Baron de Bournazel, a very fine, estimable noble, from Gascony, was imprisoned for having killed another noble of his own country, named La Tour, by great trickery, it is said. The widow strove with such energy to secure punishment that every effort was made to bring the news of her activity to the chamber of the King and Queen, for the proposal was to have him beheaded. The nobles and ladies were soon in a state of alarm and all worked hard to save his life, and the King and Queen were twice interceded with to grant a pardon, but each time the Chancellor[964] opposed it and claimed that justice should be done. The King was strongly for mercy, since he was young and would gladly have reprieved him, for de Bournazel was one of the court gallants, and Lord de Sypierre[965] too urged it strongly. Meanwhile the hour of execution drew near, with everybody aghast, when Lord de Nemours[966] intervened. He was fond of the poor baron, who had supported him valiantly in tough corners in the wars, and he flung himself on his knees before the Queen and pleaded with her to grant him the life of that poor noble, and beseeched her so eloquently that a reprieve was granted, when without delay a captain of the guard was sent for him, to get him out of prison, and arrived just as he was being taken to execution. Thus he was saved, but only after such mental agony as remained for ever stamped on his face, for though Lord de Bournazel made a good escape, he never recovered his former looks, as I both saw and also heard from Lord de St-Vallier.[967]

All this time however the widow was not idle, and the following day she went to the King just as he was going to Mass and flung herself at his feet, and held out to him her son, who may have been three or four years old and said : 'Sire, at least, if you reprieved the murderer of this boy's father, I beg you here and now to reprieve this boy for the act he will perform when he grows up and takes revenge and kills that miscreant.' After which, I have been told, every morning the mother wakened her boy and showed him the bloodstained shirt which his father had worn when killed and three times said to him : 'Look well at this and never forget when

469

you grow up to revenge it, or I shall disinherit you!' What hatred!

When I was in Spain[968] I heard the story told how Antonio Roque, one of the pluckiest, most valorous, keen, punctilious, able, celebrated and at the same time most chivalrous bandits there ever were in Spain (this is agreed upon) had first wanted to be a priest, but when the day came for him to conduct his first Mass, and he was just leaving the vestry and most gravely proceeding to the main altar of his church, in full vestments for the office, chalice in hand, as he passed her he heard his mother say: 'Oh, what a wretched, scurvy son you are, far better to have avenged your father's death, not sung Masses.' Those words touched him to the quick. He turned sternly back, though half-way to the altar, and went to the vestry, where he derobed, saying he had a heart attack and must post the service to another day. And he went straight off into the mountains, to join the brigands, and there became so famous and was so valued that he was made bandit chief. He committed many crimes and robberies and thus avenged the death of his father, who was said to have been killed by another man. The story was told me by none other than one of the bandits who had formerly been under his command, and he praised Roque to the fourth heaven and said that the Emperor Charles[969] never could touch him.

To come back to the Duchess de Nemours, the King did not long keep her imprisoned, and Lord d'Escars[970] was partly the cause of this, for it was he had her taken out and sent to Paris to Lords du Maine[971] and de Nemours[972] and other princes of the league to bear them words of peace and oblivion of the past— 'Let the dead bury the dead, let we be friends as we once were.' The King made her swear on oath to carry out this embassy. When she arrived there was nothing at first but weeping and laments and regrets for their loss, after which she delivered her message. Lord du Maine's reply was to ask her if she herself thus advised. All she replied was: 'My son, i have not come here to advise you, but only to give you the message I am charged to pass to you. It is for you to decide whether you are right or whether you should follow the suggestion of which I am the bearer. Your decision must come from your heart and your conscience. As for me, I have accomplished what I undertook to do.' But secretly she found good ways of stirring the fire, and it smouldered on for a long time after.

There were many people who were most surprised that the King, who was so wise, and one of the clever men of his kingdom, should have made use of this lady for such an embassy, since it must have outraged her and she would have been without heart or feeling had she really aided his cause the least in the world, and indeed she did make a fool of him. It was said that this was done by the fine counsel of the Marshal de Retz,[973] who once gave similar advice to King Charles,[974] to send Lord de La Noue to la Rochelle[975] to persuade the inhabitants to conclude peace and be obedient and dutiful subjects, going so far that, so this emissary might have their confidence, he allowed him to be hot and lively on their side and for their party, waging a war to the death and counselling them against the King, the only condition being that when ordered and summoned (by the King or his Lieutenant-General,[976] to come out[977] of La Rochelle, he should do so. Lord de la Noue did both the one and the other thing, he made war, and he came out, but in the meantime he had so encouraged those people of la Rochelle and so made them militant, taught them such good lessons and stirred them up so, that they could cock a snook at us. There were very many people who thought there was no cleverness at all in that. I saw it, and hope to describe it all elsewhere. But that was all de Retz was worth to his King and France, and people thought him more a cheat and deceiver than a good counsellor and marshal of France.

One more brief note on the Duchess de Nemours. I have been told that when the League was being formed and she saw the records and lists of the towns which had joined it, and noticed that Paris was not yet among them, she kept telling her son that this was no achievement, they must add Paris. 'And if you do not get Paris, you have achieved nothing, so see you get Paris!' And 'Paris!' was all you could hear her say, so that civil war was bound in due course to ensue.

There you see how a great heart always aims at the very summit, which reminds me of a little tale I read in a Spanish novel entitled *La Conquista de Navarra*,[978] The Conquest of Navarre. When that town had been seized from the King by King Jean[979] of Aragon,[980] King Louis XII sent an army there[981] under Lord de La Palice,[982] to reconquer it. By this lord the King[983] sent a message to Queen Donna Catherina,[984] to move to the court of France and there stay with his consort, Queen Anne,[985] while the King and Lord de La Palice made their attempt to recover the Kingdom. The Queen's hot-tempered reply was : 'What is this, sir? I thought your master the King had sent you to take me with you to my Kingdom and restore me in Pampeluna, and have me go with you, as I was resolved and ready to do, yet here you are inviting me to go and stay at the court of France. That is a sinister augury and poor hope for me. I see I shall never get back to my Kingdom.' And as she foresaw, so it was.[986]

When King Henry was on his death bed and there was little hope he might recover, the Duchess de Valentinois[987] was told this and ordered to retire to her Paris house and not come to his bedchamber again, both so as not to disturb him in his thoughts of God and on account of the hostility which some men felt for her. When she had obediently withdrawn to her house, somebody was sent to her for certain rings and jewels which belonged to the crown, and she was to give up. She at once asked the messenger if this meant that the King was dead. 'No, Madame,' the messenger said, 'but he cannot last long.' 'Well, so long as there is a spark of life in him,' she said, 'I would like my enemies to know that I do not fear them, and I shall not obey them so long as he is alive. I am still relentlessly courageous, while, when he does die, I myself shall have no desire to live and any bitterness they think then to cause me will be sweet in comparison with my loss. That being so, I have no fear of my enemies, whether the King is dead or not.'

In this that lady showed real greatness of heart. But, some will say, she did not die as she said. All the same, she did not fail to feel death very near more than once. Besides, it was better to want to live, than to have died, just to show her enemies that she had absolutely no fear of them and that though she had on many occasions seen them tremble and grovel before her, she was not going to do the same before them, but show herself so determined in bearing and at heart that they would never dare do her any displeasure. However, even better than this, in two years' time they sought her more than ever, and, as I saw, resumed friendly relations, which is the way among great men and women, whose friendships are little lasting and who like thieves at the fair easily patch up their differences, equally easily blowing to friendship or hatred, which we lesser folk do not do, for we either have to fight and avenge and die or end the state of war by clearly defined, well sifted and very formal agreements, which we find more satisfactory.

There is no question but that one must admire that lady for this feature, by which as a rule such great ladies when involved in affairs of State always go one better than the usual behaviour of ordinary people. That is why our last monarch, the late King Henry III, and the Queen his mother had no love for the ladies of their court who would so poke their noses into state business and concern themselves in it, liking to do it either for mere gossip or as really concerned about the state of the Kingdom, as if (said their Majesties) they themselves had some great interest in it or should also have inherited it. Their Majesties disliked it especially since it was not even as if they engaged the sweat of their bodies or used their hands, as the men did, to maintain it, but merely, at ease in their arm-chairs or on their cushions, or on their couches, or enjoying themselves and gossiping in an ingle-nook, would eternally spread themselves about the world and the realm of France, as if it was they who did everything. *A propos* of which there was one well-known lady, whom I shall not name, who had her say at the first Estates at Blois,[988] whereupon their Majesties uttered a sharp reprimand and said she had far better concern herself with her domestic affairs and her prayers, when she replied : 'In the days when Kings, princes and great lords donned the cross to go overseas and achieve great things in the Holy Land, admittedly we women were only permitted to

473

pray, tell our beads, make vows and fast, so God might give the men safe passage and safe return. But since today we see the men do no more than we ourselves, we have a right to talk about everything, for why indeed should we pray for them now, when they do no more than we do?'

There is no question about it, this was too boldly said, and this lady thought it was going to cost her dearly, and had great trouble getting the pardon and reconciliation which she had to beg, and were it not for a certain consideration which I could mention, she would have suffered a really condign punishment. There are times when it does not do to tell the truth the moment it is on the tip of one's tongue, as she did here, and I have known many ladies who failed to curb themselves, for they are more restive than any Barbary steed, and when they have a good mouthful ready to spill must spit it out, sparing neither relations nor friends nor the great. I have known many such temperaments at our courts, men and women, and we have a name for them: 'mouthful marquis' or 'mouthful marquise' we say, though as often as not they pay for it.

And now, having described the great-heartedness of some ladies in certain great deeds done by them, I would like to record some who have shown great-heartedness in their deaths. And without borrowing any examples from the ancient world, what better than that instance of the late Lady Regent of France, the mother of great King François?[989] In her time, as I have heard both men and women who saw and knew her relate, she was a very lovely person, and very noble-hearted too, even in her declining years. For this reason, whenever anybody mentioned death, she loathed the subject, even when priests spoke of it in their sermons. 'As if,' she once said, 'we did not know we all have to die some day, but, when they can think of nothing else to say in their sermons and in their ignorance have exhausted all they ever learnt these preachers will seize on death.' Her daughter, the late Queen of Navarre,[990] was no greater lover of such hymns or sermons than her mother.

So when she had come to her fated end, and lay in bed, three days before she died, she saw the night in her room as brightness, as if shining through the window, and scolded her women watching over her for making so bright and dazzling a light. They replied that there was only a very low glimmer and it was the moon that was shining in and giving the light, 'What nonsense!' she said, 'we are at the wane, it cannot light the room now.'

Then, having the curtains drawn, she saw a comet throwing its light straight on her bed. 'Oh!' she said, 'there is a sign which never appears for people of low quality. God brings it out for us great ones. Close the window. It is a comet, announcing my end, I must get ready.' And, the following morning, sending for her confessor, she accomplished the duty of a good Christian, although the doctors assured her she was not dying. 'Had I not see the sign of my death, I would believe what you say, for I do not feel so low,' she said, and then told them all of the appearance of her comet. Three days after that[991] she left this world's dreams, and passed on.

I cannot deny a conviction that great ladies, those who are lovely, young and estimable, are as a rule more loth to leave the world than other people are, and yet I propose to cite some who were not in the least concerned, but readily accepted death, even though at the first instant its annunciation was bitter and hateful to them.

The late Countess de la Rochefoucauld, of the Roye family,[992] in my opinion, as in that of others, one of the really lovely and charming women of France, when told by her minister (for, as everybody knows, she was of the reformed faith,) that she should think no more of this world, her hour had come, and she was now to leave the worldly concerns which were all nothing in comparison with the blessing of Heaven, and go to God, who was calling her, she said : 'That, Reverend sir, is a good thing to tell those who have no great satisfaction or delight in this world and already have one foot in the grave, but to me, in the green of my years and with all my delight in this world and my beauty, your sentence is very bitter, but yet although I have better reason to like to be in this world than in any other and to regret to die, I would show you my greatness of heart and assure you that I accept death willingly, as would the most vile, abject, low, ugly and aged woman there ever was.' And then, having with great piety sung some psalms, she passed away.

Lady d'Epernon, of the house of Candale,[993] was taken with such a sudden illness that in less than six or seven days she was carried off. Before dying, she tried every known means of cure, imploring God and men alike for aid, with very devout prayers, and all her friends, attendants and servants were also most vexed that she should come to die at so early an age. But when she had been told plainly that there was no question but that she was doomed, there was no remedy left to try : 'Is that true?' she said, 'then leave me to myself, I must face it and be resigned.' As she uttered those very words, she raised her lovely white arms and lay her hands together, then with open countenance and heart at peace lay back, ready to accept death patiently and with very Christian words leave the world which she now began to loathe, and died most piously, a good Christian, at the age of twenty-six, one of the lovely, charming ladies of her age.

It is said that it is not nice to praise one's own folk, but on the other hand truth that is comely should not be concealed, and that is why I propose here to praise Lady d'Aubeterre, a niece of mine, daughter of my eldest brother,[994] and those who saw her at the court or elsewhere will affirm with me that she was one of the most beautiful and gifted ladies one could ever have seen, both in body and soul. Her person plainly showed its true nature, by her comely, charming countenance, her figure, her grace and her fine bearing, and as for her soul, that was really heavenly, alive to everything. She was finely spoken, direct, without any over larding, the words flowing from her lips with great charm, whether on serious matters or in gay exchange. Never did I see a woman whom I found more like our French Queen Marguerite,[995] both in her outstanding features and in her bearing too. And so I once heard the Queen Mother[996] say. That is recommendation enough to render no other necessary, so I say nothing, and any who have seen her will I am sure not gainsay a word I have written, but praise her. She was suddenly attacked by an ailment which baffled the doctors, who could not make out what it was, though she thought she had been poisoned, I will not say by whom, though God avenges everything and so men may do so too. She did all she could to get cured, not that she was afraid, she said, of dying, for after the death of her husband[997] she had lost all fear of that, though he was in no way her equal, nor had deserved her, nor the lovely tears shed by her lovely eyes at his death. But yet she would much have liked to live a little longer for love of her daughter,[998] whom she left at a tender age, which was a fine, worthy motive for wanting to live, whereas her regrets for a foolish, aggravating husband were very vain and frivolous. So when she saw there was no means of recovery, and felt her pulse begin to weaken (she knew all about this,) two days before the end she sent for her daughter and enjoined her most beautifully and piously how to live her life, and I doubt if there could be a mother who would have put it to her more finely or beautifully, both how to conduct herself in this world and how to acquire the grace of God, after which she blessed her and ordered her not to fret any more with tears about the ease and rest she was now going to find with God. Then she asked for her glass, and, staring hard at herself, said : 'Oh, traitorous face, why has my sickness not changed you?' (For it showed her to be as lovely as ever). 'But soon Death, which is drawing near, will teach you and rot you and consume you with the worm!' She also put most of her rings on her fingers, and these she examined, hand and rings together, all so lovely, and said : 'See the worldly show I loved so much in days gone by, but now with good heart I leave, to make myself ready for ornament more lovely, in the other world.' And, seeing her sisters[999] weeping bitterly at her side, she consoled them and begged them to agree with her in this that it pleased God to send for her, as they had always loved one another so, they should not be sad at what now brought her joy and satisfaction, the love she had always felt for them would last in them for ever, and she begged them to love her in the same way and likewise her daughter. And seeing them weep still more copiously, she said further : 'My sisters, if you love me, why do you not rejoice with me in the exchange I am

477

making of a wretched existence for one that is very fortunate? Weary of so much labour, my soul craves to be released and be in its place of repose with Jesus Christ my Saviour, yet here you are wanting it to remain tied to this frail body which is its prison, not its real dwelling. So, dear sisters, I beg you, do not be sad any longer.' So many other fine, Christian things she said, that there is no great brain of the church that could utter finer. With which I pass on. But above all she wanted to see Lady de Bourdeille, her mother, whom she asked her sisters to fetch to her, pleading with them again and again : 'But, dear sisters, is Lady de Bourdeille never coming? Oh, how slow your messengers are ! They would not be much good to handle the mails.' In the end Lady de Bourdeille did come, but not to find her still alive, she had died one hour before.

She had also much asked for me, calling me her dear uncle, and sent us her farewell. She wanted her body opened up after her death, a thing she had always hated, in order, she told her sisters, that the cause of her death could be made more plain and it would be reason for them and her daughter too to look after themselves as they should, 'For,' she said, 'I must admit that I suspect that together with my Uncle de Branthôme and my sister the Countess de Durtal I was poisoned these five years since, but I took the bigger portion. Not indeed that I wish to accuse anybody, lest it be false and I have the accusation on my conscience, for I would rather my soul were clear of any reproach or bitterness, hatred or sin, so it may fly straight to God, who created it.' I would never end were I to relate all, for she spoke at such great length, not at all like what one would have expected of a debilitated body or an enfeebled, dying mind. At this point, a noble who was her neighbour (a great man for a joke, with whom she had always liked talking and backchatting) appeared. 'Ah, my dear friend,' she said to him, 'the close season's come for lip and wit, God's calling it all in.' Her doctor and her sisters wanted to have her take a restorative, but she begged them not to bring her any. 'Such things can't do any good now,' she said, 'only drag out my distress and keep me from my rest.' And she begged them to leave her, and was then frequently heard to say : 'Heavens,

478

how sweet dying is! Whoever would have thought it?' Then, gradually yielding her soul, she closed her eyes, without any of those ugly, frightful signs that death produces in some people. Lady de Bourdeille, her mother, was not very long in following her,[1000] for the grief which she felt for that estimable girl carried her off in eighteen months, after a seven months illness, during which she alternated between hope of recovery and despair, though at the very outset she had declared she would never come through it, and was not in the least afraid of death, and she never prayed for life or health but only for patience to bear her sickness, and in particular a gentle death, without pain or suffering. Which was granted her, for in a moment when we thought she had only fainted, she rendered her soul to God, so gently that one did not see a single movement of feet, arms or legs, nor was there any ugly contortion of the face, she just turned up those eyes which were as lovely as ever and passed away, as beautiful dead as she ever was, when at her very best, she had been alive. There can be no question, it is a great pity when such as she and these other lovely ladies die so early, were it not that I believe that Heaven is not satisfied with the lovely torches which since the creation of the world embellish the vault, but in addition craves new stars to give light, as such ladies did with their lovely eyes when alive.

This is all of her, no more.

In recent days there was Lady de Balagny, in every way a true sister of brave de Bussy.[1001] When Cambrai was besieged,[1002] she did all she could there, with her stout, noble heart, to prevent its seizure. But after making every effort with every kind of defence she could try, when she saw it was the end and that the town was in the grip of the enemy and the citadel was also going to fall, she was unable to bear the pain of leaving her principality (for her husband and she had themselves called the Prince and Princess of Cambrai, a title which many nations held to be detestable and much too arrogant, since they were mere nobles) she passed away, dying of grief in the place of honour. Some say she committed suicide, and declared it was an act more pagan than Christian, but even so one has to

479

praise the great-heartedness of it and also the remonstrance she made to her husband when she came to the end, for she said to him : 'Balagny, what is there left for you to live for after your wretched downfall, but merely to serve as laughing stock and spectacle for the world, which will point the finger of scorn at you, for falling, after having risen so high from such great estate, to the low condition which I see awaits you unless you do what I am doing. Learn then from me how to die well and not survive your misfortune and disgrace.'

It is a rare instance indeed when a woman teaches us how to live and die. But de Balagny refused to think so, or agree, for seven or eight months later, forgetting the memory of that bold woman, he married again, taking Lady de Monceaux's[1003] sister as wife, who was indeed a lovely, estimable girl, and thereby showing many people that after all the only thing to do is to live, however one achieves it.

No doubt about it, life is sweet and good, but a great-hearted death is also much to be praised, like that of this lady who, dying thus from depression, was the opposite in nature of some ladies, for woman's nature may be said to be the opposite of that of men, for they die from delight to delight.

I will cite merely the following story of the elder Limeuil girl,[1004] who died at court. She was one of the Queen's maids-of-honour. During the illness from which she died, her tongue never stopped working, she talked all the time, for she was a terrible talker, with a spicy wit, always ready with stories, and very much to the point too, and was also lovely. When the hour for her death came, she called in her gentleman-in-waiting (for maids-of-honour each have one to themselves), Julien was his name, and he played the violin very well. 'Julien,' she said, 'take your violin and play to me and keep on playing till you see I am dead (for I am dying), and play *The Defeat of the Swiss*,[1005] as well as you can, and when you get to the words *all is lost*[1006] in the song, play them over four or five times, as sadly as ever you can.' Which he did, with her accompanying him with her voice, and when they got to *all is lost* she sang the words twice, then, turning to the other side of the bed-head, said to her girl companions : 'Yes, no doubt about it, all is lost,' and she was gone, just like that. Now there was a glad and pleasant death for you! I had the story from two of her girl-comrades worthy of belief, who saw the drama played out.

If there are some women who die of delight or in delight, there are certainly men who have done the same, as we read of that great Pope Leo,[1007] who died of delight and gladness of heart when he saw us French chased right out of the state of Milan, he hated us so.

The late Lord Grand Prior of Lorraine once conceived the idea of sending two of his galleons on a voyage into the Levant under Captain Beaulieu, one of his lieutenants, of whom I speak elsewhere.[1008] Beaulieu very gladly undertook the charge, for he was a bold and valorous man. When he drew near the Archipelago, he came upon a large Venetian vessel which was heavily laden and heavily armed, and he began firing at it. But the Venetian ship returned a fierce fire and completely carried away two banks of men at the sweeps, together with Beaulieu's lieutenant, Captain Panier, i.e., Captain 'Grapeskep', a boon companion, who however just had time before he died to cry: 'So long, Skipper, the vintage is over.' That quip made his death so much the pleasanter. Beaulieu was then obliged to retire, for he could not possibly take that Venetian ship.

In the first year of Charles IX's reign, at the time of the July Edict,[1009] when the King was residing in the *Faubourg St Germain*, we saw a young pickpocket hanged there who had stolen six silver dishes from the kitchen of Prince de la Roche-sur-Yon.[1010] When he was on the steps, the condemned lad asked the executioner to allow him a moment to make a last statement, and then held forth, assuring the crowd that he was being wrongly hanged: 'For,' he said, 'I never stole from any poor person, beggar or ruffian, only from princes and great men who are all bigger thieves than we folk are and rob us every day, so it is really doing but right to take back from them what they have taken from us.' He also babbled a lot of other amusing nonsense that it would be superfluous to recount and would have gone on longer, had not the priest, who

481

had climbed the ladder with him, turned to the crowd and, when they noticed him, cried : 'Gentlemen, this poor victim claims your kind prayers, we will all say a *Pater noster* and an *Ave Maria* for him and his soul, and then sing a *Salve*. And will the crowd please join in with the responses !' The fellow he called *this poor victim* shot the priest a glance, lowered his head, bellowed insultingly like a calf, to make fun of the priest, though very amusingly, then gave the priest a kick and sent him flying down to the ground off the steps, with so bad a fall that he broke a leg. 'Oh, Mr. Priest, by God !" the condemned man cried, 'I was sure I could push you off there ! Oh, and he's had it, too, the scoundrel !' And, hearing the priest's cries of pain, he roared with laughter, then himself leapt into the wind. I do assure you that the King's court had a really good laugh at that one, though the poor priest did come off rather badly. Now there you had a death which was hardly dismal.

The late Lord d'Estampes[1011] had a fool named Colin, a very amusing fellow. When his death drew near, d'Estampes asked how Colin was doing. He was told : 'Poorly, my lord, he's going to die, he can't take anything.' 'Here,' said d'Estampes, who was at table at that moment, 'take him this potage and tell him that if he does not take something for the love of me, I shall never like him again, say I have heard he won't take anything.' The message was delivered to Colin, when the fool, who was on the very point of passing over, said : 'And who was it told my lord I would not take anything?' And then surrounded by a million flies as he was, (for it was in Summertime) he waved his hand about through them, as one sees pages and serving boys and other lads do, then, suddenly, with a little twist of the hand better drawn than described, grabbing a couple at once, said : 'Now tell my lord what I have just taken for love of him, say that anyway I am on my way to the Kingdom of flying things.' And, turning to the other side, the gallant fellow died.

A propos of this, I have heard some philosophers say that when it comes to dying some people tend to recall things they have most loved and each man, soldier, noble, huntsman, artisan, recall his own calling, and as they die, so say something about it. This has been observed and can often be seen.

Women too will say something in the same way, even the whores. I heard tell of a lady of rather fine quality who as she died exulted in babbling about her love affairs and all the pleasant and lewd things she had done. Indeed, she then told more than the world had ever known, though she had certainly been suspected of being very whorish. Perhaps what she said was only a dream, but it may have been the truth, which was not to be hidden, that brought her to speak so, or she may have wanted to unburden her conscience and repent, for there were some cases which she was most specific about, with such detailed comment that the whole thing was amply clear. 'Really,' somebody remarked, 'she must have found time heavy on her hands to choose this moment to sweep out so much that's disgraceful and all of one kind too.'

I have been told of a lady who was much given every night to dreaming, and who in her sleep would tell everything she had done during the day, so that in the end she quite disgraced herself in her husband's eyes, for he at last began to pay attention to all her delirious chatter, till he really took notice of her dreams and trances and then got very wroth with her.

It was not long ago that a well-known noble in a province which I will not name, as he was dying did the same and revealed all his love-affairs and debauchery, specifying the ladies and the unmarried girls with whom he had had dealings, and where and when they had met to do it, and how they did it too, confessing all of it loudly, begging the divine pardon in front of everybody. He did worse than the woman, for she only disgraced herself, whereas he disgraced quite a number of women. Fine gallants those, both male and female!

It is said that misers, men or women, have a tendency at their deaths to dream a lot about their hoards of money, and can never keep silent about them. About forty years ago a lady of Mortemar, one of the richest ladies of Poitou[1012] and the most miserly too, when she was on her death bed thought only of the crowns in her closet, and although she was ill got up twenty times a day to go and make sure the hoard was all right.

At last, getting very near the end, with the priest speaking earnestly to her about eternal life, she made no response, and the only thing she could say was : 'Give me my petticoat, give me my petticoat, the wretches are taking it away,' her only thought being to get up to go to her closet, and thus, struggling at all costs to get out of bed, the good lady passed out.

At the close I have got a bit varied on my original theme, but after morals and tragedy comes farce. With which I end.

NOTES

1. Fourth son of Henri II and Catherine de Medici. Born 1554, François, Count of le Perche, was granted the Duchy of Alençon in 1566, and when his brother the Duke of Anjou ascended the throne as Henri III, he followed him as Duke of Anjou.

2. François, who never reigned, since during the reign of Henri III he died suddenly of a haemorrhage. The favourite of François II, Charles IX and Henri III, he would otherwise have succeeded the latter.

3. His *Lives of Great Military Leaders*.

4. The future Henri IV.

5. The second Balafré, Henri I of Lorraine, Duke of Guise, who was to have been assassinated by Henri III's orders (1550-1588).

6. Brother of the above, Charles de Lorraine by name, who later became Duke of Mayenne and, when Balafré died, headed the League (1554-1611).

7. Alexander Farnese, Governor of the Low Countries and one of Philippe II's finest military leaders (1545-1592).

8. The *Illustrious Ladies*, part of Brantôme's compendious memoirs.

9. See Note 2.

10. Exaggerated praise for a prince all of whose schemes failed. Alençon-Anjou tried to seize the throne when Charles IX died. After this, by sacrificing his favourite, La Mole, he was restored to Henri III's good books. He then headed the Flemings who rebelled against Philippe II and in 1582 tried to secure recognition as sovereign of the Low Countries. He then went to England and courted Queen Elizabeth, after which he returned to the Low Countries, to be disavowed by his subjects. His traitorous character and his unfortunate physiognomy, marked by an enormous, pimply nose, earned him among other bouquets the following epigram :

> *Oh, Flemings, Nature no miracle discloses*
> *If François seems to have two noses,*
> *She was honest thus to grace*
> *A man with such a double face.*

11. In his *Lives of Great Military Leaders*.

12. The story told by Marguerite of Navarre—the 18th tale of her *Heptameron*. In this account, however, the 'loveliest lady in all the land', after having had her love go to bed with her 'without requiring more of her than talk and kissing,' wonders whether she should not put him to other love tests before 'keeping her promise'.

13. If we are to believe Brantôme, 'it was usual in those days for protonotaries, even those of good family, scarcely to be literate, but to give themselves a good time'.

14. Almost certainly Bussy d'Amboise, lover of Françoise de Maridor, Countess of Montsoreau, stabbed to death by the Count before

her adulterous eyes on August 19th, 1579, after the Count had made her draw the gallant into a trap.

15. Cosmo I of Medici, first Grand-Duke of Tuscany (1519-1574), said to have poisoned his faithless wife, Eleonora of Toledo, after having had her lover done to death.

16. The lovely, clever Isabella (1542-1576), whom he had married to Paolo Orsini, Duke of Bracciano. One of her husband's bodyguard, Troilus Orsini by name, got her with child, then took refuge in France, but was tracked down there and assassinated. A few months after Cosmo of Medici's death Paolo enticed Isabella to his Cerreto estate and there on July 16th 1576 strangled her. Cf. Litta, *Medici,* Vol. IV, *tavola* xiv.

17. The Duchess of Bracciano had good reason to confide to her father confessor that Cosmo's love for his daughter had tended to exceed what should be permitted a father. It was about 1557, Vasari was busily painting the ceiling of one of the rooms of the Palazzo Vecchio—and was hidden by scaffolding—when he saw Isabella come in. It was midday and hot. Unaware that she was not alone, Isabella lay down on a divan and fell asleep. Cosmo then came in and saw his daughter. His lust stirred, he hastily closed all the doors. Immediately after Isabella cried out, but Vasari prudently took care neither to see nor to be seen, but pretended to be asleep, which was wise of him, for a moment later, Cosmo remembered that Vasari might be there and climbed up on to the scaffolding, dagger in hand. But, seeing Vasari apparently sound asleep, he slipped the weapon back into its sheath and concluded that Vasari did not know what had taken place.

18. René de Villequier, who killed his wife Françoise de la Marck, natural daughter of Lord de Montbazon, in open court at Poitiers, where Henri III was at the time, on September 1st 1577.

19. Henri III's *Journal* gives us to understand that he indeed ordered the complaisant husband to commit this murder, to avenge himself for something the young woman had said about him 'though he had had his unlawful pleasure of her a long time, by the intermediary of her husband, who was his pimp'.

20. With the same dagger he also slit the throat of a maidservant 'who was holding a mirror for him and helping him titivate.'

21. An epitaph of the time condemned both the victim and the murderer:

> *But let them be, such wives are better dead*
> *Who welcome other men into their bed,*
> *And it was meet for him to have to hand her*
> *What she got, who'd been her constant pander.*

Cf. L'Estoile: *Journal de Henri III,* September 1577.

22. Sampietro, husband of Vanina d'Ornano. Summoned to court after the murder, all he had to say was: 'What does it matter to France whether Pierre and his wife got on together or not?' And he was considered not to be guilty. Cf. Lalanne edition of Brantôme, Vol. VI, p. 214.

23. The Duke of Bracciano, husband of Isabella of Medici, cf. note 16.

24. Vittoria Accoramboni, whom he married after the death of Isabella, first having her husband done to death. Cf. Litta, *Orsini,* Vol. VII, *tavola* xxix.

25. Paul de Stuer de Caussade, Count of Saint Mégrin, one of Henri III's favourites and first Gentleman of the Bedchamber to that King. He was killed leaving the Louvre, by Henri de Guise—le Balafré's man, for having seduced his wife, Catherine de Cleves (1578). Of this the King of Navarre (Henri IV to be) said: 'I think the Duke of Guise was quite right not to let a little bedchamber whipper-snapper like Saint Mégrin cuckold him. That's the way we ought to settle the hash of all the other little court gallants who think fit to approach ladies of the royal blood to dally with them.'

26. Coming from an old Neapolitan family which had originated in Spain, Dona Maria d'Avalos had married Charles Gesualdo, Prince of Venosa. She was a niece of the Alfonzo d'Avalos, Marquis of Pescara and Guasto, of whom Brantôme elsewhere remarks that he was such an effeminate creature that he even scented his horses' saddles.

27. It did not seem too lengthy to Anatole France, who relates it in his *Puits de Sainte-Claire.*

28. This is Ferdinand François d'Avalos, Marquis of Pescara (1489-1525), uncle of the Marquis mentioned in Note 26, one of Charles V's most able officers. His valour won the battle of Pavia for the imperial forces.

29. Françoise de Daillon, wife of Jacques de Rohan.

30. She was saved by a miracle in 1526, according to Jean Bourdigné's *Chronicle.*

31. Béroalde de Verville, in Chapter 58 of *Le Moyen de Parvenir,* ascribes a similar desire to the commandant of Compefiers, 'who wanted to be like three kinds of animal, namely, like a swan, which gets lovelier as it grows older, like a dog, whose sexual organ grows with the years, and like a stallion or a stag, which perform the act the more frequently as they grow older.'

32. No doubt this is a reference to the sister of the famous Count de Lautrec and Marshal de Foix. Françoise de Foix (1495-1537) was married at the age of twelve to the Count de Chateaubriand, of the house of Laval: 'she could do whatever she wished, says a memoir of 1606, and wished many things which she ought not to have done.'

33. Probably Philippe II, who had his wife Elisabeth de Valois, daughter of Henri II, suspecting she had committed adultery with the *Infante,* Don Carlos, who was his own son.

34. Gaillard Castle, not far from Andelys, is a feudal fortress built by Richard the Lion Heart, in 1197, commanding the Seine at that point. In 1314 Louis X the Stubborn imprisoned his wife, Marguerite of Burgundy, there. He suspected her of adultery, and she was strangled. Some years later Charles V 'the Handsome' had his wife Blanche of Burgundy put to death there 'cruelly' for the same reason.

35. In 1331 Gaston II de Foix persuaded Philippe VI of Valois to intern his own mother, Jeanne d'Artois there, for being very lascivious.

36. Henry VIII.

37. The charming, spirited Anne de Boulan, Boulem or Boleyn,

whom Henry VIII sent to the scaffold, charged with adultery—so he might marry Jane Seymour.

38. As we all know, Henry VIII had six wives in succession: sweet, resigned Catherine of Aragon, Anne Boleyn, then Jane Seymour, Anne of Cleves (with whose portrait he fell in love, but whom he repudiated as soon as he had had her), Catherine Howard (whom he had beheaded, like Anne Boleyn, because her virginity was not sufficiently beyond dispute) and finally that argumentative but cautious theologian, Catherine Parr, who had the good sense to allow her husband to convert her.

39. Here Brantôme has mixed up Baudoin II, who married Morphie, the daughter of the Prince of Melitena and who had had no previous wife, and Baudoin I, who one after another repudiated the daughter of the Prince of Armenia and Adela de Montferrat. See: Guillaume de Tyr, Book II, chapter xv.

40. Not a wise act. By it Louis VII the Younger lost Aquitaine, which his wife had brought him that very same year (1152). It now went to Henry II of England, whom she married.

41. Here Brantôme follows Suetonius *(Caesar VI)* who says: 'In place of Cornelia Caesar married Pompeia, daughter of Quintus Pompeius, whom he divorced later, on suspicion of her having had an adulterous liaison with Claudius. The story that he had smuggled himself into her room during a public ceremony had become so insistent that the Senate had decided to accept the allegation of sacrilege.'

42. Cicero made no such speech.

43. Brantôme repeats this story in another place (Works, Lalanne edition, Vol. VIII, p. 198) but without any more detail.

44. Cf. Suetonius, Caesar, LI: *Urbani, servate uxores; maechum calvum adducimus.*

45. Suetonius in Augustus, LXII, says that he divorced her because he was disgusted by the degree of her depravity.

46. All details taken from Suetonius, *Augustus* LXIX.

47. Fulvia, according to Sallustus—*Catilina*, XXIII, and *Augustus* XIX and LXV.

48. Taken from Suetonius, *Augustus.*

49. Taken from Suetonius, *Caligula,* XXV. Caligula's wife was named not Livia Hostilia, but Orestilla.

50. Taken from Suetonius, *Caligula,* XXV. The name should be Lollia Paulina, not Tullia Paulina.

51. Taken from Suetonius, *Claudius, XXVI.* This wife of Claudius's was named not Plantia Herculalina, but Urgulanilla.

52. Cf. Satires, VI, 115-132.

53. Allusion to an ancient statue found in a field near the Priory of Saint Martin, near Bordeaux, on July 21st, 1594, believed to represent Messalina. Transported on the Garonne in a sloop, which sank, during the following century, the piece of statuary disappeared for ever. It depicted a tall woman, with bare breasts and curled hair.

54. Brantôme is in error—he killed her. Cf. Suetonius, *Nero,* XXV.

55. Details taken from Suetonius, *Domitian,* III.

56. Taken from the *History of Augustus.*

57. *Ibid.*

58. Severus was no doubt thinking of the two Julias, daughter and grand-daughter respectively of the Emperor Augustus. Both were notorious for their excesses.

59. Ingeburge or Ingelburge (1176-1236), sister of Canute VI of Denmark, whom Philippe Auguste married in Amiens Cathedral on August 14th, 1193, to secure the alliance of the Danes against Richard the Lion Heart, but whom he repudiated twenty-eight days later, having discovered, so it is believed, that she suffered from a secret and displeasing infirmity. In 1196 he married Agnès de Méranie, but Pope Innocent III three years later excommunicated him, compelling him to leave Agnès and—in 1201—accept Ingeburge again.

60. Charles VIII repudiated his fiancée, Marguerite of Austria, daughter of the Arch-duke Maximillian, to marry Anne of Brittany in 1491. Louis XII repudiated his wife Jeanne, daughter of Louis XI, to marry the widow of Charles VIII, from fear of losing the Duchy of Brittany for France.

61. Philippe II, who had taken his niece Anne of Austria as his fourth wife, by whom he had a son in 1578—the future Philippe III, who reigned from 1598 to 1621.

62. Alphonse V 'the Magnanimous', King of Aragon, Naples and Sicily, who followed his father Ferdinand the Just in 1416 and died at Naples in 1458. A warm-hearted, enlightened, genial personality, he left a collection of maxims, assembled by Antonio de Palermo.

63. The story told in the 32nd story.

64. The Bernage mentioned, lord of the manor of Sivray, near Amboise, was Chief Groom to King Charles VIII. In 1495 he was in receipt of 300 *livres* per annum as emolument for this post.

65. In 1557.

66. According to Herodotus and Justinus (I, VIII, 12) it was not Semiramis, but Tamyris who plunged Cyrus's head into a skinful of blood and said: 'Drink your fill, you were always thirsty for it and never had enough.' Xenophon however tells us that Cyrus died a natural death.

67. Albert de Gondi, Marquis of Belle-Isle, Marshal of France. In 1565 he married Claude Catherine de Clermont, Baroness de Retz, and was made Duke de Retz by Henri III. He was said to have tried all Aretin's poses. His wife was pilloried in a pamphlet entitled *Madame de Montpensier's Library*.

68. This refers to Elephantis, a Greek woman author, who lived towards the close of the first century B.C., and wrote a number of works on the various fashions of making love. The most celebrated was quite frankly entitled *Katakliseis*.

69. Not only the 'great ladies and princesses,' but also the Emperor Tiberius, who according to Suetonius *(Tiberius,* XLIII) 'had in a number of places had rooms decorated with pictures and statuettes representing the most lascivious scenes and poses, and with the works of Elephantis at hand, so that when he demanded this or that position there was always a model at hand.'

70. Cyrene, Aristophanes' *dodekamikhanos,* or lady with the dozen variations.

71. Taken from Lampride: *Heliogabalus*.

72. Sixtus Quintus, Pope from 1585 to 1590. The Cardinal de Lorraine, du Perron and some others were similary depicted with Catherine de Medici, Marie Stuart and the Duchess of Guise, in two pictures mentioned in the *Légende du Cardinal de Lorraine*, folio 24, and in the *Réveille Martin des Français*, pp. 11 and 123.

73. Louis d'Este (1538-1586), son of Hercule II, Duke of Ferrara, and Renée of France, Archbishop of Auch, Cardinal in 1561 and Dutch uncle of Henri III. He is mentioned a number of times in Montaigne's *Travel Notebook* and Montluc's *Commentaries*.

74. This must be the Duke of Alençon.

75. This fable about lions and lionesses derives from an error of Aristotle's, which naturalists went on repeating till the eighteenth century.

76. Ode 2, Book VI.

77. The rich Florentine Louis di Ghiaceti (French: Adjacet) who had married a Lady d'Atrie. Buying the estate of Châteauvilain for 400,000 *livres*, he was made a Count. He was famous for his good luck and his escapades. It was he who had gowns made for three of his mistresses, with his secret mark on them and without their knowing it made them everybody's laughing stock for a whole evening. He died in 1593, at the hand of an officer, leaving behind him (according to Tallemant—Mongrédien edition, Vol. III, p. 88) 'affairs in disorder.'

78. *Orlando furioso*, Canto XLII, stanza 98:

> *Ecco un donzello a chi l'ufficio tocca*
> *Por sù la mensa un bel nappo d'or fino. . . .*

79. This pun Brantôme stole from Ariosto, Canto IX, stanza 27:

> *Credeano che da lor se fosse tolto*
> *Per gire a Roma, e gito era a Corneto.*

There is indeed a town near Rome which bears this name. It is near ancient Tarquinia.

80. Bernardin Turissan.

81. *La Somme de Benoît* is the work of a monk of Brittany named Jean Benoît. The full title is: *La Somme des péchés et les Remèdes d'iceux*, printed at Lyons by Charles Pesnot in 1584 (a quarto) and often reprinted since. Though he dedicated his book to the Virgin, he did not hesitate to pack it with filth and scurrility, just as the Jesuit, Sanchez, with his notorious treatise *De Matrimonio*.

82. Taken from Spartien—*Life of Commodus*.

83. Claude de Sanzay, who came of a Poitiers family which settled in Brittany.

84. He was the third of four brothers: René, Christophe being senior, to him, and Charles younger than he was.

85. Anne Ist de Montmorency, Constable, mortally wounded at the battle of Saint Denis in 1567.

86. René de Sanzay. Cf. Note 84.

87. Philippe Strozzi, Colonel General of the French infantry, later Lieutenant-General of the naval forces (1541-1582).

88. Among others, the story of Gyges' ring is related by Herodotus, (I, 8-13) and Cicero, *De officis*, Book III, Chapter IX. Further,

La Fontaine, remembering his Brantôme, drew from the incident what is one of his best stories : *King Candaule.*

89. Louis I of Orleans, the second son of Charles V (1371-1407), assassinated at the Barbette Gate of Paris, at the corner where the rue Vieille du Temple and the rue Barbette meet, by men posted there by Jean the Fearless, Duke of Burgundy.

90. Among other mistresses, this Louis I of Orleans had numbered Queen Isabeau of Bavaria, who was his sister-in-law. The lady in question here was Mariette d'Enghien, the wife of Aubert de Cany, mother, as stated later by Brantôme, of handsome Dunois, known as 'the Bastard of Orleans.'

91. Emmanuel Philibert, known as 'Iron Head' or the 'Prince with the Hundred Eyes'. He was tenth Duke of Savoy (1528-1580) and after the Peace of Cateau Cambrésis had married Marguerite of France, sister of Henri II.

92. Henri III.

93. Sainte Solonie, who deserted his general, Philippe Strozzi (Note 87) at the battle of the Iles Tercères.

94. Virgil, in the *Aeneid* (VI, 447) places this Evadne in hell, among the victims of love, in the company of Phaedra, Procris, Pasiphae, Laodamia and Dido. Ovid, Propertius and Statius also tell her story.

95. She was later brought back to Hell by Hercules.

96. This was the hero of the First Crusade, who died at Antioch in 1112. Just before he died he sent for his wife and young Pons, son of the Count of Tripoli, and counselled them to marry each other when he was gone. Cf. Guillaume de Tyr, Book XI.

97. Lovely, ambitious Mertrade de Montfort, wife of Foulques le Réchin, Count of Anjou and Touraine, who at the end of four years agreed to leave her husband and join Philip I, King of France, at Orleans, bearing him, among other children, Cécile, who married Tancrède.

98. Brantôme may have been thinking of Councillor Lavoix or Levoix, who slashed and disfigured his mistress, the wife of a lawyer named Boulanger, when she tried to break off with him, but was set free by the court which tried him—he had bribed the judges.

99. Blanche d'Auverbruckt, Viscountess of Arsy, becoming apprehensive lest her husband, Guillaume de Flavy, killed her, to inherit her estates the sooner—he had already done his parents-in-law to death in prison—had his throat slit by his barber. After this she fled with her lover, one Pierre de Louvain, Captain of a hundred lancers of the Royal garrison, and soon obtained letters of indemnity from Charles VII. In any case, Flavy had treated his wife very badly, as we learn from Matthieu de Coucy, the chronicler, who wrote : 'His wife being present, he often had in bed with him at the same time young wenches with whom he took his carnal pleasure and whenever his wife tried to raise objection would threaten to wall her up and kill her.'

The same Flavy is also said to have betrayed and sold Joan of Arc, as when she returned from a sortie against the English she found the gates of Compiègne closed against her, and Flavy was then governor of the town. But there is nothing to confirm this story.

100. Cf. *Annales d'Aquitaine, folio 140 verso*.

101. Jeanne de Montal, wife of Charles d'Aubusson, lord of the manor of la Borne, a rascally fellow who begot four children by the Prioress of Blessac, who was his mistress, and ended with his head cut off at the pillory, in Paris, February 23rd, 1533, for acts of brigandry in a number of convents in the district. Cf. Anselme, Vol. V, p. 335.

102. Cf. Brantôme, Lalanne edition. Vol. VIII, p. 148. It is not quite true notwithstanding our author, that Jeanne I, Queen of Naples, had her third husband, the Infanta of Majorca, Jacques d'Aragon, decapitated. On the other hand, their union was not a happy one, and in fear of suffering the fate of Jeanne's first husband, André d'Hongrie, who was strangled on the Queen's orders in Caserta Castle on September 18th, 1345, he fled to Spain, where he died in 1375.

103. The belief that a female ferret dies when on heat if she cannot find a male to satisfy her was still held by naturalists in the 18th century, even in the early 19th century. It seems to have arisen from the fact that the female ferret on heat does indeed put great energy into finding a partner.

104. It is the third story that is in question. 'The Queen of Naples found solace in the revenge which she had of her husband, King Alphonse, who did her wrong, with a noble whose wife the King had made his mistress, and this liaison lasted all their lives, without the King's even suspecting it.

105. Possibly Marguerite of France, the daughter of François I (1523-1574), the protector of Ronsard and Du Bellay. She finally married Emmanuel Philibert, Duke of Savoy, but not at the age of 45 —at 36.

106. The second day—the seventh story.

107. Bemynedab. He was however Sultan of Babylon, not Egypt.

108. No doubt the King of Algarva, the south-west part of Portugal.

109. Isabeau de la Tour d'Auvergne, Lady de Limeuil. It was during the visit of Charles IX to Lyons, in May, 1564, that this lady gave birth in the Queen-Mother's wardrobe. Some contemporary authors, mainly basing themselves on the *Confession de Sancy*, say that the child died at once, but in fact Isabeau sent the baby to the Prince 'in a basket of straw, like a young hunting pup,' the father admitted the paternity, the child was given to a wet nurse and survived. Cf. Champion: *Cathérine de Médici*, pp. 119-124.

110. The Rich Italian banker, Scipio Sardini.

111. This may have been Cosmo I, Duke of Tuscany, mentioned above. Cf. Note 17.

112. Ferdinand II, King of Naples, who had married his aunt, the sister of King Alphonse II, and daughter not of the King of Castille, but of Naples.

113. Cf. Suetonius: *Caligula*, XXIV. 'He maintained shameful relations with all his sisters.'

114. *Ibid*.

115. *Ibid*.

116. *Ibid*. Almost all these details are taken directly from Suetonius.

117. Suetonius: *Caligula*, XXV.

118. Suetonius, *Caligula*, LIX.

119. Similar practices by which the newly married feign virginity are given in Aretin's *Nanna,* in the chapter entitled *Married Women.*

120. Henri IV, the Impotent, who reigned over Castille 1454-1474. Brantôme drew this story from Baptista Fulgosius's collection, *Factorum et dictorum memorabilium libri;* book IX, chapter 3.

121. The consort of Henri IV. Jeanne de Portugal, by this commerce with a nobleman chosen by himself has a daughter, Jeanne of Castille, who never reigned, Castille preferring the King's sister, despite the fact that Henri had furnished himself with a certificate of virility given by a council of doctors.

122. He made him Duke of Albuquerque.

123. Probably an allusion to Jeanne de Tignonville who according to Agrippa d'Aubigné 'virtuously resisted the importunings of Henri IV (King of Navarre) being a maiden,' but became his mistress as soon as she was married—in 1581, to the Count of Pangeas, Chamberlain in Ordinary to the King and Governor of Armagnac, the one whom the King's sister, whose Lady in Waiting his wife was, on one occasion spoke of as 'that great buffalo Pangeas.' Cf. also the *Confession de Sancy,* Volume II, p. 128, in the *Journal d'Henri IV.*

124. Baudoin I, whose first wife was the daughter of the Prince of Armenia. Cf. above, p. 15 and Note 39.

125. Jean de Poitiers, Count of Saint Vallier, Captain of the Hundred Guards of François I, an accomplice of the traitorous de Bourbon and condemned to death, was indeed saved from the executioner's axe at the last moment, but not, as says the legend which Hugo included in *Le Roi s'Amuse,* because his daughter, lovely Diane de Poitiers, bought her father's life with her honour, but because his son-in-law, Louis de Brézé and Count de Maulévrier intervened in the nick of time.

126. The executioner had already in customary fashion asked the condemned man's forgiveness for killing him and was preparing to do his work when a clerk of the criminal court, Mathieu Dolet, rose and read out the King's letter commuting death to imprisonment. This was in February 1523.

127. The Order of St. Michael, created August 1st 1469 by Louis XI, was to have been limited to thirty-six knights of noble birth, but in successive reigns it fell into complete discredit, so many being added that, as Castelnau says in his *Mémoires* (I, p. 163), it came to be known as the *'collier à toutes bêtes,'* i.e. a collar made to fit any animal.

128. The Order consists of a cross bearing on oval medallion, showing St. Michael trampling the dragon underfoot.

129. The Duke of Etampes, Governor of Brittany and the complaisant husband.

130. François de Vivonne, lord of the manor of la Chastaigneraie, killed by Jarnac in a duel which was famous, and notorious himself both for his good luck and his biting sarcasm.

131. Whence Brantôme drew this obscure story is not known.

132. Marguerite de Valois, lavish with her body, regularly rewarded her men with such presents.

133. Henri III. Having had his pleasure of light Charlotte de la

Trémouille, who was the wife of the Huguenot leader, de Condé—Henri I de Bourbon—he palmed her off on to one of his pages. She was then said to have plotted her husband's death by poison with this young courtier. Certainly Condé did die in circumstances which give rise to suspicion, March 5th, 1588.

134. Marie de Clèves, daughter of François I, Duke of Nevers (1553-1574), the lady whom the poets of the time so enviously referred to as 'lovely Marie.' When she came to court, Henri III at once fell in love with her, and 'had first-fruit of her,' although she was affianced to her first cousin, Prince de Condé, whom indeed she married within two months (1572). This fair Huguenot was to renounce Calvinism on the eve of the St. Bartholemew's Day massacre and she died in childbed at the age of twenty, after giving birth to a daughter. The Charlotte de la Trémouille of the previous note followed her both as wife of Condé and mistress of the King.

135. Louis Bérenger du Guast was one of Henri III's favourites (1540-1575). He was killed by Baron de Vitteaux on the order of Marguerite de Valois—for having disclosed Marguerite's liaison with Bussy d'Amboise.

136. Charles d'Espinay (about 1530-1591), consecrated Bishop of Dol in 1558, was the author of a collection of love sonnets which scarcely befitted his episcopal position. These appeared in 1559. He was altogether a nobleman in the grand style and a great soldier, who when it was besieged, defended Dol most valiantly.

137. Agrippa d'Aubigné.

138. Brantôme forgot that d'Aubigné was wielded not only the pen, but also the sword.

139. See Note 136.

140. St. Mathurin was then reputed to cure madness and this was known as 'St. Mathurin's colic.'

141. Brantôme here recalls Spartien's—*Life of Hadrian*, but embroiders and embellishes to suit his own purpose.

142. Commodus came after the death of Faustina. Cf. Capitolin : *Life of Marcus Aurelius, xix.*

143. She was in fact merely sprinkled with it. Cf. Capitolin, l.c.

144. Marguerite de Valois and the Duchess of Nevers, whose 'serving men,' La Môle and Coconas, were leaders of a faction of 'malcontents' whose secret purpose it was to bring the Duke of Alençon to the throne when Charles IX at last died, were arrested and beheaded in the Place de Grève on April 30th, 1574, not, as Brantôme tries to convince us, 'killed fighting in battle.' The two mistresses were heartbroken. They took the bodies to burial in their coaches and had the heads embalmed—and preserved them. Cf. *Mémoires de Nevers*, I, p. 75. Alexandre Dumas the elder made good use of this dramatic event in his novel *Queen Margot.*

145. The same Philippe Strozzi as in Note 87.

146. Thomas de Foix, lord of the manor of L'Escu or Lescun, a brother of Lady de Chateaubriand, who was the mistress of François I, was made Marshal of France in 1515. It was he who when governor of Milan in the absence of his brother Lautrec was driven out of the province because of his excessive demands on it. Besieged in Cremona in 1522 (after losing the battle of the cocked-hat), he

signed a convention by which he undertook to withdraw from Lombardy if not relieved within forty days, and thereby lost all Italy for France. Finally, it was he who in 1525, died in the house of the lady of whom Brantôme speaks, after being mortally wounded by a shot in the abdomen.

147. The celebrated Gaston de Foix (1489-1522).

148. He had been given the soubriquet of The Thunderbolt of Italy.

149. Paul Jove (Italian Paolo Giovio)—1483-1552—wrote a great number of historical works notable for the elegance and purity of their language. Among them was the *Dialogo delle imprese militari ed amorose,* of which Brantôme speaks here. Cf. the edition of 1559, p. 13.

150. The well-known author of the *Commentaries,* Blaise de Montluc, who was with Brantôme in the siege of la Rochelle in 1573 and made Marshal of France the following year.

151. An allusion to a work of Joachim du Bellay's entitled *Counter Repentance.* One may compare *La Courtisanne repentie* and *La Vielle Courtisanne,* by the same author.

152. In his didactic poem *Remède d'amour.*

153. Rabelais, Book Three, Chapter ix.

154. Henri II.

155. The Saint Germain des Près fair, one of the most famous of olden Paris. Under Henri II it lasted from the beginning of Carnival week to Palm Sunday.

156. In the Print Room of the *Bibliothèque Nationale* there is a satirical print by Léonard Gautier entitled: *Of the Cuckold who carries the Key while his wife Keeps the Lock.* A woman seated on a bed is handing a man standing by her the key which locks a girdle of chastity, which she is wearing, while behind the bed-curtains we see another man, the lover, who is taking out his purse to pay for a duplicate key which a maid is handing him. There is a fool trying to keep some bees in a basket and a cat waiting for a mouse.

157. To all appearances it was indeed on the other side of the Alps that such obstacles were first devised. The innovation seems to go back to the middle ages, to a certain François de Carrara, provost of Padua, who in his anxiety to ensure his honour during frequent absences from home invented an iron device which went round his wife's middle and the whole of the lower part of her body. It was provided with a lock, and the husband always carried the key. De Brosses in his *Lettres sur l'Italie* (No. 16 in the Bézard edition) mentions seeing it and remarks: 'The lady must have had a deal of honour, for the lock is a devilish large one.'

As everyone knows, Rabelais makes Panurge say: 'Devil take me if I don't buckle my wife up in Bergamo fashion', and Diderot refers to this feminine device as the 'Florentine instrument.' In his *Mémoires* Count de Bonneval relates his love affair with a lady of Como who wore a belt of this sort.

158. Cf. Lampride: *Alexandre Sévère,* xxii.

159. Nicolas d'Estonteville, lord of the manor of Villeconnin, a Gentleman of the Bedchamber, who died in Constantinople, in February 1567.

160. Albert de Gondi, Marquis of Belle Isle, Marshal of France,

ambassador to Austria and England, who in 1565 married Claude Cathérine de Clermont, Baroness de Retz. He was made Duke of Retz and peer by Henri III, and died in 1603. He was the Great-uncle of the celebrated cardinal.

161. Charles de Téligny the Huguenot, son-in-law of Coligny and brother-in-law of La Noue, who was massacred on St. Bartholemew's Night.

162. Surname of the English theologian Duns Scotius, opponent of St. Thomas Aquinas and defender of 'realism' (1276-1308).

163. St. Lucia of Syracuse, who died a martyr's death in 304, whose acts are depicted in a fresco in the San Giorgio chapel at Padua, the work of Jacopo Avanzi, a fourteenth century painter. The principal events are : St. Lucia before the Governor of Syracuse, St. Lucia being dragged off to a House of Prostitution, the martyrdom of the saint and the exhibition of her body.

164. The celebrated Roman woman who was so upset when raped by Tarquin the Splendid (510 B.C.), that she committed suicide.

165. St Sabina did not commit suicide, as Brantôme avers, but died a martyr's death during the persecutions under Hadrian (2nd century). It would seem that he has got it all mixed between two saints, Sabina and Seraphia. According to the apocryphal Acts, the latter was an Antiochian virgin who lodged with a widow named Sabina at Vendinum. The prefect Beryllus sent for her then, in some games, handed her over to two debauched young Egyptians, but she was miraculously saved from them by a mysterious illness which carried them off. Having mocked the Prefect for his disappointment, she brought the young men back to life. Beryllus, however, had her tortured, then beheaded. Sabina gave her a funeral in the tomb prepared for herself—for which she too was beheaded.

166. Brantôme really means St Sophonia. The Christian wife of the Prefect of Rome, she was desired by the Emperor Maxentius, her husband stating his readiness for Maxentius to have her. She then went to her room on pretence of having preparations to make with ointment and so forth, and there ran herself on to a sword. She was however never canonized, which makes it possible for Brantôme to have confused her with Seraphia. Cf. Note 165.

167. This concerns the capture of Cyprus, then in Venetian hands, by the Sultan Selim, allied to the King of France, in 1571.

168. This Guillot le Songeur is the Don Guilanel Cuidador of *Amadis de Gaule.* It was a common phrase of the sixteenth century to speak of being or going or sending somebody to see Guillot the Dreamer. Note Rabelais, Book three, chapter xiii : Whereupon Panurge declared : 'Indeed I am at Guillot the dreamer's.'

169. There is no trace of this essay in Brantôme's works.

170. Henri III.

171. From the end of 1558 to December 1559.

172. Princess Danae, daughter of King Acrisios of Argos, was locked up by her father in a brazen tower, but Jupiter came in under the door, in the shape of golden rain, and coupled with her.

173. An allusion to Duke Henri of Guise, whose wife, Catherine de Clèves, had many a bed-partner besides Saint Mégrin.

174. Dion Cassius does indeed say that there was a 'love bond'

between Trajan's consort Plotina and her nephew Hadrian, but he does not say the attraction was a guilty one.

175. There were indeed two at least. One is the Square Mansion, the other is now no more than ruins.

176. A reference to his journey to Scotland to accompany Queen Mary Stuart, setting out from St Germain on July 25th, 1561.

177. Probably Catherine de Medici.

178. Mary Stuart.

179. David Rizzio, or Riccio, a guitarist of Turin, who, brought to Scotland by the French Ambassador, the Count of Moret, in 1564, won the Queen's favours, in spite of his ugly face and misshapen body, and was made her French secretary. His throat was eventually slit by Ruthven, on Darnley's orders, in the Queen's presence, in 1566!

180. Two Spanish *infantas*—Isabella Clara Eugenia (who later married Albert of Austria) and Catarina (who married Charles Emmanuel of Savoy in 1585)—both were daughters of Philippe II and Elisabeth.

181. Elisabeth's sister was Queen Marguerite of Navarre.

182. Two of the four brothers of this name—Joyeuse,—Anne Scipion, Knight of Malta, Grand Prior of Toulouse—1565-1592, and Henri, known in his youth as the Count of Bouchage. This was a very 'joyous' rascal. When his wife died, he took vows in a Capuchin monastery, but twelve years later left this, to put himself at the head of Catholic gangs which pillaged Languedoc. He submitted to Henri IV in exchange for a marshal's baton, and then became a monk again. He lived 1567-1608.

183. Guillaume II, Viscount of Joyeuse, who owed it much more to his elder son, Anne, than to his own merits, to be made Marshal of France (1519-1592).

184. Marie de Batarnay.

185. One was Marguerite de Lorraine, who had married Anne Joyeuse, admiral of France, favourite of Henri III, who made a peerage of the title, and Henriette de Joyeuse, Duchess of Montpensier.

186. Possibly François de Vendôme, Vidame de Chartres—the one mentioned in the *Aventures du baron de Foeneste*.

187. Cf. Ariosto, *Orlando furioso*, Canto V, stanza 67—

> *Io non credo, signor, che ti sia nova*
> *La legge nostre . . .* etc.

188. In 1557.

189. Beaulieu-Chastaignier, referred to again later, pp. 232, 288 of Garnier edition—two pages from the end of the fourth *Discours* and two pages from the end of the 5th *Discours* respectively.—A. B.

190. François de Lorraine, son of the Duke of Guise, Grand Prior of France and General of the Galleys.

191. The Comtesse de Senizon, who got into trouble later.

192. Cf. Livy, xxvi, xxiii.

193. The Countess of Salisbury, who was the mistress of King Jean II the Good of France, held prisoner in London after Poitiers (1356-1360) whose love persuaded him to return to London, according to some historians, to be prisoner again, when his son the Duke

of Anjou, who had been serving as hostage for him, had fled the country.

194. Cf. p. 35.

195. Cf. Juvenal, *Satires* VI, 206 and 211-2. Juvenal says:

Si tibi simplicitas uxoria, deditus uni
Est animus. . .

196. Cf. Note 171.

197. He found this in Boccaccio's *Decameron*, Fifth Day, 10th story.

198. At Pérouse. Cf. Boccaccio, l.c.

199. Pietro de Vinciolo. Cf. Boccaccio, l.c.

200. Ercolano in Boccaccio's story, l.c.

201. Christine de Lorraine, daughter of Duke Charles, married to Ferdinand de Medici, Grand-duke of Florence.

202. Port de Piles, a small town on the Vienne, between Touraine and Poitou.

203. In all probability, the Princess de Condé. Cf. above, p. 72 and Note 133.

204. Bussy d'Amboise.

205. Possibly—as Bouchot avers—Louise de Vitry, Lady de Simiers, who in sequence lost Charles d'Humières at Ham, Admiral de Villars at Dourlens, then the Duke of Guise, Count de Randan and others. Or else it may be—as Lalanne and Mariéjol suppose—Marguerite de Valois, whose lovers were innumerable.

206. Brantôme confuses the Séjan horse with Seius's horse *(equus Seianus)*. Cf. Aulu-Gelle, Nuits attiques, book III, chapter ix: 'A certain Cn Seius had a horse foaled at Argos in Greece. Persistent tradition has it that this animal was descended from a race of race horses which had belonged to Diomedes of Thrace and which Hercules brought to Argos after killing Diomedes. These were very tall, upstanding animals, of bay colour. The mane was shot with gold and the breed was outstanding in all qualities. However, these horses were cursed, and whoever owned one was doomed to die and his family with him. Thus the first owner, Cn. Seius, was condemned to death by Marc Antony . . . and died in torment. At the same time, Cornelius Dolabella, a Consul, who was leaving for Syria, was attracted by the famous animal and travelled by way of Argos and bought the horse for one hundred thousand *sesterces*. He too was killed, in Syria, during the civil war, in a besieged town. His horse passed to C. Cassius, who had been besieging Dolabella, and we all know what happened to him—seeing his side defeated and his army routed, he found a wretched death of his own seeking. After Cassius had gone, it was the turn of Antonius, who, having won the battle, claimed the famous horse, only to be at once defeated in turn and, abandoned by his men, to suffer a miserable death. Hence the proverb which comes to mind whenever one thinks of a man who seems to be pursued by fate, so that one often heard people say: "He's got Seius's horse".'

207. Louis Bérenger du Guast. Cf. p. 73 and Note 135.

208. Here Brantôme rather turns upside down a compliment which Théodore de Bèze applied to the ladies of Italy *(Epigrammata, xciv, In italiam)*.

209. There were a number of Cajetans in the fifteenth and six-

teenth century who wrote about religion and it is impossible to know which one Brantôme meant.

210. The figures got mixed: it was the 91st, not the 119th epigram of Book I.

211. Bandello also mentions this famous courtesan.

212. Georges d'Armagnac, born towards 1500, Bishop of Rodez, Ambassador to Venice in 1536, to Rome in 1539, Cardinal in 1544, Archbishop of Toulouse in 1562, appointed co-legate of Cardinal de Bourbon in 1562 at Avignon, where he ended his life in 1585 as Achbishop. Montaigne speaks of him in his travel diary and Montluc mentions him in his *Commentaires*.

213. In the *Dialogues des Courtisanes*, (V, *Clouarion et Léaina*): 'She's a terribly masculine woman. I don't see what you mean, unless she is tribadic, because I've been told there are such masculine women on Lesbos, who won't let a man approach them but take women as if they were men themselves.'

214. Brantôme did not quite understand his own quotation. Here *crissantis* (not: *grissantis*) is not a proper name, but a verb. Juvenal (Satires VI; 322) was most precise about lascivious Saufeia.

'Ipsa Medullinae fluctum (or frictum) crissantis adorat.'

215. Lucian *Amores*, xxviii.

216. De Philinna, Lucian's courtesan.

217. Henri de Clermont, Viscount of Tallard, killed in the siege of La Rochelle, April 1573.

218. Cf. Note 212.

219. Refers to the legend of which Ovid makes much in his *Heroidae* (xv) by which when in her fifties Sappho fell in love with a handsome young sailor of Mitylene, named Phaon, and when he left her, flung herself into the sea from Cape Leukadia.

220. An ambiguous passage. Is Brantôme talking about himself or merely telling us what he was told in confidence? It would seem that faulty punctuation causes the puzzle—if after 'time' instead of a full-stop (as in the original) one places a comma, the text is perfectly clear.—A. B.

221. Martial, *Epigrams*, I, xcl. Cf. Note 210.

222. It is not clear to what this refers in Martial.

223. *Dialogues des Courtisanes*, V.

224. Louis Bérenger du Guast. Cf. Note 135.

225. Agnolo Firenzuola, poet and Florentine translator, pupil and friend of Aretino and author, among other such works, of a *Dialogue on Feminine Beauty*, translated into French by J. Pallet in 1578.

226. This 'famous' and 'lovely' Margaret of Austria was not, as Brantôme asserts later, the Duchess of Savoy (who died about 1530) but an illegitimate daughter of the Emperor, whose first husband was Alexander de Medici, and second, Octavio Farnese.

227. The church of Brou, near Bourg en Bresse, built (1517-1536) by Margaret of Austria, widow of the Duke of Savoy and Count of Bresse, Philibert le Beau (the Handsom) whom Brantôme here confuses with Margaret de Medici. In any case, Margaret of Austria died in 1530, before the church she founded was completed.

228. Charles V.

229. The Peace of Cambrai or 'Ladies' Peace,' which was signed

by Meritregau of Austria, Charles V's aunt and Louise of Savoy, mother of François I and Regent of France (August 5th, 1523).

230. Henri Corneille Agrippa, alchemist and cabalistic philosopher, physician to Louise of Savoy, secretary of Maximilian I, counsellor to Charles V, author of a number of works on the occult and also of one entitled *De nobilitate et praecellentia feminei sexus declamatio*, published in Antwerp in 1529 and many times republished or translated in the sixteenth century.

231. Rabelais (Book 3, chapter 25, Lefranc edition, Vol. V, p. 191), recalls this song where he makes Panurge say to Her Trippa: 'When all the cuckolds get together, you will be standard-bearer.'

232. These words of Jean de Meung, in the *Roman de la Rose*, were proverbial in the Middle Ages.

233. The 26th tale of the *Heptameron*.

234. Gabriel d'Albret, lord of Avesnes and Lesparre, fourth son of Alain, lord of Albret, known as *le Grand*, and brother of Jean d'Albret, King of Navarre. He died a bachelor in 1504.

235. The author of this half-line, often quoted as of Ovid, is unknown. Ovid it is not. It has been completed as:

> *Errat que dixit: Casta est quam nemo rogavit;*
> *Scilicet banc, nemo si rogat, ipsa rogat.*

'He was wrong who said the woman is chaste whom nobody wants, because if a man does not want her, she will want him.'

236. Livy, XXIX, 14: 'Ladies of the highest society in the city received Cybele; the name of one of them, Claudia Quinta, is famous; her previous doubtful reputation all the more brought out her chastity for posterity after she had accomplished so sacred a mission.'

237. In the *Decameron*.

238. Claudia Quinta.

239. 204 B.C.

240. Marguerite of Navarre.

241. Keraton in Greek means 'horned.' Cf. Plutarch, Misc. LXXVII (Vol. II, p. 167—1808 edition).

242. The fashion of wearing drawers dates from about 1575. Brantôme apparently means to say that a lady might not put on drawers at all, or else wear her farthingale over them without any petticoats, which were very heavy. The text apparently needs repunctuation.

243. Terms of a game which was popular in the fifteenth and sixteenth centuries. Cards were classified as *blank* (without pips, or with few) and so crying *blank* meant one had bad luck, whereas *benefice* meant the opposite—a knave, a queen or a king, the king of hearts being the strongest card. 'Our children,' nicely said Pasquier, 'are what luck of birth brings us, so that we get more *blanks* than *benefices* from them.'

244. Without success. See preceding Note.

245. Like those of Bonaventure des Périers or Noël du Fail.

246. L. Perceau has not included this amusing little poem in his collection of 'rhymes of my youth' by Brantôme, yet it may well have been by him, like the two poems which precede it.

247. The famous judge and jurist, Etienne Pasquier (1529-1615) author among other works of the celebrated *Recherches de la France* and 22 volumes of *Letters*.

248. This *'discours'*—a letter to Ronsard—is in Vol. II, p. 38, of the 1723 edition of the *Oeuvres complètes* of Pasquier.

249. 'Which,' wrote Pasquier, 'yields a lover the greater pleasure, to feel and touch his love without talking to her, or to see her and talk to her without touching her?' In the dialogue of Thibaut de Champagne and Count de Soissons, Thibaut held that talking was the more enjoyable.

Brantôme is to be excused for not knowing Thibaut's works, for the first edition did not appear till 1742, when it was published by Bishop de la Ravallière, under the title *Poésies du roi de Navarre avec des notes et un glossaire français* (a small octavo work in two volumes). Known as the *Faiseur de chansons* (song-maker), Thibaut was of course the King of Navarre, otherwise Count of Champagne and Brie.

250. In the Platonic, chivalric sense of the word, for whatever is said to the contrary, it would still seem that Thibaut's love for Blanche of Castille never went beyond the limits of pure love.

251. Isabeau de Bavière?

252. A veiled reference to Queen Catherine de Medici and her favourites.

253. Here Brantôme was either thinking of the passage in Plutarch on Diogenes the Cynic (De Stoicorum repugnantiis, Chapter xxi), or of the life of Diogenes (VI, lxix) by Diogenes Laertius, referred to by Montaigne too (Essays II, Chapter xii) where he says: 'Masturbating in public, Diogenes told onlookers that he wishes he could satisfy his belly by rubbing it.'

254. Not Lamia, but Thônis. Cf. Plutarch, *Demetrius,* Chapter xxvii (Amyot's translation, Vol. II, p. 669): 'There was a young man in Egypt who fell in love with a courtesan named Thônis, but she asked such a high price to sleep with her that the young man could not afford it; finally the young lover, so full of desire was he, dreamt that he was in bed with her and taking his pleasure of her, so vividly that the awareness and satisfaction of the pleasure were so great in his sleep that when he woke up he no longer wanted her. When she learned this, the courtesan sued him for the pleasure he had had of her in his imagination. Hearing this, Bocchoris ordered the young man to bring to court at the next sitting the exact amount that she had asked of him, in a pot, and had him shake it about in front of the courtesan, so that she had merely the shadow and sight of it, since he said, imagination and concepts are but shadows of the truth.'

The story is to be found in various forms also in Elien, *Histoires diverses,* book xii, chapter 63, *De Archedice scorto* (of 'Archedyce the whore') in the 23rd tale of the *Grand Passage des Nouvelles nouvelles,* by Nicolas de Troyes; in Bandello, *Novelle,* part IV, story 2; in Rabelais, *Book Three, Chapter 37,* etc. La Fontaine also used it for one of his best stories: *Le cas de conscience, (Contes,* Part IV, iv).

255. 43rd story of the Heptameron.

256. The 'kerchief': in the original a *touret de nez.* This was as it were the lower part of a mask, attached to the headgear and worn under the eyes by ladies when it was cold. It was popularly known as the *drip collector.* In the *Cymbalum mundi,* 3rd dialogue we read: Item, to tell the ladies not to forget their kerchief masks when they

go about town, as these are fine for laughing and making fun of this or that without anybody's being able to know.

257. Masks did not come in till Charles IX's reign.

258. Velvet in those times was not everyday wear, as the *Heptameron* tells us, but only usual dress for ladies of eminent family and authority.

259. This detail Brantôme has invented.

260. As Ennasuitte—cf. *Heptameron*, stories 4, 19, 27, 36 and others.

261. Cf. Note 131.

262. François de Compeys, Lord of Gruffy, of a noble Savoyan family, entered François I's service in 1518.

263. Since the siege of 1528, when Lautrec, who was the besieger, also died, of some infection.

264. The portrait of handsome Gruffy is to be seen in the Versailles museum.

265. According to Luis Baratona (*Lagrimas de Angelica,* Canto 4) the perfect lover should have not three, but four S's—*sabio, solo, solicito* and *segreto*—be circumspect, sole, solicitous and secret. Chapter 34 of Cervantes' Don Quixote also shows how fashionable initial letters were in Spain.

266. What queen is this? Jeanne of Navarre, consort of Philippe the Handsome? Marguerite of Boulogne? Isabeau of Bavaria? We do not know, but the legend of Nesle Tower was popular in Paris in the fifteenth and sixteenth centuries. Villon wrote:

> *And also tell me where's that queen*
> *Who ordered Buridan be thrown*
> *Sewn in a sack into the Seine?*
> *Yes, where is now last winter's snow?*

267. Built by Amaury de Nesle (whose name is preserved by it) this building stood where the streets of Nevers, Anjou Dauphine and Guénégaud meet (where the mint now stands) and reached as far as the Philippe Hamelin Gates and Tower, where the graceless Institute now stands.

268. Cf. Plutarch, *Vie d'Antoine*, 32 (page 638 of Amyot's translation, which Brantôme follows). Plutarch says that when Cleopatra saw how inept Mark Antony's repartee was she became very bold with him.

269. Cf. Pliny, Book 26, Chapter 3 (page 154 of Vol. 2 of Antoine du Pinet's translation, published by Cl. Senneton at Lyons in 1562, as *L'histoire du monde de C. Pline second*, which Brantôme follows.

270. This letter of Mark Antony to Octavius is in Suetonius—Augustus, 69 (page 118 of the translation entitled *Vie des XII Césars* by Georges de La Boutière, published in Paris in 1569, which Brantôme follows). But Brantôme got some of the names wrong: Tortala, Leontila and Salura Litisema should be Tertula, Terentila and Salvia Titisenia.

271. Livy, Book 30, Chapter 15.

272. Appian, *De rebus punicis,* 27.

273. Brantôme had greatly enjoyed Trissino's tragedy *Sofonisba*, in Mellin de Saint Gelais's translation, performed at Blois on April 3rd, 1554, by Princesses Elisabeth and Claude.

274. This line is taken from *La Vielle Courtisanne*, by Joachim du Bellay (*Oeuvres poétiques*, 1597, verso of folio 449).

275. Taken from Lucian, *Amours*, 15.

276. Brantôme seems to have been very fond of scents, if we are to judge from the list of things he left when he died, for in his room in 1614 he had three pairs of perfumed gloves, four perfumed sachets and a 'chain of scent.' Cf. H. Omont, *La Succession de Pierre de Bourdeille, seigneur de Brantôme,* in the *Annuaire-Bulletin de la Société d'Histoire de France,* 1900, p. 221.

277. To whom Catherine de Medici, as Brantôme records elsewhere *(Eloge de la reine Marguerite)* one day said : 'Wherever you go, the court will take its fashions from you, not you from the court.'

278. The Duke of Anjou. However, the *Divorce satyrique* ascribes this device to Marguerite de Valois, who tried it to make her husband, the King of Navarre, more amorous and lascivious.

279. Pliny the Elder (Du Pinet's translation, Vol. II, folio 643) mentions this Helena of Zeuxis. 'In Philippe's doorways and galleries of Rome there is a Helena by Zeuxis.' Boccaccio, however, (*De claris mulieribus,* translated by Vérard, 1493, folio 55) ascribes this portrait of Helena to Herakleotes : 'From all the women,' he says, 'he picked out the five loveliest, worthy of being admired for their outstanding beauty, and by the liveliness of his hand gathered and combined all the beauties of form of these women that he could and so made a figure and depicted the body and features of this Helena as best he could.'

280. These lines are taken from an old French book entitled : *De la louange et beauté des dames.* François Comiger put them into 18 lines of Latin verse. Vincentio Calmeta translated them into Italian, beginning with *Dolce Flaminia.* We may also compare Cholières, *Matinées,* published by P. Lacroix in 1879, p. 182, where the details are set forth in a sonnet.

281. In Ronsard's *Mélanges*, which appeared in 1555, the elegy beginning :

> *Pein moy, Janet, pein moy . . .*

written to the son of the famous painter Clouet (François or Janet Clouet) painter in ordinary to Kings Henri II and Charles IX.

Ronsard reprinted the elegy in the first book of his *Amours*.

282. Cassandre Salviati, 'concealed' by Ronsard not by the 'cover name' of Cassandre, but by her surname. She married Jean de Peigné, lord of the manor of Pré, near Vendôme.

283. Ronsard never plainly disclosed of whom he wrote as Marie, but from a remark of Claude Binet's in his *Vie de Ronsard* that it was a girl of Anjou, whom he often refers to as 'the Pine of Bourguiel' most Ronsardists are in agreement that she was Marie Dupin or Pin, a 'plain peasant girl' as Baïf said.

284. Ariosto, *Orlando furioso*, Canto VII, Stanzas 11-15.

285. In the sixteenth century poets disputed whether fair or dark women were the more lovely, Marot was for brunettes, cf. *Epistres*, the poem entitled *Des jartières blanches*, and also *Chansons*, 26, where he deals with the matter at length.

Similarly the lawyer Louys d'Orléans (*Bibliothèque nationale*, ms. fr. 863, folio 649) and Belleau, in *Bergeries, 2-e journée.*

286. One of the lovely woman warriers of *Orlando furioso,* whom Ariosto describes in *canto* 13, and whose deeds fill *cantos* 18-20.

287. Raymond Lully, the famous alchemist and philosopher of Spain, born, most authorities concur, in 1235 at Palma, Majorca, and died in Africa 1315.

288. Arnauld de Villeneuve, another famous alchemist of the 13th century, who lost his life in a shipwreck in 1313.

289. Oldrade, an Italian lawyer of the 13th century, who came from Lodi.

290. The *Code de la fausse monnaie* by d'Oldrade is unknown.

291. Charles de Bovelle, a Picardy man, author, among other minor works, of a life of Raymond the Hermit, which Ascensius published in Paris in 1521. Folio 34 contains the points Brantôme has referred to.

292. Aimeric de Rochechouart (1545-1580) who followed his uncle Albin de Rochechouart as Bishop of Sisteron, and according to l'Estoile (*Journal,* Vol. I, p. 375) was 'a typical Epicurean and one of the ugliest and dirtiest of the lot whose death was like his life.' Théodore de Bèze (Histoire ecclés. Vol. I, p. 894) in his usual vehement manner speaks of him as a 'court buffoon and pimp, one of the most idiotic of his kind.'

293. Brantôme is wrong about the temple, as the passage in Pliny to which he refers shows (*Histoire naturelle,* Chapter 4, Du Pinet's translation, Vol. II, p. 576). This refers to the temple of Minerva, at Lyndos.

294. This was Françoise Babou de la Bourdaisière, wife of Antoine de Coevures, lynched together with her lover, Yves d'Alègre, by the people of Issoire, when 'so alleged a gentleman of honour who was a very intimate friend of the d'Estrées family' strange things were discovered. Cf. *Journal de Henri III,* 1720 edition, Vol. I, p. 275.

295. Apparently the story of the Duchess of Montpensier and Henri III who is said to have found her so misshapen 'under her linen' and so disappointing to him that he went so far as to 'spit on her.'

296. In *Pantagruel,* Chapter 15.

297. Elizabeth I of England.

298. Charles de La Rochefoucauld, Count of Randan, Colonel General of Infantry, who died of wounds at the siege of Rouen on November 4th, 1562.

299. Jacques de Savoie, Duke of Nemours, who married Anne d'Este, widow of the Duke of Guise (1531-1585).

300. François de Vendôme, Vidame of Chartres.

301. François III, Count de la Rouchefoucauld, who married Sylvie Pic de La Mirandole, then Charlotte de Royé, took part in the civil wars and perished on St Bartholomew's night.

302. Melchior de Près, lord of the manor of Montpezat, who was Senechal of Poitou (1502-1572).

303. René d'Anglure, lord of the manor of Givry, killed in the battle of Dreux in 1562.

304. François d'Hangest, lord of the manor of Genlis, who died at Strasbourg in 1569.

305. Henri II.

306. Catherine de Medici.

307. Taken from Pierre Belon's *Observations de plusieurs singularitez et choses memorables trouvées en Grèce, Asie . . .* (1553) Book 3, chapter 29: 'The Sophi, who is Moslem, calls the Turks heretics because Turkish women are not circumcized, as are the women of his country; they also go to the mosque, which the women of Turkey do not do.'

308. Lady Claude Blosset of Torcy, daughter of Jean Blosset and Anne of Cognac. In 1553 she married Louis de Montberon or Montbron, Baron of Fontaine and Chalandray, one of the gentleman of the Royal Bedchamber.

309. *La belle Torcy* had been presented to Eleonora of Austria, widow of King Manoel of Portugal, (who had become queen of France by her marriage to François I, July 4th, 1550), by Lady de Canaples, who was the enemy of the Duchess of Etampes.

310. The poets of the time sang praise of the goodness and piety of Queen Eleonora rather than of her good looks. In admiration of the care with which she maintained peace between her husband, François I and her brother, Charles V, Theodore de Bèze, addressed to her his 24th Latin epigram:

> *Nil Helena vidit Phoebus formosius una:*
> *Te, Regina, nihil pulchrius orbis habet;*
> *Utraque formosa est; sed re tamen altera major:*
> *Illa serit lites, Helionora fugat.*

311. Jeanne d'Albret, Queen of Navarre.

312. Jeanne d'Albret spent some time with the court at Moulins early in 1566.

313. In the Fourth Book, chapter 32.

314. *Suetonius: Life of Augustus,* 119 Brantôme copies the La Boutère translation, folio 118, almost word for word: 'they took mothers of families and ripe Virgins and visited each in turn, as if Thoranus the slave pimp sold them.'

315. In 1573.

316. Henri de Guise, Scarface (le Balafré).

317. The Duke of Alençon.

318. The following year (November 1574) Brantôme was entrusted with the negotiation of a peace with La Noue and the garrison of la Rochelle.

319. Written four years after the assassination of the Duke of Guise.

320. No doubt Marguerite de Valois.

321. Apparently Bussy d'Amboise.

322. Reference to Actaeon's strange fate—when he came upon Diana bathing in a stream, he was transformed into a stag, and his own hounds devoured him. Cf. Ovid, *Metamorphoses,* III, 143-252.

323. Refers to Henri II's love for Diane of Poitiers, Duchess de Valentinois.

324. The author of the *Divorce satyrique* says of the Queen of Navarre: 'I have been told that her father was similarly bewitched by Lady de Valentinois.'

325. Catherine de Medici.

326. Probably Jacqueline de Longwy, Duchess of Montpensier.

327. This great lady may well be Queen Catherine de Medici. If we are to accept Henri III's diary for May 15th, 1577, on the occasion of festivities at Chenonceaux, she had Ladies de Retz and de Sauves wait on her stark naked.

328. Pic de la Mirandole, in his *Disputationes adversus astrologos* (Petit's 1517 edition of the complete works, Book III, chapter 22).

329. In 1558 or 1565.

330. François Ferdinand of Avalos, Marquis de Pescaire, who died in 1571. Cf. Note 28.

331. The story of the lord leaving a glove in the lady's bed goes back to the Middle Ages. Jacques d'Acqui's Latin chronicle—this author was born towards the end of the 13th century—ascribes it to the emperor Frederic II.

332. In *Antiquités judaïques*, Book 15, Chapter vii.

333. Cf. Plutarch, *Life of Alexander*, 39. However, Brantôme seems to have borrowed his version of the story of Alexander and Darius's daughters literally from *Pérégrinations orientales*, by Nicolay.

334. The land of Hafiz and Saadi, famous for its wines and the loveliness of its women.

335. Here, to hide his source, Brantôme has scratched out his reference to the original text.

336. Pierre Belon: *Observations de plusieurs singularitez et choses memorables trouvées en Grèce, Asie* (1553) Book 3, Chapter 10, pp. 178-179.

337. Cartagena.

338. Taken from Antoine de Guévara, *Epistres dorées et discours salutaires*, translated into French by de Guterry (1588), Vol. III, p. 42. But in his usual way Brantôme alters the names, for Guévara calls the Prince of the Celtiberians Liceius.

339. This story is in *Livy*, 38, chapter 24, in Boccaccio's *De claris Mulieribus*, 74, and in Antoine du Verdier, *Les diverses leçons* (1580) p. 338. The king is usually called Ortiagon. His wife, lovely Chiomara, was, we are told, frowned upon by her husband, who was so punctilious about 'honour' that he reproached her with not keeping her word to the Roman centurion.

340. Taken from Suetonius, *Life of Caesar*, 52 La Boultière's French version, folio 34. Julius Caesar is said also to have loved a number of queens, among these being Eunoe Maura, wife of Bogud, giving her and her husband many magnificent presents. . .

341. *Livy*, 30, Chapter 15.

342. Brantôme is wrong when he ascribes to Scipio this story of widowed Cato and a young slave girl who disgraced his son. See Plutarch: *Cato the Elder*.

343. François I.

344. Charles of Guise, second Cardinal of Lorraine (1524-1574), François II's all-powerful minister known as 'the Great' to distinguish him from his brother Louis (1527-1578), who was first Cardinal of Guise, and his nephew Louis (1555-1588), who was second Cardinal of Guise.

345. The armistice of Vauxcelles, between the Emperor and Henri II.

346. The Cardinal of Lorraine was entertained by the Republic of Venice, January 16th-24th, 1556.

347. The name 'Master Gonnin' symbolized buffoon to Brantôme. History records three men of that name. The first, the one in question, was a conjuror attached to the court of François I, the second, grandson of the first, was a contemporary of Charles IX, and the third juggled on the Pont Neuf under Louis XIII. Lerous de Lincy quotes a proverb which preserves Gonnin's reputation.

348. Bonaventure des Périers agrees with Brantôme in praising this conjuror, whom Jean Bodin charged with sorcery.

349. The Neapolitan jurist Alessandro Alessandri, in a work entitled *Geniales dies* (published at Lyons by Rouville in 1536) in Book 6, pp. 827 and 1,006, certainly does refer briefly to the cult of Apis, but Brantôme elaborates greatly apparently vaguely recalling Book II, Chapter 9 of Herodotus on the cult: 'Women with castagnets make a din . . . others sing, clapping their hands . . . still others shout and mock the good wives of the town, while others dance and some stand and raise their skirts.' All this takes place not at Alexandria, but Bubastis. . . .

350. This information on the Swiss bathing customs is no doubt taken from Belon: *Observations de plusieurs singularitez,* (1553), book 3, Chapter 35, p. 198. But it is tempting here to compare what Brantôme and Belon say with what Montaigne writes on the baths of Rome in his posthumous *Diary of a Journey in Italy through Switzerland and Germany,* where 'it is the custom to take what woman friends you please and these are massaged together with you by boys.'

351. All these details concerning Flora are taken from Guévara's *Epistres dorées,* Vol. I, pp. 306-317. Brantôme slightly modifies the notice, which the Spanish author gives as: 'King, Prince, Dictator, Consul, Censor, Pontiff and Questor may knock and enter here.'

352. The cult of this courtesan, whose real name was Acca Taruntia, became confused with that of Flora, whose name she assumed. The grammarians and poets of ancient Rome (Varron: *De lingua latina,* Book 5, Chapter 3, and Ovid's, *Fastes,* Book IV, 947 and V, 351) concerning her fortune tell us that when she began, Acca was introduced to the Temple of Hercules by a watchman to pass a night with the God. The following day, Hercules, satisfied, invited her to embrace the first man she came upon as she left the temple, and this happened to be elderly and very rich Taruntius, who married her and made her his heir. Cf. also Macrobius, *Saturnales,* Book I, Chapter 10, 12-17, who says the man who married Acca was Carutius.

353. According to Guévara, *op. cit.,* quoting Suetonius, *Life of Galba.*

354. According to Guévara, *op cit.,* who after quoting Suetonius on the introduction of the floral celebrations by the Emperor Galba, adds: 'The authors of all said here are Pausanias the Greek and Manilius the Latin, from the books they wrote on famous women who loved.' But neither Pausanias nor Suetonius nor Manilius wrote any books about women, and the author clearly refers to casual mention of women in their other writings.

355. The oldest sanctuary of the goddess at Sparta contained an armed Aphrodite. There is also a Laconian coin of the 3rd century B.C. which depicts a divinity wearing a tightly drawn gown, a helmet on her head, in her right hand a lance and in the left a bow. Julius

Caesar, who boasted descent from Venus, wore a ring, so Suetonius tells us, depicting an armed Venus and the motto (which refers to the *Judgement of Paris*):

Vincere si possum nuda, quid arma gerens?

(If I can conquer naked, what when armed?)

356. Cf. p. 170 and Note 280.

357. Queen Catherine de Medici. Elsewhere (Works, Lalanne edition, Vol. 7, p. 342) Brantôme informs us that she 'had a well-turned leg and thigh and took great pleasure in good stockings, well drawn and tight.'

358. 'All the ladies wore breeches or drawers attached to their stockings below the knee by garters, which could be the more ornate since there was thus less unseemliness in letting them be seen and sometimes showing them off. Indeed, horse-riding or any quick movements tending to reveal the leg very often, so the stockings worn were richly embroidered and the garters real pieces of jewellery.' L. de Laborde in *Notice des émaux du Louvre, II,* 348.

359. Suetonius, *Life of Vitellius, II,* Georges de La Boutière translation (1563), p. 358: Lucius Vitellius 'asked Messalina, in return for a very great gift she was according him, to be allowed to take off her shoes for her, and having taken off the the little slipper of the right foot, he carefully put it between his cloak and his toga, kissing it very passionately a number of times.' But La Boutière, whom Brantôme follows, somewhat embroidered what Suetonius said, which was merely: *Messalina petiit ut sibi pedes praeberet excalciandos.*

360. The 57th story of the Heptameron, in which de Montmorency, ambassador of Louis XI in England, sees a 'lord of a great house' sit down next to him at a banquet 'with a little woman's glove fastened by gold pins to his cloak, the fingers of this being much ornamented with diamonds, rubies, amethysts and pearls, so that the glove was worth a great deal of money.'

361. Most likely refers to François de Lorraine, Grand Prior and General of the Galleys (1534-1562) who went to Scotland with his niece, Mary Stuart, 'the loveliest lady in the world'—or else perhaps to René d'Elbeuf or Aumale, who were in the company on this journey.

362. Pliny the Elder, Pinet translation, Vol. 2, p. 587: 'Nous avons veu de nostre temps l'imperatrice Poppea, femme de l'empereur Nero, faire ferrer d'or les pecques de ses coches qu'eele aymoit le plus.'

363. Beginning with Otho (Suetonius, *Life of Otho, III*) who seduced her when, after taking her from her first husband, the noble Crispinus Rufius, Nero handed her over to him.

364. Henri III.

365. The book mentioned, *Le Voyage du Prince,* printed in Antwerp in 1552 and translated by J. Petit, was reprinted in Brussels in 1871.

366. Philippe II.

367. Charles V.

368. Marie of Austria, sister of Charles V and widow of King Louis II of Hungary.

369. Bains in Hainaut.

370. In the *Life of Henri II,* cf. Brantôme, *Works,* Lalanne edition, Vol. III, pp. 253-265.

372. Eleonora of Austria.

373. Philippe II.

374. Béatrix Pacheco, who had been maid of honour to Queen Eleanora prior to 1544, and by marrying Sebastien, Count of Entremont and Montbel, had become Countess of Entremont. Her daughter was Jacqueline d'Entremont, whose second husband was Admiral de Coligny (March 25th 1571). She was arrested in 1585 on orders of the Duke of Savoy, in whose lands she had taken refuge, and charged with having 'invoked, worshipped and burned incense to devils,' and despite the efforts of Henri IV she died in prison in December, 1599. Cf. H. Bordier, *La Veuve de l'amiral de Coligny*, in the *Bulletin de la Société de l'histoire du protestantisme français*, 1875, p. 357.

375. The Queen of France had twelve ladies in waiting at this time. The senior was Jeanne de lHôpital, Lady de Boucard. The others were Thomette d'Arpajon, Claude Blosset (la belle Torcy), Cécile de Boucard, Marguerite de Breuil, Claude de Grany, Léonor de La Chapelle, Sidonie de Mervillez, Barbe de Pons, Cathérine de Sanctan, Béatrix de Savoie, Marie de Tombes and Marie de la Billalons. Cf. *Comptes de la reine Eléonore*, Arch, nat., KK 105.

376. The story of Henri II's entry of Lyons in September 1548 is taken by Brantôme—with certain cuts and some additions—from a small contemporary book: *La magnificence de la superbe et triomphante entrée de la noble et antique cité de lyonfaicte au très chrestien roy de France Henry, deuxiesme de ce nom, et à la royne Catherine, son épouse, le XXIII de septembre MDXLVIII*, à Lyon chez Guillaume Roville, à l'Escu de Venise (1549).

377. The obelisk and courtyard of which Brantôme speaks were illustrated by wood engravings in the above booklet of 1549.

378. The final three words were added by Brantôme.

379. The bloodhounds and 'other leash dogs' were added by Brantôme.

380. The reference to Diane of Poitiers is added by Brantôme.

381. The dogs which were baying were not in the 1549 book.

382. The poem (pp. 32-4 of the Lyons booklet)—which M. Bertrand Guégan ascribes to Maurice Scève (Cf. *Poésies complètes* de Scève, in the Garnier classics edition) is as follows:

> Le grand plaisir de la chasse usitée
> Auquel par montz, vallées et campaignes
> Je m'exercite avecques mes compaignes,
> Jusqu'en voz boys, Sire, m'ha incitée
> Où ce Lion d'amour inusitée
> S'est venu rendre enceste notre bande,
> Lequel soudain, à sa privauté grande,
> J'ay recongneu, et aux gestes humains,
> Estre tout vostre. Aussi entre voz mains
> Je le remetz et le vous recommande.

383. The Duchy and peerage of Valentinois was given to Diane of Poitiers by Henri II for life enjoyment three weeks after his reception at Lyons (hence Brantôme slightly anticipates). It was quite near to Lyons, with Valence as capital and Montélimar, Crest and Donzère as principal towns.

384. Catherine de Medici was very fond of dancing, and Brantôme elsewhere describes the famous ballet which the Queen Mother gave on August 19th 1573 in honour of the Ambassadors of Poland.

385. The waltz of the age. Spinning round, we read in Thoinot Arbeau's *Orchéographie* (folio 63) that the girl placed her right hand on her partner's collar, behind, and 'with her left hand on her hip to steady her skirts, lest as they caught the wind they revealed her shift or her naked thigh. . . . And after having turned as many phrases of music as you like, you put the girl back where she was, quite dizzy, and yourself too just as much. I leave it to you to judge for yourself whether it is very seemly for a young girl to take big strides and open her legs. And whether in this *volta* honour and health are not jeopardized or even damaged.'

386. 1552.

387. Brantôme uses Montluc's *Mémoires*: 'All the ladies of the city of Siena formed three troops. The first was led by Signora Forteguerra, who was dressed in violet, and all who followed her were attired like nymphs, in short dresses, revealing their boots, the second was Signora Piccollomini, dressed in scarlet satin, and her troops in the same, and the third was Signora Livia Fausta, dressed all in white, as were those with her, with their white banner. Their weapons were picks, shovels, hods and faggots.'

388. Hippolyte d'Este, Cardinal of Ferrara, Lt.-General at Siena in October 1552.

389. Paul de Labarthe, Lord Termes, Marshall of France in 1558, died 1562.

390. Henri II.

391. Here Brantôme takes inspiration from Nicolay *op. cit.* p. 51: 'The Ladies of Cios dress so well and with such appeal that one would rather think them Nymphs of Goddesses than mortal women or girls.'

392. These grandstands, says a contemporary account (*Le Sacre et Couronnement du tres-chretien roy de France et de Pologne Henry III, Reims*, 1575,) 'between two columns ornate with gold fleurs-delys on blue satin,' to the right of the main altar. 'Above were seated a considerable number of ladies and girls of great houses, and below were the Queen and her ladies.'

393. *Les Blasons anatomiques du corps féminin* include two coats of arms of a foot, the work of Lancelot de Carle and Sagon.

394. In 1564.

395. *Il Filicopo* is Boccaccio's striking story of the chivalric adventures of Florio and Blanchfleur.

396. Cf. above, p. 442, Note 876.

397. A bench of the High Court of Paris the judges of which by rota were taken half from the *Chambre des Enquêtes* and the *Grand-Chambre*.

398. Barbe de Cilley, second wife of the German Emperor Sigismond, who by his excesses earned the title of the Messalina of Germany. He died in 1415.

399. (translation) Cf. above, p. 139, Note 234.

400. Cf. above, p. 139, Note 233.

401. Cf. above, p. 452, Note 888.

402. Cf. above, p. 172, Note 286.

403. No doubt Lady de Villequier (Françoise de Lamarck), referred to above.

404. Cf. above, pp. 219-225, Note 395.

405. Isabeau de la Tour de Limeuil, whose story Brantôme here gives. Cf. above, p. 53, Note 111.

406. Louis I of Bourbon, Prince de Condé. Cf. above, Note 109.

407. With Sardini the Banker. Cf. above, Note 110.

408. bis. The Bourbon Hall is the hall of the palace called the 'Petit Bourbon.' It was built by Louis II de Bourbon in the 14th century and demolished under Louis XIV. It was big enough to hold the whole court on solemn occasions, such as the marriage of Marguerite de Valois. It was this princess who together with Maria de Clèves, the young Princess de Condé, invented the whole entertainment. Cf. Mariéjol, *Marguerite de Valois*, pp. 56-7.

409. This little tale is taken from the *Cent nouvelles nouvelles*—in which it is No. 25.

410. Philippe Strozzi. Cf. above, p. 41, Note 87.

411. In 1566.

412. Ronsard: *Second Book of Love Poems, Sonnet* XLVII.

413. Honoré Castellan, physician to Catherine de Medici.

414. Cf. Note 872.

415. The Duke de Nevers was a Gonzaga.

416. Guillaume du Prat, Baron de Vitteaux, mentioned above: it was he who killed Louis Béranger du Guast.

417. Nicolas Le Grand, a famous contemporary physician.

418. Ovid, from whom Brantôme took his 'fable' (*Metamorphoses, 3*, 316-338) adds that Jupiter 'as compensation for losing the light of day accorded Tiresias knowledge of the future.' According to Apollodorus (3, 6, para. 7) Tiresias's reply was that a woman got nine times the pleasure that a man did out of the act of love. There is an amusing reference to Tiresias's reply and his misfortune in the Third Book of Rabelais, Chapter 22 (Lefranc edition, Vol. V, p. 169).

419. The story of Bublos's incestuous love for her twin brother Caunis is also taken from the *Metamorphoses*, 9, 419-665.

420. Paolo Emilio, an Italian historian, born at Verona, died in Paris May 5th, 1529. As Paul Emile, he became 'orator and chronicler to the King' under both Charles VIII and Louis XII. Coming after the monks of St Denis, he was the first lay historian of the monarchy. He wrote an account of the French monarchy entitled *De rebus gestis Francorum*. It ran from the beginning to 1488, in twelve books. The four first appeared in 1516, two more in 1517, and the final four between 1539 and 1540, being published posthumously by a compatriot and friend named Zavarizzi.

421. Baudoin I, Emperor of Constantinople 1204-1205. This Count of Flanders and Hainaut, who had become a crusader, was defeated by the Bulgarian King Joanitza. According to tradition he died under great torments, inflicted by his conqueror. Other accounts say that he returned to Flanders, but his daughter Jeanne (mentioned earlier by Brantôme) refused to recognize him.

422. Here Brantôme gets his history mixed. Marguerite of Constantinople, known as Marguerite the Black, or 'the Black Lady,' daughter of Baudoin I, and younger sister of Jeanne, whom she succeeded, first had two illegitimate sons, who were subsequently legitimized by her Preceptor, Bouchard, Lord d'Avennes, in holy orders. These were the two children, Jean and Baudoin, of whom Brantôme speaks here. Becoming a widow, she married again, her second husband being Guillaume de Dampierre, by whom she had three sons and two daughters.

423. Innocent V.

424. From King Henri III.

425. The Queen Mother, Catherine de Medici. Cf. Brantôme, *Works, On Illustrious Ladies*, Lelanne edition, Vol. 7, pp. 373-4.

426. Almost certainly Marguerite de Navarre, author of the *Heptameron*.

427. What Horace said at the end of Ode 33 of Book 1, was in fact:

> *Sic visum Veneri, cui placet impares*
> *Formas atque animos sub juga aenea*
> *Save mittere cum, joco.*

'Thus Venus would have it, who with cruel ingenuity pleases to harness together beings and souls which differ.'

428. The story is taken from Plutarch, *Life of Caesar*.

429. Tradition has it that Monserrat, twenty-five miles west of Barcelona, was rent from top to bottom when Christ breathed his last. The Madonna here is an object of pilgrimage held to aid women in childbirth.

430. Catherine de Medici when forty.

431. Marie de Clèves, mother of Louis XII, who married Jean de Rabodanges, while still in mourning for her husband.

432. Jean, Cardinal de Lorraine. Cf. Note 755.

433. In 1560.

434. These are the eighteen knights created on the same occasion, of whom the Duchess of Crussol concocted the pun, what good fortune it was that there were not twenty of them, for that would have been *'vingt nouveaux'*—i.e., twenty new ones, or 'young wines' *(vins nouveaux)*—the point being that the wine just pressed in that year were all of poor quality.

435. Odet de Foix, Viscount de Lautrec, killed in the siege of Naples in 1528.

436. Elisabeth of Austria, the daughter of Maximilian and widow of Charles IX.

437. Coligny.

438. Henri III.

439. Richard Lion Heart.

440. Louis Bérenger du Guast.

441. Nicolas de Lorraine, Lord de Vaudemont.

442. Philippe II.

443. She was thirty-eight years old.

444. Marguerite de Valois.

445. Château d'Usson, in Auvergne.

446. Louis de St Gelais, Lord de Lansac (from about 1512 to 1589) Gentleman of the Bedchamber to Henri II. Tutor of his sons, François II and Charles IX, Knight of Honour to Catherine de Medici and Superintendent of his finance, Councillor of State, Ambassador to England, then to Duke Maurice of Saxony and Albert of Brandenburg and thrice Ambassador to the Pope, Captain of the Second Company of the Hundred Nobles of the Royal Household, 1568-1578. He is frequently mentioned in Montluc's *Commentaires*.

447. Philippe Altoviti, Baron de Castellane, Captain of the Galleys at Marseilles, who had married lovely Renée de Rieux, known as the 'fair Châteauneuf,' and fell in a duel against the Grand-Prior of Angoulême, the Grand-Prior also being killed in the same instant. Lovely, fairheaded Renée had been courted by d'Aremberg, Strozzi, and Brantôme, before becoming the mistress of the Duke of Anjou (1571-1574).

448. Jeanne, married to Prince Jean of Portugal, died 1578.

449. In 1564.

450. November 28th of the same year, 1578.

451. Marie of Austria, Queen of Hungary. Cf. p. 210, Note 368.

452. After the abdication of Charles V (1555) being 52 years old, Marie retired to Cigales, in Spain.

453. Charles V after his abdication retired to the Monastery of Yuste.

454. At the age of 23.

455. Louis II, King of Hungary, whom she had married in 1521.

456. The Battle of Mohacs (1526), won by Sultan Suleiman II.

457. Sebastian, King of Portugal, posthumous son of the Infanta Jean, who three years previously had followed his ancestor Jean III (1557) to the throne, reached his majority in 1569 and died in 1578.

458. In the plan of Alcaçarquivir, where he clashed with the powerful army of the ageing Mulej Abd-el-Melek and was killed by a Moorish captain, his army being utterly routed.

459. Philippe II shortly after this annexed the Kingdom of Portugal to the Spanish crown. It only broke away again in 1640, by the revolution which brought the house of Braganza to the throne.

460. In the expedition of 1556-1557, the command of which Henri II had placed in his hands, but in which he failed to conquer the Kingdom of Naples.

461. François, second Duke de Guise (1519-1563).

462. Pope Paul IV.

463. Charles, Second Cardinal of Lorraine, who became cardinal in 1557.

464. Eleonora of Austria, sister of Charles V.

465. Dukes Philippe the Bold, Jean the Fearless, Philippe the Good and Charles the Bold.

466. Marguerite of Austria (1480-1530) daughter of Maximilian.

467. The betrothal of Marguerite and the Dauphin, Charles, the future Charles VIII, was broken off.

468. The child died a few months later.

469. After four years of happy marriage she lost her husband (1501-1505).

470. In 1558.

471. In 1535.

472. The so called Rebellion of the Germanats, in Spain, was in 1522.

473. Guillaume de Croy, Lord de Chièvres.

474. In 1540.

475. I.e., of Tunis, in 1535.

476. From 1531 to 1555.

477. Folembay Castle, not far from Laon, was the residence of François I and Henri II. Henri IV negotiated there with Mayenne during the League war. The castle was destroyed by fire.

478. Bains, in Hainaut. Cf. p. 210, Note 369.

479. When Queen Elisabeth came to Bayonne (June 15th, 1565) there were magnificent festivities, tournaments of all sorts, tilting at the ring, masked jollity, comedies and so forth. Cf. *Ample discours de l'arrivée de la royne catholique, soeur du roy, à Sainct-Jehan-de-Lus, de son entrée à Bayonne et du magnifique recueil qui luy a été faict.* Paris, 1565.

Lavish furniture had been brought from Royal castles, including a famous Flemish tapestry *(Le triomphe de Scipion)* which François I had bought for 22,000 crowns. The hospitality was most lavish. Elsewhere *(Oeuvres,* Lalanne edition, Vol. 3, p. 123) Brantôme tells us that 'the great lords of Spain had a chance of seeing how well France could entertain at board, for so long as they were there all alike, big or little, had all found them and were treated to the Royal kitchen, as I saw, and the things they were used to were never missing, all of fine quality, excellent, outstanding. . . .' Cf. P. Champion, *Catherine de Medici,* pp. 276-299.

480. Claude Blosset, known as Torcy, Lady de Fontaine-Chalandray. Cf. Notes 308 and 309.

481. In 1529, when after twenty savage attacks Suleiman II had at once to deal with the Danube's overflowing its banks and his janissaries indiscipline.

482. In 1525, at Pavia.

483. This concerns André, Viscount de Bourdeille, who was taken prisoner at the Battle of Hesdin (1552), while his other brother, Jean, known as *Captain Bourdeille,* had his head carried away by a cannon ball.

484. Lille.

485. Charles V died in 1558, Queen Eléonora in 1559, Marie of Hungary in 1560.

486. Christine of Denmark, daughter of Christiern II, married first to François Marie Sforza, Duke of Milan, then, when widowed, to Duke François I of Lorraine (1540).

487. Catherine de Medici.

488. Marie of Hungary.

489. Claude Blosset, known as Torcy, Lady de Fontaine-Chalendray. Cf. Notes 302 and 480.

490. Charles II of Lorraine.

491. Lord de La Brosse-Mailly.

492. Henri II.

493. Guy du Faur de Pibrac, (1528-1584), author of the famous *Quatrains,* who was on various occasions *'Juge Mage'* at Toulouse,

Ambassador to the Council of Trent, Attorney-General to the High Court of Paris, Councillor of State, Chancellor of the Duke of Anjou, when he became King of Poland, a high official of Henri III's, and Chancellor of Queen Marguerite.

494. Charles the Bold.

495. Mary Stuart.

496. Cercamp.

497. Cf. Note 486.

498. Anne d'Este, daughter of Renée of France and grand-daughter of Louis XII.

499. December 4th, 1549.

500. Livy, Book 30, chapters 30, 31.

501. Mary Stuart.

502. In April 1561 when he went to Lorraine as a member of the Duke de Guise's entourage.

503. May 5th, 1561.

504. These were highly esteemed animals believed to be a cross between the Arab and the Persian horse.

505. Renée, wife of Guillaume V, Duke of Bavaria.

506. Tortona, Dertona of the ancient world, 15 miles east of Alexandria in Italy.

507. Blanche de Montferrat, of the famous Lombardian house of that name, which sent more heroes to the crusades than any other noble family. Married to Charles I the Warrior, Duke of Savoy, King of Cyprus and Jerusalem, she survived him by twenty years, dying in 1509 at the age of 43.

508. Charles II of Savoy (1488-1497) only a few months old when his father died. His mother was his guardian.

509. In 1494.

510. Charles II (Cf. Note 508), then five and a half.

511. Paradin, *Chronicle de Savoie*, III, 85.

512. Louise de Daillon, wife of André de Vivonne, Seneschal of Poitou, who told his grandson Brantôme many of the little stories which we have in this book.

513. Nicolas de Lorraine-Vaudemont, father-in-law of Henri III.

514. Françoise d'Orléans, widow of Louis I, Prince de Condé, who died in 1601. Cf. p. 369.

515. Cf. above, Note 431.

516. Louise, daughter of Nicolas de Lorraine-Vaudemont, who in 1571 became the consort of Henri III and died in 1601.

517. In L'Estoile's *Journal*, January, 1579, we read: 'Friday, January 23rd, the King went to Olinville to bathe and cleanse himself, and the same was done by his wife the Queen, whom he left in Paris, then he went to Candlemas in Chartres church and prayed and made vows to the Virgin, and there took two shirts from Our Lady of Chartres, one for himself, the other for the Queen his wife, which having done, he returned to Paris to lie with her, hoping to get her with child, of which he was incapable, because of the pox which consumed him and the loose living which had exhausted him.'

518. Catherine de Medici.

519. Jean de Talleyrand, Lord de Grignols or Grinaux, sometime ambassador to Rome.

520. In the *Life of Anne of France*.

521. Louise of Savoy, Duchess of Angoulême.

522. Marguerite of Lorraine, who first married Duke Anne de Joyeuse, and then the Duke of Piney.

523. In August and September 1589.

524. The Duke of Mayennes, and then the Duke of Maine.

525. Aymard de Chastes, Commander of the Order of Malta and Governor of Dieppe.

526. François de Luxembourg, Duke of Piney. Cf. Note 522.

527. Catherine de Clèves, Countess d'Eu, née Nevers. Herself a Huguenot, she had married Antoine de Croy, Prince de Porcien, another Huguenot, who died May 5th, 1567, aged 26.

528. Cf. p. 465.

529. Françoise d'Orléans, widow of Louis I, Prince of Condé, who was killed at Jarnac, March 13th, 1569.

530. Jacqueline de Rohan, Marquise de Rothelin, known as 'la belle Rohan' and of whom it was said 'she would get her husband with child before he would her.' Cf. p. 369, Note 687.

531. Fulvie Pic de La Mirandole, married to Charles de La Rochefoucauld, Count of Randan, often mentioned by Brantôme earlier in this book. Cf. Note 298.

532. An epigram of Ausonius' (51) *Lais dicans Veneri speculum suum*, of which Brantôme here takes the first and last lines only. The full text is:

> *Lais anus Veneri speculum dico: dignum habeat se*
> *Aeterna aeternum forma ministerium.*
> *At mihi nullus in hoc usus, quia cerenere talem*
> *Qualis sum nolo, qualis eram nequeo.*

> Lais grown old her mirror gives to Venus,
> As good for lasting loveliness, because
> No use to her it is, to see herself as she is,
> Who cannot see herself as once she was.

Ausonius's epigram is indeed his own version of an earlier piece of the Greek Anthology, usually ascribed to Plato. (Votive epigr. 1).

533. Henri de Guise, the second Balafré (Scarface).

534. Françoise de la Baume, first widow of the Count de Montravel de Saint Sorlin, then of François de Kernevenog or Carnavalet, mentioned above, cf. p. 363, Note 662.

535. Jean Louis de Nogaret de La Valette, Duke of Epernon, favourite of Henri III, who later joined Henri IV, and still played an important part in affairs under Louis XIII (1554-1642).

536. La Valette had gathered many grand titles—he was a member of the Order of the Holy Ghost, a Peer of the Realm, Duke of Epernon (1581), a Colonel-General of Infantry (1581), Admiral of France, and Governor in turn of the Three Bishoprics (Trois-Evêchés) (1583), of the Boulonnais (1583), of the Angoumois, of Touraine and of Anjou.

537. Jacquette de Montberon, Brantôme's sister-in-law.

538. Cf. Note 87.

539. Although the Strozzis had voluntarily banished themselves from Florence, where they had been against the Medicis, Queen Catherine still held them to belong to her family, since Pietro Strozzi, who was father of Philippe and a Marshal of France, had married a Medici (Laudamine de Medici). Catherine called Philippe 'cousin.'

540. Taken from Plutarch's *Life of Cato of Utica*.

541. Epigram 43 of Book 1 : *De Porcia uxore Bruti:*

> *Conjugis audisset fatum cum Porcia Bruti*
> *Et subtracta sibi quaereret arma dolor:*
> *'Nondum scitis, ait, mortem non posse negari?*
> *Credideram satis hoc vos docuisse patrem.'*
> *Dixit et ardentes avido bibit ore favillas.*
> *I nunc et ferrum, turba molesta, nega!*

And when she learned the fate of Brutus, Portia
  In grief would seize the knife they took from her
'Do you not know you can't deny me death,'
  she cried, 'I thought my father gave the answer there,'
And, swallowing hot coals, she took her life—
  'So now, you tiresome crowd, deny the knife !'
Before Brantôme, Guillaume Bouchet told the story in his *V-e Serée.*

542. Virgil, Aeneid, Book 6.

543. The story of the Matron of Ephesus which Brantôme gives us here, and from which La Fontaine in turn took one of his best stories, is in the Satyricon, and had been very popular in the Middle Ages. Thus we find it in Fable 33 of Marie de France *(De la Fame qui fesoit duel de son Mari,* alias *De l'Oume mort et de sa Moilier)* ; in Eustache Deschamps *(Exemple contre ceulx qui se fient en amour de femmes),* and in the 16th century cf. Gratian du Pont: *Controverses des sexes masculin et femenin* (Toulouse, 1534, folio 97). There are other instances.

544. Jean Daurat or Dorat, Ronsard's teacher and one of the seven members of the Pleiad (1508-1588).

545. Louis Bérenger du Guast, mentioned above. Cf. Note 135.

546. Balthazarini, known as Beaujoyeux, valet of the bedchamber to Catherine de Medici, a musician (performer on a number of instruments and author of ballets).

547. In 1557.

548. Not Lampridius, but Petronnis. Cf. Note 543.

549. Daurat's *De funeribus.* According to Du Verdier (Bibliothèque, p. 685) Daurat wrote more than 50,000 lines, mainly Greek and Latin, 'for,' says Bayle (*Dictionnaire,* article on Daurat) 'no person of any consequence died without Daurat's writing some lines. . . .'

550. Jean de Parthenay-l'Archevêque, Lord of Soubise, one of the leaders of the reform cause. Charged by Poltrot de Méré with being involved in the assassination of François de Guise, he was 'condemned to death' by the Catholics and was to have been assassinated in the Queen-Mother's presence by the Count de Brissac and Marshal de Bourdillon, but she intervened.

551. March 13th, 1569.

552. Niort was captured from Coligny's huguenots by the Duke of Anjou in October 1569.

553. Aubigné in his *Histoire universelle* (I, 4) tells us that the murderer took Captain de Pleuviau's widow his trousers, then saved her by marrying her!

554. There are frequent echoes in Pliny to the beliefs of his age about the sacred nature of snakes and the use made of them by the Gods for the performance of miracles.

555. That is, when he was still Duke of Anjou.

556. Henri Le Mignon, Bishop of Digne, who died in 1587.

557. In Vallès, folios 205 *verso* and 206.

558. Not Victoria but Claudia Colonna.

559. Cf. p. 9, Note 28.

560. Napoleone Orsini, who was granted the Abbey of Farfa as sinecure.

561. The Orsinis.

562. Cf. pp. 8-9, Notes 26 and 28.

563. Thomas de Foix, Lord de Lescun. Cf. p. 83, Note 146.

564. Marshal Philippe Strozzi. Cf. Note 87.

565. Jacques de Salvoison, a nobleman of Périgord, who took part in the Scottish expedition in 1547 under d'Essé, served under Brissac in Piedmont, took part in the capture of Verceil in 1553 and that of Casal in 1554 and died soon after, aged 37. Brantôme gives him a place in his *Illustrious Captains* (Works, Lalanne edition, Vol. 4, pp. 97-120), and Montluc pays him hommage in his *Commentaires*.

566. Roger de Saint Lary de Bellegarde, Marshal of France in 1574, a nephew of the Marshal de Termes and one of Henri III's favourites.

567. Jean de Bourbon Vendôme, Count of Soissons and Enghien, killed by a pistol shot in the battle of Saint Quentin (August 10th, 1528).

568. François de Gouffier, Lord de Bonnivet, Knight of Malta, not to be mixed up with the Admiral of the same name, who was François I's favourite.

569. Sébastian de Luxembourg, Viscount Martigues.

570. Jean de Bourdeille, killed at the siege of Hesdin, aged 25. Cf. above, Note 658.

571. Henri de Clermont, Viscount de Tallard, referred to above, cf. p. 130, Note 217.

572. In 1573.

573. André de Souillelas, known as d'Oraison, Bishop of Riez-en-Provence in 1576. Henri IV used charmingly to say of his mistress, who was both pious and lascivious, that she never found pleasure save 'fasting and at prayer.'

574. Marshal de Matignon (1525-1597) who spent twelve years as Governor of Guyenne and as we know was in close touch with Montaigne.

575. That great lady Philippe de Beaupoil.

576. La Châteigneraie.

577. Françoise de Caumont d'Aymé.

578. Marguerite de Lustrac.

579. Marshal de Saint André.

580. Geoffroy de Caumont, Abbé of Clairac.

581. Concerns Tristan de Monneins, Lieutenant of the King of Navarre, lynched in Bordeaux during the salt tax riots on August 21st, 1548, and mentioned a number of times by Montluc. His second wife was Françoise de Lomagne.

582. Anne d'Anglure de Givry.

583. Marshal de La Châtre, who was her second husband.

584. Blanche de Toumon, whose first husband was Jean du Bellay, and her second Jacques II de Châtillon, who died at Ferrara in 1512 as the result of a wound received at Ravenna. (Cf. Brantôme: *Works*, Vol. II, p. 427).

585. François de Bouliers de Mane, Bishop of Fréjus.

586. Philibert II de la Platière, Lord of Bordes and of Bourdillon, Counsellor and Chamberlain to the King (1498), who died September 4th, 1499. He was father of Marshal de Bourdillon.

587. Jacques de Genouillac, Lord of Assier, known as Galiot, Grand Groom of France, died 1546.

588. Germain de Bonneval, eldest son of Antoine de Bonneval and Marguerite de Foix, Cupbearer and Valet of the Bedchamber to Charles VIII, Councillor of State, Seneschal of Limousin in 1508, killed at Pavia in 1525.

589. Jacques II de Châtillon. See Note 584.

590. The fourth story, of which in his *Illustrious Men* Brantôme says: 'There is a tale in the *Hundred Stories* of the Queen of Navarre about a Royal favourite who . . . made a trapdoor from his room to the bedside wall of a great princess, to sleep with her, and did indeed do so, though, the story says, got only scratches for his pains. But that is for discussion. The tale is about him, but I am not going to say who the princess was.' It was the Queen of Navarre herself, the noble, de Bonnivet.

591. Louise de Daillon who had a sharp and ready tongue. See Note 512.

592. Odet de Coligny, Cardinal de Châtillon, brother of the celebrated admiral (1515-1571). Raised to the purple by Clement VII, when only eighteen, successively archbishop of Toulouse and Beauvais, he was converted to protestantism by reading Calvinistic literature, and under the influence of his brother Dandelot, but did not openly profess it till the first war of religion. In 1563 Pius IV struck him off the list of cardinals and excommunicated him. He then married Elisabeth de Hauteville, Lady de Loré, appeared in his cardinal's robes together with her at the coming-of-age ceremony of Charles IX, took the title of Count of Beauvais, fought at St Denis (1567) then, finally denounced by the High Court, took refuge in England, where he was poisoned by his footman !

593. Cardinal Jean du Bellay (1492-1560), an illegitimate cousin of the poet, who was French ambassador to Rome under François I and raised to the purple in 1535 by the Pope (Paul III)—'one of the wisest, most eloquent, sensible and level-headed men of his time,' as Brantôme says elsewhere.

594. Henri II.

595. Diane de Poitiers.

596. Brantôme here agrees with Marot, who in one of his 'New Year's Day gifts' to Diane de Poitiers, as Lady Seneschal, said:

> *Que voulez-vous, Diane bonne,*
> *Que vous donne?*
> *Vous n'eutes, comme j'entens,*
> *Jamais tant d'heur au printemps*
> *Qu'en automne.*

'Now, Diana, my darling,
What am I to give you? After all,
I don't think you were ever
So lucky in Spring
As you are in the Fall.'

597. Towards the year, A.D. 400 St Jerome, who records the fact. *(Epist. ad Ageruchiam, de Matrimonio)*, witnessed the lady's funeral. No doubt Brantôme borrows from Bouchet, *20e Serée*.

598. Charles de Rochechouart, Lord of Barbazan, who belonged to the Poitouan Mortemarts.

599. Françoise de Mouchy, Lady de Barbazan, daughter of Jean, Lord of Mouchy.

600. Christine de Danemark, Duchess of Lorraine, often mentioned.

601. Melchior des Prés, Lord Montpexat, mentioned above.

602. The shrub under which at Delos Latona hid her daughter, the chaste Diana. This explains why (according to Pliny the Elder in his *Natural History*, 24, 38) the Athenian women who were obliged to continence on those days, spread its leaves on their beds. Plato, Galen and Pliny all speak of the antiaphrodisiac effect of the fruit and leaves —*ad Venerem impetus cohibent*—'they inhibit the urge to make love.' In his Third Book (Chapter 31) Rabelais calls it just *vitex*, one of the herbs which 'make man cold, sickly and disinclined to generation.'

603. Cf. Lampridius, *Life of Heliogabalus*.

604. *Pantagruel*, Book 1, chapter 17.

605. Plutarch, *Life of Cleomenes*.

606. The Turks took Chios in 1566.

607. These Genoese traders had apparently told the same story and in the same terms, as Bouchet: 'At Chios widowed women pay a tax . . . called *argomoniatic*, which means . . . idle, useless parts.'

608. Cf. above, p. 31.

609. Plutarch, *Life of Lycurgus*.

610. In the 20th tale, the story of Lord de Ryant, taken from Morlini and Ariosto and imitated by Là Fontaine in the story entitled *Joconde*.

611. The folio, Gothic-letter edition of the *Histoire et plaisante chronique du Petit Jehan de Saintré*, by Antoine de La Salle.

612. In the 45th story of the *Heptameron*.

613. The celebrated Bussy d'Amboise.

614. Henri III.

615. Pierre Griffon, valet de chambre and man of confidence to King Henri III, whom he had served since 1543.

616. Alexandre de Medici, first Duke of Florence, stabbed in 1537 by his cousin Lorenzino, who had inviegled him to his house one

night by offering a love meeting with his aunt, Catherine Ginori, of whom Alexandre was enamoured.

617. Probably Lady de Chateaubriant. However, the vexatious mishap which Bonnivet experienced (according to Brantôme) we find in analogous form, except for the names, in Chapter 11 of Béroalde de Verville's *Moyen de Parvenir*.

618. Marguerite de Valois.

619. Sébastien de Luxembourg-Martigues.

620. Chambord.

621. Princess d'Eboli.

622. Philippe II.

623. Antonio Perez.

624. In the 49th story of the *Heptameron*.

625. Agnès Sorel.

626. Anne de Boleyn—Cf. Note 37.

627. Henry VIII.

628. Louise de Savoie, Duchess d'Angoulême, who was Regent after Pavia.

629. Jeanne de Poupincourt. Cf. Clairambault, *Nol. 1216, folio 60*.

630. Lady de la Brelandière. Cf. *Arch. nat., J.362*, for 1558.

631. Louise of Savoy, Duchess of Angoulême.

632. Queen Elizabeth I, 'the Virgin Queen.'

633. Louise de Charançonnet or Charansonnet, who was also linked to the family of Catherine de Medici (in 1583) and for whom twenty years earlier Bourdeille's youngest brother, Jean, had sighed. (Cf. Brantôme, *Recueil d'aulcunes rymes,* Sonnet 36.)

But the lady's aversion from marriage was not, as Bantôme suggests because she was so chaste, but because she was a Lesbian. There is a libellous ditty of 1581 which speaks of Charansonnet 'and her mistress' enjoying themselves together, and another of 1583 which runs

> *Charansonnet n'a plus ses fleurs;*
> *La bastarde s'en est lassée;*
> *Serteau elle a depucelée.*
> *Sapho et Sodome revit,*
> *Un gaudemichi et un vit.*

634. Madeleine de Bourdeille.

635. Anne de Beri, Lady de Certeau or Serteau, who in 1583 was one of Catherine de Medici's maids. Like her friend Charançonnet she too had a leaning for Lesbian delights.

636. Hélène de Fonsèque de Sirigères, daughter of René, Baron de Surgères and of Anne de Cossé-Brissac. She was Ronsard's Helen, whom he called the Tenth Muse and Wise Goddess. There is a sonnet in the manuscripts (Ms. fr : 25-45) which praises her wisdom. This chaste, dark maiden who, as Pierre Champion says (*Ronsard et son temps,* p. 255) 'remained cold as the mountains of Piedmont, where she had spent her childhood' was also sung in Latin by Dorat and in French by Baïf, Jamyn, Jodelle and Desportes.

637. Marie, *Infanta* of Portugal.

638. Eleonora, Queen of Portugal.

639. Ogier de Gourgues-Julliac.

640. In 1564.

641. Already mentioned. Cf. p. 108, Note 190.

642. François II.

643. In 1559.

644. In Valère-Maxime: *Actions et paroles mémorables*. Book 1, Chapter 1, para. 10:

'When Rome was taken by the Gauls, the flamen of Quirinus and the Vestal Virgins took the sacred impedimenta, sharing the burden. They had just crossed the Sublicius bridge and were going up the Janicula hill, when L. Albanius, who was taking his wife and children away in a chariot, noticed them. More attached to the State cult than to his personal affection, he made his family get down, took the Vestals and their goods in to the vehicle, turned aside off his way and took them to the township of Caera, where they were received with every mark of respect.'

645. Symmacus, Consul of Rome in the year when Theodosius suppressed the Vestal Virgins (389).

646. The Latin poet Prudentius (348, line 410 of his *Liber Peristephanum*).

647. In the 16th century it was the custom to whip lazy boys and girls in bed on Innocents' Day. This was called 'giving them the innocents' and the custom of course was a wonderful opportunity for all manner of horseplay. Marot wrote a nice epigram about it, entitled Innocents' Day:

> 'O sister dear, if I knew where you lay
> Your lovely body on our Innocents' Day
> Beside your bed I'd very early be. . .' and so forth.

648. Cf. Lampridius, *Life of Heliogabulus*.

649. Horace, *Epodes*, 12, lines 11-12:

> . . . *Jam[que] subando*
> *Tenta cubilia tectaque rumpit!*

'When she is in a frenzy, she makes the very frame and strappings of the bed shake.'

Subare, a verb used of any female on heat or in a frenzy, is derived, some hold, from *sus,* a sow, but according to others from *sub*—to be under the male.

650. Suetonius: *Life of Caligula*, 25.

651. Spartianus: *Life of Caracalla*, 10.

652. Henri III, who had seduced Marie de Clèves, first wife of the Duke of Condé. Cf. Note 134.

653. Géta.

654. Philippe Marie Visconti, third duke of Milan, had married Beatrice de Tende, widow of very rich Facino Cane. Cf. Litta, *Visconti di Milano,* Vol. 3, *tavola* 6.

655. Suspected of adultery with Michele Orombelli, she and her lover with her were killed by the Duke of Milan, who thus acquired her estates.

656. In 1194. Cf. Collenuccio, Book 4, year 1194.

657. Marguerite of Clermont, sister of Louise de Crussol, Duchess of Uzès, who was Abbess of Tarascon and Saint Césaire d'Arles.

658. This concerns Brantôme's brother, Jean de Bourdeille, known as Captain Bourdeille, not to be confused with the youngest of them, Jean de Bourdeille d'Ardelay.

659. Hesdin in Flanders, a much contested town in the wars of the period between the Spanish and the French. Captured by François I in 1537, it was lost by Henri II in 1551, retaken again in 1553, then lost once more in the same year, and destroyed by order of Charles V.

660. The Duchess of Ferrara protected the Huguenots.

661. Meung-sur-Loire.

662. François de Kernevenog, known as de Carnavalet, whose wife acquired the town house named Carnavalet since then, (1572).

663. Lèonor d'Orléans, Duke of Longueville (1540-1573) to whom Charles IX granted the title of prince of the blood as much for his marriage ties as his services.

664. Charles IX.

665. In 1557.

666. Henri II.

667. François de Lorraine, Duke of Guise.

668. Esclaron, a district of Vassy (Haute-Marne).

669. In the first of the wars of religion (1562-1563).

670. Louis I, Prince of Condé and head of the family of that name (1530-1569), who after the Vassey massacre put himself at the head of the Huguenots and opened civil war by the capture of Orleans and the handing over of le Havre to the English, to win Elizabeth's support (1562).

671. See Note 418.

672. Captain Avaret, who fell at Orleans, in 1562.

673. Because it was Henri II's habit to call the Constable de Montmorency 'compère.'

674. When jousting with Montgomery.

675. Emmanuel Philibert, Duke of Savoy, husband of Marguerite of France. Cf. p. 45, Note 91.

676. 'I do not know what is meant by the austerity of philosophers, the famous Corinthian courtesan used to say: they knock on my door more often than other men do.'

677. Cf. above, pp. 200-202, Note 351.

678. Octavius Augustus, Cf. Suetonius, Life of Augustus, 59.

679. Cf. Suetonius, Life of Caligula, 36.

680. Cf. Suetonius, Life of Nero, 34.

681. Henri III and his brother the Duke of Alençon.

682. Plutarch, Life of Artaxerxes-Mnemon, 26.

683. Collenuccio, History of Naples, Book V, p. 208 (Venice edition) at year 1405.

684. She was 38.

685. Diane of Poitiers.

686. Brantôme no doubt meant to write sixty-six, the age at which the fair Diane died (1499-1566).

687. Jacqueline de Rohan-Gié, married to François d'Orléans, Marquis of Rothelin.

688. Françoise d'Orléans, widow of Louis I of Bourbon, Prince of Condé, died 1569.

689. Cf. p. 363, Note 663.

690. Françoise Robertet, widow of Jean Babou, who later married the Marshal d'Aumont.

691. Catherine de Clermont, married to Guy de Mareuil.

692. Gabrielle de Mareuil, married to Nicolas of Anjou, Marquis of Mézières.

693. Thus was called the Duchess of Montpensier, wife of Duke François, the 'dauphin prince'.

694. Jacqueline, known as Jacquette de Montberon, wife of André de Bourdeille, Brantôme's eldest brother.

695. Françoise de Longwy, Lady Admiral of Brion.

696. Lady de Brion, who had married Charles de la Rochefoucaul, Lord of Barbezieux.

697. A celebrated beauty of the period, described and praised by G. Minut in an essay entitled *La Paulographie,* inserted at the end of a work by the same author on beauty (1587).

698. She was a great friend of Brantôme, who praises her a number of times.

699. Anne d'Este, daughter of Hercules d'Este and Renée, of France, daughter of Louis XII (1532-1607). She first married the second Duke of Guise (December 4th, 1549) having eight children by him, then, when her husband had been assassinated, Jacques de Savoie, Duke de Nemours.

700. Mary Stuart, who at this time (1559-1560) was Queen of France.

701. Cf. Note 699.

702. Louis XII. Cf. Note 699.

703. In September 1574.

704. 'Very kind-hearted' and also very gay, which, it is true, is a way of being kind-hearted, if we are to trust the attitudes of those times.

705. Guillaume Gonzague, Duke of Mantua, who had married Princess Eleonora, daughter of Fernand I of Germany and sister of Maximilian.

706. From the Italian *gobbino,* a diminutive of *gobbo,* hunched (Low Latin *gobbus,* for *gibbus*).

707. If we are to believe Litta *(Gonzaga di Mantova, Vol 1, tav. 6),* she was very devout.

708. Anne d'Este, Duchess of Guise, later of Nemours. Cf. Note 699.

709. Anne, Duke of Joyeuse, Admiral of France 1561-1587, a favourite of Henri III'rds who in 1582 had married Marguerite of Lorraine, the Queen's sister.

710. At the wedding of Duke Charles Emmanuel I the Great, Duke of Savoy (1562-1630) who had married Catherine of Austria, daughter of Philippe II, King of Spain.

711. Having had eight by Guise she had three more by Nemours.

712. Mary Stuart.

713. Marie of Aragon, married to Alphonse d'Avalos, Marquis del Guasto or Vasto.

714. Henri II.

715. Cf. above, p. 199, Note 345.

716. Charles de Lorraine, Cardinal de Guise in 1557, younger

brother of the second Duke de Guise. Cf. above, p. 199, Note 344.

717. François de Lorraine, Grand Prior and General of the Galleys 1534-1562. Cf. above, p. 108, Note 190.

718. Don Perafan, Duke d'Alcala, then Viceroy of Naples (since 1559).

719. No doubt Claude de l'Estrange, a noble of Languedoc.

720. Not Donna Antonina, but Donna Beatrice, who married the Count of Potenza.

721. Evidently Donna Joanna, later married to the Prince de Pulmona.

722. In 1566, when in response to the appeal of the Grandmaster Prior of La Valetta, Brantôme and his brother Ardelay went with three hundred nobles (among them Strozzi and Brissac) to defend Malta against the Turks, then allies of France.

723. Brantôme spent some time at Milan, visited Rome, then travelled *via* Naples to Messina, Catana and Syracusa, where Maltese galleys came to pick up the crusaders.

724. In 1562.

725. In the shops in the arcades of the Courts of Justice in Paris.

726. François Ferdinand d'Avalos Marquis de Pescaire, Viceroy of Sicily, who died in 1571. Cf. above, p. 9, Note 28.

727. Suleiman II.

728. Brantôme came back to France through Milan, where he spent a month, and Turin.

729. In the *Capitaines illustres*.

730. Tradition has it that *les Cent nouvelles nouvelles* were collected while Louis XI to be, as crown prince, was living at Geneppe Castle in Brabant. Concerning this 'fine rascal,' cf. Bonaventure des Périers, *Nouvelles récréations*, 6, which depicts 'this good King going from place to place in plain clothes, to hear the truth about all sorts of things better.'

731. Edward IV.

732. Louis XI's second wife, Charlotte de Savoie, says Commynes, 'was not one of those women who exactly give a man pleasure, but all the same was a very worthy lady.'

733. In other words, she was 'a foreigner.' Charlotte was the daughter of Louis, Duke of Savoy.

734. By Charlotte, Louis XI had a son Charles, who succeeded him as Charles VIII, Anne, who was married to the master of Beaujeu, Jeanne, who married Louis of Orleans, who followed Charles VIII as Louis XII, and three other children who died in infancy.

735. In 1495, in the autumn. Here Brantôme follows Commynes, in his life of Henri II : cf. *Oeuvres*, edited Lalanne, Vol. 3, p. 142.

736. When fifty-two and worn out by gout and the trials of life, he married for the third time, taking one of Henry VIII's sisters, Mary, a sixteen-year-old light and loose English girl, imagining, so Fleuranges remarks, to have a quiet domestic life. But, as Brantôme says elsewhere, he had taken a young hussy who was going to show him the short-cut to Paradise. Indeed. He died within three years of marrying —on New Year's Day, 1515. Shortly before breathing his last he told his spouse that his death was going to be her New Year's Day gift. She

accepted it gladly and married her lover, the Duke of Suffolk, while still in mourning.

737. There was a notorious liaison with a court laundress, who, it is said, was the mother of Cardinal du Bucy. There was also Thomasina Spinola, at Naples.

738. Louis of Orleans, brother of Charles VI, was assassinated on November 23rd, 1407, but not for the reason which Brantôme gives.

739. Cf. above, p. 41, Note 89.

740. Brantôme is in error. Marguerite of Bavaria outlived her husband, Duke Jean of Burgundy, by four years.

741. Another mistake. The daughter of Louis III de Bourbon married her uncle, Béraud, crown prince of Auvergne.

742. Judging women by his sister, Marguerite of Navarre, François found the ladies most self-contradictory. Writing to Montmorency on November 8th, 1537, he said that when you wanted them to stop, they always wanted to go and when you wanted them to go, would never budge. (Clairambault, 336, folio 6230 *verso,* in the *Bibliothéque nationale.*)

743. Pierre Bressart, known as Brisambourg, stable boy to the King in 1528, later carver to His Majesty. Cf. *Catalogue des actes de François I,* 1,611.

744. June 2nd, 1538, to reconcile François I and Charles V.

745. June 11th, 1538. The ladies of whom Brantôme speaks were the Queen of Navarre, Lady de Vendôme, the Duchess of Etampes, the Lady Constable de Montmorency, the Lady Admiral de Brion and thirty-eight maids of honour.

746. John Stuart, Duke of Albany, grandson of Jacques II, governor of Bourbonnais and the Auvergne (1482-1536).

747. Clément VII disembarked at Marseilles October 11th, 1533. He had been escorted from Spezia by a French squadron commanded by the Duke of Albany.

748. The wedding of Catherine de Medici, niece of the Holy Father, and Henri d'Oréans, Henri II to be, took place at Marseilles October 28th, 1533.

749. Brantôme had the story from Jean Bouchet's *Annales d'Aquitaine,* Part 4, p. 473. But Bouchet does not give any names. Brantôme's identification hardly holds, since Lady de Chateaubriant died before her husband and Lady de Canaples did not lose hers till twenty-two years later (in 1555). Lady de Châtillon, mother of Admiral de Coligny, had been a widow since 1522 (her husband having been Gaspard de Coligny, Lord de Châtillon) and Aimée Mottier de La Fayette was the widow of François de Silly, Bailiff of Caen.

750. Louise de Clermont-Tallard, whose first husband was François du Bellay, Prince d'Yvetot, her second being Antoine de Crussol, Duke d'Uzès. She died in 1536.

751. June 2nd, 1538. Cf. Note 744 and 745.

752. Cf. Note 750.

753. There is that epigram of Marot's about her—and he was a great master of repartee. She was 'second to none' and one had to admit that 'by her mere appearance there was proof that spirits came to this world, for that fair slip of a thing was nothing but spirit.'

754. Jean de Taix, knight of the order, then a gentleman of the

bedchamber. Later he was Captain General of Infantry, then Grand-master of Artillery (when Galiot de Genuilhac died—January 21st, 1547). Montluc makes frequent mention of him.

755. Jean de Lorraine (1498-1550) who was cardinal when he was twenty-five and famous in his time for his grand manner of living and his largesse—as witness his epitaph, collected by Rasse de Noeux (Man. fr. 22. 561. p. 155):

> *Or en vivant n'ay avarice onc eu,*
> *Mais comme prince aymant l'heur de noblesse,*
> *Ay par le monde espandu ma largesse,*
> *Dont durera à jamais me mémoire.*

> Now in my life I never once was mean,
> But like a prince that lives the noble way
> Generous to every man I've been
> And shall remembered be for many a day.

756. Brantôme speaks elsewhere of how harsh this overweening great lady was to soldiers of Lautrec's who took refuge in Pied-mont.

757. Antoine Perrenot, Cardinal de Granvelle (1517-1586), one of Philippe II's advisers, and in turn Archbishop of Malines and of Be-sançon.

758. Egmont was beheaded on the orders of the Duke of Alba, 1568.

759. Cf. Note 109.

760. She was daughter of Gilles de la Tour de Turenne, Lord of Limeuil in Périgord.

761. On her mother's side Catherine de Medici belonged to the la Tour de Turenne family.

762. Pierre de la Mare, Lord Matha, groom to Marguerite of France.

763. Edmée or Aimée Brossin de Méré, maid of honour to Catherine de Medici 1560-1564. She married Claude de Mavay, Lord Sorel, Royal chamberlain.

764. Lord Gersay, whom Brantôme elsewhere calls Gerzay and Ger-geay, and Agrippa d'Aubigné Jarsé, had killed Baron d'Ingrandes, as we see from the *Discours sur les duels,* and 'when recognized died outside the fort of Sainte Catherine at Rouen, in a very smart little encounter' (1562).

765. Honorat de Bueil, Lord of Fontain-Guérin, gentleman of the bedchamber, later Vice-Admiral and Lt.-General representing the King in Brittany. He was 'killed at St Mâlo while Governor by his own men' (March 14th, 1530).

766. Charles IX.

767. No doubt Françoise de Rohan, Lady de la Gamache, daughter of René de Rohan and Isabelle d'Albret. She later became Duchess de Mousunois. Cf. Bayle: *Dictionnaire.*

768. Jacques, Duke of Savoy-Nemours. Cf. above, p. 432, Note 846. She became pregnant at Blois Castle in 1556.

769. In Jhoinot Arbeau's *Orchésorgraphie, folio* 86, we read about this brandishing the torch: 'Any man who wishes to dance it takes a candlestick with the candle lighted, or a torch or flare, and dances,

527

making one or two rounds of the hall, looking for the partner he means to choose, selects the one who suits him, then, having danced with her for a little time, thanks her and leaves her alone at the end of the hall, and with a bow puts the candlestick in her hand, or the torch or flare, and dancing withdraws to his place. Holding the candlestick the girl does as she saw the young man do, and dancing round selects her partner, to whom when she has brought him to the place she gives the candlestick and so in turn the dancers invite one another to dance.'

770. It was the Duke de Gènevois.

771. To silence his claims, he had to be locked up in the Châtelet prison. Coming out in January 1585, he entered the service of Henri of Navarre and despite his mother's protest seized la Garnache Castle, in Lower Poitou.

772. *Marie de Flamin* (original ms. spelling of Brantôme's)—Lady Fleming—illegitimate daughter of James V of Scotland, Governess of Mary Stuart.

773. The liaison between Henri II and this lovely Scotswoman ended in September 1550, following a quarrel between Diane de Poitiers and the King. Cf. Lucien Romier: *Les origines politiques des guerres de religion,* Vol. 1, p. 87.

774. This Henri d'Angoulême, who, wounded in the groin in a quarrel with Philippe Altoviti, Baron de Castellane, husband of the fair Renée de Rieux, died at Aix-en-Provence, not at Marseilles, June 2nd, 1586. On his death cf. Tallemant, *Historiettes,* published by Mongrédien, Vol. 1, p. 163.

775. Thalestris. Cf. above, p. 426, Note 827.

776. Mary Stuart.

777. Catherine de Medici.

778. The Guises, that is, Duke François de Guise and Cardinal de Lorraine, who had it all in their hands, as King François II told the deputation of members of the High Court (parlement) when he ascended the throne.

779. The first Catilinade.

780. Anne of Este, wife of Duke François of Guise, and his 'near relative' the Cardinal de Lorraine.

781. Since they could not trace the author, they hanged a printer, Martin Lhomme, in the Place Maubert, July 15th, 1560—a copy of the pamphlet, entitled *Epistre envoïée au tigre de la France* having been found in his possession. The pamphlet was re-issued in 1875, by Ch. Read (published by Jouast).

782. Philibert de Marcilly, Lord de Cipierre. Cf. above, p. 469, Note 965.

783. It concerned Anne d'Este, widow of François de Guise, when in 1566 she married the Duke of Nemours.

784. Refers to the detestation of Henri III to which the Duchess of Montpensier had given voice. Cf. above, p. 465, Note 952.

785. Marie de Clèves, who in July 1572 married Henri de Bourbon, Prince de Condé. She died in childbed July 30th, 1574. 'The King loved her desperately,' says L'Estoile, 'and fainted when told she had died.'

786. At Strasbourg.

787. Charlotte de la Tremouille, second wife of the Prince de Condé.

788. This essay has never been found.

789. Brantôme himself, who never discloses his own loves, and only names a mistress in poetry which was never intended to be published.

790. Doubtless—if this does concern Brantôme himself—Lady de-Grandmont (Marguerite d'Aure), who married Jean de Durfort, Lord Duras.

791. Is this Bussy d'Amboise? Du Guast? Or Lignerolles?

792. Marie Babou de la Bourdaisière 'of the lovely hair,' who in 1560 married Claude de Beauvillier, Count of Saint Aïgnan.

793. Catherine de Medici.

794. Cecilia, daughter of the Grand-Pontiff Metellus and wife of Sylla. Cf. Plutarch : *Sylla,* 30 (Amyot's translation, folio 319).

795. Marie of Hungary, Charles V's sister, Governor of the Low Countries.

796. She had Folembray Castle, near Laon, one of François I's residences, burned down.

797. Refers to the love affair between the Queen and Jean de Ligne, Baron de Barbançon, Count d'Aremberg, defeated and killed at Heigerloo in 1568. Cf. Le Roux de Lincy, *Recueil des Chants historiques français,* Vol. II, p. 583.

798. Follows Plutarch, in Amyot's translation : *Caton d'Utique,* 35, folio 534. Cato in the Senate read 'a scrap of paper brought from outside to Caesar, to find it was a love letter written to Caesar by his sister Servilia, she being in love with him and having been debauched by him.'

799. Henri d'Anjou, Henri III to be.

800. Renée de Rieux-Châteauneuf, who became Lady de Castellane.

801. Marie de Clèves, wife of the Prince de Condé. Cf. p. 402, Note 785.

802. Louis I de Bourbon, Prince de Condé.

803. Isabeau de la Tour de Limeuil, who became Lady Sardini. Cf. Note 111.

804. Françoise d'Orléans.

805. On the reverse of folio 109 of the Brantôme manuscript is an anonymous sonnet dedicated to Jérôme Lhuillier, Lord de la Maison-fleur, about the fair Limeuil girl. It begins : 'Lhuillier, if you would see the girl to whom there's none to compare . . .' The sketch of her which is in Louvre (attributed to Benjamin Foulon) hardly justifies such language.

806. The Lyons banker Scipio Sardini, who came from Lucca and was then set up in Paris. In September 1578 Paris was placarded with denunciations of 'Messire *Poltron Scorpion Sardini,* Sardinian, and his accomplices, the gentry of Italy.'

807. Françoise de Foix, who in 1509 married Jean de Laval, Lord de Châteaubriant. Cf. p. 388, and Note 749.

808. Anne de Pisseleu, who in 1536 married Jean de Brosse and was made Duchess of Etampes in 1537.

809. In March, 1526.

810. In his essay on that Queen, Brantôme uttered the same praise of Marguerite of Navarre : 'Nobody in the world could equal her for

embroidering mottoes, in French, Latin and other tongues, and there are an infinity of them in our family, in bedding and tapestries, of her composition.'

811. Anne de Bourbon, who in 1561 married François de Clèves, Duke of Nevers and Count d'Eu.

812. When the Duke de Nevers took away his fiancée, the Queen of Spain, said a witness, 'wept and lamented so that it was the most piteous day in the Royal household.'

813. September, 1571.

814. Well known lines of the *Aeneid* (6 : 882-884.) The tradition to which Brantôme refers comes from Donat, who in his commentary on the *Aeneid* adds that after his return Octavius gave the poet 10,000 sesterces for each line in praise of his son.

815. Veiled allusion to Louis II de Montpensier, widowed in 1561, his wife having been Jacqueline de Longwy. At the age of 57 he re-married February 4th, 1570, his bride being young Catherine de Lorraine. Cf. p. 465, Note 951.

816. Cf. Rabelais, Book Three, chapter 8, *Good Mr Priapus*.

817. Elisabeth de Portugal.

818. The Marquis de Villena.

819. Gomez Suarez de Figueroa, Duke de Feria.

820. Eleonora of Portugal, who later married François I.

821. Marie of Hungary, Cf. p. 210, Note 368.

822. Cf. Note 824.

823. Cf. above, p. 9, third paragraph.

824. The daughter of Henri II,—Elisabeth de Valois, who was Queen of Spain. Cf. p. 393.

825. The *Palacio Real* (Royal Palace) of Valladolid, where the Kings of Spain often resided. This old city, farther removed from the Moors, was for a long time regarded as a more suitable capital than Madrid.

826. The most common tradition brings Penthesilea, the Amazon Queen, to Troy after the death of Hector, as Brantôme notes below : 'Though . . . some maintain that she never saw Hector at all. . . .'

827. Thalestris.

828. In the depths of Hycania after, Justinus tells us, a march of thirty-three days.

829. 'The amorous fire of this woman,' says Quintius Curtius (in *History of Alexander* 6, 5) fiercer than that of the King, decided him to halt for some days; thirteen days were spent satisfying her cravings, then she returned to her kingdom and the King went to Parthia.'

830. *Op. cit.*

831. Paul Orose, *Histoire contre les païens*, Book 5, Claude de Seissel's translation (1491).

832. Justinus, *Histoires philippiques*, II, 4, 33; XII, 3, 5-7; XLII, 3, 7.

833. In the 11th canto of the *Aeneid*. If Brantôme's use of the plural surprises, we must assume that he took it from Octavien de Saint Gelais's 1509 translation—Octavien had himself borrowed it from a sort of novel drawn from the Latin poem, and entitled *Le Livre des Enéides*, 1483.

834. Not *Armie*, but Larine—*Larina virgo* Aeneid, 11,655.

835. Aeneid, 11,656.

836. Virgil wrote: *Aeratam quatiens Tarpeia securim*: Tarpeis brandishing her bronze hatchet. (*Aeneid,* 11,656.)

837. The word comes from Virgil, *op. cit.,* 11,657: *Italides.*

838. *Aeneid,* 4, 10-13.

839. Book 9, chapter 3.

840. Bandello, *Histoires tragiques*, vol. 3, p. 1 of the quarto Venetian edition of 1568.

841. Henri III who while still Duke of Anjou was the victor of Jarnac and Moncontour.

842. Ovid, at the beginning of the *Art of Love.*

843. Sonnet 180 of the *Amours à Cassandre.*

844. Cf. above, p. 108, Note 190.

845. Henri I, Duke of Montmorency, Constable of France (1534-1614), second son of the Constable Anne de Montmorency, known as Damville or d'Amville, till the death of his elder brother François (1579).

846. Jacques de Savoie, Duke of Nemours, died in 1585. Cf. above, p. 179, Note 299.

847. Charles de La Rochefoucauld, Count of Rendan or Randan.

848. Not in Scotland, but England, where he 'negotiated peace with Scotland' (1559).

849. Philibert Le Voyer, Lord de Lignerolles and de Bellefille, diplomatic agent of the Court of France in the 16th century, assassinated at Bourguiel in 1577, for having disclosed things told him in confidence by Charles IX.

850. Veiled reference to the love of the Duke de Nemours for Anne d'Este, Duchess de Guise, whom indeed he married, when Guise was dead. Cf. Note 699.

851. In the sixteenth story.

852. Guillaume Gouffier, Lord de Bonnivet (1488-1525) companion in arms and favourite of François I, who made him Admiral of France. A brave, witty and very gallant personality.

853. Marguerite de Valois, who engaged Bussy d'Amboise as her 'serving-man' because of his reputation as a good and fortunate swordsman.

854. Jacques de Lorge, Lord de Montmorency, Captain of the Scots Guard of King François I, whose son was to kill Henri II when jousting.

855. Claude de Clermont, Viscount de Tallard, nephew of Diane de Poitiers, who, like Brantôme, sighed for fair Rouet. He was killed in the battle of Montcontour (1569).

856. François d'Hangest, Lord de Genlis, already discussed above. Cf. p. 179 and Note 304.

857. Genlis was Captain of the Louvre.

858. Either of September 28th or October 26th, 1562, in the first of the wars of religion.

859. Either Lady de Piennes senior, who later married Marcilly-Cipierre, or the younger one, who was to have married the son of the Constable de Monmorency, but did not.

860. Agnès Sorel.

861. His first wife, Tiphaine Raguenel, Countess de Longueville.

862. Raymond-Béranger IV, Count of Anjou and Provence. It concerned his daughter, Béatrix.

863. Charles, Count of Anjou and Provence, brother of Saint Louis (about 1221-1286) who in 1265 accepted the investiture of the Kingdom of Naples and Sicily, the gift of Pope Urbanus IV, and was solemnly invested by him, in Rome.

864. Charles marched against Naples, which he entered after crushing Manfred at the battle of Benevento. He then dealt with a new rival, Conradin of Suabia. Him he had tortured to death. When his brother, Saint Louis, died, he had all Italy under his control.

865. Not for any length of time. At least, Béatrix died in 1567. Her husband survived her nearly twenty years.

866. Isabeau of Lorraine, daughter of Charles the Bold, Duke of Lorraine, married when ten years old to René d'Anjou, King of Sicily, who had eleven children by her (1410-1455). Estienne Pasquier said of her that she had 'a man's heart in a woman's bodice.'

867. In 1434.

868. In 1435.

869. Cf. above, p. 165, Note 273.

870. In 1562.

871. René de La Platière, Lord des Bordes, standard-bearer in Maréchal de Bourdillon's company, killed in the battle of Dreux.

872. François de Clèves, Count d'Eu, then Duke of Nevers.

873. François de Guise, who defeated the Huguenots at Dreux.

874. Although Brantôme praises Bussy d'Amboise, he also records how he remonstrated with him about his passion for warfare and duelling.

875. Marguerite de Valois.

876. Canto 5 of Ariosto's *Orlando furioso*.

877. Cf. above, p. 429, Note 840.

878. No doubt Brantôme himself and one of his friends.

879. No doubt the Duke of Guise (Henri Scarface) and the Duke de Mayenne.

880. Probably Marguerite de Valois.

881. Catherine de Medici.

882. The episcopal palace of Reims, situated in the *le Paon* alley, off the *rue Hautefeuille*.

883. Madeleine de Saint Nectaire, wife of the Huguenot chief, Guy de Saint Exupéry, Lord Miramont, who, disguised as a man, killed Montal of the League in 1574. Cf. Anselme, Vol. 4, p. 890.

884. Cf. above, p. 215, Note 387.

885. Cf. above, p. 216, Note 388.

886. Cf. above, p. 216, Note 389.

887. *Livy,* Book 27, Chapter 37.

888. Ariosto's *Orlando furioso,* cantos 22 and 25.

889. Christophe Jouvenel des Ursin, Lord de La Chapelle, died 1588.

890. Henri II.

891. Charles V.

892. This at least is what Moreri too asserts: 'Siena was built by the Senonian Gauls after the capture of Rome by Brennus.'

893. Cf. Brantôme, *Works*, Lalanne edition, Vol. 2, p. 293.

894. Ippolita Fioramonti, wife of Louis de Malaspina, commander of the armies of the Duke of Milan. Cf. Litta, *Malaspina di Pavia,* Vol. VII, table 20.

895. February 22nd, 1573.

896. The Duke of Alençon.

897. The interview between François de La Noue, known as Iron-arm (Bras-de-fer) and the Abbé de Gadagne, representing the Duke of Alençon, took place at Amboise Mill, near the Cougné Gate.

898. Not only Philippe Strozzi, but also La Batresse.

899. In the work of Jacques de Bourbon, *La grande et merveilleuse oppugnation de la noble cité de Rhodes,* 1527.

900. In 1536.

901. In 1589.

902. Cf. Colenuccio.

903. The famous condottiere, Giacomuzzo Attendolo Sforza (1369-1424) who hired his services to Queen Joanna II and was granted the fiefs of Benevento, Manfredonia, etc., by her, and in 1414 married the sister of Alopo, the Queen's favourite.

904. Jacques de Bourbon, King of Naples, on his return, seized him at Benevento and threw him into prison (1415).

905. Sforza recovered his liberty in 1416.

906. Cf. Vopiscus, Life of Aurelian, 26-30. The story was improved on by Boccaccio in his *De claris mulieribus* (Chapter 101), whence Brantôme took it.

907. Cf. above, pp. 201-203 and 367, Notes 351 and 667.

908. By committing suicide.

909. Marie of Austria, sister of Charles V, widow of Louis II of Hungary, who died in 1558.

910. Aurelia Victorina, mother of Victorinus.

911. Catherine de Medici.

912. Isabelle, daughter of Philippe II and Elisabeth de Valois, who was governor of the Low Countries.

913. Cf. Froissart, Book 1, chapter 174.

914. Jeanne de Flandre, wife of Jean de Montfort.

915. Annebon or Hennebont, an old strongpoint in Morbihan, on the R. Blavet, besieged in 1342.

916. Henri I, Prince de Condé, who died March 5th, 1588, poisoned, so the *Journal de Henri III* alleges, by his wife, Catherine Charlotte de la Trémouille, cf. above, Note 133.

917. Jacquette de Montberon, Brantôme's sister-in-law.

918. Matha, not far from Saint Jean d'Angély.

919. Cf. above, p. 460, Note 914.

920. Cf. above, p. 460, Note 915.

921. In the *Dell-arte della guerra,* Book 5, 2.

922. Paule de Penthièvre, second wife of Jean II of Burgundy, Count of Nevers.

923. Between Peronne and Compiègne.

924. Charles the Bold.

925. Richilde, Countess of Hainaut, married to Baudoin VI of Mons, Count of Flanders, died 1091.

926. Philippe I, who reigned 1060 to 1108.

927. February 22nd, 1071.

928. Arnulphe or Arnould III, known as the Unfortunate. But he was not killed in any second battle, but in that of February 22nd, 1071.

929. Isabeau or Isabelle of France (1290-1357) who married Edward II of England, Duke of Guyenne (1309).

930. Hugh Spencer.

931. The Prince of Wales.

932. Jean, younger brother of the Count of Hainaut.

933. Having acquired Hainaut, Isabelle there found aid for an invasion of England, and landed in Suffolk in 1326. She rallied all malcontents under her banner and had Edward II arrested, proclaimed the Prince of Wales King, as Edward III, and assumed the Regency.

934. Having got rid of Spencer, Isabelle had Edward II—who was imprisoned in Berkeley Castle—put to death.

935. Roger, Count (or Duke) of Mortimer (1287-1330) who escaped from the Tower of London, to which he had been committed by Edward II at the time of the Barons' Revolt, reached France, became Isabelle's lover, and persuaded her to return to England with an army. Now all-powerful favourite of the Queen, he had the Duke of Kent put to death and imprisoned Lancaster (the two uncles of the King). But Edward III grew tired of his tyranny, had him arrested, and condemned him without waiting for Parliament to sit in judgement. He was hanged at Smithfield in 1330.

936. After Mortimer's death, Isabelle was imprisoned in Rising Castle, where she spent the last twenty-seven years of her life in obscurity.

937. Eléonore of Aquitaine (1122-1204).

938. Louis VII the Younger.

939. The Second Crusade, preached by St Bernard, which ended in the fruitless siege of Damascus (1147-1149).

940. While her husband was impotently besieging Damascus, Eléonore was making love with a handsome Saracen slave. Mézeray tells us that all the historians of the time agreed that she ran after this Turk 'without the least regard for religion or dignity.'

941. The dissolution of the marriage of Louis and Eléonore was pronounced by the Council of Beaugency on March 18th, 1152.

942. The divorce of Eléonore cost France Aquitaine, which she transferred to her second husband, Henry Plantaganet, Duke of Anjou, who inherited the English throne.

943. Outside Damascus, Eléonore had passed from the embraces of the handsome slave to those of her uncle, Raymond de Poitiers, Count of Antioch, then those of Saladin, the valiant leader of the Saracens.

944. Eléonore's example was followed by many others. A small troop formed exclusively of women was formed. The Saracens knew the captain of this as the 'lady with the golden boots.' Emad Eddem, an Arabian historian, tells us that one Frenchwoman fitted out a ship which transported five hundred armed men to Palestine, and another, Ibn Alatin, tells us that among the prisoners taken during the Second Crusade were three women who had fought on horseback, and whose sex was only realized when their wounds were dressed.

945. Thévet, not Nauclerus, as Brantôme erroneously tells us.

946. Volume II, pp. 912-3.

947. Vittoria Colonna, daughter of Fabuzio Colonna and Agnès de Montefeltro, born 1490, when she became the wife of Ferdinand François d'Avalos, Marquis de Pesaïre, often mentioned, cf. Note 28.

948. Valès, folio 205.

949. Grand-Chancellor Hieronimo Morone.

950. From Plutarch's Life of Anthony.

951. Catherine Marie de Lorraine, wife of Louis de Bourbon, Duke of Montpensier.

952. The assassination of Henri III so pleased the Duchess that she always wore thereafter a green scarf which she had had on when it happened. Cf. *Mémoires de la Ligue*, 4, p. 14.

953. The third Duke of Guise, Henri Scarface, assassinated December 23rd, 1588, and the second Cardinal de Guise, Louis, who perished the day after.

954. Anne d'Este, Duchess of Guise, then of Nemours. Cf. above, p. 370, Note 699.

955. The Duke of Mayenne.

956. Who had married a daughter of the Duke d'Aumale, another brother of Scarface.

957. Henri III was killed a year later (1589).

958. François, the second Duke of Guise, mortally wounded by Poltrot de Méré, February 18th, 1563. He died a few days later.

959. Hit by a pistol shot a little below the right shoulder, where not covered by his cuirasse, the Duke had the strength to ride home.

960. Coligny, who had secretly armed Poltrot de Méré.

961. Poltrot de Méré was quartered with such frightful cruelty that young Lady de Montmorency-Thoré, daughter-in-law of the Constable, who was present, fell dead from horror (18th March, 1563).

962. A week later, in the St Bartholemew massacre (August 24th, 1572).

963. Tavannes tells us that the moment Henri of Guise heard the first tocsin he ran to the house of the Admiral, with him his uncle the Duke d'Aumale and a small band of followers and informed Cosseins, an old warrior of the Italian wars, now Colonel of the Royal Guard, who protected the Admiral that he 'had permission to go in and kill the Admiral to avenge his father's death.' Cosseins joined the murderers.

964. Michel de l'Hopital.

965. Philibert de Marcilly, Lord de Cipierre or Cypierre, Tutor to Charles IX, later Lieutenant of his Company and Captain of Gendarmery, died 1566.

966. Cf. above, p. 179, Note 299.

967. Cf. above, p. 67, Notes 125, 126.

968. In 1564.

969. Charles V.

970. Jean de Pérusse d'Escars, Prince de Carency, Count de La Vauguyon (about 1520-1595), who in 1551 married Anne de Clermont-Tallard was Field Marshal, State Councillor, and Lt.-General of Brittany.

971. The Duke of Mayenne, elected 'Lt.-General of State and the

Crown of France,' had come hastily from Lyons (where he was when the Duke of Guise was killed), to secure Burgundy (of which he was governor), then Paris, which he entered February 12th, 1589.

972. Jacques de Savoie, Duke of Nemours, Cf. above p. 179, Note 299.

973. Albert de Gondi, Marshal and Duke de Retz. Cf. above, p. 26, Note 67.

974. Charles IX.

975. Cf. above, p. 453, Note 897.

976. François, Duke of Alençon, then aged 18.

977. Authorized to do so by the King, La Noue fought the Royal troops, calling on his co-religionaries to give in. He formed companies, strengthened the ramparts, destroyed the besiegers equipment and field work and without cease called for peace. In the end his loyalty to the King exasperated the more headstrong, and La Place, a Protestant priest, declared him 'perfidious, a traitor, a deserter of his cause' and slapped his face. Persuaded at last that he must give up any hope of persuading the people of La Rochelle to be loyal, La Noue left them and on March 12th, 1573, re-entered the Royalist camp.

978. Louis de Correa, *Historia de la conquista del reino de Navarra*.

979. Jean III d'Albret, King of Navarre 1494-1512, grand-father of Jeanne d'Albret, who had lost part of his estates to Ferdinand le Catholique (1512).

980. Ferdinand le Catholique.

981. In 1513.

982. Jacques de Chabannes, Lord of La Palice, famous military leader of Louis XII and François I, who was to fall at Pavia.

983. Louis XII.

984. Catherine de Navarre, sister and inheritor of Phoebus.

985. Anne of Brittany.

986. La Palice failed in his expedition, and the efforts made by Louis XII (1513-1514) and François I (1515) to assure Jean III his estates remained fruitless.

987. Diane de Poitiers.

988. November, 1576.

989. Louise of Savoy, mother of François I and Marguerite of Navarre.

990. Marguerite of Navarre, author of the *Heptameron*, cf. preceding note.

991. Not after three days, but about three weeks, as the comet in question did not come into view till August 6th, remaining visible till September 7th, 1531 (*Catalogus cometum*, Bâle, 1556), while Louise of Savoy died September 29th, 1531.

992. Charlotte de Roye, married to François III de La Roche-foucauld in 1557, dead 1559.

993. Marguerite de Foix-Candale, married to Jean Louis de Nogaret, Duke of Epernon.

994. Renée de Bourdeille, daughter of André de Bourdeille, elder brother of Brantôme, and Jacquette de Montberon. In 1559 she married David Bouchard, Viscount Aubeterre and she died in 1596. Brantôme was very fond of her and wrote her a verse *Epitaphe* and a prose *Funeral Oration*.

995. Marguerite of Valois, wife of Henri IV.

996. Catherine de Medici.

997. Viscount Aubeterre had been killed three years before this, in 1593, in Périgord.

998. Hippolyte Bouchard d'Aubeterre, who married François d'Esparbès de Lussan.

999. Her three sisters: Jeanne, Countess de Durtal; Isabelle, Baroness d'Ambleville; Adrienne, Lady de Saint-Bonnet.

1000. The widow of André de Bourdeille, Brantôme's sister-in-law, who died in 1598.

1001. The sister of valiant Bussy d'Amboise, Renée de Clermont, had married Jean de Balagny, illegitimate son of the Bishop of Valence. Though a most incompetent person, he was made Marshal of France in 1594. Cf. Claude Derblay, *Une héroïne de Brantôme*, Plon, Paris, 1935.

1002. October, 1595.

1003. Diane d'Estrées, sister of lovely Gabrielle d'Estrées, Lady Monceaux.

1004. Nicole de Limeuil, a sister of lovely Isabeau de Limeuil, of whom Brantôme makes such frequent mention. Cf. above, p. 516 and Note 109.

1005. *La bataille de Marignan ou la défaite des Suisses*, a song in Attaignant's collection. It was set to music by Janequin.

1006. In Attaignan's version the lines in question run:

> *Ils sont confuz,*
> *Ils sont perduz,*

'they are dismayed, they are lost.'

1007. Léon, died 1521, allied at the time to Charles V against François I.

1008. Cf. above, p. 107, Note 189.

1009. In 1561.

1010. Charles de Bourbon, Prince de la Roche-sur-Yon, died 1565.

1011. Jean de Brosse, Duke of Etampes, the complaisant husband of Anne de Pisseleu, François I's favourite. It is quite true that the duke had a fool named Colin, but Brantôme's story should be compared with that in Noël du Fail's *Contes d'Eutrapel*, about Dom Robert Jouant, who likewise died catching flies.

1012. Renée Taveau, married to François de Rochechouart, Baron Mortemart, Lord of Lussac in Poitou. She was an ancestor of Mme de Montespan, who was also born at Lussac.